About Pearson

Pearson is the world's learning company, with presence across 70 countries worldwide. Our unique insights and world-class expertise comes from a long history of working closely with renowned teachers, authors and thought leaders, as a result of which, we have emerged as the preferred choice for millions of teachers and learners across the world.

We believe learning opens up opportunities, creates fulfilling careers and hence better lives. We hence collaborate with the best of minds to deliver you class-leading products, spread across the Higher Education and Test Preparation spectrum.

Superior learning experience and improved outcomes are at the heart of everything we do. This product is the result of one such effort.

Your feedback plays a critical role in the evolution of our products and you can contact us - reachus@pearson.com. *We look forward to it.*

CLASS

7

Trishna's

PEARSON IIT FOUNDATION

Physics

Twelfth Edition

2025

Pearson

Photo Credits

Chapter 1 Opener: snehit / 123RF
Chapter 2 Opener: Alta Oosthuizen / 123RF
Chapter 3 Opener: Сергей Кострыкин / 123RF
Chapter 4 Opener: nikkytok / 123RF
Chapter 5 Opener: DVARG / Shutterstock
Chapter 6 Opener: Fabiano Panizzi / Shutterstock
Chapter 7 Opener: MilanB / Shutterstock
Chapter 8 Opener: Michael C. Gray / Shutterstock

ISBN 978-93-6159-580-6

First Impression

Published by Pearson India Education Services Pvt. Ltd, CIN: U72200TN2005PTC057128.
Head Office: 1st Floor, Berger Tower, Plot No. C-001A/2, Sector 16B, Noida - 201 301, Uttar Pradesh, India.
Registered Office: Featherlite, 'The Address' 5th Floor, Survey No 203/10B, 200 Ft MMRD Road, Zamin Pallavaram, Chennai – 600 044.
Website: in.pearson.com, Email: companysecretary.india@pearson.com

Compositor: Saksham Printographics, Delhi
Printed in India at MP Printers (A Unit of D B Corp Ltd), Noida 201305

Brief Contents

Contents

Preface

"If you have a great ambition, take as big a step as possible in the direction of fulfilling it. The step may only be a tiny one, but trust that it may be the largest one possible for now".

Mildred McAfee

The Pearson IIT Foundation Series has been created keeping in mind the learner's ambition to excel in a competitive examination like IIT-JEE. The series can be used in addition to the books being studied in school to attain that extra edge required to strengthen the concepts and prepare well for future endeavours.

Why Start Early with Pearson IIT Foundation

Classes VI to X are the base years of a learner's academic life. In these years learner explore their interests and determine the goals they wish to attain. *Pearson IIT Foundation* series is filled with interactive learning that not only nurtures a learner's interest in science and mathematics but also strengthens their concepts.

The series uses real-life examples and application-based problems to teach theoretical concepts. The objective of this series is to help learners cultivate an analytical mind.

Most of the lessons to be learnt are introduced to the learners in the books for class VI. As they get promoted to higher classes, new topics are added to these lessons. This additive method helps the learners' span their learning over four standards, from VI-X. Thus, learners are not overwhelmed by the introduction of completely new lessons every time they are promoted to a new class.

While their learning is being spanned across five years, so is their ability to resolve doubts for further conceptual clarity. For instance, they can use concepts learnt in class VI to solve questions in class VII. If, in case, they get stuck while answering a question, the learners can infer for themselves that they might be lacking in conceptual clarity. They can then approach their teachers, requesting them to explain the concept once again. This helps the learner to clarify their concepts while revising the lessons previously learnt.

Since classes VI-X are deemed to be a student's formative years, we, at Pearson, aim to provide a foundation level course which serves more than just a standard curriculum.

Here is how it makes a difference to a learner's overall learning...

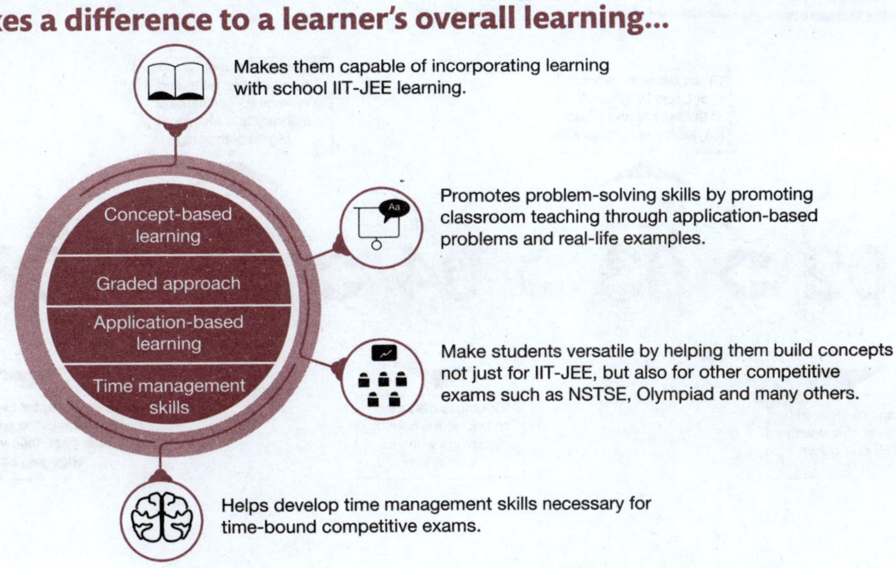

Other Uses of the Series

Instead of limiting themselves to IIT-JEE, a learner can also use this series to prepare for several other competitive examinations such as NSTSE, National and International Olympiads, NEET, BITSAT, etc. This series offers a level of concept learning that empowers learners to handle the challenging nature of questions posed in these examinations. Moreover, this will also allow the learners to have an early insight into their key strengths as well as improvement areas and help them work on themselves.

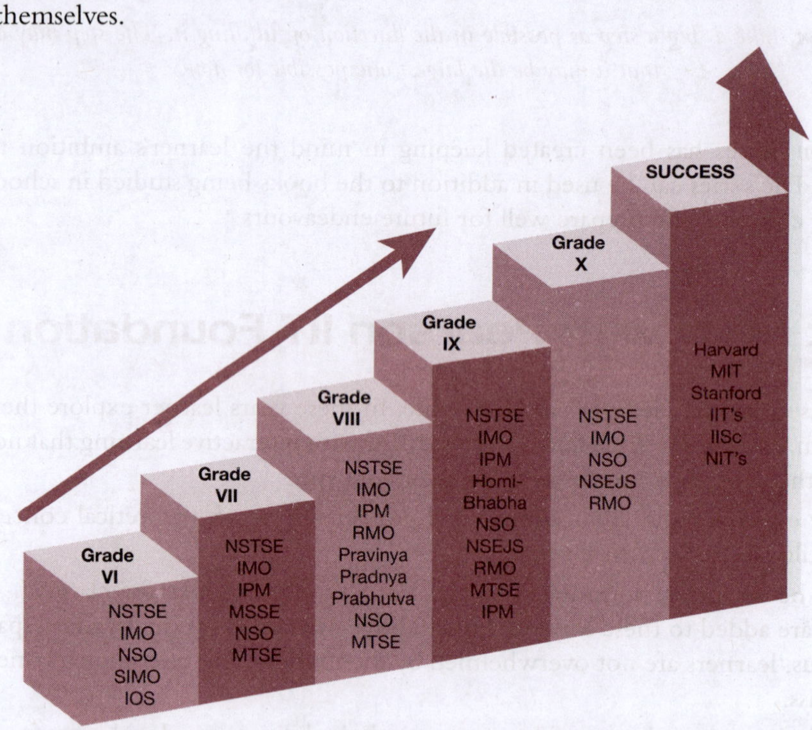

[IMO: International Mathematics Olympiad; NSO: National Science Olympiad, IOS: International Olympiad of Science, NSTSE: National Level Science Talent Search Examination, MTSE: Maharashtra Talent Search Examination, RMO: Regional Mathematical Olympiad, PPP: Pravinya Pradnya Prabhutva, NSEJS: National Standard Examination in Junior Science, IIT: Indian Institute of Technology, IISc: Indian Institute of Science, NIT: National Institute of Technology.]

Highlights of the Series

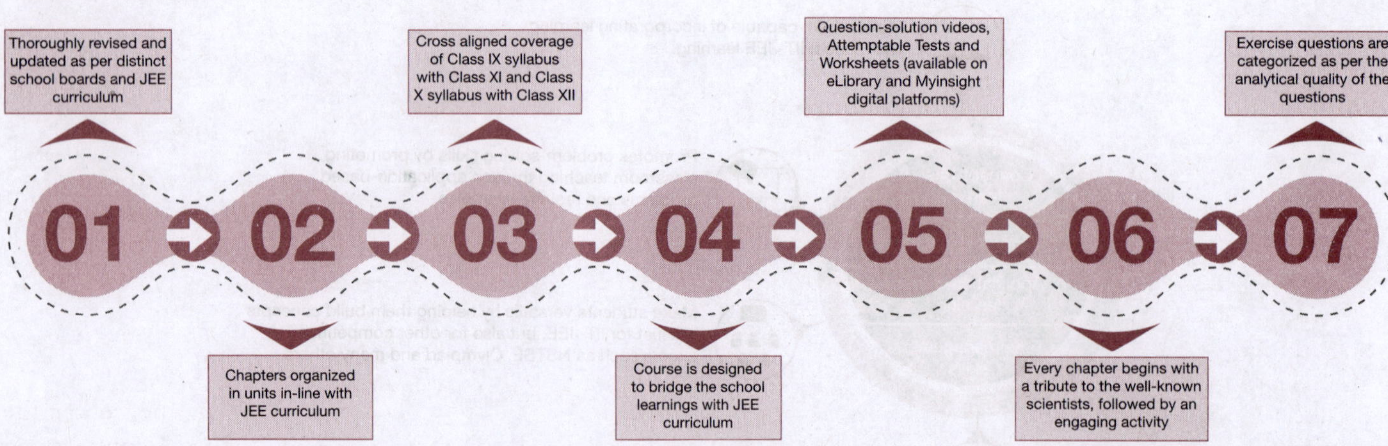

Pearson IIT Foundation series provides a perfect blend of learning through theory and practice questions with a fusion of school and JEE curriculum. It is imperative to note that this series would be as profound as you want it to be. Therefore, to get maximum benefit from this book, we recommend following the given study plan.

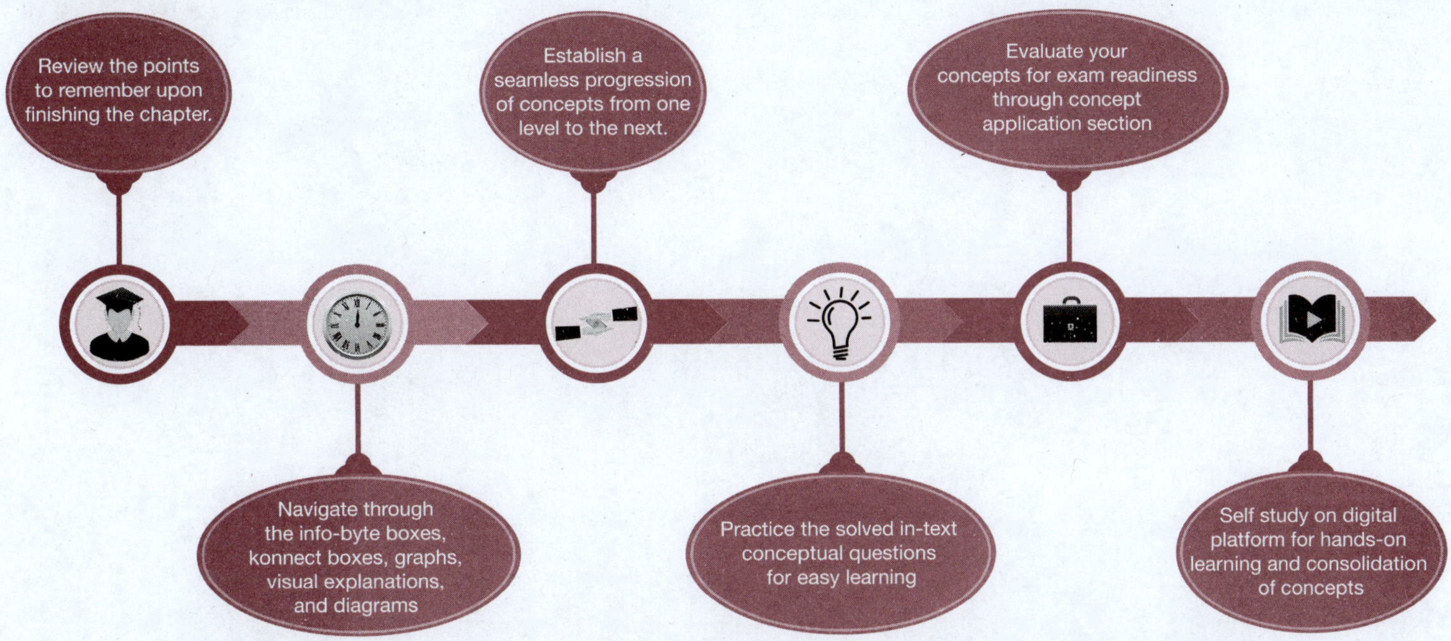

To provide a graded learning approach, the exercise part of each chapter is categorized by using four icons for question tagging. The question categorization helps the learners assess their own problem-solving and analytical skills and motivates them to improve to reach their objectives.

The following icons are used to categorize the questions with specific meanings:

Real-life Situations Questions: 

Analytical Questions: 

Conceptual Questions: 

Value-based Questions: 

With this refined and well-tuned course from Pearson, students will become more confident when they enter the competitive world for actual IIT-JEE preparation. The effort put in today will transform into a valuable asset, contributing to success in future competitive examinations.

Chapter Insights

Remember

Before beginning this chapter, you should be able to:

- Understand physical quantities
- Discuss the units for time, distance, weight, etc.

Remember section will help them to memorize and review the previous learning on a particular topic

Key points will help the students to identify the essential points in a chapter

Key Ideas

After completing this chapter, you should be able to:

- Study physical quantities and systems of units; measurement of physical quantities
- Know the difference between mass and weight

Scientific Crypt

A Tribute to William Thomson, Lord Kelvin (1824 – 1907)

William Thomson was born in Belfast, Ireland in 1824. His father was a reputed mathematician and he was given a professorship at the University of Glasgow. Thomson was quickly recognised as a child prodigy and he entered in the University of Glasgow at the age of ten. While still in his teens, he persued his graduate degree at Cambridge and Paris. His first published paper appeared when he was sixteen years old. In 1846, at the age of twenty two, Thomson was appointed as professor of natural philosophy at University of Glasgow and there he was responsible for the construction of Britain's first physics laboratory.

In 1848, he invented an absolute scale of temperature which is considered his most famous invention. The zero degree in this scale coincides with −273.1°C in Celsius scale and −459.69 °F in Fahrenheit scale. Thomson called his temperature scale the absolute scale, but after his death, in his honour the same scale is renamed as Kelvin scale. This great soul, who is an icon in the field of Science and technology, left the world in 1907.

FUN TIME

CROSSWORD

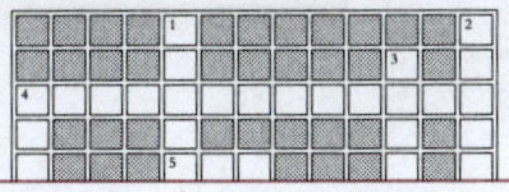

Scientific Crypt provides information about well-known scientists related to the chapter. The engaging activity is also given in the form of a crossword to keep the learners interested.

INTRODUCTION

The word 'science' is derived from the Latin word '*scire*' means to know. Science attempts to understand the unknown, and great discoveries are made in the process. The study of inanimate objects in nature is the subject of physical sciences. Its two main branches are physics and chemistry.

Physics deals with the properties of matter. For example, it talks about how dense and elastic a matter is. It deals with external behavior of matter. For example, how a matter behaves when force is applied on it. It also deals with interaction between matter and energy.

Physics explains the day-to-day phenomena happening around us. It explains, why lightning occurs during

Introduction section helps to lay the foundation of the following chapter and leads the way for further learning

Concepts are explained in a well-structured and lucid manner

Applications of Science

Science attempts to find the cause of an event. This is called 'aim'. To achieve this aim, various phenomena taking place in the inanimate and living world are observed. The reason behind a given phenomenon is determined and its correctness is verified in different situations. The science is applied through the following steps.

- **Aim:** A phenomenon is chosen to determine its cause.
- **Observation:** It involves noticing the phenomenon attentively in different conditions. For observation, sense organs as well as different instruments are used. In most cases, a phenomenon similar to the one observed in nature is created in the laboratory, which is called an experiment.

Konnect boxes are some add-on information of related topic

Konnect

Depending on the situation, different units of time are used. For example, the age of a person is expressed in years but not in minutes or hours. The time taken to go from one place to another by an aeroplane can be expressed in minutes and hours but not in months and years.

Info Bytes!

In the Imperial system, there is a unit called a "smidgen," which equals about $\frac{1}{32}$ of a teaspoon!

Info bytes are interesting trivia and facts that engage young minds and keep the grey cells ticking!

EXAMPLE 3.2 Find the amount of heat energy produced by 250 g of a fuel with a calorific value of 9500 cal g^{-1}.

SOLUTION

Given calorific value, $C = 9500$ cal g^{-1}

Mass of the fuel, $M = 250$ g

Heat energy produced; $Q = C \times M$

$Q = 9500 \times 250 = 23.75 \times 10^5$ cal $= 2.375 \times 10^6$ cal.

Examples are given in the form of in-text exercises to reinforce the concepts learnt

Illustrative examples solved in a logical and step-wise manner

PRACTICE QUESTIONS CLASSROOM WING

Very Short Answer Type Questions

Directions for questions from 1 to 5: Fill in the blanks.

1. Density of water is _____ than the density of cooking oil.
2. Weight of a body varies according to the variation in the __________.
3. The SI unit of energy is _________.
4. The density of a body is 500 kg m^{-3}. Then its equivalent value in CGS system is ______.
5. The area of a square plot is 100 m^2. Then the value of its perimeter is __________ m.

11. 5 litre of a liquid weighs 5 kgf. The density of the liquid is ________.
    (a) 1 kg m^{-3} (b) 1 g cm^{-3}
    (c) 100 kg m^{-3} (d) 100 g m^{-3}
12. 1 kilogram is equal to ________.
    (a) 1000 gram (b) 100 gram
    (c) 1000 milligram (d) 100 milligram
13. Mass is measured by using a __________.
    (a) spring balance (b) physical balance
    (c) measuring jar (d) metre scale

Points to remember summarises the concepts and topics presented in each chapter

PRACTICE QUESTIONS CLASSROOM WING

Very Short Answer Type Questions

***Directions for questions from 1 to 5:* Fill in the blanks.**

1. Density of water is _____ than the density of cooking oil.
2. Weight of a body varies according to the variation in the _________.
3. The SI unit of energy is _________.
4. The density of a body is 500 kg m^{-3}. Then its equiva-

11. 5 litre of a liquid weighs 5 kgf. The density of the liquid is ________.
    (a) 1 kg m^{-3} (b) 1 g cm^{-3}
    (c) 100 kg m^{-3} (d) 100 g m^{-3}
12. 1 kilogram is equal to _________.
    (a) 1000 gram (b) 100 gram
    (c) 1000 milligram (d) 100 milligram

s is measured by using a _________.
spring balance (b) physical balance

Short Answer Type Questions

67. The mass of a bottle filled with water is fo 150 g. The mass of the empty bottle is 50 external volume of the container is 125 cm the density of the material of the bottle.
68. Ten identical metallic balls of density 5 g c

Essay Type Questions

83. Explain the steps through which science is applied.
84. Describe how triangulation method is used to measure large distances, by taking suitable example.
85. With the help of suitable example, explain how science is applied.

Different typologies of questions have been included in the *Classroom Wing* which help students to develop the problem-solving skill

Competition Wing at the end of the chapter incorporated for competitive examination inline with JEE syllabus

Graded as per complexity: Level 1; Level 2; and Level 3

PRACTICE QUESTIONS COMPETITION WING

Level 1: Apply your Concepts

***Directions for questions from 1 to 13:* Fill in the blanks.**

1. 10 g of water occupies __________ cm^3 of volume.
2. The mass of a body does not change with change in

17. The density of the material of a solid cube of side 3 cm and a hollow cube of side 3 cm both made up of copper will have same density.
18. Mass of a body cannot be zero.

he temperature of gases increases, its density also ases.

Level 2: Review your Concepts

61. Density of the material of a paper is 0.4 g cm^{-3} mass of the paper is 0.5 g and its length and bread 10 cm and 4 cm, respectively. Determine the thic of the paper.
62. If the length, breadth and height of a cuboid increased to '*n*' times their original values, the ratio of initial and final density of air present insic cube is 8 : 1. Determine the value of '*n*'.

Level 3: Assess Your Concepts

79. Two identical containers A and B are filled wit different liquids of equal masses. The level of the l in container A is found to be one-fourth of the of the liquid in container B. What is the ratio c density of two liquids? If the density of the liqu the container A is 2 g cm^{-3}, then find the density c mixture of the two liquids.
80. Three places A, B and C form the vertices of a tria A triangle to reduced scale is drawn as shown bel the actual distance between A and C is 200 km

Is the car moving with constant speed? Find the speed of the car at the end of 2 hour and 6 hour, respectively.

69. A lorry driver sees a old man crossing the road. Suddenly he applies brakes and stops the lorry within 30 s. If the initial speed of the lorry is 108 km h^{-1}, find its deceleration.
70. A car moves the first-half of the total distance at a speed of 5 m s^{-1} and second-half of the distance at 10 m s^{-1}. What will be the average speed in m s^{-1}?
71. Define day and year. How do watches and clocks measure time? Explain.
72. What are the different points one must keep in mind while choosing a suitable scale for drawing a graph? Discuss.
73. Define velocity and explain how it is different from speed.
74. Derive the relation between acceleration, change in

77. A car starts from rest and reaches a speed of 150 km h^{-1} in $\frac{1}{6}$ h. What will be the acceleration of the car in km h^{-2}
78. Define different kinds of velocity. Give one example each kind.
79. Explain how will you change the time period of a simple pendulum.
80. I
81.

Explain, with suitable examples.

76. A ball is thrown vertically upwards with a velocity of 50 m s^{-1} and its velocity becomes zero in 5 s when it reaches maximum height. What will be the acceleration of the ball?

moon such that the time period is constant.(Take g_e = 6 g_m)

83. The length of a seconds pendulum is double. What happens to the time period of the pendulum?
84. What is a simple pendulum? Explain the terms time period, mean position and extreme positions of a simple pendulum.

Essay Type Questions

85. The $s-t$ graph shown below shows how three cars A, B and C in a race reach the target in three different times. If S_A, S_B and S_C are the speeds of the cars A, B and C, respectively, then arrange them in descending order.

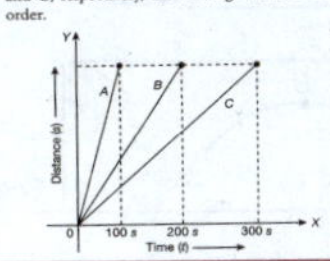

86. Describe the experimental method to determine the time period of a simple pendulum.
87. When pendulum A completes 20 oscillations, pendulum B completes 30 oscillations, what is the ratio of their time periods?
88. Explain in detail about the different kinds of motion.
89. Explain in detail about periodic motion and non-periodic motion.

The icons are used for categorisation of the questions in Classroom Wing and Competition Wing

Hints and Explanations

Classroom Wing

Very Short Answer Type Questions

1. (greater)
$d_w > d_{cooking\ oil.}$ The cooking oil will float on water because its density is less than the density of water.
2. (value of 'g')
W = mg
The weight of a body changes according to the variation in the acceleration due to gravity as the mass of the body is constant.

Mass = 5 kg

$$\text{Density} = \frac{\text{mass}}{\text{volume}} = \frac{5\text{ kg}}{5\text{ litre}} = \frac{5\times1000\text{ g}}{5\times1000\text{ cm}^3} = 1\text{ g cm}^{-3}$$

12. (a)
1 kilogram is equal to 1000 gram.
13. (b)
Mass is measured by using a physical balance.
14. (b)

Hints and Explanations for key questions of classroom wing and competition wing along with highlights on the common mistakes that students usually make in the examinations

Competition Wing

Level 1: Apply your Concepts

1. The density of water, $d = \frac{m}{v} = 1\text{ g cm}^{-3}$.
$\Rightarrow$ 1 g of water occupies 1 cm^3 of volume and 10 g of water occupies 10 cm^3 of volume.
2. The mass of a body always remains constant.
3. $\text{Pressure} = \frac{\text{Force}}{\text{Area}}$. CGS units of Force are dyne or gwt or gf and Area is cm^2.
4. As the temperature of the gas decreases, volume decreases and its density increases.
5. The least count of metre scale is 1 mm (or) 0.1 cm.
6. The method of measuring distance by forming a triangle is called triangulation method.
7. The CGS unit of weight is gram weight (gwt) or gram force (gf).
8. The CGS unit of pressure is dynes cm^{-2}.
9. The weight of a body can be zero when no gravitational force acts on it.
10. SI unit of acceleration is m s^{-2}.
11. 1 cm = 20 km
$\Rightarrow$ 35 cm = 700 km
12. Weight is the force with which the earth pulls a body towards its centre.
13. 10 cm = 100 km $\Rightarrow$ 25 cm = 2500 km
14. False. The specific gravity or relative density of a substance is not the ratio of mass of the substance by volume of the substance.
15. True. A solid sphere and a solid cube having equal volumes are made up of copper. The mass of sphere is equal to the mass of cube as density of sphere and cube is equal to density of copper.
16. The mass of a given substance does not change with change in position or location.
17. False. Mass of solid cube of side 3 cm is more than the mass of hollow cube of side 3 cm. Even both are made up of same metal copper, their densities are different.
Density solid cube > Density hollow cube.
[∴ Mass of solid cube > Mass of hollow cube]

CHAPTER 1: WORKSHEET

DW

***Directions for questions from 1 to 5:* Select the correct answer from the given options.**

1. The screw, with 22 threads on it, is placed on the scale such that initial endof the first thread and the end of 22nd thread exactly coincides with 1-cm and 3-cm mark, respectively. The distance between two successive threads (Pitch) is ________.
(a) 0.0909 mm (b) 0.909 cm
(c) 0.909 mm (d) 0.00909 cm
2. Which of the following statements given below is/are false?
(a) A sphere and a cube having equal volumes are made

9. 1 km is equal to ________.
10. One gram is equal to ____.

***Directions for questions from 11 to 15:* Answer the following questions.**

11. A semicircle is drawn to reduced scale as shown in the figure given below. If the actual perimeter of a semicircle (ABC) is 22 km, then the diameter of the circle on the graph is ________ cm.

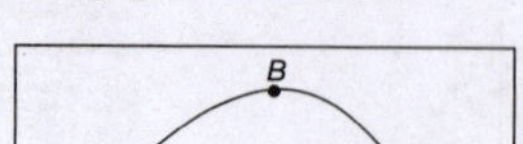

Scale: 1 cm = 2 km

DW: Downloadable worksheets supplementing textual exercises for hand-on learning

AT

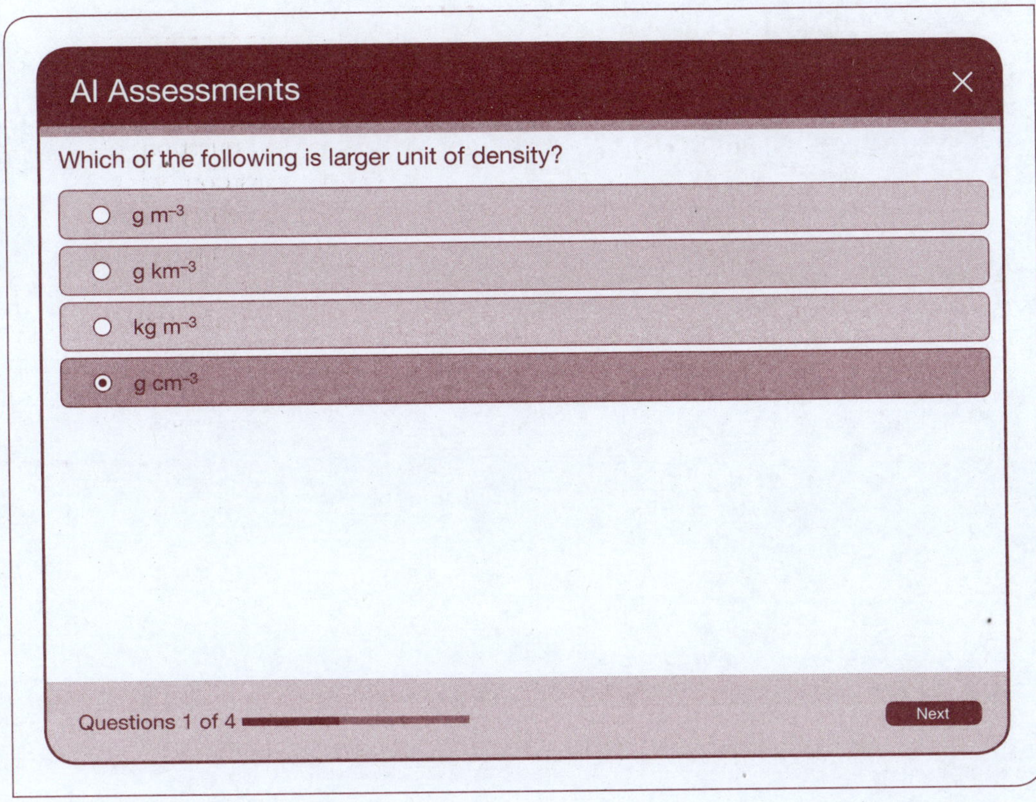

AT: Attemptable Tests for assessing understanding of concepts and getting a clear picture of your exam readiness

(B) Note the density of the given substance from the given data.

(C) Convert gram and cm in terms of kg and m.

84. Express 4 newton in terms of g cm s^{-2}.

85. Compare the following densities and arrange them in decreasing order of their magnitudes.; 4 kg m^{-3}, 10 g m^{-3}, 20 kg cm^{-3} and 40 g cm^{-3}.

Video icon: Audio and visual learning to difficult questions for effective learning and retention

CHAPTER 1

Measurements

Remember

Before beginning this chapter, you should be able to:

- Understand physical quantities
- Discuss the units for time, distance, weight, etc.

Key Ideas

After completing this chapter, you should be able to:

- Study physical quantities and systems of units; measurement of physical quantities
- Know the difference between mass and weight
- Understand density, determination of density of a solid and liquid, variation in density of liquids and gases with temperatures and its consequences
- Learn triangulation method to measure large distances

Scientific Crypt

A Tribute to William Thomson, Lord Kelvin (1824 – 1907)

William Thomson was born in Belfast, Ireland in 1824. His father was a reputed mathematician and he was given a professorship at the University of Glasgow. Thomson was quickly recognised as a child prodigy and he entered in the University of Glasgow at the age of ten. While still in his teens, he persued his graduate degree at Cambridge and Paris. His first published paper appeared when he was sixteen years old. In 1846, at the age of twenty two, Thomson was appointed as professor of natural philosophy at University of Glasgow and there he was responsible for the construction of Britain's first physics laboratory.

In 1848, he invented an absolute scale of temperature which is considered his most famous invention. The zero degree in this scale coincides with –273.1°C in Celsius scale and –459.69 °F in Fahrenheit scale. Thomson called his temperature scale the absolute scale, but after his death, in his honour the same scale is renamed as Kelvin scale. This great soul, who is an icon in the field of Science and technology, left the world in 1907.

FUN TIME

CROSSWORD

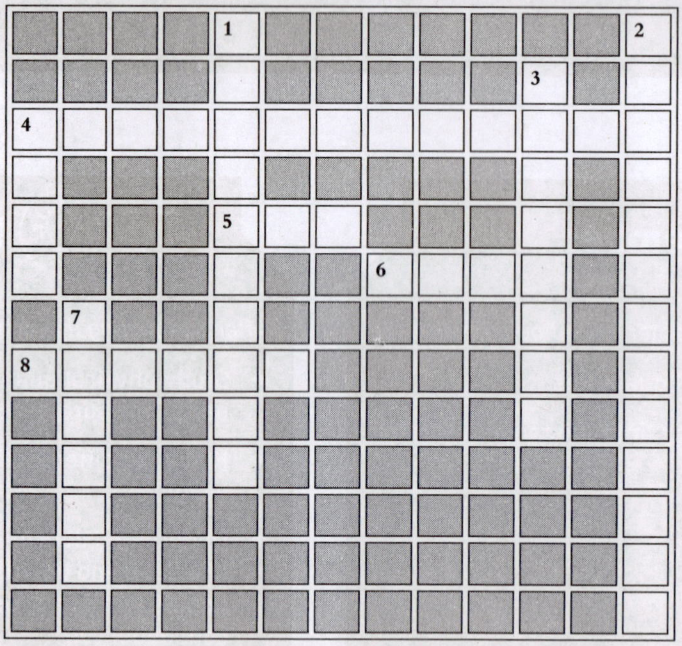

Across

4. The method used to measure the distance between our planet and the moon.
5. Product of dyne and centimetre.
6. Product of the quantity whose C.G.S unit is g cm^{-3} and the physical quantity whose unit is litre, gives a fundamental quantity which is constant everywhere in universe.
8. Pioneer of the absolute scale of temperature.

Down

1. Effect produced due to change in density of liquids with change in temperature.
2. The device used to measure a derived physical quantity whose S.I. unit is kg m^{-3}.
3. Name the mathematical operation that exist between force and area to obtain the physical quantity whose S.I unit is pascal.
4. The fundamental quantity which has the same units in all systems.
7. The physical quantity of a body whose magnitude can change from place to place on the earth.

INTRODUCTION

The word 'science' is derived from the Latin word '*scire*' means to know. Science attempts to understand the unknown, and great discoveries are made in the process. The study of inanimate objects in nature is the subject of physical sciences. Its two main branches are physics and chemistry.

Physics deals with the properties of matter. For example, it talks about how dense and elastic a matter is. It deals with external behavior of matter. For example, how a matter behaves when force is applied on it. It also deals with interaction between matter and energy.

Physics explains the day-to-day phenomena happening around us. It explains, why lightning occurs during rainy days. Why do we wear light-coloured cotton clothes in the summer and woollen clothes in the winter. It also helps us to know the working of various electrical devices, such as incandescent bulbs, fluorescent tubes, electric motors, and how *X*-rays can be used to detect fractures in a bone. It explains how ventilation in a room is achieved. Chemistry deals with transformation of substances. It classifies the substances into elements and compounds. It studies the processes involved when compounds are formed from elements. It also studies the decomposition of compounds into simpler substances.

Applications of Science

Science attempts to find the cause of an event. This is called 'aim'. To achieve this aim, various phenomena taking place in the inanimate and living world are observed. The reason behind a given phenomenon is determined and its correctness is verified in different situations. The science is applied through the following steps.

- **Aim:** A phenomenon is chosen to determine its cause.
- **Observation:** It involves noticing the phenomenon attentively in different conditions. For observation, sense organs as well as different instruments are used. In most cases, a phenomenon similar to the one observed in nature is created in the laboratory, which is called an experiment.
- **Measurement:** It involves a comparison with a standard measure known as unit. There are two systems of standard units, one is CGS (centimetre, gram, second) and the other is S.I. system (System International). In CGS system, the units of length, mass and time are centimetre (cm), gram (g) and second (s), respectively, and in S.I. system they are measured in meter (m), kilogram (kg) and second (s), respectively. The following table gives the CGS and S.I. units of some of the physical quantities.

Table 1.1 CGS and S.I. Units of Some of the Physical Quantities

Physical Quantity	CGS Unit	S.I. Unit
Area	Square centimetre (cm^2)	Square metre (m^2)
Volume	Cubic centimetre (cm^3 or cc)	Cubic metre (m^3)
Density	gram per cubic centimetre (g cm^{-3})	kilogram per cubic metre (kg m^{-3})
Velocity or speed	centimetre per second (cm s^{-1})	metre per second (m s^{-1})
Acceleration	centimetre per second per second (cm s^{-2})	metre per second per second (m s^{-2})
Force	dyne	newton (N)
Weight	gram weight (gwt) or gram force (gf)	kilogram weight (kgwt) or kilogram force (kgf)
Pressure	dyne per square centimetre (dyne cm^{-2}) or gram weight per square centimetre (gwt cm^{-2})	newton per square meter (N m^{-2}) or kilogram weight per square metre (kgwt m^{-2})
Temperature	Degree centigrade (°C)	kelvin (K)
Energy	erg	joule (J)

- **Systematization:** After measuring the physical quantities, they are arranged in a specific way. This is called systematization.
- **Inference:** A conclusion is then drawn after studying the measurements, which is called inference.

A simple example where the method of science is applied is given below:

- **Aim:** To show that the volume of a liquid displaced by a solid, which is insoluble and completely immersed in a liquid, increases with increase in the volume of the solid.
- **Observation:** Different objects, such as stone, glass, plastic, etc., of different volumes are immersed in different liquids (taken in overflowing jars), such as water, kerosene, alcohol, etc. The phenomenon is observed at different places and different times.
- **Measurement:** The displaced liquid is collected in a beaker and its volume is measured with the help of measuring cylinder.
- **Systematization:** The volume of displaced liquid of each kind is arranged in increasing or decreasing order.
- **Inference:** From studying the measurements arranged systematically, it is concluded that the liquid displaced by a solid increases with increase in the volume of the solid. This holds good for all kind of liquids.

Measurement of Some Physical Quantities

A physical quantity is one that can be measured and quantified using measures and units that provide standard for comparison.

Measurement of Mass

Mass is defined as the amount of matter contained in a body. In SI system, the unit of mass is kilogram (kg). The multiple units of mass are quintal and metric tonne, and submultiple units are gram (g) and milligram (mg), where

$$1 \text{ quintal} = 100 \text{ kg}; 1 \text{ tonne} = 1000 \text{ kg}; 1 \text{ gram} = \frac{1}{1000} \text{ kg}$$

$$1 \text{ milligram} = \frac{1}{1000} \text{ g} = \frac{1}{10,00,000} \text{ kg}$$

Info Bytes!

As the altitude increases, weight increases as gravity decreases.

Mass of a body does not change with place or time. It remains constant. Mass is measured by using a physical balance or a beam balance.

The weight of a body is the force of gravity exerted by the earth on it. It depends on its mass as well as on acceleration due to gravity. The weight of a body changes from one place to another place as acceleration due to gravity on the earth changes from place to place.

The weight of a body also changes with altitude as acceleration due to gravity changes with the altitude. The SI unit of weight is **newton (N)** and the CGS unit is **dyne**. One newton of force is approximately equal to the force of gravity on a body of mass 100 g. The other units of weight are called gravitational units. They are kilogram force (kgf) and gram force (gf).

One kilogram force is the force exerted by the earth on a body of mass 1 kg. One gram force is the force exerted by the earth on a body of mass 1 gram.

Table 1.2 Difference Between Mass and Weight

S.No.	Mass	Weight
1.	It is the amount of matter contained in a body.	It is the gravitational force exerted by the earth on a body.
2.	It is a constant anywhere in the universe.	It varies according to the variation in the acceleration due to gravity.
3.	Its SI unit is kilogram.	Its SI unit is Newton.
4.	It is measured using a common balance.	It is measured using a spring balance.
5.	The mass of a given body cannot be zero.	The weight of a body can be zero when no gravitational force acts on it.

Measurement of Volume

The volume of a body is the space occupied by it. The volume of regularly shaped solid bodies can be determined easily by applying appropriate formula. For determining the volume of an irregular solid, a measuring cylinder is used. The measuring cylinder is also used to measure the volume of a liquid.

A measuring cylinder is a cylindrical vessel with graduations in millilitre or cubic centimetre. In order to measure the volume of a given liquid, it is poured in an empty cylinder and the marking corresponding to the upper surface of the liquid is noted, which gives the volume of the liquid.

The volume of an irregularly shaped solid can be determined by immersing it into water, contained in a measuring cylinder. For example, to measure the volume of a stone, the stone is tied with the thread and is lowered into the measuring cylinder. The water level rises. The volume of the stone equals the difference between the volume of water before and after the stone is immersed.

Measurement of Density

If we compare the masses of different substances of the same volume, we find the mass to be different. For example, the mass of a certain volume of iron is greater than the mass of the same volume of wood. Why is it so? This is because the atoms in iron are more densely packed than the atoms in wood. In other words, density of iron is more than the density of wood. The density is defined as the mass per unit volume of a substance. Thus,

$$\text{Density } (D) = \frac{\text{mass}\,(m)}{\text{volume}\,(V)}.$$

The SI unit of density is kg m^{-3} and CGS unit is g cm^{-3}.

$$1 \text{ kg m}^{-3} = 1000 \text{ g cm}^{-3}$$

$$\text{Density of water} = 1 \text{ g cm}^{-3} = 1000 \text{ kg m}^{-3}$$

> **Info Bytes!**
>
> In the Imperial system, there is a unit called a "smidgen," which equals about $\frac{1}{32}$ of a teaspoon!

Determination of Density of a Solid by Using a Measuring Cylinder

The mass of a solid can be determined accurately by using a physical balance. The volume of an irregularly shaped solid can be determined by using a measuring jar (cylinder).

To measure the volume of a solid, note the initial reading in the measuring jar and immerse the solid into the jar. Note down the final reading. The difference between the final and the initial readings give the volume of the solid. Divide the mass by the volume and find out the density.

Determination of Density of a Liquid by Using a Density Bottle

A density bottle is a specially designed glass bottle available in different capacities. Generally, a density bottle of capacity 50 mL is used for finding the density of various liquids.

A density bottle is a long-necked bottle provided with a ground glass stopper as shown in Fig 1.1.

The stopper has a capillary tube. When the bottle is filled with a given liquid and the stopper is inserted, the liquid rises through the capillary tube and overflows. This ensures the accurate volume of a liquid being taken in the density bottle, whenever it is filled with different liquids. In order to find the density of a given liquid, the density bottle is washed with distilled water and dried in hot air. The mass of the density bottle with the stopper is determined by using a physical balance. The density bottle is then filled with distilled water and the stopper is inserted. The water that overflows is wiped and the mass is determined (using a physical balance). After determining the mass of the bottle with distilled water, the distilled water is poured out and the bottle is dried in hot air. Now, the bottle is filled with the liquid and the stopper is inserted. The liquid that overflows is wiped out and the mass of the density bottle filled with the liquid is measured using a physical balance.

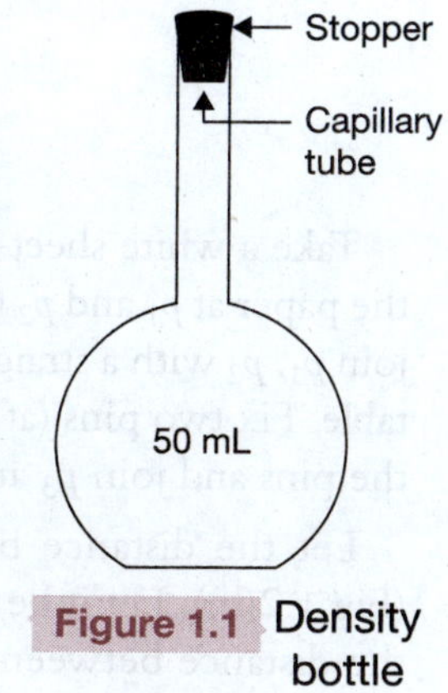

Figure 1.1 Density bottle

We can find the mass of a liquid and the distilled water by subtracting the mass of empty density bottle from the mass of density bottle filled with liquid and distilled water.

The density of liquid can be found as follows:

$$\text{Relative density} = \frac{\text{mass of liquid}}{\text{volume of liquid}} \div \frac{\text{mass of water}}{\text{volume of water}} = \frac{\text{mass of liquid}}{\text{mass of water}}$$

Konnect

The volume of liquid is equal to the volume of water. Since the density of water is 1 g cm^{-3}, its volume in CGS system is equal to its mass in CGS system.

Variation in Density of Liquids and Gases with Temperature

The expansion of solids with rise in temperature is so small that it is negligible. As volume remains almost constant, the density of solid ($d = m/V$) does not change with minor changes in temperature (from 20 °C to 40 °C).

The liquids and gases, however, expand appreciably with a rise in temperature so that the change in their density with change in temperature is large.

When water filled in a beaker is heated, it is hotter at the bottom than at the top. The hot water at the bottom, being lighter rises up and the cold water at the top, being heavier sinks in. This creates a sort of current called **convection current**. The liquids heat up due to convection current.

On being heated, gases behave in the same way as liquids. Convection currents are set up in gases also. The convection currents in gases are responsible for formation of the sea and the land breezes, the monsoon and the westerlies. The ventilation in a room is possible due to the convection current in the air. The convection current also explains why a flame point is in the upward direction.

The Triangulation Method

We use the triangulation method to measure large distances, such as the distance between planets and stars, width of river, height of hills, etc., where survey chains or big tapes cannot be used. Such huge distances are found out by constructing triangles, and therefore, this method is known as the **triangulation method**.

Let us see how the triangulation method can be applied to measure the distance between the corner of a table (A or B) and the toy placed on the table (C) as shown in the Fig 1.2 (a).

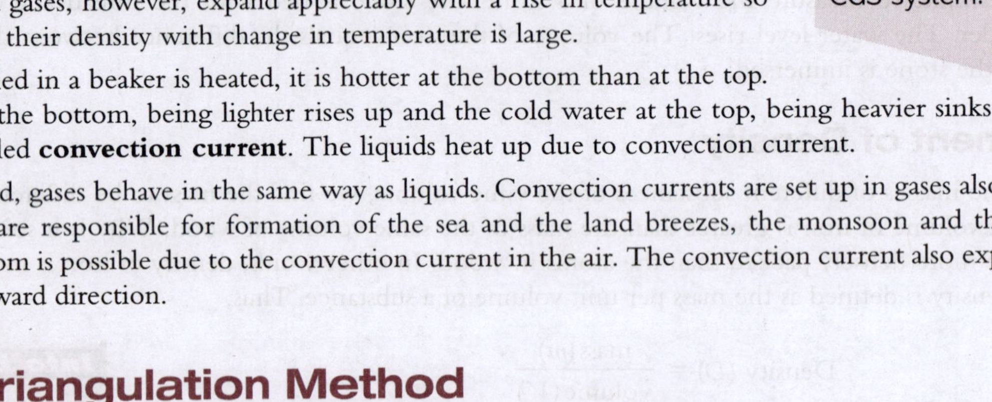

Figure 1.2 Illustration of triangulation method

Take a white sheet of paper and place it along the edges of the table. Now, look at the toy (placed at C). Fix two pins on the paper at p_1 and p_2 (at the corner of table) such that the two pins and the toy are in a straight line. Remove the two pins and join p_1, p_2 with a straight line. Now move to the other corner of the table and place the same paper along the two edges of the table. Fix two pins (at the corner of the table) at p_3 and p_4 such that the two pins and the toy are in the straight line. Remove the pins and join p_3 and p_4. After producing, the two straight lines meet at certain point, say p as shown in the Fig 1.2(b).

Let the distance between A and B on the table be 1 m. Measure the distance between p_1 and p_3 in the diagram (Fig 1.2(b)). Let it be 5 cm. This implies that 1 cm length in the diagram is equal to the actual distance of 20 cm. To know the distance between you (you are at p_1) and the toy, measure the length p_1p in the diagram. To get the actual distance, multiply the length p_1p by 20 cm.

POINTS TO REMEMBER

- ✔ The word science is derived from the Latin word '*scire*'.
- ✔ Physics and Chemistry are the two main branches of physical sciences.
- ✔ The main steps in the method of application of Science are:
  (a) aim (b) observation
  (c) measurement (d) systematization
  (e) inference
- ✔ Volume of a body is the space occupied by it.
- ✔ A measuring cylinder is used to measure the volume of irregular solids.
- ✔ Mass is defined as the amount of matter contained in a body.
- ✔ The SI unit of mass is kg. Its CGS unit is gram (g).
- ✔ The weight of a body is the force of gravity exerted by the earth on it.
- ✔ The SI unit of weight is newton. The CGS unit of weight is dyne.
- ✔ Density is defined as the mass per unit volume of a substance. The unit of density in SI system is kg m^{-3}. CGS unit is g cm^{-3}.
- ✔ Density of a liquid is measured by using a density bottle.
- ✔ Density of liquids and gases changes with temperature.
- ✔ Triangulation method is used to measure large distances, such as distances between planets and stars, width of river, height of hills, etc.

DW

PRACTICE QUESTIONS CLASSROOM WING

Very Short Answer Type Questions

***Directions for questions from 1 to 5:* Fill in the blanks.**

1. Density of water is ______ than the density of cooking oil.

2. Weight of a body varies according to the variation in the __________.

3. The SI unit of energy is __________.

4. The density of a body is 500 kg m^{-3}. Then its equivalent value in CGS system is ______.

5. The area of a square plot is 100 m^2. Then the value of its perimeter is __________ m.

***Directions for questions from 6 to 43:* For each of the questions, four choices have been provided. Select the correct alternative.**

6. The smallest measurement that can be measured by using a wall clock is __________.
(a) 1 second (b) 1 minute
(c) 1 hour (d) 2 second

7. The length and breadth of a rectangle are 2 m and 5 m, respectively, the area of the rectangle is _______.
(a) 10 m^2 (b) 100000 cm^2
(c) 1 km^2 (d) Both (a) and (b)

8. If the density of a substance is 2×10^3 kg m^{-3}, then the mass of 5 m^3 of this substance is _______.
(a) 1000 kg (b) 10000 g
(c) 10000 kg (d) Both (a) and (b)

9. The mass of a body of weight 200 gf is _______ g.
(a) 200 (b) 300
(c) 400 (d) 20

10. A pile of identical one rupee coins are placed over a metre scale as shown in the figure. The thickness of a one rupee coin is _______.

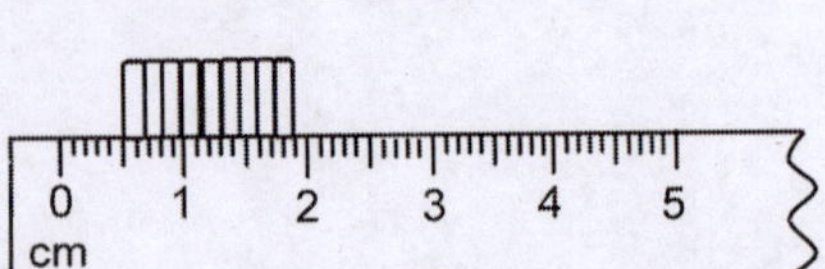

(a) 1.56 mm (b) 1.56 cm
(c) 1.67 mm (d) 1.67 cm

11. 5 litre of a liquid weighs 5 kgf. The density of the liquid is _______.
(a) 1 kg m^{-3} (b) 1 g cm^{-3}
(c) 100 kg m^{-3} (d) 100 g m^{-3}

12. 1 kilogram is equal to _________.
(a) 1000 gram (b) 100 gram
(c) 1000 milligram (d) 100 milligram

13. Mass is measured by using a __________.
(a) spring balance (b) physical balance
(c) measuring jar (d) metre scale

14. 1 kg m^{-3} = __________
(a) 1000 g m^{-3} (b) $\frac{1}{1000}$ g cm^{-3}
(c) 10000 kg cm^{-3} (d) 1 g cm^{-3}

15. The distance between two cities A and B in a map is 7.5 cm. The scale taken for drawing this map is 1 cm = 1,50,000 m. The actual distance between A and B is __________ km.
(a) 1125000 (b) 20000
(c) 200 (d) 1125

16. 1 m^3 = _______ litre.
(a) 1 (b) 10
(c) 100 (d) 1000

17. The whole length of a metre scale is divided into 500 equal parts then the smallest measurement that can be measured by using the scale is _______.
(a) 0.5 m (b) 0.005 m
(c) 50 mm (d) 2 mm

18. Which of the following is the CGS unit of energy?
(a) Degree centigrade (b) Erg
(c) Square centimeter (d) Newton

19. Which of the following statements is/are incorrect?
(a) The weight of a body can be zero.
(b) The weight of a body can be greater than zero.
(c) The mass of a body can be zero.
(d) Both (a) and (c)

20. Volume of an irregular shaped solid can be measured by using a ________.

(a) density bottle (b) spring balance
(c) measuring cylinder (d) physical balance

21. Which of the following statements is incorrect?
(a) As the temperature of a gas increases, its volume increases.
(b) As the temperature of a gas increases, its density decreases.
(c) As the temperature of a gas increases, its density increases.
(d) Both (a) and (c)

22. An atlas of a country is shown in the figure, the distance between cities A and B is ______.

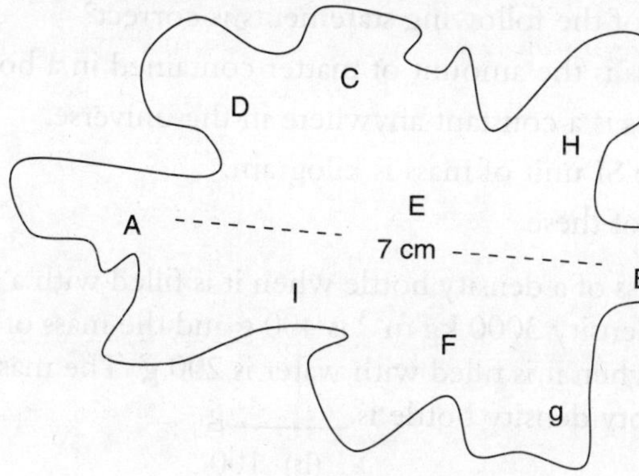

(a) 35 km (b) 3500 m
(c) 350 km (d) Both (a) and (b)

23. Arrange the following steps in a sequence to find the volume of an irregular shaped solid body.
(A) The irregular shaped solid is tied with the thread and is lowered into the measuring cylinder.
(B) A measuring cylinder with graduations in millilitre or cubic centimetre is taken.
(C) The level of water in the measuring cylinder rises after immersion of the solid. (Say V_2)
(D) First, it is filled with water to a certain level or volume. (Say V_1)
(E) The volume of the stone is equal to the difference between the volume of the water before and after the immersion of the stone. $(V_2 - V_1)$.
(a) ABCDE (b) BCADE
(c) BDACE (d) EDACB

24. Density of the material of a paper is given as 0.5 g cm^{-3}. The mass of the paper is 1 g and its length and breadth are 10 cm and 5 cm, respectively. Arrange the given steps in a sequence to find the thickness of the paper.
(A) The thickness of the paper is $= \dfrac{\text{volume } (V) \text{ of the paper}}{\text{length} \times \text{breadth}}$
(B) The density (d) of the material of the paper is $= \dfrac{\text{mass of the paper}(m)}{\text{volume of the paper}(V)}$
(C) Then the volume (V) of the paper $= \dfrac{\text{mass of the paper } (m)}{\text{density } (d) \text{ of the paper}}$
(D) The volume (V) of the paper is = length × breadth × thickness of the paper.
(a) ABCD (b) BADC
(c) ABDC (d) BCDA

25. Which among the following is/are the unit(s) of pressure?
(a) N m^{-2} (b) gwt cm^{-2}
(c) kgwt m^{-2} (d) All of the above

26. Triangulation method is used to measure ______ distances.
(a) Large
(b) Small
(c) Both (a) and (b)
(d) None of these

27. If the radius of a sphere is doubled without changing its mass, then the density of the sphere is ______ times its original value.
(a) 1/2 (b) 2
(c) 4 (d) 1/8

28. The SI unit of density is ______.
(a) g cm^{-3} (b) g cm^{-2}
(c) kg m^{-3} (d) kg m^{-2}

29. ______ is constant anywhere in the universe.
(a) Mass (b) Weight
(c) Volume (d) Density

30. 1 quintal is equal to
(a) 10 kg (b) 100 kg
(c) 1000 kg (d) None of these

31. The measuring cylinder is used to measure the ______ of a liquid.
(a) Mass (b) Volume
(c) Density (d) Weight

32.

	Column A		Column B
(A)	Liquid displaced by a solid	(a)	10^5 g
(B)	1 quintal	(b)	10^9 mg
(C)	1 tonne	(c)	Unit of pressure
(D)	kgwt m^{-2}	(d)	Volume of the solid

(a) A → a, B → b, C → c, D → d
(b) A → d, B → c, C → b, D → a
(c) A → d, B → a, C → b, D → c
(d) A → d, B → b, C → c, D → a

33. **Assertion (A):** The mass of 150 m^3 of iron is greater than the mass of 150 m^3 of wood.
Reason (R): The density of iron is less than the density of wood.
(a) Both A and R are true and R is the correct explanation of A.
(b) Both A and R are true, but R is not the correct explanation of A.
(c) A is true but R is false.
(d) Both A and R are false.

34. **Assertion (A):** The magnitude of volume of any liquid is equal to the magnitude of its mass when measured in CGS system.
Reason (R): Density of the liquid = mass of the liquid × volume of the liquid.
(a) Both A and R are true and R is the correct explanation of A.
(b) Both A and R are true, but R is not the correct explanation of A.
(c) A is true but R is false.
(d) Both A and R are false.

35. Write the following steps in a sequential order to show that the volume of a liquid displaced by a solid, which is insoluble and completely immersed in a liquid, increases with increase in the volume of the solid.
(a) The displaced liquid is collected in a beaker and its volume is measured with the help of a measuring cylinder.
(b) Different objects, such as glass, stone, etc., of different volumes are immersed in different liquids, such as water, kerosene, etc.
(c) The phenomenon is observed at different places and different times.
(d) It is observed that the volume of displaced liquid increases as the volume of the solid increases.

(a) a d b c (b) c b a d
(c) b a c d (d) b d c a

36. The unit of force in SI system is newton and it is given as 1 newton = 1 kg m s^{-2}. In CGS system its unit is dyne and it is given as 1 dyne = 1 g cm s^{-2}. Arrange the following steps in a sequential order to relate the SI unit and CGS unit of force.
(a) Write the conversions of kg and m, into g and cm, respectively.
(b) Substitute the conversions in 1 newton = 1 kg m s^{-2}.
(c) Write the relation between 1 newton and 1 dyne.
(d) Write in place of 1 g cm s^{-2} as 1 dyne.

(a) a c b d (b) a b d c
(c) b d a c (d) c d a b

37. Which of the following statements is correct?
(a) Mass is the amount of matter contained in a body.
(b) Mass is a constant anywhere in the universe.
(c) The SI unit of mass is kilogram.
(d) All of these

38. The mass of a density bottle when it is filled with a liquid of density 3000 kg m^{-3} is 400 g and the mass of the bottle when it is filled with water is 200 g. The mass of the empty density bottle is ______ g.
(a) 10 (b) 100
(c) 50 (d) 500

39. If the smallest measurement that can be measured by using a scale is 0.1 mm, then the length of 1 m in the scale is divided into ______ equal parts.
(a) 1000 (b) 5000
(c) 10000 (d) 50000

40. **Assertion (A):** Two identical spheres are taken and one is immersed in water and the other in kerosene. The volume of displaced water and displaced kerosene are equal.
Reason (R): The volume of displaced liquid is equal to the volume of the immersed part of a body.
(a) A and R are true and R is the correct explanation of A.
(b) A and R are true, but R is not the correct explanation of A.
(c) A is true but R is false.
(d) Both A and R are false.

41. Which of the following scale gives more accurate reading?
(a) One metre in a scale is divided into 1000 equal parts.
(b) One cm in a scale is divided into 2 equal parts.
(c) One mm in a scale is divided into 2 equal parts.
(d) One cm in a scale is divided into 5 equal parts.

42. If the density of a sphere is reduced to 1/8 of its original value, then the radius of the sphere is _______ times its original radius (assume that there is no change in mass).

(a) 2 (b) 4

(c) 1/2 (d) 1/4

43. Assertion (A): Spring balance is used to measure weight.

Reason (R): The weight of a body cannot be zero.

(a) A and R are true and R is the correct explanation of A.

(b) A and R are true, but R is not the correct explanation of A.

(c) A is true but R is false.

(d) Both A and R are false.

***Directions for questions from 44 to 46:* Match the entries given in Column A with the appropriate ones in Column B.**

44.

Column A	Column B
A. Science	a. Gravitational pull by Earth
B. The volume of cube of side 'S'	b. Due to convection current
C. CGS unit of temperature	c. The atoms packed within the substance
D. Density of liquid	d. Latin word 'Scire'
E. Weight	e. S^3
F. Liquids heat up	f. $\frac{\text{Mass of liquid of volume } V}{\text{Mass of water of same volume } V}$
G. The difference in densities of substances	g. Degree centigrade (°C)

45.

Column A	Column B
A. 1 g cm^{-3}	a. 1000 kg m^{-3}
B. Convection current	b. cm^3
C. Volume	c. Measurement of large distances
D. Triangulation method	d. Mass/volume
E. Mass	e. Change in density
F. Density	f. kg

46.

Column A	Column B
A. Density bottle	a. m s^{-1}
B. Temperature decreases	b. Density of liquids
C. Triangulation method	c. 1 kg
D. 10^6 mg	d. Distance between the stars
E. Velocity	e. Density of liquids increases

***Directions for questions from 47 to 66:* Answer the following questions.**

47. Fifteen identical coins are placed one beside another as shown in the figure given below. Find the thickness of a coin.

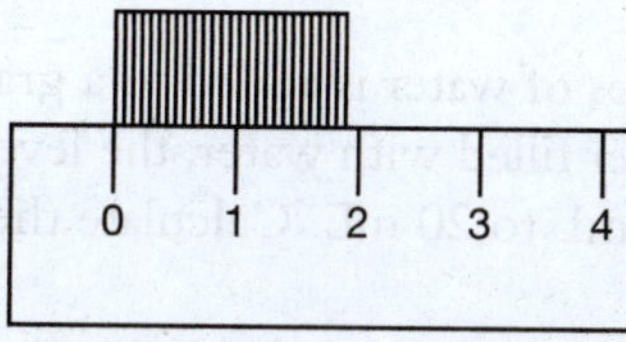

48. Express the density 2 g cm^{-3} in SI system.

49. How does the density of a solid change with minor changes in temperature?

50. Name the device used to measure the volume of an irregular solid.

51. How is the volume of a regular solid determined?

52. What is the consequence of change in density of liquids with temperature?

53. Name the method used to measure the distance between stars.

54. Define one kilogram weight.

55. Define one gram force.

56. Will mass of the solid body changes with change in its volume?

57. Define convection current. When is it formed?

58. What are the common multiple and submultiple units of mass? Express them in terms of kg.

59. Write CGS units of area, force, temperature and heat.

60. What are the main branches of physical sciences?

61. Name the steps through which science is applied.

62. What causes the formation of the land and sea breezes?

63. How does the weight of a body change with the change in altitude?

64. Convert 1 m s^{-2} into cm s^{-2}.

65. Why is the density of solid remains constant for minor changes in temperature?

66. What is systematization?

Short Answer Type Questions

67. The mass of a bottle filled with water is found to be 150 g. The mass of the empty bottle is 50 g and the external volume of the container is 125 cm^3. Find out the density of the material of the bottle.

68. Ten identical metallic balls of density 5 g cm^{-3} when dropped into water, the volume of the water displaced is found to be 500 cm^3. Determine the mass of each metallic ball.

69. When 20 drops of water is added to a graduated cylindrical container filled with water, the level of the liquid rises from 10 mL to 20 mL. Calculate the mass of each water drop.

70. A semicircle is drawn to reduced scale as shown in the figure given below. If the actual perimeter of a semicircle (ABC) is 22 km, then the diameter of the circle on the graph is ________ cm.

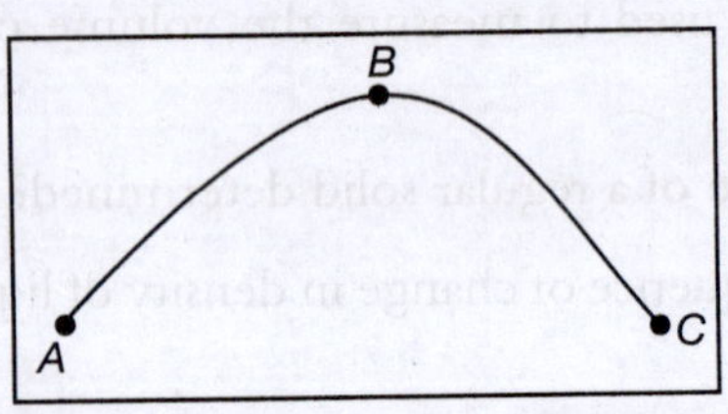

71. A meter scale (P) is divided into 200 equal parts, a rod (Q) of length 5 cm is divided into 20 equal parts. Another, meter scale (R) is divided into 100 equal parts. Rank P, Q, R in order of their accuracy.

72. The mass of an empty density bottle of 100-mL capacity is 100 g. When it is completely filled with a liquid, the mass of the bottle is found to be 200 g. Calculate the density of the liquid.

73. The screw, with 22 threads on it, is placed on the scale such that initial end of the first thread and the end of 22nd thread exactly coincides with 1-cm and 3-cm mark, respectively. Calculate the distance between two successive threads (Pitch).

74. The volume of mercury and water is 50 mL each. What is the ratio of their mass, if their densities are in the ratio 68 : 5?

75. Find the density of cuboid of dimensions 3 cm × 5 cm × 7cm and having mass 1 kg in SI system.

76. Is it possible to find density of a given liquid using a density bottle of unknown capacity and physical balance? Explain.

77. The density of a metallic sphere of radius 3 cm is 7 g cm^{-3}, then the weight of the sphere is ________ (g = 10 m s^{-2}).

78. Explain how the ventilation in a room is possible.

79. Explain why a flame point is in the upward direction.

80. Find the mass of 1 m^3 of gold in kg when density of gold is 19 g cm^{-3}.

81. If 5 kg of glycerine occupies 0.004 m^3, determine the density of glycerine in g cm^{-3} and kg m^{-3}.

82. Take two cubes each of side 4 cm made up of iron and aluminium. Why is there difference in masses of two spheres inspite of having same volume?

Essay Type Questions

83. Explain the steps through which science is applied.

84. Describe how triangulation method is used to measure large distances, by taking suitable example.

85. With the help of suitable example, explain how science is applied.

86. When half of the total volume of an empty beaker of mass 100 g is filled with water, its mass is found to be 500 g and when the remaining volume of the beaker is filled with a liquid, its mass is found to be 1 kg. Calculate the density of the liquid.

87. The following question is based on the data given below.

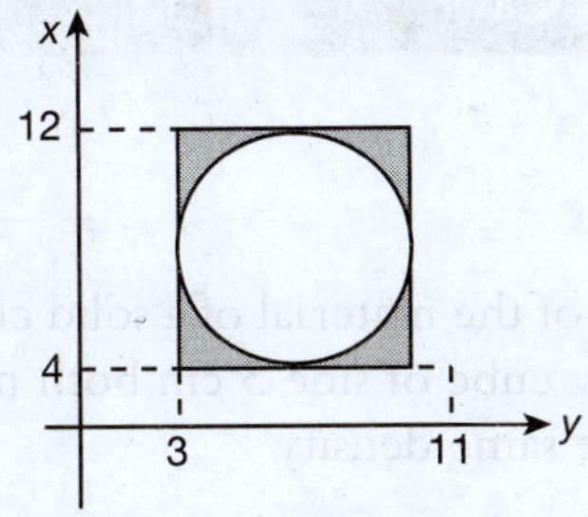

A square paper with a circle in it is placed on a graph paper as shown in the figure given above. Here each division on X and Y axes represents a distance of 2 cm. Find the area of the shaded region.

88. A right angled cone of height 9 cm and radius 3.5 cm has a density of 8 g cm^{-3}. What is the weight of the cone? (Volume of cone, $V = \frac{\pi}{3} r^2 h$) ($g = 10$ m s^{-2})

89. Test tube A contains 10 mL of liquid X and test tube B contains a liquid Y of volume 50 mL. The ratio of the density of Y to X is 2 : 5. Compare the mass of liquids A and B.

90. A density bottle weighs 150 g when filled completely with water and 250 g when filled with liquid. If the empty density bottle weighs 50 g, then write the following steps in correct sequence to find density of the liquid.

(A) Relative density of the liquid $= \dfrac{W_3 - W_1}{W_2 - W_1}$.

(B) Find the weight of empty bottle (W_1), weight of the liquid + bottle = (W_3), weight of water + bottle = (W_2) from the given data.

(C) Substitute the values in the above formula and find the relative density of the liquid.

(D) The density of the liquid is (Relative density) × 1 g cm^{-3}.

PRACTICE QUESTIONS COMPETITION WING

Level 1: Apply your Concepts

***Directions for questions from 1 to 13:* Fill in the blanks.**

1. 10 g of water occupies ________ cm^3 of volume.
2. The mass of a body does not change with change in ________.
3. The CGS unit of pressure is ________.
4. As the temperature of the gas decreases, its density ________.
5. The smallest length that can be accurately measured by using a metre scale is ____ cm.
6. The method of measuring distance by forming a ________ is called triangulation method.
7. The CGS unit of weight is ________.
8. The CGS unit of pressure is ________.
9. The weight of a body can be zero when ________ acts on it.
10. The SI unit of acceleration is ________.
11. An atlas of Andhra Pradesh is drawn by taking scale 1 cm = 20 km. If the actual length of road between Hyderabad and Vizag on atlas is 35 cm, then the distance between Hyderabad and Vizag on the road is ________ km.
12. ________ is the force with which the earth pulls a body towards its centre.
13. An atlas of world is drawn by taking scale 10 cm = 1000 km. If the distance from Moscow to London is 25 cm on atlas, then the actual distance between these cities is ________ km.

***Directions for questions from 14 to 22:* State whether the following statements are true or false.**

14. The width of the river cannot be measured by using triangulation method.
15. A sphere and a cube having equal volumes are made up of copper. The mass of sphere will be equal to the mass of cube.
16. Mass of a given substance does not change with change in position or location.
17. The density of the material of a solid cube of side 3 cm and a hollow cube of side 3 cm both made up of copper will have same density.
18. Mass of a body cannot be zero.
19. As the temperature of gases increases, its density also increases.
20. kgm^{-3} is a unit of density.
21. Triangulation method is used for measuring very long distances.
22. Density of kerosene is less than the density of water.

***Directions for questions from 23 to 57:* For each of the questions, four choices have been provided. Select the correct alternative.**

23. An atlas of India is drawn by taking scale 10 cm = 15000 km. If the actual distance between the cities of Bhopal and Cochin is 1500 km, the distance between the two places in the atlas will be _____ cm.
    (a) 10^2 (b) 1
    (c) 10000 (d) 1000
24. Sea breeze is due to the change in density of air with ____.
    (a) change in temperature
    (b) change in pressure
    (c) change in wind
    (d) change in weather condition
25. The density of liquid can be measured by using a ____.
    (a) spring balance
    (b) measuring cylinder
    (c) density bottle
    (d) physical balance
26. The area of a circle whose radius is 10 cm is ______.
    (a) 314 cm^2
    (b) 314 m^2
    (c) 3.1415 m^2
    (d) Both (a) and (b)
27. If the area of a square field is 100 cm^2, then the length of the side is ________.

(a) 1 cm (b) 1 m
(c) 0. 1 m (d) 10 m

28. Density of water at 4 °C is ________.
(a) 1 g cm^{-3} (b) 100 kg m^{-3}
(c) 1000 g cm^{-3} (d) 1 kg m^{-3}

29. Which among the following is the unit of density?
(a) kg m^{-3} (b) g m^{-3}
(c) kg cm^{-3} (d) All of the above

30. Unit of weight is/are ________.
(a) N (b) g f
(c) kg f (d) All of the above

31. A ball is placed between two wooden blocks as shown in the figure. The volume of the sphere is ________.

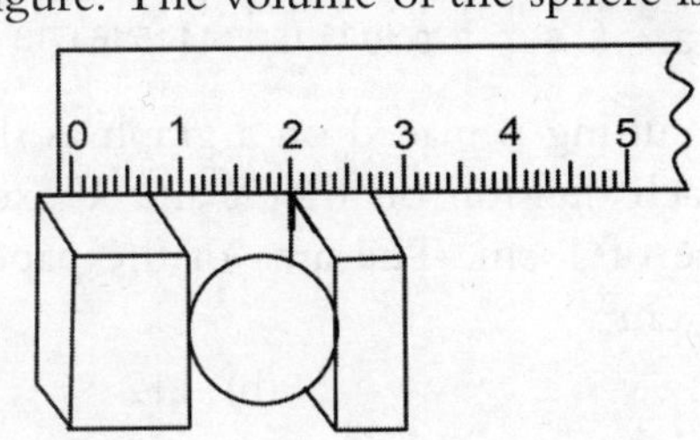

(a) 6.54 cm^3 (b) 1.15 cm^3
(c) 2.14 m^3 (d) 2.14 cm^3

32. The density of a substance in CGS system is 4 g cm^{-3}. Its density in SI system is ____ kg m^{-3}.
(a) 4 (b) 40
(c) 400 (d) 4000

33. The volume of a body having density 1 g cm^{-3} and mass 100 g is ________ cm^3.
(a) 100 (b) 50
(c) $\frac{1}{100}$ (d) $\frac{1}{50}$

34. A cylinder of height 1 m and radius 10 cm is fully filled with water, the volume of water is ________ m^3.
(a) 3.14 (b) 0.314
(c) 0.0314 (d) 314

35. 1000 kg of water at 4°C occupies
(a) 1 l (b) 0.5 l
(c) 1000 l (d) 0.75 Kl

36. 1 hectare = ________ m^2
(a) 10^2 (b) 10^3
(c) 10^4 (d) 10^5

37. 1 kg m^{-3} = ________ g cm^{-3}
(a) 100 (b) 1/100
(c) 1000 (d) 1/1000

38. If the smallest measurement that can be measured by using scale is 0.1 mm, then the length of 1 m in the scale is divided into ____ equal parts.
(a) 1000 (b) 5000
(c) 10000 (d) 50000

39. Which of the following scale gives more accurate reading?
(a) One metre in a scale is divided into 1000 equal parts.
(b) One cm in a scale is divided into 100 equal parts.
(c) One mm in a scale is divided into 2 equal parts.
(d) One mm in a scale is divided into 5 equal parts.

40. Which among the following is the unit of heat?
(a) Calorie (b) Kelvin
(c) Degree centigrade (d) All of the above

41. Which of the following statement is wrong?
(a) The mass of a body can be measured by using a beam balance.
(b) The weight of a body can be measured by using a spring balance.
(c) The mass of a body can be measured by using a spring balance.
(d) The weight of a body cannot be measured by using a beam balance.

42. The width of a stream is determined with the help of triangulation method. Arrange the following steps in a sequence to explain the process to find the width.
(A) Fix a certain stationary object like tree on the other bank of the stream.
(B) Take two pins (P_1 and P_2) and fix P_1 and P_2 at one vertex of the drawing board such that pins and tree are on the same straight line.
(C) Select two positions (say *A* and *B*) on the ground and the horizontal distance between them is noted. Let it be '*D*' m.
(D) Repeat the same process at position 'B' with other two pins (P_3 and P_4) at other vertex of the drawing board.
(E) Take a drawing board and paste a white paper on it.

(F) Fix the board at position 'A' such that one edge is directed along 'AB'.

(G) Now, produce two straight lines and let them meet at point 'P'. Complete the triangle with P, P_1 and P_3. Measure the distance between P_1 and P_3 say d. Then $\frac{D}{d}$ gives the actual distance on ground for every one cm on the drawing board.

(H) Now the width of the river will be equal to the distance from midpoint of P_1 and P_3 (let it be P_5) and P multiplied by $\frac{D}{d}$.

(a) EACFBDGH (b) EABCDFHG
(c) EDCBAFGH (d) ABCDEFGH

43. A density bottle weighs 120 g and 100 g when filled completely with oil and water, respectively. If the weight of an empty density bottle is 40 g, then arrange the following steps in sequence meant to solve the problem to get the density of oil.

(A) The density of the oil,

$$D = \frac{\text{mass of the oil}}{\text{volume of the oil}} = \frac{\text{mass of the oil}}{\text{mass of the water}}$$

$$= \frac{\text{weight of oil}}{\text{weight of the water}} = \frac{W_3 - W_1}{W_2 - W_1}$$

(B) Let the weight of the bottle + oil = W_3 = 120 g and the weight of the bottle + water = W_2 = 100 g, where bottle is completely filled with liquid, i.e., oil or water.

(C) Let the weight of the empty bottle = W_1 = 40 g

(D) Then the weight of the oil and water would be equal to $(W_3 - W_1)$ and $(W_2 - W_1)$, respectively.

(a) CBDA (b) ABCD
(c) BADC (d) DCBA

44. A stock of identical coins are placed on a scale as shown in the figure. The thickness of a coin is ______.

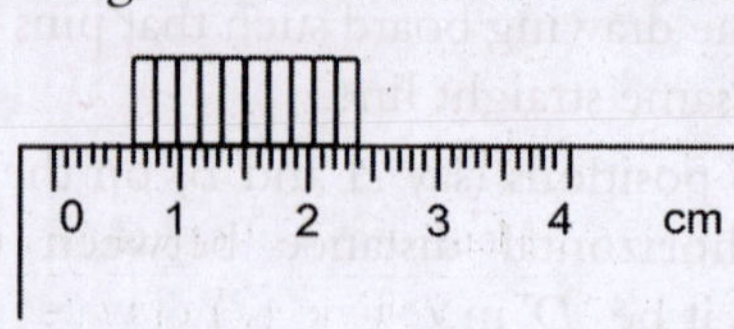

(a) 1.8 cm (b) 18 mm
(c) 1.8 mm (d) 0.18 m

45. If the density of a sphere is reduced to 1/8 of its original value, then the radius of the sphere is ______ times its original radius (assume that there is no change in mass).

(a) 2 (b) 4
(c) 1/2 (d) 1/4

46.

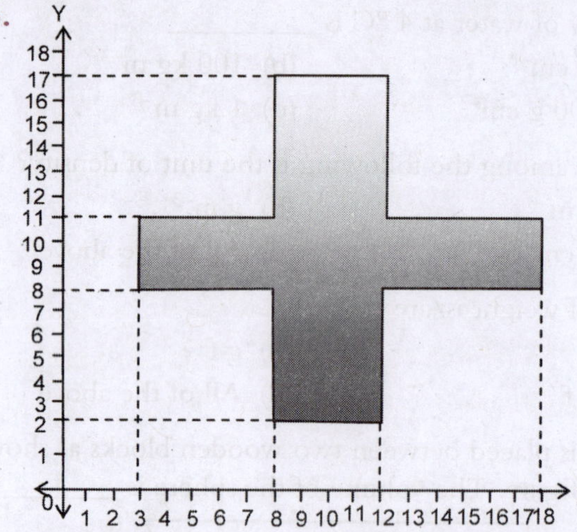

A paper cutting is placed on a graph as shown in the figure, each division on the X and Y axes represents a distance of 1 cm. The area of the paper cutting is ______ cm^2.

(a) 100 (b) 112
(c) 93 (d) 96

47. A stone of density 5×10^3 kg m^{-3} and mass 2 kg is immersed into a liquid, inside a graduated cylinder. The reading on the graduated cylinder is 1000 cm^3 before the stone is immersed into it, the reading after the stone is immersed in it is ______ cm^3.

(a) 14000 (b) 500
(c) 5000 (d) 1400

48. The weight of the given solid cylinder rod is 2512 N. The density of the body is ______ kg m^{-3}. (take g = 10 m s^{-2})

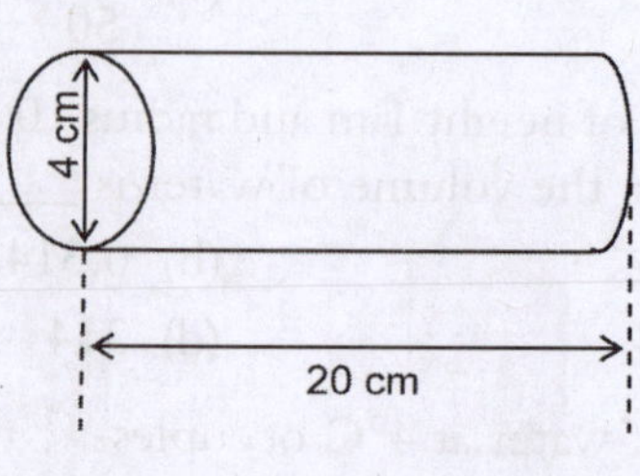

(a) 2512 (b) 25×12
(c) 10^3 (d) 10^6

49. The mass of a density bottle when it is filled with a liquid of density 3000 kg m^{-3} is 400 g and the mass of the bottle when it is filled with water is 200 g. The mass of the empty density bottle is ______ g.

(a) 10 (b) 100
(c) 50 (d) 500

50. 1 g m^{-3} = ______ kg cm^{-3}.
(a) 10^9 (b) 10^6
(c) 10^{-6} (d) 10^{-9}

51. In a particular scale *A*, one metre is divided into 500 equal parts and in scale *B* one cm is divided into 5 equal parts and in scale C one mm is divided into 2 equal parts, then the accuracy of ______.
(a) A > B > C (b) A = B < C
(c) A = B > C (d) A = B = C

52. A wire is wound over a pencil and placed over a scale as shown in the figure. The diameter of the given wire is ______.

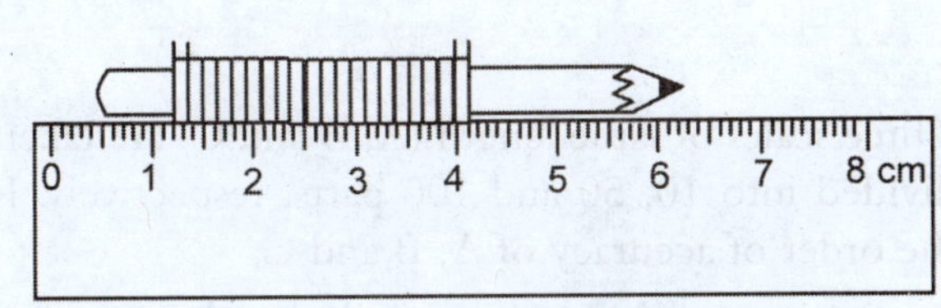

(a) 1.45 cm (b) 2.9 mm
(c) 2.9 m (d) 1.45 mm

53. If the radius of a sphere is doubled, then the density of the sphere is ______ times its original value.
(a) 1/2 (b) 2
(c) 4 (d) 1/8

54.

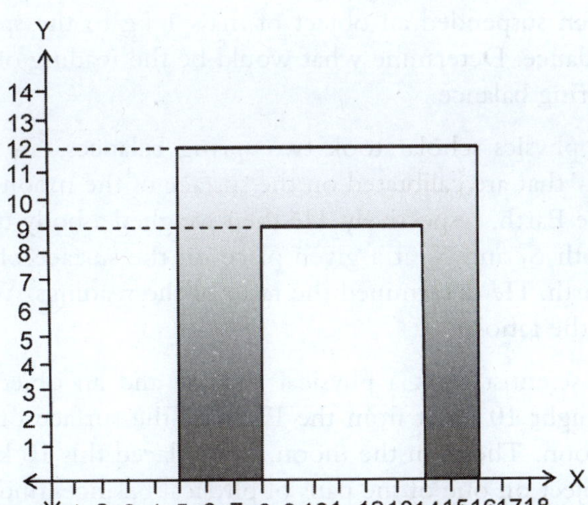

A paper cutting is placed on a graph as shown in the figure, each division on the X and Y axes represents a distance of 2 cm. The area of the paper cutting is ______ cm^2
(a) 378 (b) 186
(c) 312 (d) 156

55. The mass of an empty density bottle is 50 g. When it is completely filled with water, its mass is found to be 100 g and when it is completely filled with a liquid, its mass is 150 g. The density of the liquid is ______ kg m^{-3}.
(a) 2 (b) 2000
(c) 3.5 (d) 3500

56. Assertion (A): The mass of a given body cannot be zero.
Reason (R): Common balance is used to measure mass.
(a) A and R are true and R is the correct explanation of A.
(b) A and R are true, but R is not the correct explanation of A.
(c) A is true but R is false.
(d) Both A and R are false.

57. Assertion (A): The volume of water displaced by a solid sphere made of iron of radius 3 cm when completely immersed in water is less than that the water displaced when an iron sphere of radius 7 cm is completely immersed in water.
Reason (R): The amount of water displaced by any body depends on the total volume of the body.
(a) A and R are true and R is the correct explanation of A.
(b) A and R are true, but R is not the correct explanation of A.
(c) A is true but R is false.
(d) Both A and R are false.

Directions for questions from 58 to 60: **Match the entries given in Column A with the appropriate ones in Column B.**

58.

Column A	Column B
A. Standard measure	a. Unit
B. Physics	b. $\frac{\text{Mass of liquid of volume } (V)}{\text{Volume } (V) \text{ of water}}$
C. 1 cubic centimeter	c. Alters from place to place
D. The acceleration due to gravity	d. Weight of a body of mass 0.1 kg
E. Density of liquid	e. External behaviour of matter
F. 1 N	f. 1 mL

59.

Column A		Column B	
A.	Relative density of a substance	a.	1 mg
B.	Physical balance	b.	kg or g
C.	10^{-6} kg	c.	Density of gases decrease
D.	Temperature increases	d.	Triangulation method
E.	Measuring distances	e.	Numerical value expressed in CGS system

60.

Column A		Column B	
A.	The volume of stone	a.	kgf or kgwt
B.	The SI unit of weight	b.	Mass
C.	$\frac{1}{10,00,000}$ kg	c.	Triangulation method
D.	Common balance	d.	Cold water sinks in and hot water rises up
E.	Density bottle	e.	Difference in volume of water before and after immersion of stone
F.	Height of a mountain	f.	1 milligram
G.	Convection current	g.	The stopper has a capillary tube

Level 2: Review your Concepts

61. Density of the material of a paper is 0.4 g cm^{-3}. The mass of the paper is 0.5 g and its length and breadth are 10 cm and 4 cm, respectively. Determine the thickness of the paper.

62. If the length, breadth and height of a cuboid are all increased to 'n' times their original values, then the ratio of initial and final density of air present inside the cube is 8 : 1. Determine the value of 'n'.

63. Find the side of a cube of mass 1 kg and density 0.064 g cm^{-3}.

64. A wooden block is tied to a metallic rod of mass 100 g and immersed completely in water. When the displaced water is collected in a measuring jar, the volume of the liquid displaced is found to be 400 mL. If the density of the metallic rod is 5 g cm^{-3}, and the mass of the wooden block is 300 g, determine the density of the wooden block.

65. An atlas of a river is shown in the figure given below. Here, the river flows through A, B, C, D, E, F, G, H and I. If the length of the river from A to H is 920 km and if a glider moving directly from A to H at the speed of 400 km h^{-1}, as shown in the below figure, takes 1 h, then the distance of A from H on graph is ______ cm.

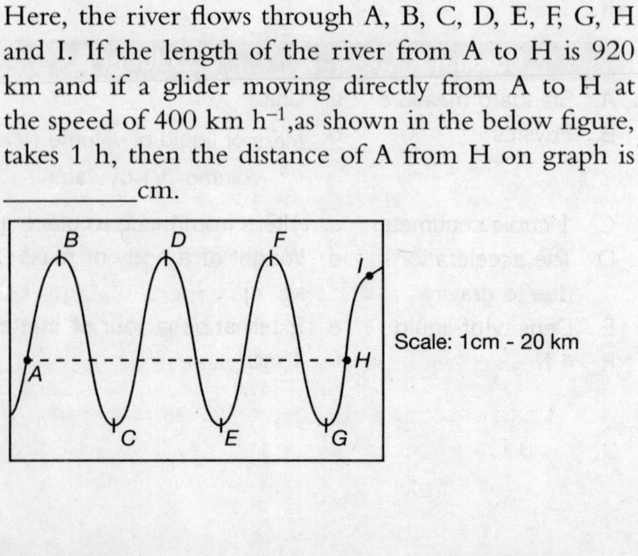

66. Three scales of same length (A, B and C) are taken and divided into 10, 50 and 100 parts, respectively. Rank the order of accuracy of A, B and C.

67. A wire is wound over a rod and placed over a scale, as shown in figure. Calculate the radius of the wire.

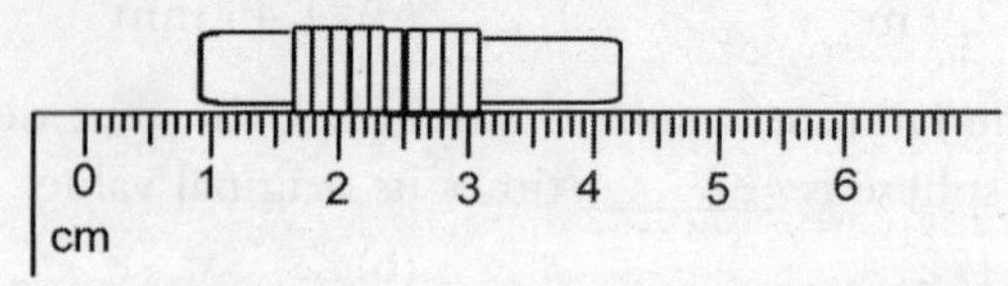

68. A student took a spring balance calibrated in gf. He then suspended an object of mass 1 kg to the spring balance. Determine what would be the reading of the spring balance.

69. A physics scholar took two spring balances, 'S_1' and 'S_2' that are calibrated on the surface of the moon and the Earth, respectively. He then weighed a body using both S_1 and S_2 at a given place on the surface of the Earth. He determined the ratio of the readings. What is the ratio?

70. A scientist took a physical balance and an object of weight 10 kgwt from the Earth to the surface of the moon. There on the moon, if he placed this 10 kgwt object on one of the pans of physical balance, find the mass of the object required to balance the physical balance.

71. A book has 100 papers in it. If the paper density is 0.2 g cm^{-3} and its dimensions are 20 cm × 15 cm × h, then find out the thickness of the book if mass of a paper is 0.1 g.

72. The change in volume of a gas with change in temperature is plotted on a graph, as shown in the figure. Calculate the ratio of density at 50 °C and 100 °C.

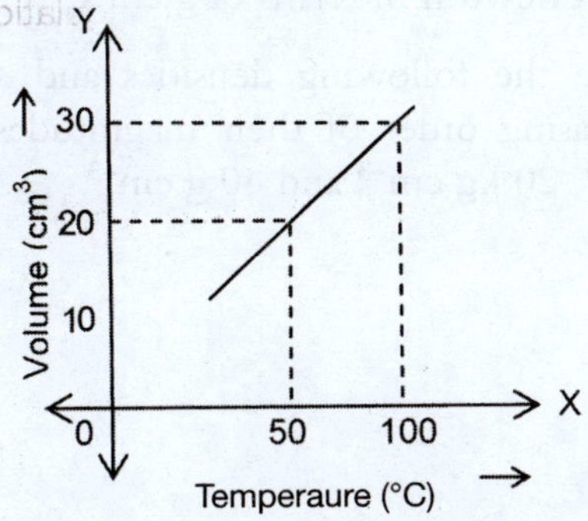

73. Ram took an empty density bottle and a weighing machine. He measures the empty bottle and found it to be 40 g. He then completely filled it with water and weighed it to be 100 g. With this data can he calculate the capacity of the density bottle? If so, what is its capacity?

74. The capacity of an empty bottle is 200 mL. An unknown liquid of mass 400 g is required to fill the bottle completely. Find the density of the unknown liquid.

75. Triangulation method is used to determine the distance between two places A and C. A triangle obtained to a reduced scale is as shown below. The ratio of the actual distances from C to another place B; and A to B is 5. Determine the distance between A and C. The actual distance between B and C is 20 km.

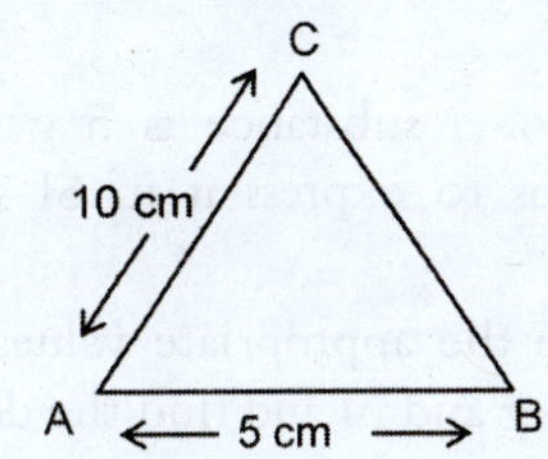

76. The weight of a body on the Earth is 500 gf. The volume of water displaced when it is immersed in water is 250 cm^3. Determine the density of the material of the body.

77. Ram took an empty balloon of mass 5 g and filled it with air. He then measured the mass of the balloon filled with air tube to be 5.05 g. He considered the density of the air filled inside the balloon as 1.5 kg m^{-3} and found the volume of air present inside the balloon. Find his answer.

78. Volume of a right circular cylinder is 88 cm^3. If the radius of the cylinder is 2 cm, then find the height of the cylinder.

Level 3: Assess Your Concepts

79. Two identical containers A and B are filled with two different liquids of equal masses. The level of the liquid in container A is found to be one-fourth of the level of the liquid in container B. What is the ratio of the density of two liquids? If the density of the liquid in the container A is 2 g cm^{-3}, then find the density of the mixture of the two liquids.

80. Three places A, B and C form the vertices of a triangle. A triangle to reduced scale is drawn as shown below. If the actual distance between A and C is 200 km, determine the actual distance from A to B and B to C.

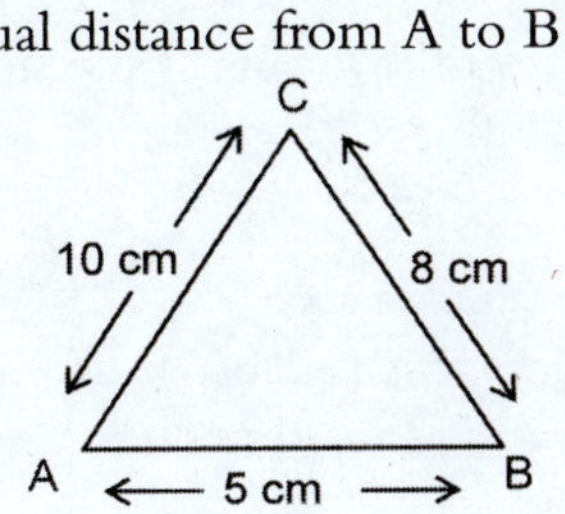

81. The following question is based on the figure and data given below.

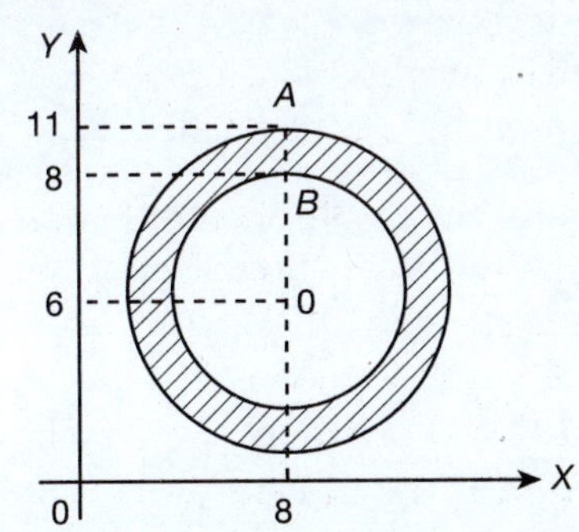

A paper cutting in shape of an annular ring is placed on a graph as shown in the above figure. Here, each division on X and Y axes represents a distance of 2 cm. The difference in the circumference of the circles passing through the points A and B is ________cm.

82. A physics student Ram was given an empty density bottle, a physical balance and a certain liquid. He first

found the weight of empty density bottle to be 50 gf. When completely filled with water, it weighs 100 gf and when completely filled with a liquid, it weighs 130 gf. He calculated the density of the liquid. What could be his answer?

83. The density of a substance is 5 g cm^{-3}. Write the following steps to express it in SI system in proper sequence.

(A) Substitute the appropriate values of g and cm in terms of kg and m and find the density of the substance in SI system.

(B) Note the density of the given substance from the given data.

(C) Convert gram and cm in terms of kg and m.

84. Express 4 newton in terms of g cm s^{-2}.

85. Compare the following densities and arrange them in decreasing order of their magnitudes.; 4 kg m^{-3}, 10 g m^{-3}, 20 kg cm^{-3} and 40 g cm^{-3}.

AT

ANSWER KEYS

Crossword

Across

4. Triangulation 5. Erg 6. Mass 8. Kelvin

Down

1. Convection 2. Density bottle 3. Division 4. Time 7. Weight

Classroom Wing

Very Short Answer Type Questions

1. greater 2. value of 'g' 3. Joule 4. 0.5 g cm^{-3} 5. 40
6. (a) 7. (d) 8. (c) 9. (a) 10. (a)
11. (b) 12. (a) 13. (b) 14. (b) 15. (d)
16. (d) 17. (d) 18. (b) 19. (c) 20. (c)
21. (b) 22. (c) 23. (c) 24. (d) 25. (d)
26. (a) 27. (d) 28. (c) 29. (a) 30. (b)
31. (b) 32. (c) 33. (c) 34. (d) 35. (c)
36. (b) 37. (d) 38. (b) 39. (c) 40. (a)
41. (c) 42. (a) 43. (c)
44. A → d, B → e, C → g, D → f, E → a, F → b, G → c
45. A → a, B → e, C → b, D → c, E → f, F → d
46. A → b, B → e, C → d, D → c, E → a 47. 1.33 mm

Competition Wing

Level 1: Apply your Concepts

1. 10 2. place and time 3. dyne cm^{-2} (or) gwt cm^{-2} 4. increases
5. 0.1 6. triangle 7. gram weight (gwt) or gram force (gf). 8. dynes cm^{-2}.
9. no gravitational force 10. ms^{-2} 11. 700 km 12. Weight
13. 2500 km 14. False 15. True 16. True 17. False
18. True 19. False 20. True 21. True 22. True
23. (b) 24. (a) 25. (c) 26. (a) 27. (c)
28. (a) 29. (d) 30. (d) 31. (b) 32. (d)
33. (a) 34. (c) 35. (c) 36. (c) 37. (d)
38. (c) 39. (b) 40. (a) 41. (c) 42. (a)
43. (a) 44. (c) 45. (a) 46. (c) 47. (d)
48. (d) 49. (b) 50. (d) 51. (b) 52. (d)
53. (d) 54. (c) 55. (b) 56. (b) 57. (c)
58. A → a, B → e, C → f, D → c, E → b, F → d 59. A → e, B → d, C → a, D → c , E → d
60. A → e, B → a, C → f, D → b, E → g, F → c, G → d

Level 2: Review your Concepts

61. 0.3125 mm
62. 2
63. 0.25 m
64. 0.79 g cm^{-3}
65. 20 cm
66. C > B > A
67. 0.75 mm
68. 1000 gf.
69. 1:1
70. 10 kg
71. 0.17 cm
72. 3:2
73. 60 cm^3
74. mA > mB > mC
75. 8 km
76. 2 g cm^{-3}
77. 33.33 cm^3
78. 7 cm

Level 3: Assess Your Concepts

79. 0.8 g cm^{-3}
80. 160 km
81. 48 m
82. 37.6 cm
83. BCA
84. 4×10^5 $gcms^{-2}$
85. 20 kg cm^{-3} > 40 g cm^{-3} > 4 kg m^{-3} > 10 g m^{-3}

Hints and Explanations

Classroom Wing

Very Short Answer Type Questions

1. (greater)
$d_w > d_{cooking\ oil.}$ The cooking oil will float on water because its density is less than the density of water.

2. (value of 'g')
W = mg
The weight of a body changes according to the variation in the acceleration due to gravity as the mass of the body is constant.

3. (joule (J))
The SI unit of energy is joule (J).

4. (0.5 g cm^{-3})
We know 1 g cm^{-3} = 1000 kg m^{-3}, then
500 kg m^{-3} = 0.5 g cm^{-3}.

5. (40)
Area = S^2 = 100 m^2
$\Rightarrow$ S = 10 m
The perimeter = 4S = 40 m.

6. (a)
The smallest measurement of a wall clock is 1 second.

7. (d)
Area of rectangle = length × breadth
= 2 × 5 = 10 m^2 = 100000 cm^2

8. (c)
$$\text{Density} = \frac{\text{mass}}{\text{volume}}$$
Mass = density × volume = $2 \times 10^3 \times 5 = 10^4$ kg
= 10000 kg

9. (a)
Weight of a body of mass 1 g is 1 gf. Therefore, mass of a body of weight 200 gf is 200 g.

10. (a)
Number of coins = 9
Total thickness = 1.4 cm = 14 mm
$$\text{So, thickness of one coin} = \frac{14}{9} = 1.56 \text{ mm}$$

11. (b)
Weight = 5 kgf
Mass = 5 kg
$$\text{Density} = \frac{\text{mass}}{\text{volume}} = \frac{5 \text{ kg}}{5 \text{ litre}} = \frac{5 \times 1000 \text{ g}}{5 \times 1000 \text{ cm}^3} = 1 \text{ g cm}^{-3}.$$

12. (a)
1 kilogram is equal to 1000 gram.

13. (b)
Mass is measured by using a physical balance.

14. (b)
$$1 \text{ kg m}^{-3} = \frac{1}{1000} \text{ g cm}^{-3}.$$

15. (d)
Scale is 1 cm = 1,50,000 m. So 1 cm in map is equal to 150 km.
So 7.5 cm = 7.5 × 150 km = 1125 km.

16. (d)
1 metre^3 = 1000 litre.

17. (d)
Total distance = 1 m is divided into 500 equal parts then the length of one
$$\text{division} = \frac{1}{500} \text{ m} = 0.002 \text{ m} = 2 \text{ mm}.$$

18. (b)
The CGS unit of energy is erg.

19. (c)
Mass of a body can never be zero and the weight can be zero if the acceleration due to gravity is zero.

20. (c)
Volume of an irregular shaped solid can be measured by using a measuring cylinder.

21. (b)
As the temperature of a gas increases its volume increases and its density decreases.

22. (c)
1 cm = 50 km
7 cm = 7 × 50 = 350 km.

23. (c) BDACE
A measuring cylinder with graduations in millilitre or cubic centimetre is taken (b) and it is filled with water to certain volume (say V_1) (d). The irregular shaped

solid is tied with the thread and is lowered into the measuring cylinder (a). Then the level of the water rises after immersion of the solid in the measuring cylinder (say V_2)(c). The volume of this stone would be equal to the difference in the volume of water before and after the immersion of the stone i.e., $(V_2 - V_1)$ (e).

24. (d) BCDA

The density of the material of the paper is ratio of mass of the paper (m) and volume of the paper (V) (b). Then the volume (V) of the paper = $\frac{\text{mass of the paper (m)}}{\text{density (d) of the paper}}$ (c).

The volume (V) of the paper is equal to length × breadth × thickness of the paper (d). Then the thickness of the paper is given by $\frac{\text{volume}(V)\text{ of the paper}}{\text{length} \times \text{breadth}}$

25. $N\,m^{-2}$, gwt cm^{-2} and kgwt m^{-2} are the units of pressure.

26. We use the triangulation method to measure large distances, such as the distance between planets and stars, width of river, height of hills, etc.

27. When the radius is doubled, then the volume will become 8 times the original.

$$\text{But density} = \frac{\text{mass}}{\text{volume}} = \frac{m}{V}$$

$$d = \frac{m}{8V} = \frac{1}{8}(d)$$

28. The SI unit of density is kg m^{-3} and CGS unit is g cm^{-3}.

29. Mass is constant anywhere in the universe.

30. 1 quintal = 100 kg; 1 tonne = 1000 kg

31. The measuring cylinder is used to measure the volume of a liquid.

32. A – d When a body with density more than the density of liquid is immersed; the volume of the displaced liquid is equal to the volume of the solid.

B – a One quintal = 100 kg

But one kg = 1000 g

∴ One quintal = 100 × 1000 g

One quintal = 10^5 g

C – b One tonne = 1000 kg

But one kg = 1000 g

⇒ One tonne = 1000 × 1000 g

And one g = 1000 mg

∴ One tonne = 1000 × 1000 × 1000 mg

One tonne = 10^9 mg

D – c kgwt m^{-2} = kgwt / m^2

kgwt is unit of force and m^2 is unit of area. Force per unit area is called pressure.

∴ kgwt m^{-2} is the unit of pressure.

33. The mass of 150 m^3 of iron is greater than the mass of 150 m^3 of wood because the density of iron is greater than the density of wood. But the reason given is density of iron is less than the density of wood.

So, A is correct and R is incorrect.

34. The magnitude of volume of any liquid is not equal to the magnitude of its mass when measured in CGS system. Only in case of water the magnitude of volume and mass are equal. So, A is incorrect.

$$\text{Density of substance} = \frac{\text{mass of the substance}}{\text{volume of the substance}}$$

So, R is also wrong.

Both A and R are incorrect.

35. Take different objects, such as glass, stone, etc., of different volumes and immerse in different liquids, such as water, kerosene, mercury, etc. The displaced liquid is collected in a beaker and its volume is measured with the help of a measuring cylinder. This phenomenon is observed at different places and different times. It is found that the volume of displaced liquid increases as the volume of the object increases.

36. The SI unit of force is newton, 1 newton = 1 kg m s^{-2}. First convert kg and m into g and cm. Substitute these conversions in, 1 newton = 1 kg m s^{-2}. Now in the place of 1 g cm s^{-2}, write 1 dyne. Finally give the relation between 1 newton and 1 dyne as, 1 newton = 10^5 dyne.

37. Mass is the amount of matter contained in a body. It is a constant anywhere in the universe. Its SI unit is kilogram.

38. Mass of the empty bottle = m_1

Mass of the bottle with water, m_2 = 200 g

Mass of the bottle with liquid, m_3 = 400 g

Density of the liquid = 3000 kg m^{-3} = 3 g cm^{-3}

$$\text{Density of liquid} = \frac{m_3 - m_1}{m_2 - m_1}$$

$$3 = \frac{400 - m_1}{200 - m_1},$$

$$400 - m_1 = 600 - 3m_1$$

$$2m_1 = 200 \text{ g}, m_1 = 100 \text{ g}.$$

39. Smallest measurement = 0.1 mm = 0.1^{-3} 10^{-3} m = 10^{-4} m

So, the length of 1 m is divided into $\frac{1}{10^{-4}}$ equal parts, that is $10^4 = 10000$

40. The volume of displaced liquid is equal to the volume of the immersed part of the body.
Hence, the correct option is (a).

41. The scale which is having the smallest least count is more accurate.

When 1 mm is divided into two equal parts

L.C. = $\frac{1}{2}$ mm = 0.5 mm.

42. Density = $\frac{\text{mass}}{\text{volume}}$

When the density is decreased to $\frac{1}{8}$th of its original value, then volume increases by 8 times the original value.

$$v = \frac{4}{3}\pi r^3$$

$$v_1 = 8v$$

$$\frac{4}{3}\pi r_1^3 = 8 \times \frac{4}{3}\pi r^3$$

$$r_1 = 8r^3$$

$$r_1 = 2r$$

43. Spring balance is used to measure weight and weight of a body can be zero, when no gravitational force acts on it.
Hence, the correct option is (c).

44. A → d The word 'science' is derived from Latin word 'scire'.

B → e The volume of a cube of side 'S' is S^3.

C → g The CGS unit of temperature is given by degree celsius or centigrade (°C).

D → f Density of liquid = $\frac{\text{Mass of liquid}}{\text{Volume of liquid}}$ = $\frac{\text{mass of liquid of volume } V}{\text{mass of water of same volume } V}$

E → a Weight of a body is equal to the gravitational pull by the Earth.

F → b Liquids stored in vessel are heated due to convection currents produced by heating.

G → c The different substances have different densities because of the difference in the density of atoms that are packed within the substance.

45. A → a 1 g cm^{-3} = 1000 kg m^{-3}

B → e Convection current in liquid is due to the change in density.

C → b Cubic centimeter is a unit of volume.

D → c Large distances are measured by triangulation method.

E → f Mass is measured in kg.

F → d Density = mass/volume.

46. (A) → b Density bottle is used to determine the density of liquids.

(B) → e When temperature decreases, the density of liquids increases.

(C) → d Triangulation method is used to find the distance between the stars.

(D) → c 10^6 mg = $10^6 \times 10^{-3}$ g = 10^3 g = 1 kg.

(E) → a Unit of velocity is m s^{-1}.

47. Given that:

15 coins → 20 mm

1 coin → $\frac{20}{15}$ mm

The thickness of the coin is 1.33 mm.

48. The density, d = 2 g cm^{-3}

$$= \frac{2\,\text{g}}{1\,\text{cm}^3} = \frac{2 \times \frac{1}{1000}\,\text{kg}}{(10^{-2}\,\text{m})^3} = \frac{2 \times 10^{-3}\,\text{kg}}{10^{-6}\,\text{m}^3}$$

$$= 2 \times 10^3\,\text{kg m}^{-3}$$

49. As volume of solids almost remains constant with change in temperature, the density of the solid remains same.

50. Measuring jar (cylinder).

51. The volume of a regular solid can be determined by measuring the dimensions using metre scale or tape and substitute in the formula of volume.

52. Density changes with temperature. Because of changing temperature, volume changes.

53. Triangulation method is used to measure the distance between the stars.

54. One kilogram weight is the gravitational force acting on a body of mass one kilogram.

55. One gram force is the gravitational force acting on a body of mass one gram

56. No. Mass of the body always remains constant.

57. Hot liquid moves up and cold liquid sinks in and creates a sort of current called convection current. When liquids are heated, convection currents are produced.

58. The unit of mass in SI System is kg and multiple units of mass are quintal and metric tonne and submultiple units are gram (g) and milligram.
1 quintal = 100 kg
1 tonne = 1000 kg
1 gram = $\frac{1}{1000}$ g;
1 milligram = $\frac{1}{1000}$ g = $\frac{1}{10,00,000}$ kg.

59. **CGS Units:**
Area = cm^2
Force = dyne
Temperature = degree celsius (°C)
Heat = erg

60. Physics and Chemistry are the main branches of physical sciences.

61. Aim, observation, measurement, systematization and inference are the steps through which science is applied.

62. The convection currents in gases produces sea and land breezes.

63. The acceleration due to gravity decreases with increase in altitude and weight also decreases because, $w = mg$.

64. We know, 1 m is equal to 100 cm.
so, 1 m s^{-2} = 100 cm s^{-2}

65. The expansion of solids with rise in temperature is negligible and volume remains almost constant. So density remains constant.

66. After measuring physical quantities, they are arranged in a specific way. This is called systematization.

Short Answer Type Questions

67. The mass of empty bottle = 50 g
Mass of empty bottle + water = 150 g
Mass of water = 150 − 50 = 100 g
Density of water is 1 g cm^{-3}. So, volume of water = 100 cm^3
Internal volume of bottle = 100 cm^3
External volume = 125 cm^3
Volume of the material of the bottle = 125 − 100 = 25 cm^3
Density of the material of the bottle = $\frac{\text{mass}}{\text{volume}} = \frac{50}{25}$ = 2 g cm^{-3}

68. Volume of water displaced = volume of ten metallic balls = 500 cc = 500 cm^3
Volume of one metallic ball = $\frac{10}{20}$ = 50 cm^3.
Density of metallic ball = 5 g cm^{-3}.
Mass of metallic ball = density × volume = 5 × 50 = 250 g

69. Volume of 20 drops = 20 − 10 = 10 mL.
Volume of 1 drop = $\frac{10}{20}$ mL = 0.5 mL = 0.5 × 10^{-6} m^3.
Density = $\frac{\text{mass}}{\text{volume}}$
Mass = density × volume = 1000 × 0.5 × 10^{-6} = 0.5 × 10^{-3} kg = 0.5 g

70. Given:
r = 22 km
R = 22 × 7/22 = 7 km
D = 2r = 2 × 7 = 14 km
Here, 1 cm = 2 km
⇒ 7 × 2 km = D
⇒ D = 7 cm

71. P → 1 part = $\frac{1m}{200}$ = 0.5 cm = 5 mm
Q → 1 part = $\frac{5\text{ cm}}{200}$ = 0.25 cm = 2.5 mm
R → 1 part = $\frac{1m}{100}$ = 0.01 m = 1 cm = 10 mm
The smallest lengths that can be measured by P, Q and R are in the order of Q < P < R.
Hence, the accuracy of P, Q, R is Q > P > R.

72. Mass of empty bottle, W_1 = 100 g
Mass of empty bottle + liquid, W_2 = 200 g
Mass of liquid = $W_2 - W_1 = m$ = 100 g
Volume of liquid, V = 100 mL = 100 cm^3
Density of the liquid
$d = \frac{m}{v} = \frac{100\text{ g}}{100\text{ cm}^3}$ = 1 g cm^{-3} = 1000 kg m^{-3}

73.

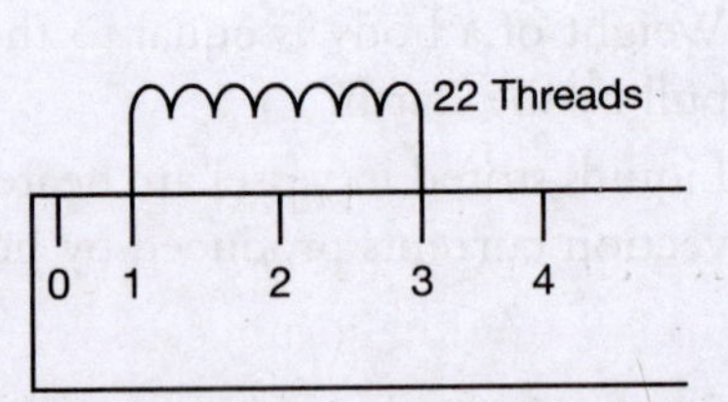

22 threads = 2 cm = 20 mm

1 thread $= \frac{2}{22}$ cm $= \frac{20}{22}$ mm

= 0.909 mm

= 0.0909 cm

74. The volume of mercury, $V_{Hg} = 50$ mL

The mass of mercury $= m_{Hg}$

The volume of water, $V_w = 50$ mL

The mass of water $= m_w$.

We know, density, $d = \frac{\text{mass}(m)}{\text{volume}(V)}$

$\Rightarrow$ mass $(m) = V \times d$

$$\frac{m_{Hg}}{m_w} = \frac{V_{Hg} d_{Hg}}{V_H\, d_w} = \frac{50\text{ ml}}{50\text{ ml}} \times \frac{68}{5} = \frac{68}{5}.$$

$mH_g : m_w = 68 : 5$

75. The volume of cuboid $v = l \times b \times h$

$= 3 \times 5 \times 7 = 105$ cm^3

The mass of cuboid $m = 1$ kg = 1000 g

$\Rightarrow$ density, $d = \frac{\text{mass}(m)}{\text{volume}(V)}$

$d = \frac{1000\text{ g}}{105\text{ cm}^3} = 9.52$ g cm^{-3} in CGS system.

And in SI system = 9.52 × 1000 = 9520 kg m^{-3}

76. Yes, it is possible.

Find the weight of empty density bottle, (bottle + water) and (bottle + liquid) with the help of physical balance. Then density of the liquid

$$= \frac{\text{Weight of (bottle + liquid)} - \text{weight of bottle}}{\text{Weight of (bottle + water)} - \text{weight of bottle}}$$

77.

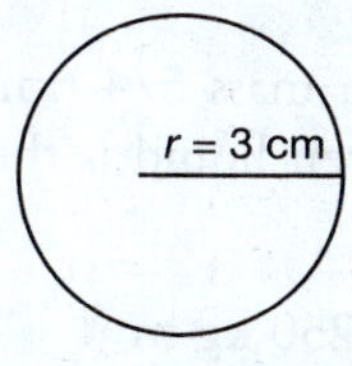

Volume of the sphere, $V = 4/3\pi r^3$

$d = \frac{m}{v} \Rightarrow m = vd = \frac{4}{3} \times \frac{22}{7} \times 3 \times 3 \times 3 \times 7$

$W = mg = 792$ gwt = 792 gf

= 7,92,000 dynes = 7.92 N

78. On being heated, gases behave in the same way as liquids. Hot air moves up and cold fresh air comes down. Thus, convection currents are set up in air. The ventilation in a room is possible due to the convection current in the air.

79. The air above the flame point gets heated and moves in the upward direction creating low pressure and the cold air below the flame point moves up to occupy the space. Because of this a flame point is in upward direction.

80. The density of gold, $d = 19$ g cm^{-3}

$= 19 \times 10^3$ kg m^{-3}

We know, $d = \frac{\text{mass of gold}(m)}{\text{volume of gold}(v)} = \frac{m}{V}$

$d = 19 \times 10^3$ kg m^{-3}

$\Rightarrow m = Vd = 1$ m$^3 \times 19 \times 10^3$ kg m^{-3}

= 19,000 kg

81. The mass of glycerine, $m = 5$ kg

The volume of glycerine $V = 0.004$ m^{-3}

The density of glycerine, $d = \frac{m}{V}$

$\Rightarrow d = \frac{5\text{kg}}{0.004\text{ m}^3} = 1250$ kg m^{-3} (SI System)

In CGS System, $d = \frac{1250}{1000}$ g cm^{-3}

= 1.25 g cm^{-3} = 5/4 g cm^{-3}

82. The volume of two cubes is same and equal to 1 cm^3. But the masses of two cubes are not equal inspite of having same volume, it is because the matter (atoms or molecules) are more densely packed in iron than in aluminium.

Essay Type Questions

83. **Method of application of science:** Science attempts to find the cause of an event. This is called the aim. To achieve this aim, various phenomena taking place in inanimate and living world are observed. The reasons behind a given phenomenon is determined and its correctness is verified in different situations. The science is applied through the following steps.

Aim: A phenomenon is chosen to determine its cause.

Observation: It involves noticing the phenomenon attentively in different conditions. For observation, sense organs as well as different instruments are used. In most cases, a phenomenon similar to the one observed in nature is created in the laboratory, which is called an experiment.

Measurement: It involves a comparison with a standard measure known as unit. There are two systems of standard units, one is CGS (centimetre, gram, second) and SI system (System International). In CGS system, the unit of length, mass and time is centimetre (cm), gram (g) and second (s) respectively, and in SI system they are measured in meter (m), kilogram (kg) and second (s) respectively.

Systematization: After measuring the physical quantities, they are arranged in a specific way. This is called systematisation. A conclusion is then drawn after studying the measurements, which is called inference.

84. **The triangulation method:** We use triangulation method to measure large distances such as the distance between planets and stars, width of river, height of hills, etc., where survey chains or big tapes cannot be used. Such huge distances are found out by constructing triangles and therefore this method is known as triangulation method. Let us see how the triangulation method can be applied to measure the distance between the corner of a table (*A* or *B*) and the toy placed on the table (*C*), as shown in the figure (*a*).

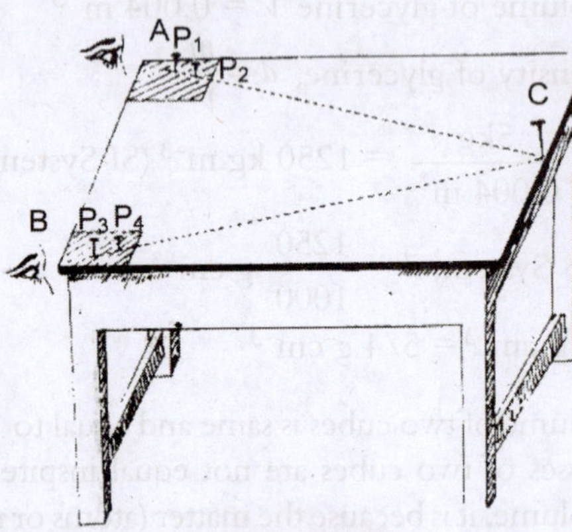

Figure (a)

Take a white sheet of paper and place it along the edges of the table. Now look at the toy (placed at *C*). Fix two pins on the paper at p_1 and p_2 (at the corner of table) such that the two pins and the toy are in a straight line. Remove the two pins and join p_1, p_2 with a straight line. Now move to the other corner of the table and place the same paper along the two edges of the table. Fix two pins (at the corner of the table) at p_3 and p_4 such that the two pins and the toy are in the straight line. Remove the pins and join p_3 and p_4. The two straight lines after producing, meet at certain point, say *p* as shown in the fig (*b*).

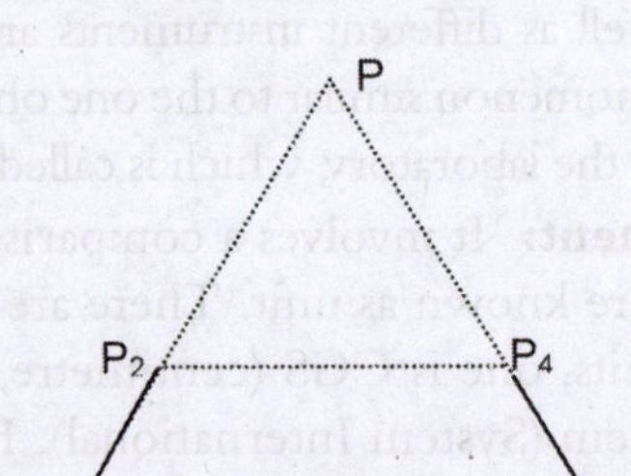

Figure (b)

Let the distance between *A* and *B* on the table be 1 m. Measure the distance between p_1 and p_3 in the diagram (figure (b)). Let it be 5 cm. This implies that 1 cm length in the diagram is equal to the actual distance of 20 cm. To know the distance between you (you are at p_1) and the toy, measure the length p_1p in the diagram. To get the actual distance, multiply the length p_1p by 20 cm.

85. A simple example where the method of science is applied:

Aim: To show that the volume of a liquid displaced by a solid, which is insoluble and completely immersed in a liquid, increases with increase in the volume of the solid.

Observation: Different objects such as stone, glass, plastic, etc., of different volumes are immersed in different liquids (taken in overflowing jars) such as water, kerosene, alcohol, etc., The phenomenon is observed at different places and different times.

Measurement: The displaced liquid is collected in a beaker and its volume is measured with the help of measuring cylinder.

Systematization: The volume of displaced liquid of each kind is arranged in increasing or decreasing order.

Inference: From studying the measurements arranged systematically, it is concluded that the liquid displaced by a solid increases with increase in the volume of the solid. This holds good for all kinds of liquids.

86. Mass of the beaker = 100 g.

Mass of the beaker with water = 500 g.

So, mass of the water (m_W) = 400 g.

Mass of the beaker with water and liquid = 1 kg.

Mass of liquid (m_l) = 1000 – 500 = 500 g.

$\frac{m_l}{m_w} = \frac{500}{400} = \frac{5}{4}$ This means that for equal volumes, the given liquid has a mass 5/4 times that of water. The density of the given liquid is therefore 5/4 times that of water.

$= \frac{5}{4} \times 1000 = 1250 \text{ kg m}^{-3}$

87.

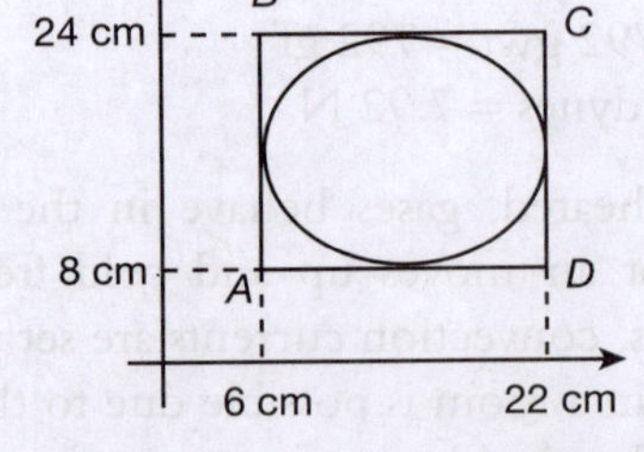

Area of ΔABCD – Area of circle

$= (22 - 6)\ \text{cm} \times (24 - 8)\ \text{cm} - \pi r^2$

$= 16\ \text{cm} \times 16\ \text{cm} - \dfrac{22}{7} \times \left(\dfrac{16}{2}\right)^2$

$= 16^2\left[1 - \dfrac{22}{28}\right] = 16 \times 16\left[\dfrac{28 - 22}{28}\right]$

$= 16 \times 16 \times \dfrac{6}{28} = 54.85\ \text{cm}^2.$

88. Given, $d = 8\ \text{g cm}^{-3}$

$V = 1/3\pi r^2 h$

$= 1/3 \times \dfrac{22}{7} \times \dfrac{7}{2} \times \dfrac{7}{2} \times 9$

$= 115.5\ \text{cm}^3.$

$\Rightarrow$ Mass, $M = V \times d = \dfrac{231}{2} \times 8 = 924$ g

Weight, $w = mg = 924$ gwt $= 924$ gf $= 924000$ dynes $= 9.24$ N

89. Given: $\dfrac{d_x}{d_y} = \dfrac{5}{2}$.

The volume of liquid '*X*' in test tube '*A*', $V_x = 10$ mL $= 10\ \text{cm}^3$.

The volume of liquid '*Y*' in test tube '*B*'. $V_y = 50$ mL $= 50\ \text{cm}^3$.

Let mass of liquids '*X*' and '*Y*' be m_x and m_y respectively.

We know, $d_x = \dfrac{m_x}{V_x}$ and $d_y = \dfrac{m_y}{V_y}$

$$\Rightarrow \frac{m_x}{m_y} = \frac{V_y\, d_x}{V_y\, d_y} = \frac{10}{50} \times \frac{5}{2} = \frac{1}{2} = 1 : 2$$

90. $W_1 = 50$ g

$W_2 = 150$ g

$W_2 - W_1 = 100$ g

$W_3 = 250$ g

$W_1 = 50$ g

$(W_3 - W_1) = 200\ g(b)$

$RD = \dfrac{W_3 - W_1}{W_2 - W_1} = \dfrac{200\,gwt}{100\,gwt} = 2\ (a, c)$

$\Rightarrow D_2 = 2 \times 1\ \text{g cm}^{-3} = 2\ \text{g cm}^{-3}\ (d)$

$= 2000\ \text{kg m}^{-3}.$

Hence, the correct order is BACD.

Competition Wing

Level 1: Apply your Concepts

1. The density of water, $d = \frac{m}{v} = 1 \text{ g cm}^{-3}$.
   $\Rightarrow$ 1 g of water occupies 1 cm^3 of volume and 10 g of water occupies 10 cm^3 of volume.

2. The mass of a body always remains constant.

3. Pressure $= \frac{\text{Force}}{\text{Area}}$. CGS units of Force are dyne or gwt or gf and Area is cm^2.

4. As the temperature of the gas decreases, volume decreases and its density increases.

5. The least count of metre scale is 1 mm (or) 0.1 cm.

6. The method of measuring distance by forming a triangle is called triangulation method.

7. The CGS unit of weight is gram weight (gwt) or gram force (gf).

8. The CGS unit of pressure is dynes cm^{-2}.

9. The weight of a body can be zero when no gravitational force acts on it.

10. SI unit of acceleration is m s^{-2}.

11. 1 cm = 20 km
    $\Rightarrow$ 35 cm = 700 km

12. Weight is the force with which the earth pulls a body towards its centre.

13. 10 cm = 100 km $\Rightarrow$ 25 cm = 2500 km

14. False. The specific gravity or relative density of a substance is not the ratio of mass of the substance by volume of the substance.

15. True. A solid sphere and a solid cube having equal volumes are made up of copper. The mass of sphere is equal to the mass of cube as density of sphere and cube is equal to density of copper.

16. The mass of a given substance does not change with change in position or location.

17. False. Mass of solid cube of side 3 cm is more than the mass of hollow cube of side 3 cm. Even both are made up of same metal copper, their densities are different. Density solid cube > Density hollow cube.
    [$\therefore$ Mass of solid cube > Mass of hollow cube]

18. Mass of a body can't be zero.

19. As the temperature of a gas increases, its volume increases or its density decreases.

20. kg m^{-3} is a unit of density.

21. Triangulation method is used for measuring very long distances.

22. Density of kerosene is less than the density of water.

23. Scale: 10 cm = 15000 km
    1500 km = 1 cm

24. The sea breeze is due to the change in density of air with change in temperature.

25. The density of liquid can be measured by using a density bottle.

26. Area of circle $= \pi r^2$
    $= \pi \times 10^2 = 314 \text{ cm}^2$

27. Area of square $= (\text{side})^2 = 100 \text{ cm}^2$
    Side = 10 cm = 0.1 m

28. Density of water at 4 °C is 1 g cm^{-3}

29. Density $= \frac{\text{mass}}{\text{volume}}$
    kg m^{-3}, g m^{-3} and kg cm^{-3} are also units of density.

30. N, kgf and gf are units of weight.

31. From the figure, we can find out the diameter. Diameter of the ball = 1.3 cm, radius $= \frac{1.3}{2} = 0.65$ cm
    Volume $= \frac{4}{3} \times \frac{22}{7} \times (0.65)^3 = 1.15 \text{ cm}^3$

32. 1 g cm^{-3} = 1000 kg m^{-3}
    So, 2 g cm^{-3} = 2000 kg m^{-3}

33. $d = \frac{m}{V}$
    $V = \frac{m}{d} = \frac{100}{1} = 100 \text{ cm}^{-3}$

34. Volume of cylinder $= \pi r^2 h = \pi \times (0.1)^2 \times 1 = 0.0314 \text{ m}^3$

35. 1000 kg of water at 4 °C occupies 1000 litres as its density is 1000 kg m^{-3} at 4 °C.

36. 1 hectare = 10000 m^2 = 10^4 m^2.

37. 1 kg m^{-3} = $\frac{1}{1000}$ g cm^{-3}

38. Smallest measurement = 0.1 mm = 0.1 × 10^{-3} m = 10^{-4} m

So, the length of 1 m is divided into $\frac{1}{10^{-4}}$ equal parts that is 10^4 = 10,000

39. The scale which is having the smallest least count is more accurate.

In the second scale, 1 cm is divided into 100 parts.

$\therefore$ L.C. = $\frac{10 \text{ mm}}{100}$ = 0.1 mm

40. Calorie is a unit of heat.

41. The density of a body cannot be measured by using a spring balance.

42. Take a drawing board and paste a white paper on it. Fix a stationary object like tree on the other bank of the stream and select two positions (say A and B) on the ground and measure the horizontal distance between them and note it as '*D*' m. Fix the drawing board at '*A*' with its edge directed along positions '*AB*' and take two pins (P_1 and P_2) and fix them at one vertex of the board such that P_1, P_2 and tree are on the same straight line. Repeat the same process at position '*B*' with other two pins (P_3 and P_4) at other vertex of the drawing board. Extend these two straight lines and let them intersect at point '*P*'. Complete the triangle with P_1, P_3 and *P*. Let the distance between P_1 and P_3 pins be '*d*'. Then D/d gives the amount of distance for every one cm on the board. Then the width of the river will be equal to the distance from the midpoint of P_1 and P_3 (let it be P_5) and *P* multiplied by D/d.

43. Consider the weight of the empty density bottle as, W_1 = 40 g. Let the weight of the bottle + oil be W_3 = 120 g and weight of the bottle + water as W_2 = 100 g. Here bottle is completely filled with given liquids, i.e., either oil or water. From above, the weight of the oil and water would be equal to $(W_3 - W_1)$ and $(W_2 - W_1)$, respectively. The density of the oil =

$$\frac{\text{mass of oil}(M_o)}{\text{volume of oil}(V_o)} = \frac{\text{mass of oil}}{\text{volume of water}}$$

$$= \frac{\text{weight of the oil}}{\text{mass of the water}} = \frac{\text{weight of the oil}}{\text{weight of the water}}$$

$$\Rightarrow D = \frac{W_3 - W_1}{W_2 - W_1}$$

(*A*) (Here density of water in CGS system is 1 g cm^{-3}).

44. Number of coins = 10

Total length = 2.4 – 0.6 = 1.8 cm = 18 mm

Thickness of one coin = $\frac{18}{10}$ = 1.8 mm

45. Density = $\frac{\text{mass}}{\text{volume}}$

When the density is decreased to $\frac{1}{8}$th of its original value, then volume increases by 8 times the original value.

$$v = \frac{4}{3}\pi r^3$$

$$v_1 = 8v$$

$$\frac{4}{3}\pi r_1^3 = 8 \times \frac{4}{3}\pi r^3$$

$$r_1^3 = 8r^3$$

$$r_1 = 2r$$

46. We can divide the given figure into 5 rectangles.

Total area = 15 + 24 + 24 + 12 + 18 = 93 cm^2

47. Density = $\frac{\text{mass}}{\text{volume}}$

$$\text{Volume} = \frac{\text{mass}}{\text{density}} = \frac{2}{5\times10^3} = 0.4 \times 10^{-3} \text{ m}^3$$

$$= 0.4 \times 10^{-3} \times 10^6 \text{ cm}^3$$

$$= 400 \text{ cm}^3$$

Final readings = 400 + 1000 =1400 cm^3

48. Volume = π × (radius)^2 × height

= π × (0.02)^2 × 0.2 = 25.12 × 10^{-5} m^3

Weight = $m \times g$

$$\text{Mass} = \frac{\text{weight}}{g} = \frac{2512}{10} = 251.2 \text{ kg}$$

$$\text{Density} = \frac{\text{mass}}{\text{volume}} = \frac{251.2}{25.12\times10^{-5}} = \frac{25.12\times10^1}{25.12\times10^{-5}}$$

= 10^6 kg m^{-3}

49. Mass of the empty bottle, m_1

Mass of the bottle with water, m_2 = 200 g

Mass of the bottle with liquid, m_3 = 400 g

Density of the liquid = 3000 kg, m^{-3} = 3 g cm^{-3}

Density of liquid $= \dfrac{m_3 - m_1}{m_2 - m_1}$

$$3 = \frac{400 - m_1}{200 - m_1}$$

$$400 - m_1 = 600 - 3m_1$$

$$2m_1 = 200 \text{ g}, \; m_1 = 100 \text{ g}.$$

50. $1 \text{ g } m^{-3} = \dfrac{1 \text{ g}}{m^3} = \dfrac{10^{-3} \text{ kg}}{\left(10^2\right)^3 \text{cm}^3} = 10^{-3} \times 10^{-6} = 10^{-9}$ kg cm^{-3}

51. Least count of $A = \dfrac{1}{500} = 0.002$ m

L.C. of $B = \dfrac{1 \text{ cm}}{5} = \dfrac{1 \times 10^{-2} \text{ m}}{5} = 0.002$ m

L.C. of $C = \dfrac{1 \text{ mm}}{2} = \dfrac{1 \times 10^{-3}}{2} = 0.0005$ m

So, L.C of $A = B >$ C or occurancy of $A = B <$ C

52. Number of turns = 20

Distance = (4.1 – 1.2) cm = 2.9 cm

So, the diameter of the wire $= \dfrac{2.9 \text{ cm}}{20} = 0.145 \text{ cm} =$ 1.45 mm

53. When the radius is doubled, then volume will become 8 times the original.

But density $= \dfrac{\text{mass}}{\text{volume}} = \dfrac{m}{v}$

$$d = \frac{m}{8v} = \frac{1}{8}(\text{d})$$

54. We can divide the paper cutting into 3 rectangles of dimension (9 × 3), (11 × 3), (9 × 2)

Area = (9 × 3) + (11 × 3) + (9 × 2) = 78;

but 1 div = 2 cm

Area = 78 × 4 = 312 cm^2

55. Mass of the empty density bottle, m_1 =50 g

Mass of the bottle with water, m_2 = 100 g

Mass of the bottle with liquid, m_3 = 150 g

Volume $v = d \times m = 1 \times 50 = 50 \text{ cm}^3$

Density of liquid =

$$\frac{\text{mass of liquid}}{\text{volume of liquid}} = \frac{m_3 - m_1}{v} = \frac{150 - 50}{100 - 50}$$

$$= \frac{100}{50} = 2 \text{ g cm}^{-3} = 2000 \text{ kg m}^{-3}$$

56. Mass is the inherent property of the body and is never equal to zero. Common balance is used to measure mass.

Hence, the correct option is (b).

57. The liquid displaced by solid increases with increase in the volume of the immersed part of the solid.

Hence, the correct option is (c).

58. A – a Measurement involves a comparison with a standard measure known as unit.

B – e Physics deals with external behaviour of matter.

C – f 1 mL (or) 1 cm^3 represents the same volume.

D – c The acceleration due to gravity changes from place to place.

E – b The density of liquid $= \dfrac{\text{mass of liquid}}{\text{volume of water}}$

F – d 1 N is the weight of a body of mass 0.1 kg.
We know
$W = \text{mg}$; $10 \; N = 1 \text{ kg} \times 10 \text{ m s}^{-2}$
$1 \text{ N} = 0.1 \text{ kg} \times 10 \text{ m s}^{-2}$

59. A → e R. D of a substance is equal to the numerical value of density when expressed in CGS system.

B → b Physical balance is used to measure mass of a substance.

C → a $10^{-6} \text{ kg} = 10^{-6} \times 10^3 \text{ g} = 10^{-3} \times 10^{+3} \text{ mg} =$ 1 mg.

D → c When temperature increases, the density of gases decreases.

E → d Triangulation method is used to measure large distances.

60. A – e The volume of stone = Difference in volume of water before and after immersion of the stone in water present in measuring vessel.

B – a The SI unit of weight is kgf or kgwt.

C – f We know, 1 kg = 1000 g = 1000 × 10^3 mg
$\Rightarrow 1 \text{ mg} = 10^{-6} \text{ kg} = \dfrac{1}{10,00,000}$ kg

D – b The mass of a body is measured using common balance.

E – g The stopper of a density bottle has a capillary tube.

F – c The height of a mountain can be measured by using triangulation method.

G – d The water in a vessel when kept on a stove, the hot water at bottom moves up and cold water at top sinks in. Thus, produces convection currents.

Level 2: Review your Concepts

61. Density of paper = 0.4 g cm^{-3}

Mass of paper = 0.5 g

Volume of paper = $\frac{0.5}{0.4} = 1.25 \text{ cm}^3$

Volume = (length × breadth × thickness)

Thickness = $\frac{1.25}{10\times4} = \frac{1.25}{40} = 0.03125$ cm

= 0.3125 mm

62. Volume of the cuboid = length × breadth × height

Volume of the new cuboid

= (n × length) × (n × breadth) × (n × height)

= n^3 (length × breadth × height)

Density = $\frac{\text{mass}}{\text{volume}}$

$\frac{8}{1} = \frac{n^3}{1}$, $n^3 = 8$, $n = 2$

63. Given, mass of the cube = 1 kg

Given, density of the cube = $0.064 \text{ g cm}^{-3} = 0.064 \times 10^3 \text{ kg m}^{-3}$.

Volume of cube = $(\text{side})^3$

Volume = $\frac{\text{Mass}}{\text{Density}}$

$\Rightarrow (\text{side})^3 = \frac{\text{Mass}}{\text{Density}}$

$\Rightarrow \text{Side} = \sqrt[3]{\frac{\text{Mass}}{\text{Density}}} = \sqrt[3]{\frac{1 \text{ kg}}{0.064\times10^3 \text{ kg m}^{-3}}}$

$= \sqrt[3]{\frac{1}{64}\text{m}^3} = \frac{1}{4}\text{m} = 0.25 \text{ m}.$

64. Mass of the metallic rod = 100 g

Volume of the metallic rod + volume of wooden block = 400 mℓ

Density of the metallic rod = 5 g cm^{-3}

Volume of the metallic rod

$= \frac{\text{mass of the metallic rod}}{\text{density of the rod}}$

$= \frac{100 \text{ g}}{5 \text{ g cm}^{-3}} = 20 \text{ cm}^3$

Volume of wooden the block = $400 - 20 = 380 \text{ cm}^3$

Mass of the wooden block = 300 g

Density of the wooden block = $\frac{\text{mass}}{\text{volume}} = \frac{300}{380} = 0.79 \text{ g cm}^{-3}$

65. We know that velocity of glider,

$V = \frac{\text{displacement (AH)}}{\text{time }(t)}$

AH = $V \times t = 400 \text{ km h}^{-1} \times 1 \text{ h} = 400$ km.

On scale, 1 cm = 20 km

⇒ 20 cm = 400 km

66. A → 1 part = $\frac{1m}{10}$ = 10 cm

B → 1 part = $\frac{1m}{50}$ = 2 cm

C → 1 part = $\frac{1m}{100}$ = 1 cm

The smallest lengths that can be measured by A, B and C are in the order of C < B < A.

The accuracy of A, B and C is C > B > A.

67. Number of turns of the wire on the object is 10

The distance between the two ends = 3.1 – 1.6 = 1.5 cm

So, the diameter of the wire = $\frac{1.5}{10}$ = 0.15 cm = 1.5 mm

So, the radius of the wire = 0.75 mm

68. Weight of 1 kg body = 1 kgf

= $1 \times 10^3 \text{ gf} = 10^3$ gf

The reading on the spring balance is 1000 gf.

69. Here, the readings on the spring balances remain the same as the weight of the same object is measured. So, each spring balance shows same reading. Hence, the ratio is 1 : 1.

70. Mass of the object is 10 kg. So, mass of the object required is equal to 10 kg.

71. The number (n) of papers in a book is given as 100. Density (d) of the paper is given as 0.2 g cm^{-3}.

Given dimensions of paper in the book, $l \times b \times h = 20 \text{ cm} \times 15 \text{ cm} \times h \text{ cm}$, where l, b and h are the length, breadth and thickness of the paper respectively.

Given, mass of the paper, m = 0.1 g

$$\text{Density} = \frac{\text{Mass}}{\text{Volume}} \Rightarrow \text{Volume} = \frac{\text{Mass}}{\text{Density}};$$

Given, $V = 20 \text{ cm} \times 15 \text{ cm} \times \text{h cm}$

$$20 \text{ cm} \times 15 \text{ cm} \times h \text{ cm} = \frac{0.1 \text{ g}}{0.2 \text{ g / cm}^3}$$

$$\Rightarrow h = \frac{1}{2} \times \frac{1}{300} = \frac{1}{600} \text{ cm}$$

$\therefore$ Total thickness of the book, $t = n \times h = 100 \times h$

$$= 100 \times \frac{1}{600} \text{ cm} = \frac{1}{6} \text{ cm} = 0.1\overline{6} \text{ cm} = 0.17 \text{ cm}$$

72. Volume at 50 °C = 20 cm^3

Volume at 100 °C = 30 cm^3

$$\text{Density} = \frac{\text{mass}}{\text{volume}}$$

$$\text{Ratio of density} = \frac{30}{20} = \frac{3}{2} = 3:2$$

73. The mass of the water = 100 – 40 = 60 g

Density of water = 1 g cm^{-3}

$$\text{Density} = \frac{\text{mass}}{\text{volume}} \Rightarrow \text{Volume} = \frac{\text{mass}}{\text{density}}$$

$$= \frac{60 \text{ g}}{1 \text{ g cm}^{-3}} = 60 \text{ cm}^3$$

74. The mass of the unknown liquid, m = 400 g

The volume of the unknown liquid,

$V = 200 \text{ mL} = 200 \text{ cm}^3$.

The density of this liquid, d =

$$= \frac{400 \text{ g}}{200 \text{ cm}^3} = 2 \text{ g cm}^{-3}$$

$= 2000 \text{ kg m}^{-3}$

75. The distance between the places A and B to reduced scale = 5 cm.

$$\frac{BC}{AB} = 5$$

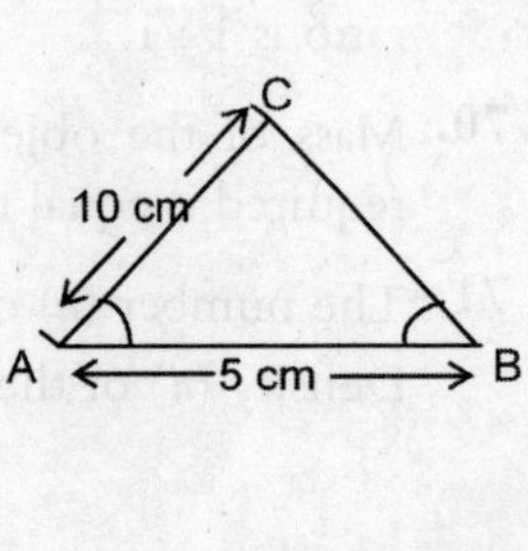

$$\frac{20}{5x} = 5$$

$$\frac{20}{25} = 4/5$$

Distance between A and $C = \frac{4}{5} \times 10 = 8$ km

76. $\text{Density} = \dfrac{\text{mass}}{\text{volume}}$

Mass of the body = 500 g

($\therefore$ mass of a body of weight 1 gf = 1 g)

Volume of the body = volume of water displaced = 250 cm^3

$$\text{Density} = \frac{500}{250} = 2 \text{ g cm}^{-3}$$

77. Mass of the balloon = 5 g

Mass of the balloon with air = 5.05 g

Mass of the air = 5.05 – 5 = 0.05 g

Density of air = 1.5 kg m^{-3} = 1.5×10^{-3} g cm^{-3}

$$\text{Volume} = \frac{\text{mass}}{\text{density}} = \frac{0.05}{1.5 \times 10^{-3}} = 33.33 \text{ cm}^3$$

78. Volume of a right circular cylinder, $V = \pi r^2 h$, where 'r' is the radius of the cylinder and 'h' is its height.

Volume of the given right circular cylinder, $V = 88$ cm^3.

Given, radius of the cylinder, $r = 2$ cm

$$\therefore \pi r^2 h = 88 \Rightarrow \frac{22}{7} \times 2^2 \times h = 88 \Rightarrow h = \frac{88 \times 7}{22 \times 4} = 7 \text{ cm}$$

Level 3: Assess Your Concepts

79. Mass of liquid A, (m_A) = mass of liquid B, (m_B)

Volume = area × height

Area of cross section of A = Area of cross section of B

Height of liquid column A = $\frac{1}{4}$ × height of liquid Column B

Volume of A = $\frac{1}{4}$ (Volume of B)

$$\text{Density} = \frac{\text{mass}}{\text{volume}}$$

$$\frac{\text{density of } A}{\text{density of } B} = \frac{m_A}{V_A} \times \frac{V_B}{m_B} = \frac{V_B}{\frac{V_B}{4}} = \frac{4}{1} = 4:1$$

If density of A is 2 g cm^{-3}, then density of B = g cm^{-3} = 0.5 g cm^{-3}

$$\text{Density of mixture} = \frac{\text{mass of mixture}}{\text{volume of mixture}}$$

$$= \frac{m_A + m_B}{v_A + v_B} = \frac{m_A + m_A}{v_A + 4v_A} \quad (\therefore m_B = m_A \text{ and } v_B = 4v_A)$$

$$= \frac{2m_A}{5v_A} = \frac{2 \times d_A \times v_A}{5V_A}$$

$$= \frac{2 \times 2}{5} = \frac{4}{5} = 0.8 \text{ g cm}^{-3}$$

80. Distance between A and C = 200 km

$\therefore$ 10 x = 200 km

x = 20 km

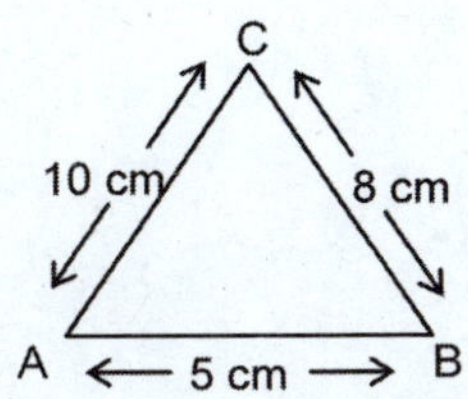

Distance between A and B = 5 × 20 = 100 km

Distance between B and C = 8 × 20 = 160 km

81. The circumference of circle though 'A' is = $2\pi r$

$$= 2 \times \frac{22}{7} \times 2(11 - 6) \text{ cm}$$

$$= \frac{440}{7} \text{ cm}^2 = 62.8 \text{ cm}$$

The circumference of circle passing through point 'B' is = $2\pi r^2$

$$= 2 \times \frac{22}{7} \times 2(8 - 6) \text{ cm}$$

$$= 4 \times 2 \times \frac{22}{7} = 25.14 \text{ cm}$$

= 62.8 – 25.14 = 37.6 cm

82. Mass of the empty bottle = 50 g

Mass of water = 100 – 50 = 50 g

Mass of the liquid = 130 – 50 = 80 g

Volume of the liquid = 50 cm^3

($\therefore$ volume of 1g water = 1mL)

$$\text{Density of the liquid} = \frac{\text{mass}}{\text{volume}} = \frac{80}{50} = 1.6 \text{ g cm}^{-3}.$$

83. Given $d = 5$ g cm^{-3} (B)

$$D = \frac{5 \text{ g}}{(1 \text{ cm})^3}$$

$D_5 = 5$ g cm^{-3}

$$1 \text{ g} = \frac{1}{1000} \text{kg} \quad \text{and} \quad 1 \text{ cm} = \frac{1}{100} m$$

$$D = \frac{5 \text{ g}}{(1 \text{ cm})^3} \text{ (C)} = \frac{5 \times \frac{1}{1000} \text{kg}}{\left(\frac{1}{100} m\right)^3}$$

$$= \frac{5}{\left[\left(1000 \times \frac{1}{10^6}\right)\right]} \text{kg m}^{-3} = 5000 \text{ kg m}^{-3}$$

Hence, the correct order is BCA.

84. $4 \text{ N} = 4 \text{ kg m s}^{-2}$

$= 4\ (10^3 \text{ g})\ (10^2 \text{ cm})\ \text{s}^{-2}$

$= 4 \times 10^{(3+2)} \text{ g cm s}^{-2}$

$= 4 \times 10^5 \text{ g cm s}^{-2}$ (or) $4 \text{ N} = 4 \times 10^5$ dyne

85. (a) $4 \text{ kg m}^{-3} = 4 \text{ kg m}^{-3}$

(b) $10 \text{ g m}^{-3} = 10 \times 10^{-3} \text{ kg m}^{-3} = 10^{-2} \text{ kg m}^{-3}$

(c) $20 \text{ kg cm}^{-3} = 20 \text{ kg} \times (1 \text{ cm})^{-3} = 20 \text{ kg} \times (10^{-2} \text{ m})^{-3}$
$= 20 \times 10^6 \text{ kg m}^{-3} = 2 \times 10^7 \text{ kg m}^{-3}$

(d) $40 \text{ g cm}^{-3} = 40 \times 10^3 \text{ kg m}^{-3} = 4 \times 10^4 \text{ kg m}^{-3}$

The decreasing order of the magnitudes of densities in terms of kg m^{-3} is:

(c) 2×10^7 > (d) 4×10^4 > (a) 4 > (b) 10^{-2}

Hence, the decreasing order magnitudes of the given densities is:

$20 \text{ kg cm}^{-3} > 40 \text{ g cm}^{-3} > 4 \text{ kg m}^{-3} > 10 \text{ g m}^{-3}$.

CHAPTER 2

Kinematics

Remember

Before beginning this chapter, you should be able to:

- Know mobile and immobile objects
- Define motion

Key Ideas

After completing this chapter, you should be able to:

- Learn the types of motion—translatory, rotatory and oscillatory
- Understand uniform and non-uniform speed
- Units of time and speed
- Understand Distance-Time graph
- Understand uniform, variable and average velocity and acceleration
- Understand simple pendulum and its application

Scientific Crypt

A Tribute to Albert Einstein (1879–1955)

Albert Einstein was born on March 14, 1879 at Ulm, Württemberg, Germany in a Jewish family. His father, Hermann Einstein, was an engineer and a salesman and his mother was Pauline Einstein. This German-born theoretical physicist with his "theory of general relativity" brought revolution in physics and he is often considered as "father of modern physics". Belonging to the classification of scientists and thinkers, his exceptional intelligence and originality has made the word "Einstein" synonymous with genius.

At age of five, Einstein received a magnetic compass from his father and then he developed a great interest to know about the invisible forces of nature. Einstein was a calm, patient child and completed his elementary education from a catholic elementary school. Einstein right from childhood spent long hours reading books of science(s), mathematics and philosophy which helped in his intellectual growth. He joined Federal Polytechnic Institute after his secondary school education and even taught in the same institute in 1900. Later, he joined a Swiss patent office and there he got an opportunity to examine others' applications. In 1905, he obtained the doctorate degree from the University of Zurich for his theory about molecular dimensions and in the same year he published four papers explaining *photoelectric effect, relativity, movement of molecules and equivalence of matter and energy* ($E = mc^2$). He received noble prize for the photoelectric effect. He became American citizen in 1940. He forewent the chance to became the President of Israel and continued his research work. He taught physics at the institute for advanced study, Princeton, U.S till his death in 1958.

FUN TIME

CROSSWORD

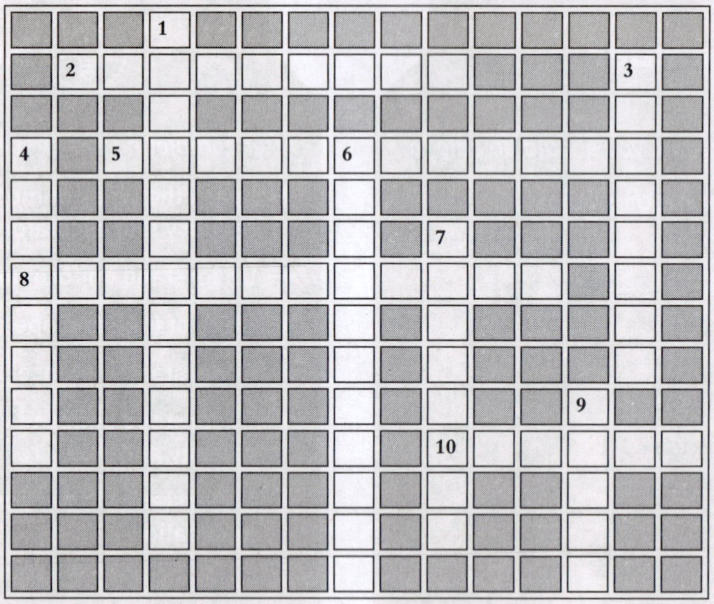

Across

2. The time period of a pendulum is _______ proportional to the square root of the acceleration due to gravity.

5. The distance travelled by a body moving with a uniform speed is _______ to the time taken.

8. Aeroplane take off from airport with a(an) _______.

10. The nature of distance time graph plotted for a body moving with a constant speed.

Down

1. $\dfrac{\text{Total distance travelled}}{\text{Total time}}$

3. Rate of change of displacement.

4. Spin motion of top.

6. A train approaching railway station.

7. Motion of moon around the earth.

9. SI unit of quantity which is the reciprocal of time period.

INTRODUCTION

In this chapter, we will learn about the different types of motion and various terms used to describe the motion of a body. The motion of a body is classified into 3 types namely translatory, rotatory and oscillatory type. Each type of motion has been described briefly. The terms used to describe the types of motion are speed, velocity and acceleration. These terms are explained in this chapter briefly. The various types of distance-time graphs have also been discussed.

Mechanics is classified into statics and dynamics.

Statics: It deals with bodies at rest under the action of forces.

Dynamics: Dynamics deals with bodies under motion and it is further classified into kinematics and kinetics.

Kinematics: It deals with the motion of bodies without considering the cause of motion.

Kinetics: It deals with the motion of bodies considering the cause of their motion.

Further, simple pendulum is discussed in this chapter.

Rest and Motion

When we look around, we find some objects are in motion whereas, some other objects are at rest. Some of the examples are: a moving bus, a moving car are in motion. To win a race, the athletes run. They are in motion. The water in a river is in motion. A book lying on the table, a lamp post, a table, a chair, a blackboard, etc., are all at rest. When do we say that an object is in motion? When do we say that it is at rest?

An object in motion is the one that changes its position with respect to its surroundings whereas, an object which is at rest is the one that does not change its position with respect to surroundings and time.

The rest and motion are relative terms. An object at rest with respect to one observer may not be at rest with respect to another observer. The same can be said about motion. For a person inside a bus, the fellow passengers are at rest but the same passengers are in motion with respect to a person standing on the ground. If we closely observe the motion of different objects, we find them performing different kinds of motion. A car moving on a straight road, the rotation of blades of a table fan, the motion of a swing which moves to and fro are all different kinds of motion.

Types of Motion

1. **Translatory motion:** A bus moving on a road, the motion of a rising balloon, the free fall of a stone under gravity, the motion of a cricket ball when it is hit by a batsman are examples of translatory motion. Translatory motion is further classified into rectilinear motion and curvilinear motion. When an object moves along a straight path, its motion is said to be rectilinear. The marching of soldiers on a straight road, the motion of a car on a straight road, the motion of carrom board coins are examples of rectilinear motion. When an object moves along curved path, its motion is called curvilinear. A bus moving on a flyover bridge, a car taking a turn, a football kicked from the ground into the air all have curvilinear motion.
2. **Rotatory motion:** In this type of motion, the object rotates about a fixed axis. The motion of blades of a ceiling fan, the spin motion of a top, the motion of turbine, the motion of the earth around the sun all have circular or rotatory motion. In some cases, the rotatory and translatory motions take place simultaneously. When a bicycle moves, its wheels undergo translatory and rotatory motion.
3. **Oscillatory motion:** A boy on a swing moves to and fro (back and forth). The motion, such as above, where an object moves to and fro is called oscillatory motion. Other examples of oscillatory motion are the motion of the pendulum of a clock, the motion of a needle of a sewing machine, the motion of a piston of an engine, etc.

A metallic wire fixed at its ends, when plucked starts moving up and down. This is also an example of oscillatory motion where an object moves to and fro at faster rate. Vibratory motion is faster than oscillatory motion. This type of motion is called vibratory motion. In the stringed instruments, such as guitar, veena, violin, etc., the motion of a string is vibratory. The motion of membrane of a drum is also a vibratory motion. It must be noted that during vibratory motion, a change in size and shape takes place.

A motion that repeats itself at regular intervals of time is called periodic motion. All oscillatory motions are periodic motions. Some rotatory motions are periodic motions. The motion of earth around the sun, the motion of the pendulum of a clock, the rotation of earth about its own axis, the motion of a swing are periodic motions. But all periodic motion are not oscillatory, e.g., rotation of earth about its axis.

A motion that repeats itself but not at fixed interval of time is called non-periodic motion. A ceiling fan when it is switched off, a drum rolling up or down on an inclined plane, the motion of a wheel of bicycle when brakes applied are all examples of non-periodic motion.

Distance and Displacement

Distance and displacement are two most commonly used terms that have same dimensions and units. These two terms are often confusing but have entirely different meanings. Let us understand these terms with the help of examples.

Distance

Distance is defined as the length of the actual path covered by a particle in motion. The unit of distance is centimetre in C.G.S. system and metre in M.K.S. or S.I. system.

Displacement

Displacement is defined as the shortest distance between the initial and final positions of a body. It is a vector quantity, whose magnitude is equal to the length of the straight line path from the initial position to the final position and the direction is along the straight line drawn from the initial to the final position.

The distance travelled by a particle depends on the path traced by the particle, whereas the displacement of a particle in motion is independent of the path traced and depends only on the initial and final positions of the particle.

Consider a particle moving along the path ABCD as shown below:

The distance travelled by the particle = 6 + 2 + 5 = 13 m.

The displacement is the vector $\overrightarrow{AD}$, whose magnitude is the length of the line segment AD.

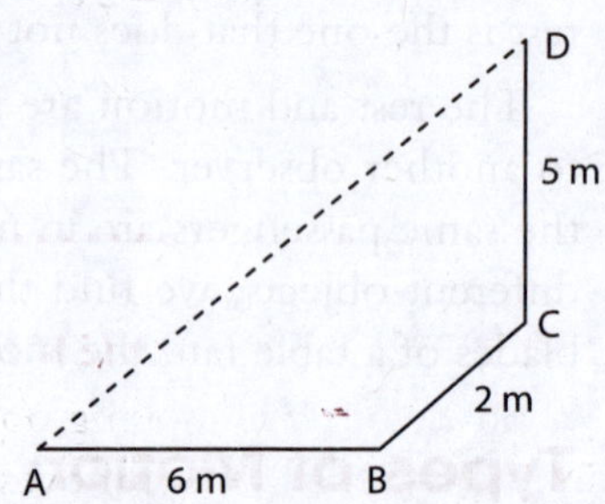

Example: A cop gets information that a thief is 5 km away from the police station. Is it possible for the cop to trace the thief with the given information?

It is not possible to trace the thief, as the cop doesn't know the direction in which to chase the thief. Thus, the information about distance alone is not sufficient to locate the position of a body.

Konnect

1. The distance covered by a body is always greater than or equal to the magnitude of displacement.
2. The distance travelled and magnitude of displacement of a particle will be equal if and only if, the particle travels along the shortest path from the initial to the final position without change in direction of motion.
3. Displacement can be zero, positive or negative whereas, distance can never be negative and distance travelled never decreases.
4. Distance does not depend on direction but displacement will depend on direction.
5. $\overrightarrow{AB} \neq \overrightarrow{BA}$, as for $\overrightarrow{AB}$ the initial position is A and final position is B and for $\overrightarrow{BA}$ the initial position is B and final position is A.
6. The magnitude of displacement is expressed in centimetre (cm) in C.G.S. system and in metre (m) in M.K.S. and S.I. system.

EXAMPLE 2.1 A horse is tied to a rope of length 5 m and the other end of the rope is tied to a pole. Find the displacement and the distance travelled by the horse in the following cases.

i. When the horse makes half revolution along a circular path.

ii. When it makes one full revolution.

iii. When it makes $\frac{3}{4}$ th of the revolution.

SOLUTION

i. Half revolution along the circular path.

Distance travelled by the horse = $\pi \times 5 = 5\pi$ m.

Displacement of the horse = diameter of the circular path, $\overrightarrow{H_1 H_2} = 10$ m from H_1 to H_2

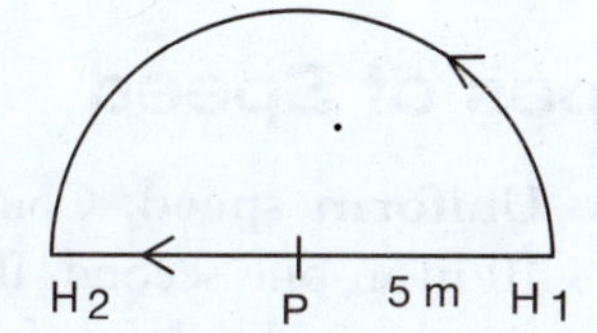

ii. When the horse makes full revolution

Distance travelled by the horse = circumference of the circular path = $2\pi r = 2\pi \times 5 = 10\pi$ m

Displacement of the horse = zero (Since initial and final position of the horse coincides)

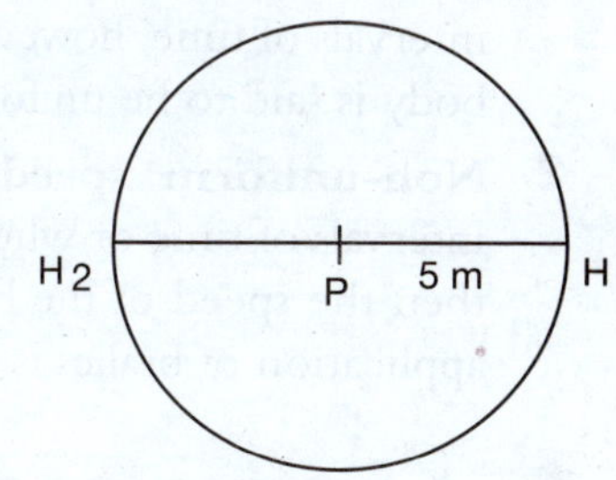

iii. When the horse makes $\frac{3}{4}$ th of the revolution

Distance travelled by the horse = $\frac{3}{4}$ th of the circumference of the circle = $\frac{3}{4}(2\pi r)$

$= \frac{3}{2} \times \pi \times 5 = \frac{15}{2}\pi = 7.5\pi$ m.

Displacement of the horse = the shortest distance between H_1 and H_2

$= \sqrt{(5)^2 + (5)^2} = 5\sqrt{2}$ [Using Pythagoras theorem]

$= 5\sqrt{2}$ m along H_1 to H_2.

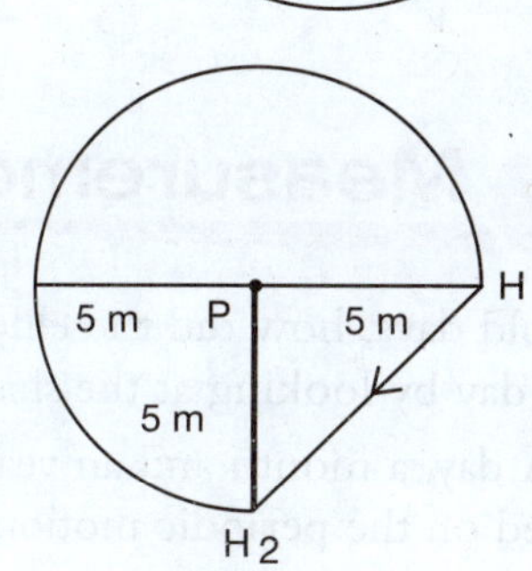

Slow and Fast Movement

When we observe moving objects, we find some of them moving faster than the others. *Cheetah* runs faster than any other animal, whereas a snail moves very slowly. A car or a motorbike runs faster than a bicycle. An aeroplane moves faster than any other vehicle moving on the road.

If the vehicles moving in the same direction are observed for a given time, it is possible to say which one is moving faster than the others. The faster vehicle covers more distance in a given time than the slower one. In this way, it races ahead of the slower one.

Speed

An object moving with higher speed covers a large distance in a given time or it covers a given distance in a shorter time. Speed is a measure of fastness or the slowness of a moving object. How to know the speed of an object? It can be calculated by finding the distance covered by an object in a unit time.

The fastness or the slowness is measured in terms of a physical quantity called speed. Thus, a faster vehicle has higher speed than a slower one.

If a bus covers a distance of 40 km in one hour, then its speed is 40 km h^{-1}. However, a bus seldom moves with a constant speed. Usually, it starts from rest, slowly picks up the speed, then for a short duration, it may travel with constant speed and stop at the traffic signal or at the bus stop. When the speed is not constant, we express the speed as average speed. It is calculated by dividing the total distance by the total time taken to cover the distance. In this book, speed is used for average speed. Thus,

$$\text{Speed} = \frac{\text{Distance}}{\text{Time}}$$

Some objects like an aeroplane can move with constant speed along a straight line for quite some time. The motion of such objects is said to be **uniform motion**.

However, most of the objects move with a speed which does not remain constant. The motion of such objects is said to be **non-uniform motion**.

Types of Speed

1. **Uniform speed:** Consider a car moving on a road such that it covers, say 10 m in one second. If it covers 10 m, in every subsequent second, then its speed is said to be uniform. Thus, when a body covers equal distances in equal intervals of time, however small the time interval may be, then the speed of the body is said to be uniform.
2. **Non-uniform speed:** When a body covers unequal distances in equal intervals of time or when it covers equal distances in unequal intervals of time, then the speed of the body is said to be non-uniform. Motion of a bus after application of brakes is an example for non-uniform speed.

$$\text{Average speed} = \frac{\text{Total speed}}{\text{Total time}}$$

Konnect

Constant speed means an object covers equal distances in equal intervals of time, but variable speed is much more common in the real world.

Measurement of Time

In old days, how did the elders know the time when there were no watches? They could tell the approximate time of the day by looking at the shadows.

A day, a month and an year are defined based on the periodic motion of the earth around the sun. A lunar month is based on the periodic motion of the moon around the earth.

Now-a-days, clocks and watches are used for the measurement of time. They measure the time by using periodic motions. Old wall clocks use periodic motion of a simple pendulum for the measurement of time.

A simple pendulum is made up of a metallic ball (called bob of the pendulum), suspended from a rigid support with the help of a thread, as shown in the Fig. 2.1. The rest position of the bob is called mean position. When the bob is taken to one side and released, it moves to and fro about the mean position. This type of to and fro motion is called an oscillatory motion (as discussed initially in this chapter). The motion of the bob of the pendulum is not only oscillatory but also periodic.

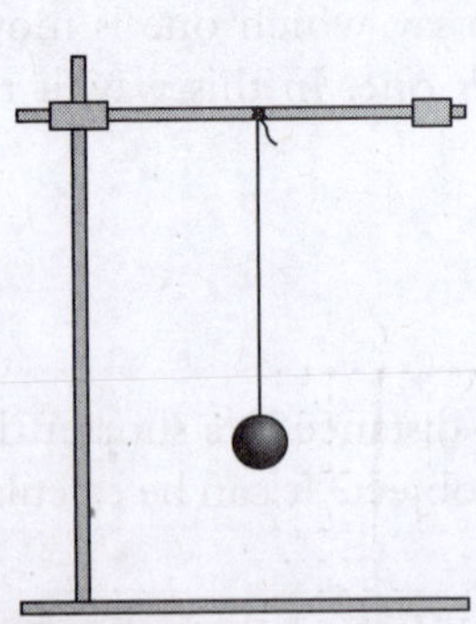

Figure 2.1 A simple pendulum

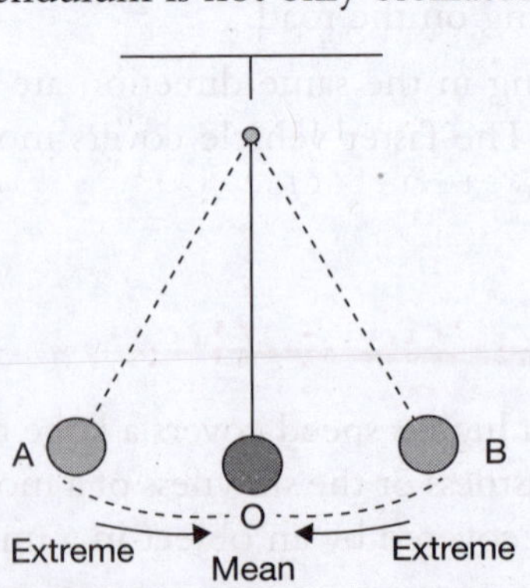

Figure 2.2 Different positions of the bob of an oscillating simple pendulum

As shown in the Fig. 2.2, O is the mean position. If the bob is displaced from its mean position and released, it starts oscillating. It goes from O to, say B. From B to A and back to O. This completes one oscillation. If the bob is released from A, it goes to B and then come back to A. This also constitutes one oscillation. The positions A and B are called extreme positions. The time taken by the bob to complete one oscillation is called its time period. The time period of simple pendulum depends on the length of the simple pendulum and is independent of mass of the bob and its size and shape. (Note: The mass of the bob should not be as light as paper).

The time period of a simple pendulum can be easily determined with the help of a stop watch. To find the time period, note the time taken, say for 20 oscillations and divide the time by 20.

Now-a-days, the watches contain an electric circuit and these watches are called quartz clocks. Quartz clocks are more accurate than pendulum and winding clocks.

Units of Time

The basic unit of time is second (s). The other units are minute and hour.

Since the speed is given by $\frac{\text{distance}}{\text{time}}$, its unit is metre per second (m s^{-1}). However, it can also be expressed as metre per minute (m min^{-1}) or kilometre per hour (km h^{-1}).

Info Bytes!

The most precise clocks are atomic clocks; they're accurate to within a few billionths of a second per day.

Konnect

Depending on the situation, different units of time are used. For example, the age of a person is expressed in years but not in minutes or hours. The time taken to go from one place to another by an aeroplane can be expressed in minutes and hours but not in months and years.

Measuring Speed and Time

The speed of an object can be calculated if we know the time taken by it to cover a certain distance. On dividing the distance by time, the speed can be found out. Let us see how the speed of a ball can be determined. Draw a straight line on the ground with a piece of chalk. Ask your friend to roll the ball along the ground. The moment the ball touches the line, start stop clock. When the ball comes to rest, stop the clock. Note the time interval when the ball touches the line and when it comes to rest. Also, measure the distance between the points where the ball touches the line and the point where it stops. Dividing the distance by the time gives the speed.

If we know the speed of an object, we can find the distance covered by it in a given time by multiplying speed and time. Thus, distance = speed × time

We can also find the time that the object would take to cover certain distance, provided we know the speed of the object. The time can be found by, time = $\frac{\text{distance}}{\text{speed}}$

Motorcycles and scooters are fitted with speedometer, which records the speed of the vehicle in km h^{-1}. In vehicles, such as buses and cars, the speedometer is fitted on the dashboard, which gives instantaneous speed only. Other than speedometer, the vehicles are provided with odometer, which measures the distance moved by the vehicle.

Distance-Time Graph

For a body in uniform motion, we can draw the distance-time graph, which is a line graph.

To draw the distance-time graph, take a graph paper and draw two perpendicular lines XOX^1 and YOY^1 intersecting each other at O, (called origin) as shown in Fig. 2.3.

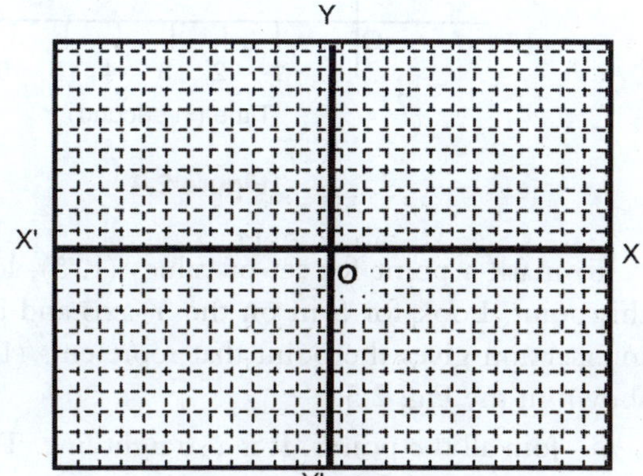

Figure 2.3

The horizontal line XOX^1 is called X-axis and the vertical line YOY^1 is called Y-axis. The distance is marked along the Y-axis and time is marked along the X-axis.

Let us draw distance-time graph of the data given in the table below, for the motion of a motorbike.

Observation Table

S. No.	Time (s)	Distance (m)
1	0	0
2	1	5
3	2	10
4	3	15
5	4	20
6	5	25
7	6	30

Info Bytes!

A steeper slope on a distance-time graph indicates higher speed, while a flat line indicates that the object is at rest.

To draw the graph, the following steps should be considered.

1. Draw two perpendicular lines, *OX* and *OY*, intersecting at '*O*' as shown in the Fig. 2.4. The line *OX* is *X*-axis and the *OY* is *Y*-axis.
2. Mark the distance along the *Y*-axis and time along the *X*-axis.
3. Choose the proper scale for time on the *X*-axis and distance on the *Y*-axis. For the above problem, the scale could be *X*-axis : 1 second = 1 cm *Y*-axis : 5 m = 1 cm
4. Mark the values of time and distance on the respective axes, in accordance with the scale chosen, as shown in the Fig. 2.4.
5. From the table, the set of values for time and distance are (0, 0), (1, 5), (2, 10), (3, 15), (4, 20), (5, 25) and (6, 30). The first number of the set represents time and the second number represents the corresponding distance.

To mark a point the set of values (0, 0), look at 0 s on the *X*-axis and 0 m on *Y*-axis. This point is the origin.

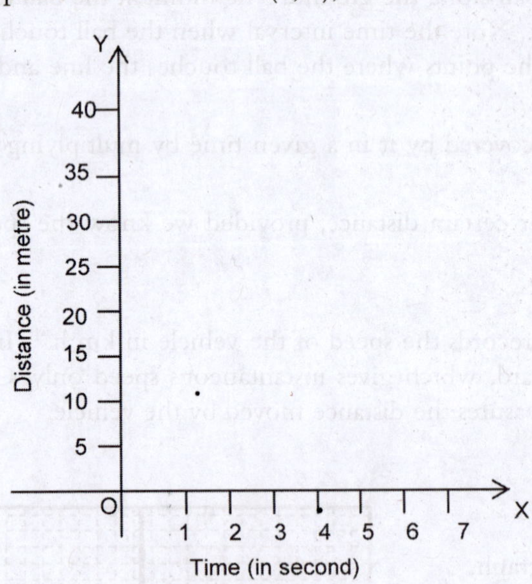

Figure 2.4

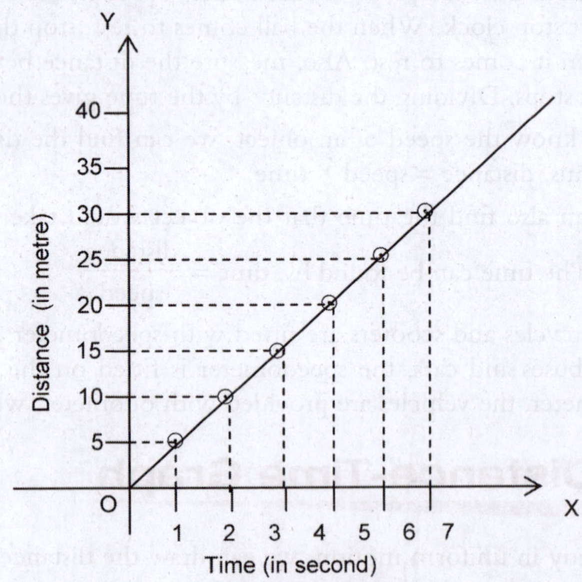

Figure 2.5

To mark a point for set of values (1, 5), look for 1 s on *X*-axis. Draw a line parallel to *Y*-axis and passing through this point. Look for 5 m on the *Y*-axis and draw a line parallel to the *X*-axis passing through this point. The point of intersection gives the point that represents (1, 5). In the same way, the points for other set of values can be plotted, as shown in the Fig. 2.5.

6. Join all the points. It is a straight line. The straight line is the distance-time graph for the motion of the motorbike.
7. The distance-time graph of a body moving with a constant speed is a straight line. However, if the body does not move with constant speed, then its distance-time graph will give a curved line.

The choice of scale in general, is not a simple one. Consider the table shown below, which shows distance covered by a bus at different times.

Observation Table

Time	Distance from the starting point
10.00 a.m.	0 km
10.30 a.m.	20 km
11.00 a.m.	40 km
11.30 a.m.	60 km
12.00 a.m.	80 km

If we choose the scale 1 km = 1 cm on the *Y*-axis, we need to draw an axis of length 80 cm which is not possible to draw on a sheet of paper. On the other hand, if we choose 10 km = 1 cm, the length of the axis would be 8 cm, which is convenient to draw. However, with the above scale, the graph covers a small part of the graph paper. While choosing the scale, the following points should be kept in mind.

1. The difference between the highest and the lowest values of the quantities.
2. The intermediate values so that they should be plotted easily with the scale chosen.
3. Utilization of the maximum part of the graph paper.

If the size of the graph paper is 20 cm × 25 cm, then for the above example, the appropriate scale would be, distance: 5 km = 1 cm, time : 6 min = 1 cm.

On studying the table, we can find the distance travelled by a body in definite time. It is not possible to find the distance at any instant of time. However, from the distance-time graph, we can find the distance moved by a body, at any instant of time.

Velocity

When an object moves with certain speed, it is not clear in which direction it is moving. To overcome the shortcoming, velocity is used. In a way, velocity is speed in a specified direction. Thus, velocity consists of two parts out of which one part is direction. For example, a car moving with 10 m s^{-1} in east direction has the magnitude of velocity as 10 m s^{-1} and the direction is east. Velocity can be classified into:

1. **Uniform velocity:** When a body moves with uniform speed in a specified direction, it is said to be moving with uniform velocity.

   Thus, a body moves with uniform velocity when its magnitude as well as its direction remains the same.

   Example: Aeroplane moving with 500 km h^{-1} towards east.

2. **Variable velocity:** When a body moves such that either magnitude of speed or direction or both change, then it is said to be moving with variable velocity.

   Example: A car moving on a straight road such that its speed changes from time to time has variable velocity. A car taking a turn has variable velocity as its direction changes.

3. **Average velocity:** When a body moves with variable velocity, the average velocity of the body is equal to the ratio of total displacement of the body to the total time taken.

$$\text{Average velocity} = \frac{\text{Total displacement}}{\text{Total time taken}}$$

Acceleration

The change in velocity of a body per unit time is called acceleration or the rate of change of velocity is called acceleration.

Example: If the velocity of the car, moving along a straight path changes from 5 m s^{-1} to 25 m s^{-1} in 4 second, then it is called acceleration.

$$\text{Acceleration } (a) = \frac{\text{change in velocity}}{\text{total time}} = \frac{25 - 5}{4} = \frac{20}{4} = 5\,\frac{\text{m s}^{-1}}{\text{s}} = 5 \text{ m s}^{-2}.$$

The SI unit of acceleration is m s^{-2}. The other units of acceleration are cm s^{-2} and km h^{-2}.

Consider a body moving with initial velocity u. Let its velocity change to v, in time 't'. Then, the change in velocity is $= v - u$.

The change in velocity per unit time $= \frac{v-u}{t}$

By definition, the change in velocity per unit time is acceleration, a. Thus,

$$a = \frac{v-u}{t} \text{ or } v - u = at$$

$$v = u + at$$

When a body is released from certain height, it moves downward due to the gravitational force. Its velocity changes continuously and an acceleration is produced in it which is called acceleration due to gravity.

Info Bytes!

- Acceleration occurs not just when an object speeds up, but also when it slows down or changes direction.
- The average value of acceleration due to gravity is 9.8 m s^{-2}.

Simple Pendulum

You are already familiar with simple pendulum. Let us define few more terms associated with the simple pendulum.

The maximum displacement of the bob of the simple pendulum, from its mean position is called amplitude. The length of the pendulum (l) is the distance between the point of suspension and the midpoint of the bob. The number of oscillations made by the pendulum in one second is called its frequency (denoted by n).
In SI system, the unit of frequency is hertz (Hz).

A pendulum whose time period is two seconds is called second pendulum.

The time period (T) of a simple pendulum is given by

$$T = 2\,\pi\sqrt{\frac{l}{g}}$$

where, 'l' is the length of the simple pendulum and 'g' is the acceleration due to gravity. At a given place, since 'g' value remains constant, $T \propto \sqrt{\ell}$ which means time period increases (or decreases) with increase (or decrease) in length. The experimental set-up to find the time period of a simple pendulum is as shown in the Fig. 2.6.

Determine the radius of the bob of the pendulum by placing it between two wooden blocks and measuring the gap between the wooden blocks with the help of a scale. The gap gives diameter from which the radius can be calculated. Suspend the bob by passing thread through a vertically cut cork and holding tight the cork between the clamps.

For the length of the pendulum to be 70 cm, the length of the thread should be (70 – R) cm where, R is the radius of the bob.

Take the bob of the pendulum to one side so that the pendulum makes 5° with the vertical and release the bob. Start the stop watch when the bob is at the mean or extreme position and find the time taken by the pendulum to complete 20 oscillations. Dividing the time for 20 oscillations by 20 gives the time period (T) of the pendulum. The above experiment can be repeated for different lengths (80 cm, 90 cm, 100 cm, etc.) and the time period for each length can be determined. It will be noticed that with increase in length, the time period also increases.

The experimental set-up for determining the time period of a simple pendulum is shown as follows:

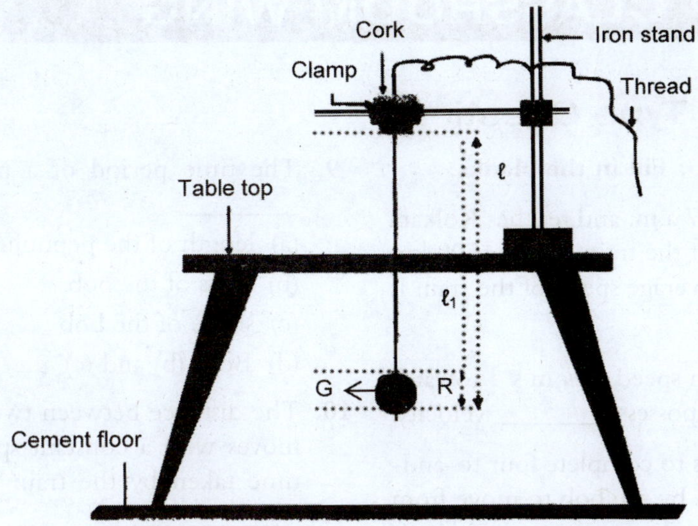

Figure 2.6 Time period of a simple pendulum

POINTS TO REMEMBER

- ✔ Rest and motion are relative in nature with respect to the surroundings.
- ✔ Different kinds of motions are
  - (a) translatory motion
  - (b) rotatory motion
  - (c) oscillatory motion
- ✔ Speed $= \dfrac{\text{distance}}{\text{time}}$
- ✔ When a body covers equal distances in equal intervals of time, however small the time intervals may be, the speed of the body is said to be uniform.
- ✔ When a body covers unequal distances in equal intervals of time or equal distances in unequal intervals of time, the speed of the body is said to be non-uniform.
- ✔ Average speed $= \dfrac{\text{total distance}}{\text{total time}}$
- ✔ Velocity is speed in a specified direction.
- ✔ When a body moves with uniform speed in a specified direction, it is said to be moving with uniform velocity.
- ✔ When a body moves such that either its magnitude or direction or both change, then it is said to be moving with variable velocity.
- ✔ Acceleration $= \dfrac{\text{change in velocity}}{\text{time interval}}$
- ✔ Time period (T) of a simple pendulum of length (ℓ) is $T = 2\pi\sqrt{\ell / g}$ where 'g' is the acceleration due to gravity.

PRACTICE QUESTIONS CLASSROOM WING

Very Short Answer Type Questions

***Directions for questions from 1 to 3:* Fill in the blanks.**

1. A train leaves Hyderabad at 7 a.m. and reaches Kolkata by 1 p.m. on the next day. If the train travels 1500 km to reach Kolkata, then the average speed of the train is ________ km h^{-1}.

2. A body moves with uniform speed of u m s^{-1} towards east, then the body is said to possess ________ velocity.

3. A simple pendulum takes 8 s to complete four to-and-fro motions. The time taken by the bob to move from one extreme position to another extreme position is ______ s.

***Directions for questions from 4 to 37:* For each of the questions, four choices have been provided. Select the correct alternative.**

4. Choose the correct statement:

(a) The magnitudes of speed and velocity are same when a body travels in a straight line path.

(b) Average speed of a moving body can be equal to zero, but its average velocity cannot be equal to zero.

(c) To describe the velocity, direction is necessary.

(d) Both (a) and (c)

5. The ratio of unit of acceleration and velocity gives unit of the physical quantity ________.

(a) time (b) frequency

(c) amplitude (d) speed

6. Unit of speed is ________.

(a) m min^{-1} (b) km h^{-1}

(c) km s^{-1} (d) All of the above

7. Which of the following deals with bodies at rest?

(a) Statics (b) Dynamics

(c) Kinematics (d) Kinetics

8. The speed of the tip of a second hand of length 5 cm of a clock is ______ m s^{-1}.

(a) 1 (b) 60

(c) 5.3×10^{-3} (d) 3.4×10^{-5}

9. The time period of a pendulum is independent of ________.

(a) length of the pendulum

(b) mass of the bob

(c) shape of the bob

(d) Both (b) and (c)

10. The distance between two stations is 20 km. If a train moves with a constant speed of 60 km h^{-1}, then the time taken by the train to reach the next station is ________.

(a) 2 hour (b) 20 minute

(c) 20 second (d) 40 minute

11. The distance-time graph of an object is a straight line parallel to the time axis, then the object is ________.

(a) at rest

(b) in uniform motion

(c) moving with a uniform speed

(d) moving with a non-uniform speed

12. A car moves with a speed of 60 km h^{-1} for 20 min and then at a speed of 30 km h^{-1} for the next 20 min. The total distance covered by the car is ________ km.

(a) 10 (b) 20

(c) 30 (d) 40

13. The distance-time graph of a body is as shown in the figure. The part of the graph that represents the uniform speed of the body is

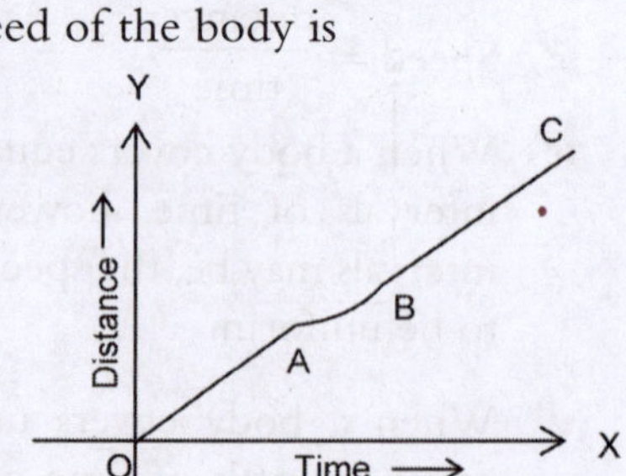

(a) OA (b) AB

(c) BC (d) Both OA and BC

14. A body moves with a uniform speed of 10 km h^{-1} for 2 h. The average speed of the body is ________ km h^{-1}.

(a) 10 (b) 20

(c) 5 (d) 25

15. The distance-time graph of a moving vehicle is as shown in the figure.

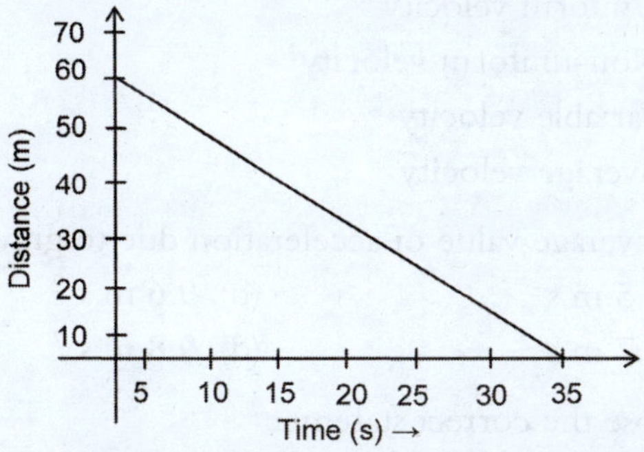

(a) The speed of the vehicle is increasing with time.
(b) The speed of the vehicle is decreasing with time.
(c) The final speed of the vehicle is zero.
(d) Graph is not possible.

16. 1 km h^{-1} = __________ m s^{-1}.

(a) $\frac{50}{3}$ (b) $\frac{5}{18}$
(c) $\frac{18}{5}$ (d) $\frac{5}{8}$

17. Choose the correct statement(s).
(a) Speed and velocity both have same units.
(b) If a body has a speed of 50 m s^{-1} in a straight line path, then its velocity is 180 km h^{-1}
(c) Speed of a vehicle is measured by a device called speedometer.
(d) All of the above

18. A person starts from a point P and travels along a path PQRP as shown in the figure. Then speed of the person is __________ m s^{-1}

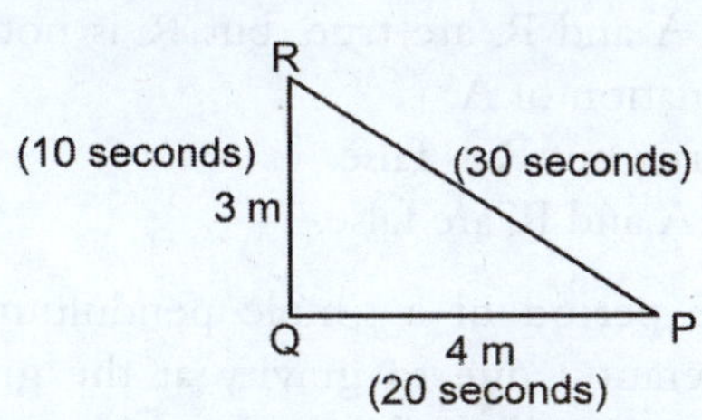

(a) 0.2 (b) 20
(c) 12 (d) 0.4

19. A simple pendulum was given to a physics student to determine its time period. Arrange the following steps in sequential order to determine its time period.
(A) Calculate the radius of the bob 'R' by dividing the diameter by 2.
(B) Take a metre scale and measure the length of the string from the point of suspension to the lower tip of the bob (ℓ_1).
(C) Place the bob over a metre scale and hold it in position with two wooden blocks or stiff cardboards. Measure the diameter (D) of the bob.
(D) Now, the length of the pendulum (ℓ) is given by ($\ell_1 - R$).
(E) Consider the formula $T = 2\pi.\sqrt{\frac{\ell}{g}}$ Calculate the time period of the simple pendulum.

(a) ABCDE (b) EDCBA
(c) BCADE (d) DEABC

20. A body covers 20 m in 2 s and another 20 m in next 4 s. Arrange the following steps in sequential order to find the average velocity of the body.
(A) Find the displacements of the body in first 2 s and next 4 s from the given data.
(B) Find the total displacement of the body.
(C) Find the total time taken by the body to complete the total displacement.
(D) Use the formula, average velocity = $\frac{\text{Total displacement}}{\text{Total time taken}}$

(a) ABCD (b) ADCB
(c) DCBA (d) DBCA

21. Rate of change of velocity is called
(a) Speed (b) Distance
(c) Displacement (d) Acceleration

22. A pendulum whose time period is two seconds is called
(a) First pendulum (b) Second pendulum
(c) Third pendulum (d) None of these

23. The SI unit of frequency is
(a) Hertz (b) m/sec
(c) Newton (d) None of these

24. Which of the following is the unit of distance in CGS System?
(a) cm (b) m
(c) cm/sec (d) m/sec

25. Displacement can be
(a) Zero (b) Positive
(c) Negative (d) All of these

26. Which of these is/are example(s) of non-periodic motion?
(a) A ceiling fan when it is switched off
(b) a drum rolling up or down on an inclined plane

(c) the motion of a wheel of bicycle when brakes applied

(d) All of these

27. The motion of a body is depicted graphically as shown in the given figure. Then the average speed of the body is ______ m s^{-1}.

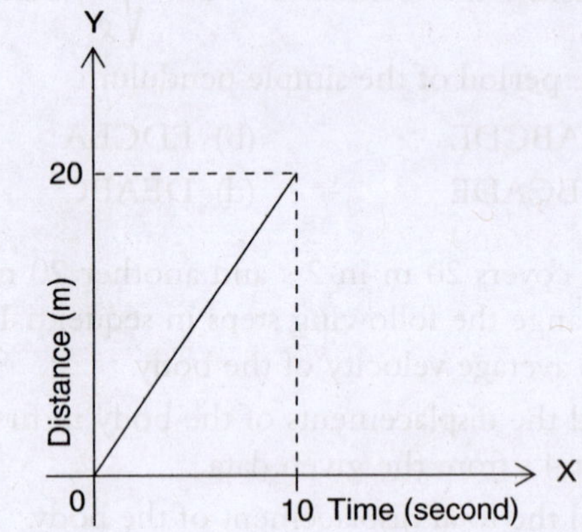

(a) 2 (b) zero

(c) 200 (d) 20

28. Which of the following statements is True?

(a) Distance does not depend on direction.

(b) Distance depends on direction.

(c) Displacement will not depend on direction

(d) All of these

29. The ratio of the unit of acceleration and velocity gives the unit of the physical quantity ________.

(a) time (b) frequency

(c) amplitude (d) speed

30. The motion of a body is depicted graphically as shown in the figure. The average speed of the body is ________ m s^{-1}.

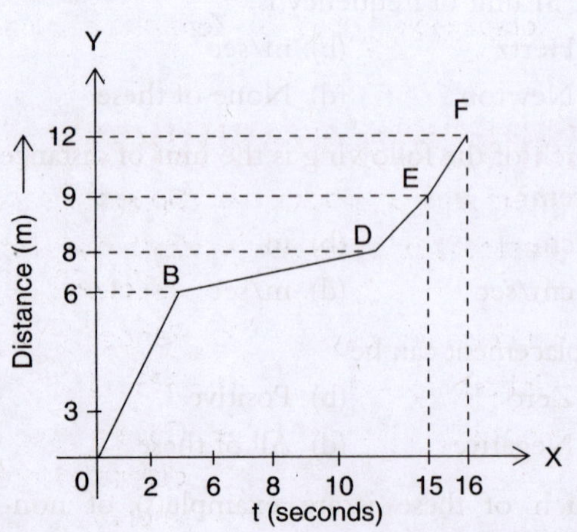

(a) 3/4 (b) 9/8

(c) 4/3 (d) 8/9

31. An aeroplane moving with 500 km h^{-1} towards east is moving with

(a) Uniform velocity

(b) Non-uniform velocity

(c) Variable velocity

(d) Average velocity

32. The average value of acceleration due to gravity is

(a) 9.5 m s^{-2} (b) 9.6 m s^{-2}

(c) 9.7 m s^{-2} (d) 9.8 m s^{-2}

33. Choose the correct statement.

(a) Unit of acceleration is m s^{-2}.

(b) Speed = distance/time.

(c) Magnitude of displacement made by a body is less than or equal to the distance travelled by the body.

(d) All of the above

34. **Assertion (A):** Quartz clocks are more accurate than pendulum clocks.

Reason (R): Quartz clocks use periodic motion of simple pendulum for the measurement of time.

(a) Both A and R are true and R is the correct explanation of A.

(b) Both A and R are true, but R is not the correct explanation of A.

(c) A is true but R is false.

(d) Both A and R are false.

35. **Assertion (A):** The acceleration of a body moving with constant velocity is zero.

Reason (R): Acceleration is the rate of change in velocity.

(a) Both A and R are true and R is the correct explanation of A.

(b) Both A and R are true, but R is not the correct explanation of A.

(c) A is true but R is false.

(d) Both A and R are false.

36. The time period of a simple pendulum is 4 s and the acceleration due to gravity at the given place is 9.8 m s^{-2}. Write the following steps in sequential order to find the length of the pendulum.

(A) From the above formula, write the value of ℓ as $\ell = \frac{T^2 g}{4\pi^2}$.

(B) Note the given values of the time period (T) and acceleration due to gravity (g).

(C) Write the formula, $T = 2\pi\sqrt{\frac{\ell}{g}}$, where '$\ell$' is the length of the pendulum.

(D) Substitute the given data and get the value of 'ℓ'.

(a) CDBA (b) ABCD

(c) BCAD (d) ADBC

37. A car starts from rest and attains a velocity of 54 km h^{-1}. If the acceleration of the car is 3 m s^{-2}, write the following steps in sequential order to find the time taken to accelerate the car.

(A) Write the relation between *u*, *v*, *a* and *t*, where *t* is the time taken to accelerate the car.

(B) Note the final velocity (*v*) and convert it into SI unit.

(C) Note the initial velocity of the car as $u = 0$ and note its acceleration.

(D) Substitute the given values and obtain the value of *t*, using $t = \frac{v-u}{a}$.

(a) ADBC (b) ABCD

(c) CADB (d) CBAD

Directions for questions from 38 to 40: **These questions are based on the following information given below.**

A graph is drawn between the displacement and time taken for the oscillations of a simple pendulum.

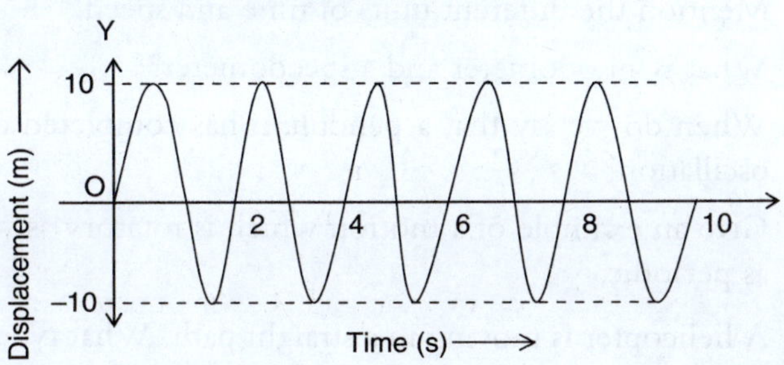

38. The number of oscillations performed by the bob at the end of 10 s is ________.

(a) 7 (b) 5

(c) 6 (d) 8

39. The length of the pendulum is ________ m (if $g = 10$ m s^{-2} and $\pi^2 = 10$).

(a) 2 (b) 1

(c) 3 (d) 4

40. The frequency of oscillation is ________ Hz.

(a) 0.5 (b) 1

(c) 50 (d) 100

Directions for question 41: **Select the correct alternative from the given choices.**

41. ________ does not depend on direction but ________ will depend on direction.

(a) Distance, displacement

(b) Displacement, Distance

(c) Velocity, distance

(d) Speed, distance

Directions for questions from 42 to 46: **Match the entries given in Column A with the appropriate ones in Column B.**

42.

Column A	Column B
A. Rest and motion	a. Fan
B. Oscillatory motion	b. Relative
C. Rotatory motion	c. Simple pendulum
D. Translatory motion	d. A car moving on the road

43.

Column A	Column B
A. Curvilinear motion	a. Motion that repeats itself at irregular intervals of time
B. Rectilinear motion	b. Wings of a ceiling fan
C. Rotatory motion	c. A shell fired from artillery gun
D. Body moving with uniform velocity	d. A stone dropped from a tower
E. Length of a pendulum	e. Point of suspension to the midpoint of the bob
F. Time period of a simple pendulum	f. Square root of the length of the pendulum
G. Non-periodic motion	g. Zero acceleration

44.

Column A	Column B
A. Pendulum of clocks	a. Speed
B. Fastness or slowness	b. Both magnitude and direction
C. Uniform velocity	c. Periodic motion
D. Uniform speed	d. FPS unit of velocity
E. Foot s^{-1}	e. Covers unequal distances in equal intervals of time

45.

	Column A		Column B
A.	Rest and motion	a.	A car taking a turn
B.	Oscillatory and periodic	b.	Relative
C.	Translatory and rotatory	c.	Motion of the bob of a simple pendulum
D.	Variable velocity	d.	Motion of the wheels of a bicycle in motion

46.

	Column A		Column B
A.	A body covers 5 m in every subsequent second.	a.	Lunar month
B.	Equal distances in unequal intervals of time	b.	Non-uniform speed
C.	Periodic motion of the moon around the earth	c.	Years
D.	Appropriate unit to express the age of a person	d.	Constant speed

Directions for questions from 47 to 65: **Answer the following questions.**

47. When can the speed and average speed of a vehicle be equal?

48. While determining the time period of a simple pendulum, why is the time for 20 or more oscillations found?

49. Define amplitude and frequency. Write their SI units.

50. Name the physical quantity that measures fastness or slowness of a moving object.

51. Two cars A and B move on a straight road for the same time. Car A covers 80 m and car B covers 100 m. Which one of the two is faster?

52. What are quartz clocks? Which one is more accurate, a clock using pendulum or a quartz clock?

53. If the speed of an object is known, how can we find the distance covered by it in a given time?

54. Name the different types of graphs used to represent motion of a body.

55. Give an example where translatory and rotatory motion occurs simultaneously.

56. Define rest and motion.

57. Define acceleration and state its SI unit.

58. What is a second pendulum? What is its approximate length? ($g = 10$ m/s^2)

59. Find the relationship between the time period of the pendulum and the length of the pendulum.

60. In a 100 m race, A touches the finishing line in 10.5 second and B touches it in 11 second. Who is faster, A or B?

61. What is meant by average speed? How is it calculated?

62. Mention the different units of time and speed.

63. What is an odometer and a speedometer?

64. When do we say that a pendulum has completed one oscillation?

65. Give an example of a motion which is rotatory as well as periodic.

66. A helicopter is moving in a straight path. What type of motion will the propeller of helicopter execute?

Short Answer Type Questions

67. If an oscillating simple pendulum performs 20 oscillations in 32 s, then the time taken to move from mean position to extreme position is ______ s.

68. The distance–time graph of a car is as shown in the figure.

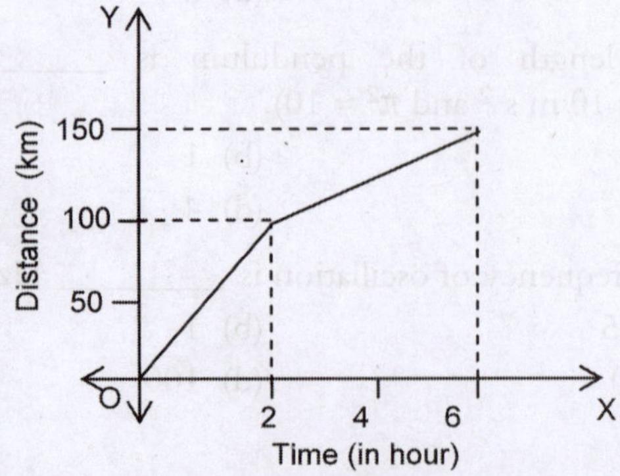

Is the car moving with constant speed? Find the speed of the car at the end of 2 hour and 6 hour, respectively.

69. A lorry driver sees a old man crossing the road. Suddenly he applies brakes and stops the lorry within 30 s. If the initial speed of the lorry is 108 km h^{-1}, find its deceleration.

70. A car moves the first-half of the total distance at a speed of 5 m s^{-1} and second-half of the distance at 10 m s^{-1}. What will be the average speed in m s^{-1}?

71. Define day and year. How do watches and clocks measure time? Explain.

72. What are the different points one must keep in mind while choosing a suitable scale for drawing a graph? Discuss.

73. Define velocity and explain how it is different from speed.

74. Derive the relation between acceleration, change in velocity and time.

75. What are uniform speed and non-uniform speed? Explain, with suitable examples.

76. A ball is thrown vertically upwards with a velocity of 50 m s^{-1} and its velocity becomes zero in 5 s when it reaches maximum height. What will be the acceleration of the ball?

77. A car starts from rest and reaches a speed of 150 km h^{-1} in $\frac{1}{6}$ h. What will be the acceleration of the car in km h^{-2}.

78. Define different kinds of velocity. Give one example of each kind.

79. Explain how will you change the time period of a simple pendulum.

80. In a race, two athletes A and B reach the finishing point in 20 second and 22 second, respectively.
    (a) What is the ratio of their speeds?
    (b) If both are allowed to run with their respective speeds for a given time, what is the ratio of the distance covered by them?

81. The odometer of a motorcycle shows a reading of 10,237 km at 8.30 a.m. At 9.00 a.m., it shows a reading 10,267 km. What is the speed of the motorcycle in km h^{-1}?

82. A simple pendulum of length 'ℓ' and time period 'T' on earth is taken onto the surface of moon. How should the length of the simple pendulum be changed on the moon such that the time period is constant.(Take g_e = 6 g_m)

83. The length of a seconds pendulum is double. What happens to the time period of the pendulum?

84. What is a simple pendulum? Explain the terms time period, mean position and extreme positions of a simple pendulum.

Essay Type Questions

85. The $s - t$ graph shown below shows how three cars A, B and C in a race reach the target in three different times. If S_A, S_B and S_C are the speeds of the cars A, B and C, respectively, then arrange them in descending order.

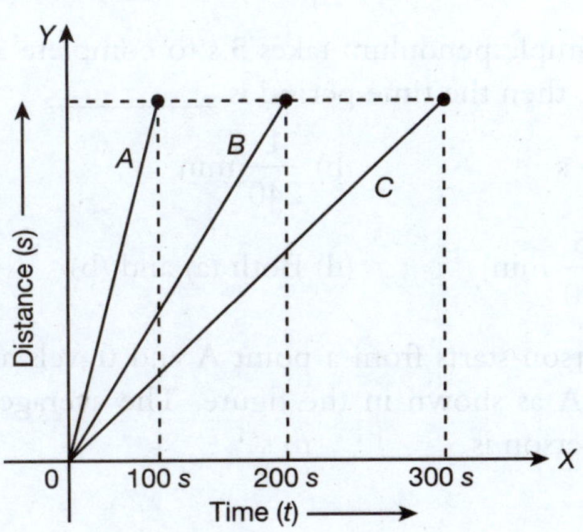

86. Describe the experimental method to determine the time period of a simple pendulum.

87. When pendulum A completes 20 oscillations, pendulum B completes 30 oscillations, what is the ratio of their time periods?

88. Explain in detail about the different kinds of motion.

89. Explain in detail about periodic motion and non-periodic motion.

PRACTICE QUESTIONS COMPETITION WING

Level 1: Apply your Concepts

***Directions for questions from 1 to 13:* Fill in the blanks.**

1. The ratio of the unit of displacement to that of acceleration is ________.
2. The motion of molecules in a solid is an example for ________ motion.
3. One millisecond is ________ part of a second.
4. A body moving with a velocity of 10 m s^{-1} increases its velocity to 20 m s^{-1} in 2 s. Then the rate of change in velocity is ________.
5. A car moves with a constant velocity, its average velocity is equal to its ________.
6. ________ measures the distance moved by a vehicle.
7. A body is said to be moving with uniform speed if it covers equal distances in ________.
8. One microsecond is ________ of a second.
9. SI unit of speed is ________.
10. A marathon swimmer runs with a uniform speed of 20 km h^{-1} for 2 h and reaches the same point from where he started the marathon. The distance covered by him is ________ km
11. The time taken by the pendulum to complete one oscillation is called ________.
12. The distance covered by an object in a unit time is known as the ________ of the object.
13. If $T = 2\pi\sqrt{\frac{\ell}{g}}$ is the time period of a simple pendulum, then $\frac{1}{2\pi}\sqrt{\frac{g}{\ell}}$ is ________ of the simple pendulum.

***Directions for questions from 14 to 23:* State whether the following statements are true or false.**

14. The $s - t$ graph of three bodies (P, Q and R) is as shown below figure.
The speed of P is greater than that of Q and R.

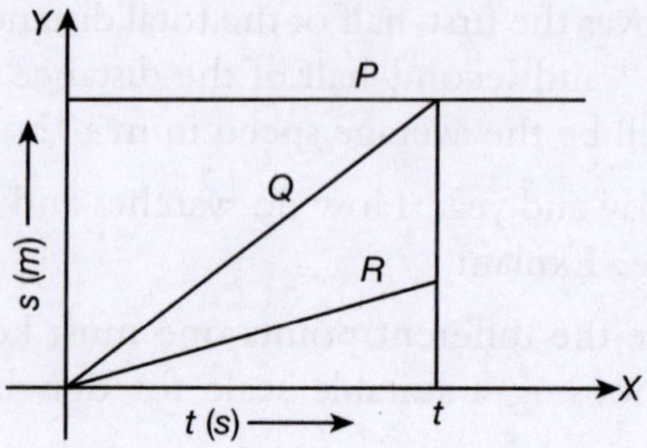

15. The motion of a simple pendulum is an example for oscillatory motion.
16. A nanosecond is one billionth of a second.
17. When an object is moving with a uniform speed, its average speed is equal to its velocity.
18. We can use a simple pendulum to measure the time.
19. By using distance-time graph, we can find out the average speed of an object.
20. Speedometer is used to measure the distance travelled by a vehicle.
21. The distance-time graph of the motion of an object moving with a constant speed is a straight line.
22. The speed of the bob of a simple pendulum is maximum at its extreme position.
23. The time period of a simple pendulum of length 1 m is 2 seconds.

***Directions for questions from 24 to 39:* For each of the questions, four choices have been provided. Select the correct alternative.**

24. If a simple pendulum takes 5 s to complete 20 oscillations, then the time period is ________.

(a) $\frac{1}{4}$ s (b) $\frac{1}{240}$ min

(c) $\frac{5}{20}$ min (d) Both (a) and (b)

25. A person starts from a point A and travels along path ABCA as shown in the figure. The average speed of the person is ________m s^{-1}.

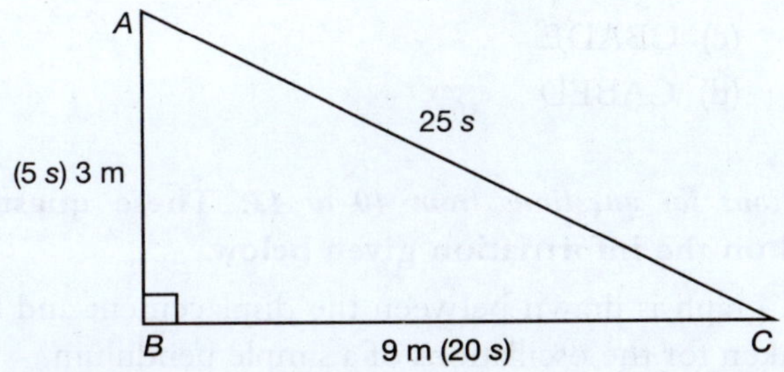

(a) $\frac{3\sqrt{10}}{25}$ (b) $\frac{3\sqrt{10}}{50}$

(c) $3\sqrt{10}$ (d) $\frac{3\left(4+\sqrt{10}\right)}{50}$

26. The speed of a body can never be __________.

(a) positive (b) negative

(c) zero (d) Both (a) and (c)

27. The motion of a body is depicted graphically as shown in the given figure. Then

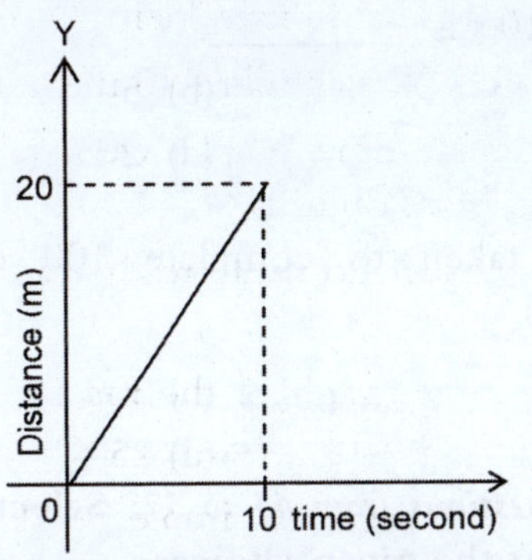

(a) The average speed of the body is 2 m s^{-1}.

(b) The average speed of the body is zero.

(c) The body changes its direction twice.

(d) All of the above

28. A body travels 10 m in 2 s then the speed of the body is __________ m s^{-1}.

(a) 20 (b) 40

(c) 5 (d) 10

29. A body moves with a speed of 2π m s^{-1} in a circular path of radius 1 m, then the time taken to complete one revolution is __________ s.

(a) 1 (b) 2

(c) 3 (d) 4

30. The odometer of a bus reads 6700 km when it starts from the station at 9 a.m., and when it comes back to the station at 10 p.m. the odometer reading is found to be 6960 km, then the average speed of the bus in the whole journey is __________ km h^{-1}.

(a) 10 (b) 20

(c) 30 (d) 40

31. A pendulum completes 120 oscillations in one minute then the time period of the pendulum is __________ s.

(a) 0.5 (b) 120

(c) 2 (d) 3

32. A body moves with a constant speed of 10 m s^{-1} for 1 hour. The distance travelled by the body is ______.

(a) 36,000 km (b) 36 km

(c) 24 km (d) 24 $\times 10^3$ m

33. It takes 1 s for the bob to move from one extreme position to other extreme position. Then the time period of the pendulum is ________ s.

(a) 1 (b) 2

(c) 3 (d) 4

34. A body projected upwards from the top of a building is an example of ______.

(a) uniform motion

(b) non-uniform motion

(c) periodic motion

(d) oscillatory motion

35. Distance versus time graph of an object is as shown in the figure. The average speed of the object is __________ m s^{-1}

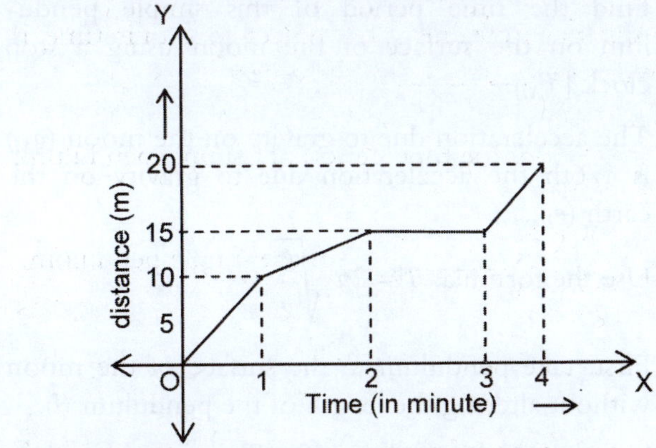

(a) 0.08 (b) 0.5

(c) 1 (d) 2

36. 20 m s^{-1} = __________ km h^{-1}

(a) 12.5 (b) 72

(c) 50/9 (d) 32

37. Choose the correct statement:

(a) Unit of acceleration is m s^{-2}.

(b) Speed = distance/time.

(c) If a body moves with uniform velocity, its acceleration is zero.

(d) All of the above

38. A car driver accelerates the car to increase its speed from 30 km h^{-1} to 60 km h^{-1} in 5 min. Arrange the following steps in a sequence to obtain the acceleration of the car.

(A) Use the formula, rate of change of velocity = $\dfrac{\text{Total change in velocity}}{\text{Total time required for change}}$

(B) Obtain the final velocity (v) of the car.

(C) Find the time taken to increase the speed of the car from u to v. Let it be 't'.

(D) Find the initial velocity (u) of the car.

(E) Substitute the values in the formula and calculate the acceleration of the car.

(a) EABCD

(b) ABCDE

(c) DBCAE

(d) EDCBA

39. Find the acceleration due to gravity on the surface of the moon by taking a seconds pendulum from the earth's surface. Arrange the following steps in sequential order to solve the above problem.

(A) Find the time period of this simple pendulum on the surface of the moon using a stop clock [T_M].

(B) The acceleration due to gravity on the moon (g_M) is 1/6th the acceleration due to gravity on the earth (g_E).

(C) Use the formula, $T = 2\pi\sqrt{\dfrac{\ell}{g}}$

(D) First, take pendulum to the surface of the moon without altering the length of the pendulum (l).

(E) Substitute the value of 'T_M' in (a), then $\dfrac{T_E}{T_M} = \sqrt{\dfrac{g_M}{g_E}}$, and obtain the value of (g_M).

(a) ABCDE

(b) DACEB

(c) CBADE

(d) CABED

***Directions for questions from 40 to 42:* These questions based on the information given below.**

A graph is drawn between the displacement and time taken for the oscillations of a simple pendulum.

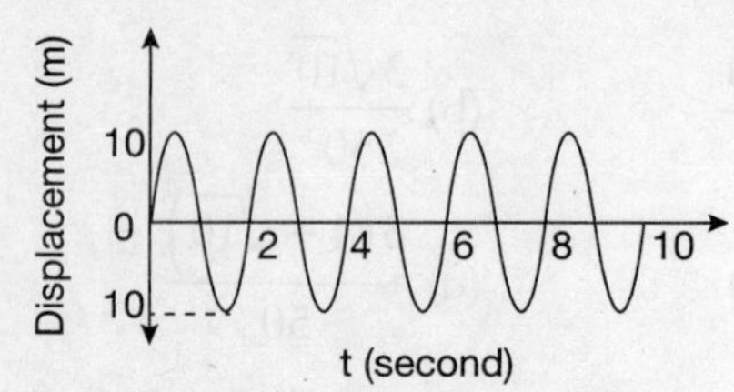

40. The frequency of oscillation is ________ Hz.

(a) 0.5 (b) 2 h

(c) 50 (d) 100

41. The number of oscillations performed by the bob at the end of 10 s is ________.

(a) 4 ½ (b) 5

(c) 6 (d) 2 ½

42. The time taken to complete 100 oscillations is ________s.

(a) 100 (b) 200

(c) 50 (d) 25

***Directions for questions from 43 to 57:* Select the correct alternative from the given choices.**

43. An athlete moves along a path PQRSTUVP, in 44 seconds as shown in the figure, then the average speed of the athlete is ________ m s^{-1}.

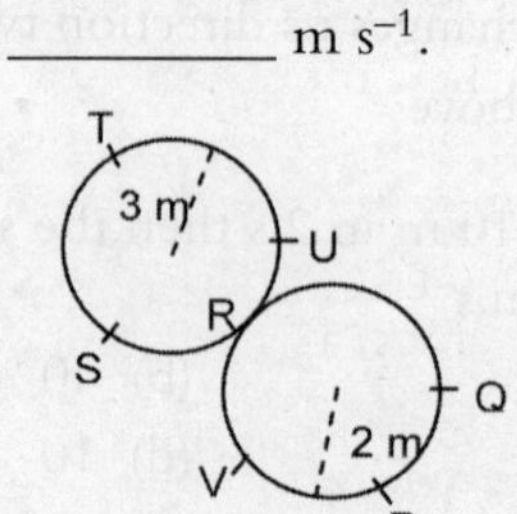

(a) zero (b) $\dfrac{5}{7}$

(c) $\dfrac{5}{11}$ (d) None of these

44. A train of length 200 m is moving along a circular path as shown in the figure. If it completes one rotation with a speed of 54 km h^{-1}, then the time taken by it to trace the path is ________ seconds.

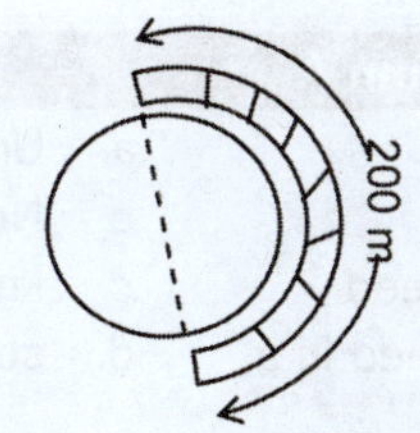

(a) 25 (b) 13.33

(c) 26.66 (d) 26

45. A body is dropped from the top of a tower. If its average velocity, when it reaches the ground, is 10 m s^{-1} and the time taken by it to reach the ground is 2 s; the height of the tower is ________ m.

(a) 20 (b) 10

(c) 40 (d) 25

46. A vehicle travels along a straight path between two places α and β. It travels first half of the distance with a velocity of 72 km h^{-1} and the remaining distance with a velocity of 36 km h^{-1}. Then the average velocity of the vehicle is ________ m s^{-1}.

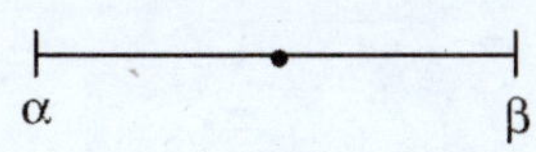

(a) $11.\overline{3}$ (b) $13.\overline{3}$

(c) 15 (d) 14

47. An electric motor winds 200 turns of a thin copper wire on a uniform rod of diameter 10 cm, in 2 seconds. Then the length of the wire that is wound over the rod in one second is ________ m.

(a) 30 (b) 10π

(c) 20π (d) None of these

48. ________ deals with the motion of bodies considering the cause of their motion.

(a) Statics (b) Dynamics

(c) Kinematics (d) Kinetics

49. An athlete runs along a circular track of radius 14 m with a speed of 11 m s^{-1} then the time taken by the athlete to complete 6 rounds is ________.

(a) 48 s (b) 0.8 min

(c) 0.0133 h (d) All of the above

50. A car is moving along a semicircular track as shown in the figure in a duration of 2π second from P to Q, then choose the correct statement(s).

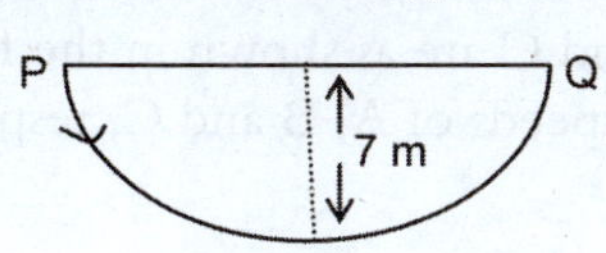

(a) The distance covered by the car is 14 m.

(b) The average velocity of the car is 2.23 m s^{-1}.

(c) The average speed of the car is 3.5 m s^{-1}.

(d) Both (b) and (c)

51. A boy dropped a ball from the top of a tower of height 125 m then the average velocity of the ball at the end of 5 second if it takes 5 s to reach the ground ________ m s^{-1}.

(a) 25 (b) 125

(c) 50 (d) 250

53. Assertion (A): A metallic wire fixed at its ends when plucked executes periodic motion.

Reason (R): A motion that repeats itself at regular intervals of time is called periodic motion.

(a) A and R are true and R is the correct explanation of A.

(b) A and R are true, but R is not the correct explanation of A.

(c) A is true but R is false.

(d) Both A and R are false.

54. Assertion (A): The time period of a simple pendulum increases with an increase in the length of the simple pendulum.

Reason (R): The time period (T) of the simple pendulum is directly proportional to the square root of the length of the simple pendulum.

(a) A and R are true and R is the correct explanation of A.

(b) A and R are true, but R is not the correct explanation of A.

(c) A is true but R is not false.

(d) Both A and R are false.

54. An ant moves along the identical steps from P to Q as shown in the figure in a duration of 8.5 seconds, then the speed and velocity of the ant respectively are ________ m s^{-1} and ________ m s^{-1}

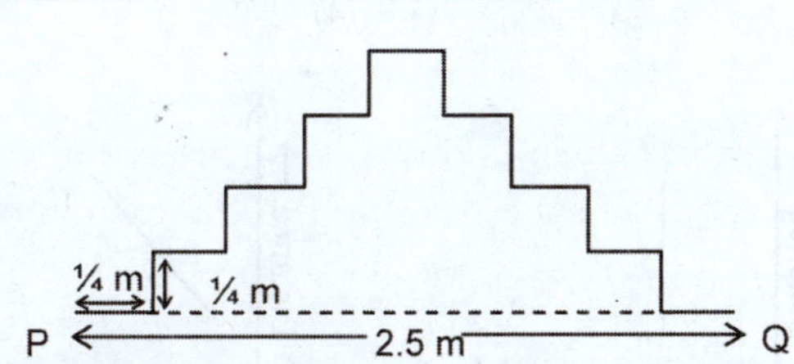

(a) 0.5, $\frac{5}{17}$ (b) 0.5, 0.5

(c) $\frac{5}{17}$, $\frac{5}{17}$ (d) Cannot be determined

Directions for questions from 55 to 57: **Match the entries given in Column A with the appropriate ones in Column B.**

55.

Column A		Column B
A. Vibratory motion	a.	Distance – time graph is not a straight line
B. Rotatory motion	b.	Speed × time
C. Seconds pendulum	c.	Musical instruments
D. Distance travelled	d.	The rate of change of motion in specific direction
E. Variable speed	e.	Potter's wheel
F. Velocity	f.	2 s

56.

Column A		Column B
A. Speed	a.	Uniform motion
B. Time	b.	Non-uniform motion
C. Average speed	c.	km h^{-1}
D. Uniform speed in a straight line	d.	second
E. Freely falling body	e.	Change in time period
F. Change in length of a pendulum	f.	$\frac{\text{Total distance}}{\text{Total time}}$

57.

Column A	Column B
A. Guitar string	a. km h^{-1}
B. Speedometer	b. Vibratory motion
C. Odometer	c. Acceleration
D. Rate of change of velocity	d. Distance moved

Level 2: Review your Concepts

58. A simple pendulum makes 20 oscillations in one second on the surface of the earth. Determine the time period of the simple pendulum on the surface of a planet where the acceleration due to gravity is one fourth of the acceleration due to gravity on the surface of the earth.

59. Which of the following distance-time graphs is not possible? Explain why?

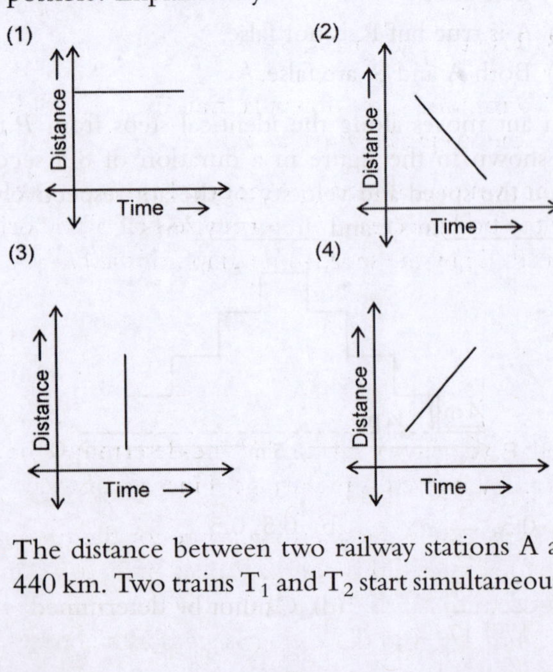

60. The distance between two railway stations A and B is 440 km. Two trains T_1 and T_2 start simultaneously from the stations A and B, respectively, and move towards each other. The train T_1 moves with a constant speed of 60 km h^{-1} and the train T_2 moves with a speed of 50 km h^{-1}. Determine the point where they meet and the time taken for this.

61. A body travels a distance of 500 m in 10 minute. Find out the speed of the body in km h^{-1}.

62. A student goes to school with a uniform speed of 3 km h^{-1} and returns to his home with a speed of 2 km h^{-1}. If the student takes 1 hour in all, then find out the distance between the school and the house.

63. Kishore walking with a uniform speed covers 20 km in 5 h. Find the distance he covers in 7 hours.

64. Determine the speed of the tip of a minute hand of length 10 cm of a wall clock.

65. A child counted 20 oscillations in his pendulum clock observed that it took 40 s for that. Find the frequency and time period of the pendulum.

66. The distance-time graph for the motion of three vehicles A, B and C are as shown in the figure. S_A, S_B and S_C are the speeds of A, B and C, respectively.

Compare the speeds of A, B and C.

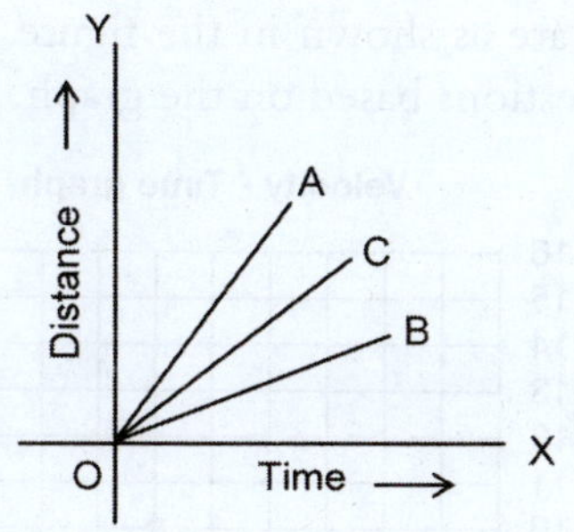

67. Usha participated in a marathon walk and completes the journey in 10 h. If she travels half the distance with a speed of 10 km h^{-1} and rest of the distance with the speed of 15 km h^{-1}, then calculate the total distance of the marathon walk.

68. Venkat went to his college from his house on his car with a uniform speed of 60 km h^{-1} and returns to his house with a different speed. If the average speed of the car for whole journey is 50 km h^{-1}, then find the speed of his car when it travelled from college to house.

69. Bantu and Mannu are good friends. One day they had a race in which Bantu covered 20 m in 10 s and Mannu covered 15 m in the same time. Find the ratio of their average speeds.

70. A boy goes to a cycle shop by walk at 5 km h^{-1} and comes back home by cycle at a speed of 15 km h^{-1}, find out the average speed of the boy.

71. The distance between two stations A and B is 200 km. A train travels from A to B at a uniform speed of 60 km h^{-1}. After half an hour another train leaves B towards A with a uniform speed of 80 km h^{-1}. Determine the distance of the point from A where the two trains meet each other.

72. Ram starts his bike from rest and moves along a straight path. If he attains a speed of 72 km h^{-1} in 10 s, determine his acceleration.

73. Sujatha noted the speedometer reading of her bike as 30 kmph at 8:00 am 40 kmph at 8:05 am, and 50 kmph at 8:10 am. Find the acceleration of her bike.

74. Raj dropped a cricket ball of mass 700 g from the top of a tower and the ball takes 5 s to reach the ground. He then determined the maximum velocity of the body by taking acceleration of the ball as 10 m s^{-2}. Find out the value of maximum velocity.

75. An ant moves along a rectangular path as shown in the figure. It starts from A and moves with a uniform speed of 0.01 m s^{-1}. Determine the average speed after 1 hour.

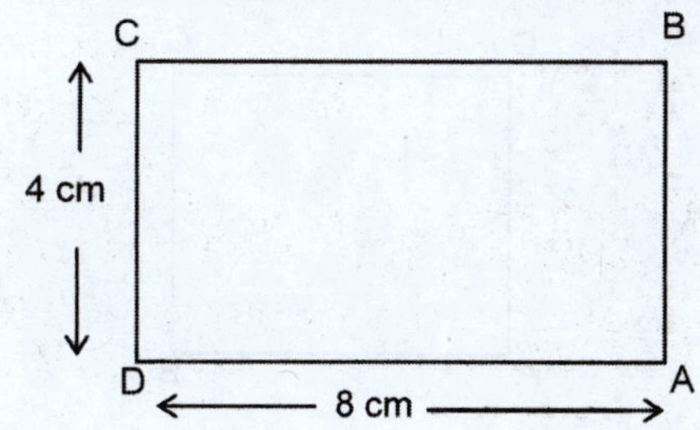

76. Write the following steps in sequence to determine the frequency of a simple pendulum of length (ℓ).

(A) Let the time period of simple pendulum be T

(B) Use the formula, $T = 2\pi\sqrt{\dfrac{\ell}{g}}$

(C) Determine the length (ℓ) of the simple pendulum from the given data.

(D) The frequency, $n = \dfrac{1}{T}$ Hz

77. Write the following steps in sequence to determine the final velocity of a stone dropped from a certain height (h) which takes t s to reach the ground (g = 10 m s^{-2}).

(A) Consider the initial velocity of the stone as zero.

(B) Use the formula, $a = \dfrac{v - u}{t}$.

(C) From the above formula, find the final velocity of the stone as $v = u + at$.

78. A body moves along a straight line. In every t s the speed of the body decreases uniformly to half of the original speed. Draw the speed-time graph of the body.

Level 3: Assess Your Concepts

79. A robot runs forward with 5 m s^{-1} for 10 s and immediately backwards with 5 m s^{-1} for 5 s. The average velocity of the robot is _______.

80. A physics student observed a train of 100 m long crossing a bridge of length 245 m. If the train is moving with a velocity of 54 km h^{-1}, he determines the time taken by it to cross the bridge. Find his answer.

81. A body travels along a straight line for the first half of the total time with a constant speed of 20 m s^{-1} and for the second half of the total time with a constant speed of 30 m s^{-1}. Find the average speed of the body.

82. Speed of light in air and glass are 3×10^8 m s^{-1} and 2×10^8 m s^{-1}, respectively. If a light ray travels 9×10^8 m in air and 16×10^8 m in glass, then what is the total time taken by it?

83. A body starts moving from a point A along the boundaries of a square field as shown in the figure and reaches the point C after 30 s. If its speed is 1 m s^{-1}, what is the shortest distance between A and C?

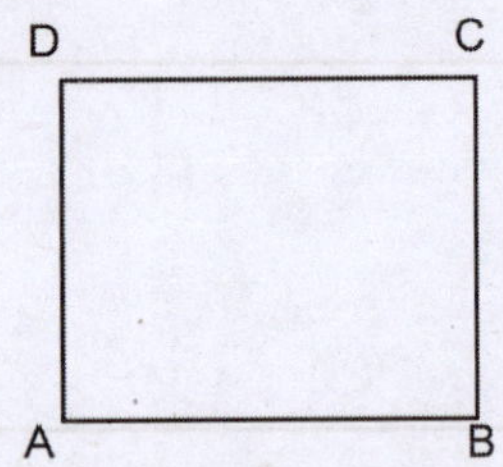

84. Ram and Raj travel along a straight line from X to Y with different uniform speeds. Ram started from X and reaches the place Y in t s. If Raj travels half of the total distance between X and Y in $2t$ s, determine the ratio of speeds of Ram and Raj.

85. A car moving along a straight road with a speed of 72 km h^{-1}, is brought to rest within 3 s after the application of brakes. Calculate the deceleration produced by the brakes.

86. The velocity Vs time positions representing the motion of a body are as shown in the figure. Answer the following questions based on the graph.

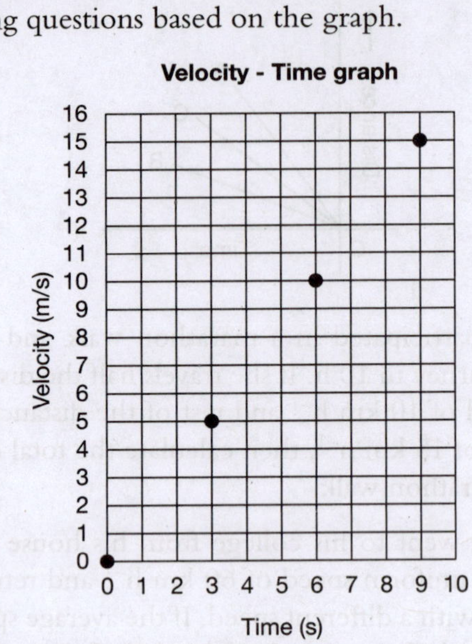

(i) What is the nature of motion?

(ii) Is the body accelerating?

(iii) If it is accelerating mention the kind of acceleration

(iv) Is it is uniformly accelerating, find its value.

ANSWER KEYS

Crossword

Across

2. Inversely 5. Proportional 8. Acceleration 10 Linear

Down

1. Average speed 3. Velocity 4. Rotatory 6. Retardation 7. Circular
9. Hertz

Classroom Wing

Very Short Answer Type Questions

1. 50 km h^{-1}	**2.** uniform	**3.** $\frac{T}{2} = 1s$	**4.** (d)	**5.** (b)
6. (d)	**7.** (a)	**8.** (c)	**9.** (d)	**10.** 40 km
11. (a)	**12.** (c)	**13.** (d)	**14.** (a)	**15.** (d)
16. (b)	**17.** (d)	**18.** (a)	**19.** (c)	**20.** (a)
21. (d)	**22.** (b)	**23.** (a)	**24.** (a)	**25.** (d)
26. (d)	**27.** (a)	**28.** (a)	**29.** (b)	**30.** (a)
31. (a)	**32.** 9.8 m s^{-2}	**33.** (d)	**34.** (c)	**35.** (a)
36. (c)	**37.** (d)	**38.** (b)	**39.** (b)	**40.** (a)

41. (a) **42.** A → b, B → c, b, C → a, D → d

43. A → c, B → d, C → b, D → g, E → e, F → f, G → a

44. A → c, B → a, C → b, D → e, E → d

45. A → b, B → c, C → d, D → a **46.** A → d, B → b, C → a, D → c

51. $V_A < V_B$ **60.** $V_A > V_B$ **66.** Both rotatory and translatory motions

Competition Wing

Level 1: Apply your Concepts

1. s^2	**2.** vibratory	**3.** $\frac{1}{1000}$	**4.** 5 m s^{-2}	**5.** velocity
6. Odometer	**7.** equal intervals of time		**8.** $\left(\frac{1}{10^6}\right)$	**9.** m s^{-1}
10. 1000	**11.** time period	**12.** speed	**13.** frequency	**14.** False
15. True	**16.** True	**17.** False	**18.** True	**19.** True
20. False	**21.** True	**22.** False	**23.** True	**24.** (a)
25. (d)	**26.** (b)	**27.** (a)	**28.** (a)	**29.** (a)
30. (b)	**31.** (a)	**32.** (b)	**33.** (b)	**34.** (b)
35. (a)	**36.** (b)	**37.** (d)	**38.** (c)	**39.** (b)
40. (a)	**41.** (b)	**42.** (b)	**43.** (b)	**44.** (c)
45. (a)	**46.** (b)	**47.** (b)	**48.** (d)	**49.** (d)

50. (d) 51. (a) 52. (a) 53. (a) 54. (a)

55. A → c, B → e, C → f, D → b, E → a, F → d

56. A → c, B → d, C → f, c, D → a, E → b, F → e

57. A → b, B → a, C → d, D → c

Level 2: Review your Concepts

58. 0.1 s
59. Graphs 2 and 3
60. 240 km; 4 h
61. 3 km h^{-1}
62. 1.2 km
63. 28 km
64. 1.75×10^{-4} m s^{-1}
65. 0.5 Hz; 2 s
66. $S_A > S_C > S_B$
67. 120 km
68. 42.86 km h^{-1}
69. $\frac{4}{3}$
70. 7.5 km h^{-1}
71. 102.86 km
72. 2 m s^{-2}
73. 120 km/h^2
74. 50 m s^{-1}
75. 0.01 m s^{-1}
76. CABD
77. ACB

Level 3: Assess Your Concepts

79. 1.66 m s^{-1}
80. 23 s
81. 25 m s^{-1}
82. 11 s
83. 21.2 m
84. 4 : 1
85. −6.67 m s^{-2}
86. 1.67 m/s^2

Hints and Explanations

Classroom Wing

Very Short Answer Type Questions

1. Total time taken, t = 1 p.m. − 7 a.m. = 30 h
Total distance travelled, s = 1500 km

$$\text{Average speed} = \frac{\text{Total distance}(s)}{\text{Total time taken}(t)}$$

$$= \frac{1500 \text{ km}}{30h} = 50 \text{ km h}^{-1}.$$

2. uniform

The body moves with uniform velocity of u m s^{-1} towards east direction.

3. Given 4T = 8 s ⇒ T = 2 s

Then time taken by the bob to move from one extreme position to another extreme position is $= \frac{T}{2} = 1$ s.

4. (d)

(i) When a body travels in straight line path, its distance and displacements are equal and hence in a given time, velocity is equal to speed.

(ii) Average velocity of a body may be equal to zero if the total displacement of is body is equal to zero, but average speed will not be equal to zero unless and until distance covered is zero (i.e., body at rest).

(iii) To describe the velocity, direction is necessary as velocity is speed in a specific direction.

5. (b)

Unit of acceleration = m s^{-2}

Unit of velocity = m s^{-1}

The ratio of unit of acceleration to the velocity

$$= \frac{m\,s^{-2}}{m\,s^{-1}} = s^{-1}$$

It is the unit of frequency.

6. (d)

All are units of speed.

7. (a)

Statics deals with bodies at rest under the action of forces.

8. (c)

$$\text{Speed} = \frac{\text{distance travelled}}{\text{time}}$$

For one rotation distance travelled = 2 πr.

= 2 × π × 5 = 31.42 cm = 0.3142 m

Time = 1 minute = 60 s

$$\text{Speed} = \frac{0.3142}{60} = 5.3 \times 10^{-3} \text{ m s}^{-1}$$

9. (d)

The time period of a pendulum is dependent on the length of the pendulum and is independent of the mass of the bob and its shape.

10. (b)

$$\text{Speed} = \frac{\text{distance}}{\text{time}}$$

$$\text{Time} = \frac{\text{distance}}{\text{speed}} = \frac{20 \text{ km}}{60 \text{ km h}^{-1}} = \frac{1}{3} \text{ h}$$

$$= \frac{1}{3} \times 60 = 20 \text{ minutes}$$

11. (a)

The object is at rest.

12. (c)

Distance travelled in the first 20 min = speed × time = $60 \times \frac{20}{60} = 20$ km

Distance travelled in the second 20 min = speed × time $= 30 \times \frac{20}{60} = 10$ km

Total distance travelled = 20 + 10 = 30 km

13. (d)

Both *OA* and *BC* show constant speed of the body.

14. (a)

The average speed = uniform speed = 10 km h^{-1}

15. (d)

Distance of a body do not decrease with time.

16. (b)

1 km h^{-1} = 10^{3}m × h^{-1}

$$= \frac{1000\text{m}}{1\text{h}} = \frac{1000\,\text{m}}{60 \times 60\,\text{s}}$$

$= \frac{10}{36}$ m s^{-1} $= \frac{5}{18}$ m s^{-1}

17. (d)

(i) The unit of speed and velocity is m s^{-1}.

(ii) If a body is moving in a straight line path then its speed is equal to velocity

50 m s^{-1} = 50 × $\frac{18}{5}$ km h^{-1} = 180 km h^{-1}.

(iii) Speed of a body (vehicle) can be measured by a device called speedometer.

18. (a)

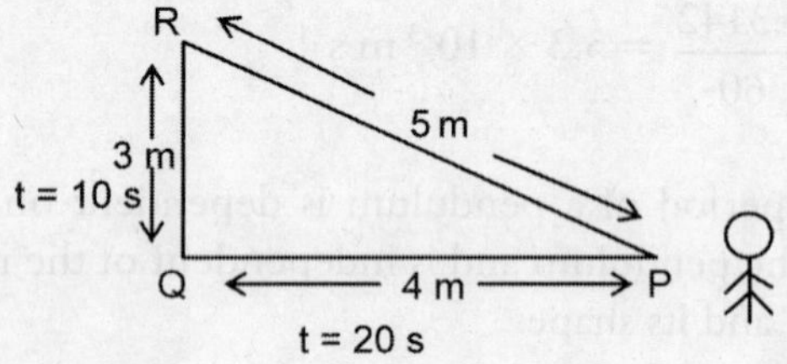

From the given figure, by pythogorous theorem

$PR^2 = PQ^2 + RQ^2$

$PR^2 = 4^2 + 3^2$

$PR^2 = 16 + 9$

$PR = \sqrt{25}$

$PR = 5$ m

Average speed = $\frac{\text{total distance}}{\text{total time}} = \frac{4\,\text{m} + 3\,\text{m} + 5\,\text{m}}{20\,\text{s} + 10\,\text{s} + 30\,\text{s}} = \frac{12\,\text{m}}{60\,\text{s}}$ = 0.2 m s^{-1}

19. (c)

Take a metre scale and measure the length of the string from the point of suspension to the lower tip of the bob (ℓ_1) (*b*). Now, place the bob over a meter scale and hold it in position with two wooden blocks or stiff cardboards and measure the diameter (*D*) of the bob (*c*). Calculate the radius *R* of the bob by dividing diameter by 2 (*a*). Then the length of the pendulum $\ell = (\ell_1 - R)$ (*d*). Consider the formula $T = 2\pi\sqrt{\frac{\ell}{g}}$ and find the time period of the simple pendulum by substituting the value of 'ℓ' (e).

20. (a)

Find the displacements of the body in 2 s i.e., (S_1) and next 4 s i.e., (S_2) (a). Add both the displacements i.e., $S_1 + S_2$ (b). Find the total time taken to cover $S_1 + S_2$ i.e., t = (2 + 4) s

⇒ t = 6 s (c). Find average velocity using the formula, $\frac{S_1 + S_2}{t}$ (d).

21. (d)

The change in velocity of a body per unit time is called acceleration or the rate of change of velocity is called acceleration.

22. (b)

Pendulum whose time period is two seconds is called second pendulum.

23. (a)

In SI system, the unit of frequency is hertz (Hz).

24. (a)

The unit of distance is centimetre in C.G.S. system and metre in M.K.S. or S.I. system.

25. Displacement can be zero, positive or negative whereas, distance can never be negative and distance travelled never decreases.

26. A motion that repeats itself but not at fi xed interval of time is called non-periodic motion. A ceiling fan when it is switched off, a drum rolling up or down on an inclined plane, the motion of a wheel of bicycle when brakes applied are all examples of non-periodic motion.

27. From the figure:

The distance moved by the body = 20 m.

The time taken to trace the path, (t) = 10 s

(1) The average speed = $\frac{\text{total distance}}{\text{total time}}$

$= \frac{20}{10} = 2$ m s^{-1}.

28. Distance does not depend on direction but displacement will depend on direction.

29. Unit of acceleration m s^{-2}.

Unit of velocity = m s^{-1}.

The ratio of unit of acceleration to the velocity

$= \frac{\text{m s}^{-2}}{\text{m s}^{-1}} = \text{s}^{-1}$.

It is the unit of frequency.

30. From the graph:

The total distance moved by the body = OF = 12 m.

The total time taken = 16 s.

Average speed = $\frac{\text{total distance}}{\text{total time}} = \frac{12}{16}$ m s^{-1} $= \frac{3}{4}$ m s^{-1}.

31. When a body moves with uniform speed in a specified direction, it is said to be moving with uniform velocity.

32. The average value of acceleration due to gravity is 9.8 m s^{-2}.

33. (1) The unit of acceleration is m s^{-2}.

(2) Speed = $\frac{\text{distance}}{\text{time}}$

(3) Displacement is the shortest distance between the initial and final positions in a specified direction. So, the magnitude of displacement travelled by a body is less than or equal to the distance travelled by the body.

34. Quartz clocks contain an electric circuit and are more accurate than pendulum clocks.

35. Acceleration is the rate of change in velocity. Hence, it is zero for a body moving with constant velocity.

36. (B) Note the given values of time period (T) and acceleration due to gravity (g).

(C) Write the formula, $T = 2\pi\sqrt{\frac{\ell}{g}}$ where 'ℓ' is the length of the pendulum.

(A) From the above formula, write the value of ℓ as $\ell = \frac{T^2 g}{4\pi^2}$.

(D) Substitute the given data and get the value of 'ℓ'.

37. (C) Note the initial velocity of the car as $u = 0$ and note down its acceleration.

(B) Note the final velocity (v) and convert it into *SI* unit.

(A) Write the relation between u, v, a and t, where t is the time taken to accelerate the car.

(D) Substitute the given values and obtain the value of t, using $t = \frac{v - u}{a}$.

38. As the bob is performing '1' oscillation in 2 s, the number of oscillations completed in 10 s = $\frac{10}{2}$ = 5 oscillations.

39. As the time period of the oscillation, (T) = 2 s,

$$T = 2\pi\sqrt{\frac{\ell}{g}}$$

$$T^2 = 4\pi^2\frac{\ell}{g}$$

$$\ell = \frac{gT^2}{4\pi^2} = 1\,\text{m}.$$

40. The frequency of the bob, i.e., the number of oscillations completed in one second = ½ Hz = 0.5 Hz.

41. Distance does not depend on direction but displacement will depend on direction.

42. A → b; B → c; C → a; D → d

43. A → c The motion of a shell fired from artillery gun is curvilinear.

B → d A stone dropped from a tower moves vertically downwards. It is in rectilinear motion.

C → b The wings of a ceiling fan undergo rotatory motion.

D → g Acceleration, a =. $\frac{v-u}{t}$ If body moves with uniform velocity, then $v = u \Rightarrow a = 0$.

E → e The length of the pendulum is the distance from the point of suspension to the mid-point of the bob.

F → f We know, $T = 2\pi\sqrt{\frac{\ell}{g}} \Rightarrow T \propto \sqrt{\ell}$.

G → a The motion of a body that repeats itself at irregular intervals of time is known as non-periodic motion.

44. (A) → c Pendulum of a clock performs periodic motion.

(B) → a Speed of a body is its fastness or slowness.

(C) → b Uniform velocity is a vector quantity and has both magnitude and direction.

(D) → e The speed of a body is uniform when it covers equal distances in equal intervals of time.

(E) → d FPS unit of velocity is foot s^{-1}.

45. A – b Rest and motion are relative.

B – c Motion of the bob of a simple pendulum is oscillatory as well as periodic.

C – d The wheels of a bicycle in motion perform both rotatory and translatory motions.

D – a A car taking a turn is an example of variable velocity.

46. A – d A body covering 5 m in every subsequent second moves with constant speed.

B – b If a body covers equal distances in unequal intervals of time, then it is said to move with non-uniform speed.

C – a A lunar month is based on the periodic motion of the moon around the earth.

D – c The age of a person is expressed in years.

47. The speed and average speed of the vehicle can be equal if the vehicle moves with uniform speed or constant speed.

48. To get more accurate time period.

49. The maximum displacement of the vibrating particle is called amplitude. S.I unit is m.

The number of vibrations per second is frequency. SI unit is hertz (Hz).

50. The fastness or slowness is measured in terms of a physical quantity called speed.

51. $V_A = \frac{d_A}{t}$; $V_B = \frac{d_B}{t}$

$d_A = 80$ m and $d_B = 100$ m

$V_A = \frac{80}{t}$; $V_B = \frac{100}{t} \Rightarrow V_A < V_B$. 'B' is faster than 'A'.

52. The watches with electronic circuits are called quartz clocks. Quartz clocks are more accurate than pendulum clocks.

53. Speed = $\frac{\text{Distance travelled}}{\text{Time taken}}$

⇒ distance travelled by the body = speed of the body × time taken.

54. Distance-time graph, displacement–time graph, velocity–time graph.

55. Ball delivered by a spin bowler.

56. A body which does not change its position with respect to surroundings is said to be at rest and if the position of the body changes with respect to the surroundings it is in motion.

57. The rate of change of velocity is acceleration.

Acceleration, $a = \frac{v - u}{t}$

SI unit is m s^{-2}.

58. A simple pendulum that has time period of 2 s is called seconds pendulum. Its length is approximately 100 cm or 1 m.

59. We know $T = 2\pi\sqrt{\frac{\ell}{g}} \Rightarrow T \Rightarrow \sqrt{\ell}$

$T^2 = 4\pi^2 \frac{\ell}{g} \Rightarrow T^2 \propto \ell$

From above relationships, it is clear that as the length of simple pendulum increases, time period also increases and vice versa.

60. $V_A = \frac{d}{t_A}$; $V_B = \frac{d}{t_B}$ $\frac{V_A}{V_B} = \frac{t_B}{t_A} = \frac{11}{10.5}$

$V_A > V_B$ ∴ 'A' is faster than 'B'.

61. The average distance per unit time, when the body is moving with variable speed, is called average speed, Average speed = $\frac{\text{Total distance travelled}}{\text{Total time taken}}$

62. Unit of time in *SI* and *CGS* systems is second (s).

Unit of speed in *SI* and *CGS* systems are m s^{-1} and cm s^{-1} respectively.

63. Odometer is used to find the distance travelled by the vehicle and speedometer is used to find the speed of the vehicle.

64. When pendulum completes one to and fro motion.

65. Earth spinning on its own axis.

66. The propeller of the helicopter will execute both rotatory and translatory motions, since the propeller of the helicopter rotates and moves along with the helicopter and covers the distance.

Short Answer Type Questions

67. 20 oscillation → 32 s and 1 oscillation ____Ts

$T = \frac{32 \times 1}{20}$ s

$\Rightarrow \frac{T}{4} = \frac{32}{4 \times 20} = 0.4$ s.

68. The graph is not a straight line. So, car is not moving with constant speed.

Speed at the end of 2 h = $\frac{100 \text{ km}}{2 \text{ h}} = 50$ km h^{-1}

Speed at the end of 6 h = $\frac{150 \text{ km}}{6 \text{h}} = 25$ km h^{-1}

69. The initial velocity, $u = 108$ km h^{-1} = 30 m s^{-1}

The final velocity, $v = 0$ m s^{-1}

The time taken to stop lorry, $t = 30$ s.

The acceleration of the lorry, $a = \frac{v-u}{t} = \frac{0-30}{30}$

$= -1$ m s^{-2}

70. Let's assume the total distance to be 2D.

Time taken to cover the first half (at 5 m/s) = D/5

Time taken to cover the second half (at 5 m/s) = D/10

Total Time = (D/5)+(D/10) = 3D/10

Average Speed = (2D×10)/3D = 20/3 m s^{-1}

71. The time taken by the earth to rotate once on its own axis is day. The time taken by the earth to revolve once around the sun is year.

The watches and clocks measure the time by using periodic motions.

72. To draw the graph, the following steps should be considered.

(i) Draw two perpendicular lines, *OX* and *OY*, intersecting at '*O*' as shown in the figure. The line *OX* is *X*-axis and the *OY* is *Y*-axis.

(ii) Mark the distance along the *Y*-axis and time along the *X*-axis.

(iii) Choose the proper scale for the given physical quantities on *X*-axis and *Y*-axis.

73. Velocity is the ratio of displacement to time. When an object moves with certain speed, it is not clear in which direction it is moving. To overcome the shortcoming, another term, velocity is used. In a way, velocity is speed in a specified direction.

74. Consider a body moving with initial velocity *u*. Let its velocity change to *v*, in time '*t*'. Then, the change in velocity is $= v - u$.

The change in velocity per unit time $= \frac{v-u}{t}$

By definition, the change in velocity per unit time is acceleration, a. Thus,

$$a = \frac{v-u}{t} \text{ or } v - u = at$$

$$v = u + at$$

75. (i) Uniform speed: When a body covers equal distances in equal intervals of time, however small the time interval may be, then the speed of the body is said to be uniform. Consider a car moving on a road such that it covers, say 10 m in one second. If it covers 10 m in every subsequent second, then its speed is said to be uniform.

(ii) Non-uniform speed: When a body covers unequal distances in equal intervals of time or when it covers equal distances in unequal intervals of time, then the speed of the body is said to be non uniform. Motion of a bus after application of breaks.

76. Given that:

$u = 50$ m s^{-1}

$v = 0$

$t = 5$ s

$a = \frac{v-u}{t} = \frac{0-50}{5} = -10$ m s^{-2}.

77. Given that:

$u = 0$

$v = 150$ km h^{-1}

$t = \frac{1}{6}$ h

$a = \frac{v-u}{t} = 900$ km h^{-2}.

78. **(a)** Uniform Velocity: When a body moves with uniform speed in a specified direction, it is said to be moving with uniform velocity.

Thus, a body moves with uniform velocity when its magnitude as well as its direction remains the same.

Example: Aeroplane moving with 500 km h^{-1} towards east.

(b) Variable velocity: When a body moves such that either its magnitude or direction or both change, then it is said to be moving with variable velocity.

Example: A car moving on a straight road such that its speed changes from time to time has variable velocity. A car taking turn has variable velocity as its direction changes.

79. Take the bob of the pendulum to one side so that the pendulum makes 5° with the vertical and release the bob. Start the stopwatch when the bob is at the mean or extreme position and find the time taken by the pendulum to complete 20 oscillations. Dividing the time for 20 oscillations by 20 gives the time period (T) of the pendulum. The above experiment can be repeated for different lengths (80 cm, 90 cm, 100 cm etc.,) and the time period for each length can be determined. It will be noticed that with increase in length, the time period also increases.

80. (a) Let the distance travelled be 'd'.

The speed of 'A', $v_A = \frac{d}{20}$ m s^{-1}

The speed of 'B', $v_B = \frac{d}{22}$ m s^{-1}.

$$\Rightarrow \frac{v_A}{v_B} = \frac{\frac{d}{20}}{\frac{d}{22}} = \frac{22}{20} = \frac{11}{10} = 11 : 10$$

(b) Let them run for 't' s.

Then, $d_A = v_A \times t = \frac{d}{20} \times t$

$d_B = v_B \times t = \frac{d}{22} \times t$

$$\Rightarrow \frac{d_A}{d_B} = \frac{\frac{d}{20}(t)}{\frac{d}{22}(t)} = \frac{22}{20} = \frac{11}{10} = 11 : 10$$

81. The distance moved by motor cycle, $d = 10267 - 10237$ $= 30$ km

The time taken, t = 9:00 am − 8:30 am = 30 min

$= \therefore \frac{h_1}{h_2} = \frac{t_1{}^2}{t_2{}^2}$ h.

The speed of motor cycles $v = \frac{5}{h_2} = \frac{1}{2^2} = \frac{1}{4}$

$= \frac{30 \text{ km}}{\frac{1}{2}\text{ h}} = 60$ km h^{-1}.

82. Let the time period of the simple pendulum on the earth be 'T'.

We know, $T = \frac{v_1}{v_2} = \frac{t_1}{t_2} = \frac{2}{4} = \frac{1}{2}$, where, ℓ_e, g_e are length of the simple pendulum and acceleration due to gravity on the earth.

Then, $2\pi\sqrt{\frac{l_m}{g_m}}$ where, ℓ_m, g_m are length of the simple pendulum and acceleration due to gravity on the moon.

$$T = 2\pi\sqrt{\frac{l_e}{g_e}} = 2\pi\sqrt{\frac{l_m}{g_m}}$$

$$\frac{l_e}{g_e} = \frac{l_m}{\frac{1}{6}g_e} \quad [\{\, g_e = 6\, g_m] \quad \Rightarrow \ell_m = \frac{l_e}{6}$$

$\therefore$ The length of the pendulum should be decreased to 1/6th of the original length.

83. We know, $T = 2\pi\sqrt{\frac{l}{g}}$

The time period of seconds pendulum, $T_1 = 2$ s

The length of the second pendulum $\ell_1 = 100$ cm $= 1$ m

Now, the new length of the pendulum $\ell_2 = 2\ell_1$

$\Rightarrow \ell_2 = 200$ cm $= 2$ m

Let the new time period of the pendulum be $= T_2$

$\Rightarrow T \propto \sqrt{l}$

$$\Rightarrow \frac{T_1}{T_2} = \sqrt{\frac{l_1}{l_2}} \Rightarrow T_2 = T_1\sqrt{\frac{l_2}{l_1}}$$

$$T_2 = 2 \times \sqrt{\frac{2l_1}{l_1}} = 2\sqrt{2} \text{ s.}$$

The time period becomes $2\sqrt{2}$ times the original one.

84. A simple pendulum is made up of a metallic ball (called bob of the pendulum), suspended from a rigid support with the help of a thread, as shown in the figure (a). The rest position of the bob is called the mean position. When the bob is taken to one side and released, it moves to and fro about the mean position. This type of to and fro motion is called an oscillatory motion. The motion of the bob of the pendulum is not only oscillatory but periodic also.

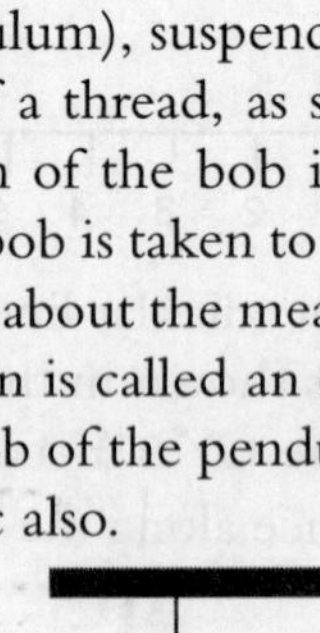

Figure (a) A simple pendulum

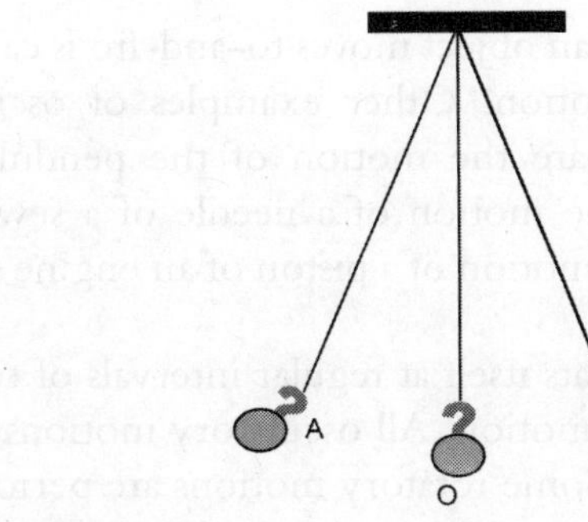

Figure (b) Different positions of the bob of an oscillating simple pendulum

As shown in the figure (b), 'O' is the mean position. If the bob is displaced from its mean position and released, it starts oscillating. It goes from 'O' to, say B, from B to A and back to 'O'. This completes one oscillation. If the bob is released, from 'A' it goes to B and then comes back to 'A'. This also constitutes one oscillation. The positions 'A' and 'B' are called extreme positions. The time taken by the bob to complete one oscillation is called its time period.

Essay Type Questions

85. Let, d_A, d_B and d_C be the distances covered by the cars. A, B and C are the cars.
Given that: $d_A = d_B = d_C$
Let t_A, t_B and t_C be the time taken by cars A, B and C.
Then, $t_A < t_B < t_C$

We know $S_A = \frac{d_A}{t_A}$; $S_B = \frac{d_B}{t_B}$ and $S_C = \frac{d_C}{t_C}$

$\Rightarrow S_A > S_B > S_C$.

86. The time period (T) of a simple pendulum is given by

$$T = 2\pi\sqrt{\frac{l}{g}}$$

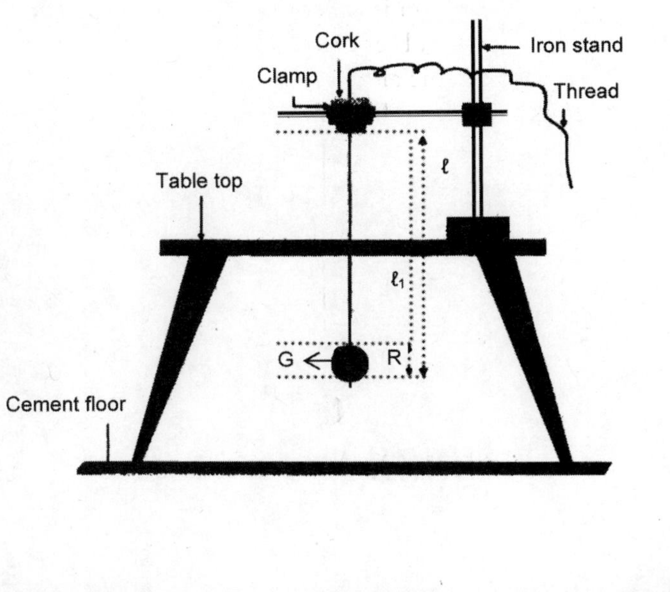

Where, 'ℓ' is the length of the simple pendulum and 'g' is the acceleration due to gravity. At a given place, since 'g' value remains constant, $T \propto \sqrt{l}$ which means time period increases (or decreases) with increase (or decrease) in length. The experimental set up to find the time period of a simple pendulum is as shown in the figure given below.

Determine the radius of the bob of the pendulum by placing it between two wooden blocks and measuring the gap between the wooden blocks with the help of a scale. The gap gives diameter from which the radius can be calculated. Suspend the bob by passing thread through a vertically cut cork and holding tight the cork between the clamps.

For the length of the pendulum to be 70 cm, the length of the thread should be (70 – R) cm where, R is the radius of the bob.

Take the bob of the pendulum to one side so that the pendulum makes 5° with the vertical and release the bob. Start the stopwatch when the bob is at the mean or extreme position and find the time taken by the pendulum to complete 20 oscillations. Dividing the time for 20 oscillations by 20 gives the time period (T) of the pendulum. The above experiment can be repeated for different lengths (80 cm,90 cm, 100 cm etc.,) and the time period for each length can be determined. It will be noticed that with increase in length, the time period also increases.

87. The time period of 'A' is, $T_1 = \frac{T}{20}$.

The time period of 'B' is, $T_2 = \frac{T}{30}$

The ratio of time periods of 'A' and 'B' is $\frac{T_1}{T_2}$

$$= \frac{\frac{T}{20}}{\frac{T}{30}} = \frac{30}{20} = \frac{3}{2}$$

$T_1 : T_2 = 3 : 2$

88. The different kinds of motion are:

(i) Translatory motion: A bus moving on a road, the motion of a rising balloon, the free fall of a stone under gravity, the motion of a cricket ball when it is hit by a batsman are examples of translatory motion. Translatory motion is further classified as rectilinear motion and curvilinear motion. When an object moves along a straight path, its motion is said to be rectilinear motion. The marching of soldiers on a straight road, the motion of a car on a straight road, the motion of carrom board coin are examples of rectilinear motion. When an object moves along curved path, its motion is called curvilinear motion. A bus moving on a fly-over bridge, a car taking a turn, a football kicked from the ground into air all have curvilinear motion.

(ii) **Rotatory motion:** In this type of motion, the object rotates about a fixed axis. The motion of blades of a ceiling fan, the spin motion of a top, the motion of turbine, the motion of the earth around the sun are all circular or rotatory motion. In some cases, the rotatory and translatory motions take place simultaneously. When a bicycle moves, its wheels undergo translatory and rotatory motion.

(iii) **Oscillatory motion:** A boy on a swing moves to-and-fro (back and forth). The motion such as above, where an object moves to-and-fro is called oscillatory motion. Other examples of oscillatory motion are the motion of the pendulum of a clock, the motion of a needle of a sewing machine, the motion of a piston of an engine etc.

89. A motion that repeats itself at regular intervals of time is called a periodic motion. All oscillatory motions are periodic motions. Some rotatory motions are periodic motions. The motion of the earth around the sun, the motion of the pendulum of a clock, the rotation of the earth about its own axis, the motion of a swing are periodic motions.

A motion that repeats itself but not at fixed interval of time is called a non-periodic motion. A ceiling fan when it is switched off, a drum rolling up or down an inclined plane, the motion of a wheel of bicycle when brakes are applied are all examples of non-periodic motion.

Competition Wing

Level 1: Apply your Concepts

1. The unit of displacement is meters (m).
The unit of acceleration is meters per second squared ($m\ s^{-2}$).
Now, to find the ratio of the unit of displacement to that of acceleration = s^2

2. vibratory
The molecules in solid undergo vibratory motion.

3. $\frac{1}{1000}$
1000 millisecond = 1 s
$\Rightarrow$ 1 millisecond = $\frac{1}{1000}$ th part of a second.

4. $5\ m\ s^{-2}$
$$a = \frac{v - u}{t} = \frac{20 - 10}{2} = 5\ m\ s^{-2}$$

5. velocity
When a car moves with constant velocity, its average velocity is equal to its velocity.

6. Odometer measures the distance travelled by a vehicle.

7. A body is said to move with uniform speed if it covers equal distances in equal intervals of time.

8. One microsecond is one millionth of a second.

9. SI unit of speed is $m\ s^{-1}$.

10. $v = 20\ km\ h^{-1}$
$T = 2\ h$
$v = \frac{s}{t} \Rightarrow 5 = v \times t = 20 \times 2 = 40$ km.

11. The time taken by the pendulum to complete one oscillation is called time period.

12. The distance covered by an object in a unit time is known as the speed of the object.

13. If $T = 2\pi\sqrt{\frac{\ell}{g}}$ is the time period of a simple pendulum,
then $\frac{1}{2\pi}\sqrt{\frac{g}{\ell}}$ is frequency of the simple pendulum.

14. False. Body *P* is at rest from time 0 to t_s.

15. The motion of a simple pendulum is an oscillatory motion.

16. A nanosecond is one billionth of a second.

17. When an object is moving with constant speed the average speed is not equal to velocity.

18. The motion of a simple pendulum is periodic.

19. By using distance-time graph we can find out the average speed of an object.

20. Speedometer is used to measure the speed of a vehicle.

21. The distance-time graph of the motion of an object moving with a constant speed is a straight line.

22. The speed of the bob is maximum at its mean position.

23. The time period of a simple pendulum of length 1 m is 2 second.

24. Number of oscillations = 20
Total time taken for 20 oscillations = 5 s
Time period (T) = Total time taken / Number of oscillations
T = 5 s / 20
T = 0.25 s
Thus, the time period is 0.25 s.

25. To determine the average speed of the person, we need to calculate:
1. Total distance travelled by the person.
2. Total time taken for the journey.
From the figure:
Distance AB = 3 m
Distance BC = 9 m
Distance CA (using Pythagoras theorem) = $3\sqrt{10}$ m
Total distance = AB + BC + CA
Total distance = 3 m + 9 m + $3\sqrt{10}$ m
Total distance = 12 m + $3\sqrt{10}$ m
Time taken for path AB = 5 s
Time taken for path BC = 20 s
Time taken for path CA= 25 s
Total time = 5 s + 20 s + 25 s = 50 s
Now, average speed = Total distance / Total time
Average speed = (12 m + $3\sqrt{10}$ m) / 50 s
$$= \frac{3\left(4+\sqrt{10}\right)}{50}$$

26. The speed of a body cannot be negative.

27. From the figure:
The distance moved by the body = 20 m

Time taken to trace the path, $(t) = 10$ s

(i) average speed $= \dfrac{\text{total distance}}{\text{total time}} = \dfrac{20}{10}$

28. Speed $= \dfrac{\text{distance}}{\text{time}} = \dfrac{10}{2} = 5 \text{ m s}^{-1}$

29. Speed $= \dfrac{\text{distance}}{\text{time}}$

Time $= \dfrac{\text{distance}}{\text{speed}} = \dfrac{2\pi \times r}{2\pi} = \dfrac{2\pi \times 1}{2\pi}$ 1 s

30. Average speed $= \dfrac{\text{total distance}}{\text{total time}}$

$= \dfrac{6960 - 6700}{13} = 20 \text{ km h}^{-1}$

31. Time period $= \dfrac{60}{120} = 0.5$ s

32. Speed $= \dfrac{\text{distance}}{\text{time}}$, distance = speed × time

$= 10 \times 60 \times 60 = 36000 = 36 \times 10^3$ m

$= 36$ km

33. Time period = time taken for one oscillation = 2 s

34. A body projected upwards from the top of a building is an example of a non-uniform motion.

35. Average velocity $= \dfrac{\text{total displacement}}{\text{total time}} = \dfrac{20}{4 \times 60}$

$= 0.08 \text{ m s}^{-1}$

36. $1 \text{ km h} = {}^{5}\!/_{18} \text{ m s}^{-1}$

$1 \text{ m s}^{-1} = {}^{18}\!/_{5} \text{ km h}^{-1}$

$20 \text{ m s}^{-1} = 20 \times \dfrac{18}{5} \text{ km h} = 72 \text{ km h}^{-1}$

37. (1) Unit of acceleration is m s^{-2}

(2) Speed $= \dfrac{\text{distance}}{\text{time}}$

(3) As the body is moving with uniform (constant) velocity, i.e., there is no change in the velocity of body, and hence, acceleration of the body = zero.

38. First find the initial velocity and final velocity of the car from given data (D, B). From the problem, find the time taken to increase the velocity (C). Use the formula acceleration $= \dfrac{\text{Total change in velocity}}{\text{Total time required for change}}$

i.e.,

$$a = \frac{v - u}{t} \text{ (A).}$$

Substitute the values of u, v, t and attain the value of 'a' [E].

39. Take the pendulum to the surface of the moon and keep the length of the pendulum constant (D). Find the time period of this simple pendulum using stop watch on the surface of the moon (T_m) (A). Use the formula $T = 2\pi\sqrt{\dfrac{l}{g}}$ (C). Substitute the values of 'T_m' in $T = 2\pi\sqrt{\dfrac{l}{g}}$, and obtain $\dfrac{T_E}{T_M} = \sqrt{\dfrac{g_M}{g_E}}$.

From this, obtain the value of (g_M) (E). The acceleration due to gravity on the moon (g_M) is 1/6th the acceleration due to gravity on the earth (g_E) (B).

40. Frequency of the bob, i.e., number of oscillations completed in one second = ½ Hz = 0.5 Hz.

41. As the bob is performing '1' oscillation in 2 s, the number of oscillations completed in 10 s $= \dfrac{10}{2} = 5$ oscillations.

42. From the graph,

The time taken for one oscillation, i.e., time period of oscillation (t) = 2 s

Time taken to complete 100 oscillations

$= 2 \times 100$ s $= 200$ s

43. Total distance traced by the athlete = sum of perimeter of two circles

$= 2\,\pi\, r_1 + 2\pi\, r_2 = 2\pi\,(r_1 + r_2)$

$= 2\,\pi\,(2 + 3) = 10\,\pi$

Time taken to trace the path, $(t) = 44$ s

Average speed $= \dfrac{\text{total distance}}{\text{total time taken}}$

$= \dfrac{10\pi}{44}$

$$= \frac{10\times22}{7\times44} = 5\!\big/_{7} \text{ m s}^{-1}$$

44. Length of the trains, $l = 200$ m

Number of rotations completed = 1

Speed with which it is moving along the circular path = 54 km h^{-1}

$= 54 \times 5\!\big/_{18}$ m s^{-1} = 15 m s^{-1}

As the train is completing 1 rotation, the distance moved by the train = 2 × 200 = 400 m

$$\text{Speed} = \frac{\text{distance}}{\text{time}}$$

$$\text{Time} = \frac{400 \text{ m}}{15 \text{ m s}^{-1}} = \frac{80}{3} \text{ s} = 26.666 \text{ s} = 26.\bar{6} \text{ s}$$

45. $\text{Average velocity} = \dfrac{\text{total distance}}{\text{total time}}$

$$10 = \frac{h}{2}$$

$$h = 20 \text{ m.}$$

46. Let the distance between 'α' and 'β' be x m

The velocity during its first half of journey = 72 km h^{-1}

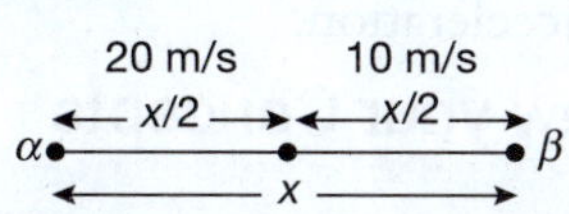

$= 72 \times 5\!\big/_{18}$ m s^{-1}

= 20 m s^{-1}

The velocity during its second half of journey = 36 km h^{-1}

$= 36 \times 5\!\big/_{18}$ m s^{-1}

= 10 m s^{-1}

Time taken to travel first half of distance

$$(t_2) = t = \frac{x\!\big/_2}{20} = \frac{x}{40} \text{ s}$$

Similarly, time taken to travel second half of the distance

$$(t_2) = \frac{x\!\big/_2}{10} = \frac{x}{20} \text{ s}$$

$$\text{Total time taken, } (T) = t_1 + t_2 = \left(\frac{x}{40} + \frac{x}{20}\right)\text{s}$$

$$= \left(\frac{x + 2x}{40}\right)\text{s} = \frac{3x}{40} \text{ s}$$

$$\text{Average velocity} = \frac{\text{total displacement}}{\text{total time taken}}$$

$$= \left(\frac{x}{3x\!\big/_{40}}\right) \text{m s}^{-1} = \frac{40}{3} \text{ m s}^{-1}$$

$= 13.33$ m s^{-1}

$= 13.\bar{3}$ m s^{-1}

47. Number of turns wound over rod = 200

Diameter of the rod, (d) = 10 cm

$R = 5$ cm = 0.05 m

Time taken to wind, (t) = 2 s

$$\text{Length of the wire wound in one second} = \frac{\text{distance}}{\text{time}}$$

$$= \frac{200\times2\pi r}{2} = \frac{200\times2\pi\times0.05}{2} = 10\pi \text{ m}$$

48. **Kinetics** deals with the motion of bodies considering the cause of their motion.

49. Speed of the athlete = 11 m s^{-1}

Radius of circular track = 14 m

Number of rounds completed = 6

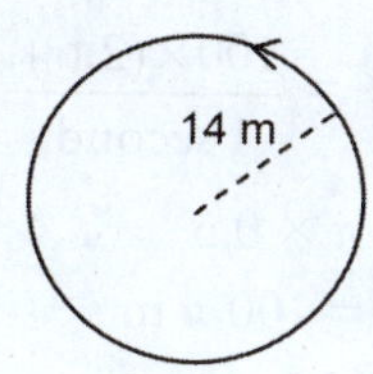

Total distance traced by the athlete = $6 \times 2\pi r$

$$= 6 \times 2 \times \frac{22}{7} \times 14$$

$$\text{Speed} = \frac{\text{distance}}{\text{time}}$$

$$\text{Time taken} = \frac{6\times2\times22\times14}{7\times11} = 48 \text{ s}$$

= 0.8 min = 0.0133 h

50. Time taken to travel = 2π s

Total distance travelled

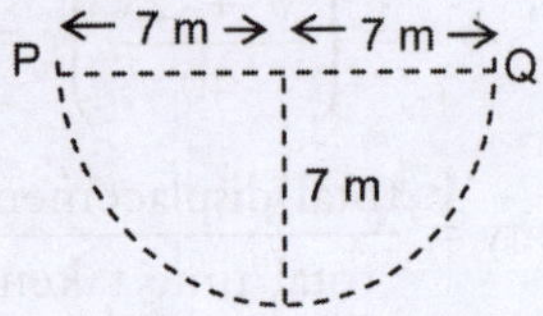

$$\text{(d)} = \frac{2\pi r}{2} = \pi r$$
$$= \pi\,(7)$$
$$= 7\pi \text{ m}$$

$$\text{Average speed of the car} = \frac{7\pi}{2\pi} = 3.5 \text{ m s}^{-1}$$

$$\text{Average velocity} = \frac{\text{total displacement}}{\text{total time taken}} = \frac{(7+7)}{2\pi}$$
$$= \frac{14\times 7}{2\times 22}$$
$$= \frac{49}{22} \text{ m s}^{-1}$$
$$= 2.23 \text{ m s}^{-1}$$

51. $$\text{Average velocity} = \frac{\text{total displacement}}{\text{total time}}$$
$$= \frac{125}{5} = 25 \text{ m s}^{-1}$$

52. Radius of the circular path traced by fan = 0.5 m

The number of rotations per second = 100

$$\text{Speed} = \frac{\text{distance}}{\text{time}} = \frac{100\times(2\pi r)}{1 \text{ second}}$$
$$= 100 \times 2\,\pi \times 0.5$$
$$= 50 \times 2\pi = 100\,\pi \text{ m s}^{-1}$$

53. A plucked metal wire moves up and down and repeats this motion itself at regular intervals of time. It executes periodic motion.
Hence, the correct option is (a).

54. We know, $T = 2\pi\sqrt{\frac{l}{g}} \Rightarrow T \propto \sqrt{l}$.

Hence, the correct option is (a).

55. A – c Musical instruments produce sound due to vibratory motion of air molecules or strings.

B – e Potter's wheel undergoes rotatory motion.

C – f The time period of a seconds pendulum is 2 s.

D – b We know speed = $\frac{\text{Distance travelled}}{\text{Time taken}}$

$\Rightarrow$ Distance travelled = speed × time taken.

E – a The distance–time graph of a body moving with variable speed is not a straight line.

F – d The rate of change in motion in a specific direction is called velocity.

56. A – c km h^{-1} is a unit of speed.

B – d Unit of time is second.

C – f,c average speed = total distance covered/ total time km h^{-1} is a unit of average speed.

D – a An object moving along a straight line with a constant speed is said to be in uniform motion.

E – b Freely falling body is an example of non-uniform motion.

F – e Change in length of a simple pendulum results in change in its time period.

57. (A) → b Guitar string performs vibratory motion.

(B) → a Speedometer reads speed of the vehicle in km h^{-1}.

(C) → d Odometer of the vehicle reads the distance moved by the vehicle.

(D) → c Rate of change of velocity is called acceleration.

Level 2: Review your Concepts

58. $T_1 = \frac{1}{20}$ s $\quad T_1 = 2\pi\sqrt{\ell/g_1}$

$$\Rightarrow \frac{1}{20} = 2\pi\sqrt{\ell/g_1} \qquad (1)$$

$$T_2 = 2\pi\sqrt{\ell/g_2} \qquad (2)$$

$$\frac{(2)}{(1)} \Rightarrow \frac{T_2}{\frac{1}{20}} = \frac{2\pi\sqrt{\ell/g_2}}{2\pi\sqrt{\ell/g_1}}$$

$$20T_2 = \sqrt{\frac{\ell}{g_2}\times\frac{g_1}{\ell}} = \sqrt{\frac{g_1}{g_2}}$$

$$T_2 = \frac{1}{20}\sqrt{\frac{g_1}{g_2}}$$

$$\text{But } g_2 = \sqrt{\frac{g_1}{4}}$$

$$=\frac{1}{20}\sqrt{\frac{g_1}{\frac{1}{4}g_1}}=\frac{1}{20}\sqrt{4}=\frac{2}{20}=\frac{1}{10}\text{ s; } 0.1\text{ s}$$

59. In graph-I the distance travelled by the body is not changing with time. Thus, the body is at rest. In graph-II distance travelled by the body decreases with time. It is not possible. In graph-III the body has different distances at the same time. This graph is also not possible. In graph-IV the distance increases with time. Therefore, the body is moving with a uniform speed. Thus, the graphs 2 and 3 are not possible.

60. Time for which the two trains travel before they meet are equal.

That is $t_A = t_B$.

But $t_A = \frac{d_A}{S_A}$, $t_B = \frac{d_B}{s_B}$

Let the two trains meet at a distance of x km from A. Then the distance travelled by the other train is $(440 - x)$ km

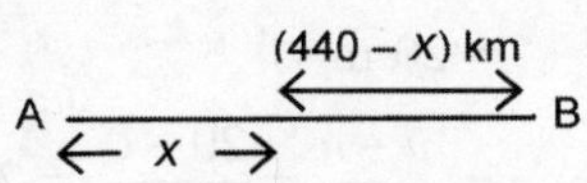

$$\frac{x}{60} = \frac{440 - x}{50} \Rightarrow 5x = 2640 - 6x$$

$\Rightarrow 11x = 2640 \Rightarrow x = 240$ km

The two trains meet each other at a distance of 240 km from A.

Time taken, $t = \frac{d_A}{s_A} = \frac{240}{60} = 4$ h

61. $\text{Speed} = \frac{\text{distance}}{\text{time}} = \left(\frac{500}{10\times60}\right)\text{ m s}^{-1}$

$$= \left(\frac{500\times18}{10\times60\times5}\right)\text{ km h}^{-1} = 3\text{ km h}^{-1}$$

62. $\text{Speed} = \frac{\text{distance}}{\text{time}}$

Let the distance be x, $\frac{\text{distance}}{\text{speed}} = \text{time}$

$$t_1 + t_2 = \frac{x}{3} + \frac{x}{2} = 1, \Rightarrow \frac{2x+3x}{6} = 1$$

$$\Rightarrow 5x = 6;\ x = \frac{6}{5} = 1.2\text{ km}$$

63. $\text{Speed} = \frac{\text{distance}}{\text{time}} = \frac{20}{5} = 4\text{ km h}^{-1}$

Distance covered in 7 hours $= 4 \times 7 = 28$ km

64. $\text{Speed} = \frac{\text{distance}}{\text{time}}$

For one full rotation it takes 1 hour.

Distance travelled in one full rotation is $= 2\,\pi \times r$.

$$\text{Speed} = \frac{2\times\pi\times0.1}{60\times60}\text{ m s}^{-1} = 1.75\times10^{-4}\text{ m s}^{-1}$$

65. Number of oscillations = 20

Time taken, $t = 40$ s

$$\text{Frequency, } n = \frac{\text{Number of oscillations}}{\text{Time taken}} = \frac{20}{40} = 0.5\text{ Hz}$$

$$\text{Time period} = \frac{\text{Time taken}}{\text{Number of oscillations}} = \frac{40}{20} = 2\text{ s}$$

66. The speed of body is the slope of distance-time graph. The slope of $A >$ slope of $C >$ slope of B

$\therefore S_A > S_C > S_B$.

67. Let the total distance be x km.

$\text{Speed} = \frac{\text{distance}}{\text{time}}$

$\text{Time} = \frac{\text{distance}}{\text{speed}}$

$$t_1 = \frac{x}{2\times10} = \frac{x}{20}$$

$$t_2 = \frac{x}{2\times15} = \frac{x}{30},\quad t_1 + t_2 = 10\text{ hours}$$

$$\frac{x}{20} + \frac{x}{30} = 10$$

$30x + 20x = 6000$

$50x = 6000;\ x = 120$ km

68. Let the speed of the car from college to house be x km h^{-1}.

$\text{Average speed} = \frac{\text{total distance}}{\text{total time}}$

Take the distance between A and B as d.

Time taken from A to B

$$\text{Time} = \frac{\text{distance}}{\text{speed}} = \frac{d}{60} = t_1$$

Time taken from B to A $t_2 = \dfrac{d}{x}$

$$\text{Average speed} = \frac{\text{total distance}}{\text{total time}} = \frac{d+d}{t_1+t_2}$$

$$\frac{2d}{\dfrac{d}{60}+\dfrac{d}{x}} = 50$$

$120x = 3000 + 50x$

$70x = 3000;\ x = 42.86 \text{ km h}^{-1}$

69. Distance covered by Bantu, $s_B = 20$ m

Time taken, $t = 10$ s.

$\therefore$ Average speed of Bantu, $v_{avB} = 20 / 10 = 2$ m/s

Distance covered by Mannu, $s_M = 15$ m

Time taken, $t = 10$ s.

$\therefore$ Average speed of Mannu, $v_{avM} = 15 / 10 = 1.5$ m/s

Hence, the ratio of their average speeds

$$= \frac{v_{avB}}{v_{avM}} = \frac{2}{1.5} = \frac{20}{15} = \frac{4}{3}$$

70. $\text{Speed} = \dfrac{\text{distance}}{\text{time}}$

$\text{Time} = \dfrac{\text{distance}}{\text{speed}}$

Take the distance as x.

Time taken to reach the cycle shop $t_1 = \dfrac{x}{5}$.

Time taken to return $t_2 = \dfrac{x}{15}$

$$\text{Average speed} = \frac{\text{total distance}}{\text{total time}} = \frac{x+x}{t_1+t_2}$$

$$= \frac{2x}{\dfrac{x}{5}+\dfrac{x}{15}} = \frac{2x}{\dfrac{3x+x}{15}}$$

$$= \frac{15\times 2x}{4x} = \frac{30}{4} = 7.5 \text{ km h}^{-1}$$

71. Let the two trains meet at a distance of x km from A.

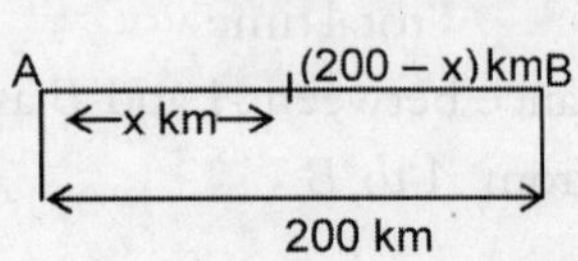

$$\text{Speed} = \frac{\text{distance}}{\text{time}}$$

Time taken for the train which starts from A is

$$\text{time} = \frac{\text{distance}}{\text{speed}} = \frac{x}{60}$$

Time taken for the train which starts from B is

$$\text{time} = \frac{(200-x)}{80} \text{ h}$$

Difference in the time is equal to ½ hour.

$$\frac{x}{60} - \frac{200-x}{80} = \frac{1}{2}$$

$$\frac{80x - 60(200-x)}{60\times 80} = \frac{1}{2}$$

$$\frac{80x - 12000 + 60x}{4800} = \frac{1}{2}$$

$140\,x - 12000 = 2400$

$140x = 14400$

$x = 102.86$ km

72. Initial velocity, $u = 0$

Final velocity, $v = 72 \text{ km h}^{-1} = 72 \times \dfrac{5}{18}$

$= 20 \text{ m s}^{-1}$

Acceleration, $a = \dfrac{v-u}{t} = \dfrac{20-0}{10} = 2 \text{ m s}^{-2}$

73. The speed of the bike at 08:00 am, $v_1 = 30$ km / h

The speed of the bike at 08:05 am, $v_2 = 40$ km / h

The speed of the bike at 08:10 am, $v_3 = 50$ km / h

Time interval between 08:00 am to 08:05 am,

$t = 5 \text{ min} = \dfrac{5}{60} = \dfrac{1}{12}$ h

Time interval between 08:05 am to 08:10 am,

$t = 5 \text{ min} = \dfrac{5}{60} = \dfrac{1}{12}$ h

The increase in speed of the bike from 08:00 am to 08:05 am, $\Delta v = v_2 - v_1 = 40 - 30 = 10$ km / h

The increase in speed of the bike from 08:05 am to 08:10 am, $\Delta v = v_3 - v_2 = 50 - 40 = 10$ km / h

Thus, she goes with equal increase in speed in equal intervals ⇒ acceleration is uniform.

Acceleration of the bike,

$$a = \frac{\Delta v}{t} = \frac{10 \text{ km / h}}{\dfrac{1}{12}\text{h}} = 120 \text{ km / h}^2$$

74. Acceleration, $a = \frac{v-u}{t} = 10 \text{ m s}^{-2}$

$\frac{v-0}{t} = 10, \quad v = 10 \times 5 = 50 \text{ m s}^{-1}$

Maximum velocity = 50 m s^{-1}

75. It moves with a uniform speed. So, average speed is equal to 0.01 m s^{-1}.

76. To determine the frequency of a simple pendulum of length ℓ, the following steps should be followed:

(i) Determine the length (ℓ) of the simple pendulum from the given data.

(ii) Let the time period of simple pendulum be T

(iii) Use the formula, $T = 2\pi\sqrt{\frac{\ell}{g}}$

(iv) The frequency, $n = \frac{1}{T}$ Hz

Hence, the correct order is CABD.

77. To determine the final velocity of a stone dropped from a certain height h which takes t seconds to reach the ground with $g = 10 \text{ m/s}^2$, the following steps should be followed:

(i) Consider the initial velocity u of the stone as zero since it is dropped (not thrown) from rest.

(ii) Use the formula, $a = \frac{v-u}{t}$.

(iii) Use the second equation of motion to determine the final velocity, v = u + at. Given that u = 0 (from step 1), this equation simplifies to v = at. Here, a is the acceleration due to gravity 10 m/s^2 and t is the time taken to reach the ground.

Hence, the correct order is ACB.

78. As the speed of the body is becoming half of its initial value, for every *t s*, the graph of speed versus time is as follows:

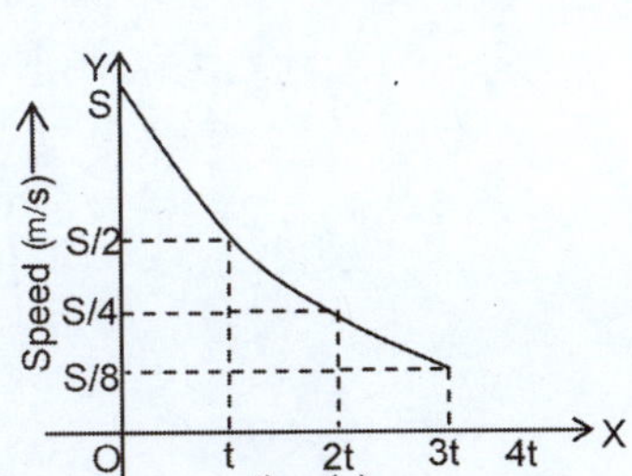

Level 3: Assess Your Concepts

79. Given that:

Forward direction:

$V = 5 \text{ m s}^{-1}$.

$T_1 = 10$ s

$\Rightarrow s_1 = u \times t_1 = 5 \times 10 = 50$ m

Backward direction:

$v = 5 \text{ m s}^{-1}$

$T_2 = 5$ s

$\Rightarrow s_2 = v \times t_2 = 5 \times 5 = 25$ m

Average speed, $v_{avg} = \frac{\text{Total distance}}{\text{Total time taken}}$

$= \frac{s_1 + s_2}{t_1 + t_2} = \frac{50+25}{10+5} = \frac{75 \text{ m}}{15 \text{ s}}$

$= 5 \text{ m s}^{-1}$

Average velocity, $v_{avg} = \frac{\text{Total displacement}}{\text{Total time taken}}$

$= \frac{50-25}{10+5} = \frac{25}{15} = \frac{5}{3}$

$= 1.66 \text{ m s}^{-1}$.

80. Velocity of the train,

$$v = 54 \text{ km h}^{-1} = 54 \times \frac{5}{18} \text{ m s}^{-1} = 15 \text{ m s}^{-1}.$$

In order to cross the bridge the train has to cover a distance equal to the sum of length of the bridge and the length of the train.

$$S = 100 \text{ m} + 245 \text{ m} = 345 \text{ m}$$

Time taken to cross the bridge = t.

$$= \frac{345}{15} = 23 \text{ s}$$

81. Let t be the time, for which the body travels. Distance covered in the first half of the time,

$$S_1 = 20 \times \frac{t}{2} = 10\,t.$$

And the distance covered in the second half of the time

$$S_2 = 30 \times \frac{t}{2} = 15\,t.$$

$$\text{Average speed} = \frac{\text{total distance}}{\text{total time}} = \frac{15t + 10t}{t} = 25 \text{ m s}^{-1}$$

82. Speed of light in air, $v_a = 3 \times 10^8$ m s^{-1}

Distance travelled by light in air, $s_a = 9 \times 10^8$ m

$\therefore$ The time taken by light to travel in air,

$$t_a = \frac{s_a}{v_a} = \frac{9 \times 10^8}{3 \times 10^8} = 3 \text{ s}$$

Speed of light in glass, $v_g = 2 \times 10^8$ m s^{-1}

Distance travelled by light in glass, $s_g = 16 \times 10^8$ m

$\therefore$ The time taken by light to travel in glass,

$$t_g = \frac{s_g}{v_g} = \frac{16 \times 10^8}{2 \times 10^8} = 8 \text{ s}$$

$\therefore$ The total time taken by light to travel, $t = t_a + t_g = 3 + 8 = 11$ s

83. Distance travelled = $2x$

Time, $t = 30$ s

Speed = 1 m s^{-1}

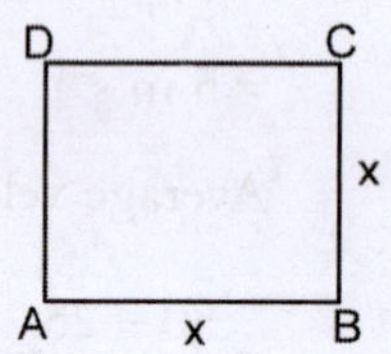

$$\text{Speed} = \frac{\text{distance}}{\text{time}} = \frac{2x}{30} = 1,$$

$$x = \frac{30}{2} = 15 \text{ m}$$

Shortest distance between A and C

$= \sqrt{15^2 + 15^2} = \sqrt{450} = 21.2$ m

84. Let 'd' be the distance covered by Raj in time t then

Speed of Ram $S_1 = \left[\frac{d}{t}\right]$ m s^{-1}.

Speed of Raj $S_2 = \left(\frac{d/2}{2t}\right) = \frac{d}{4t} = \frac{1}{4}\left(\frac{d}{t}\right)$

Ratio of speed $= \frac{S_1}{S_2} = \frac{d}{t} : \frac{1}{4}\frac{d}{t} = 1 : \frac{1}{4} = 4 : 1$

85. Initial velocity 'u' = 72 km h^{-1} = $72 \times \frac{5}{18}$ = 20 m s^{-1}

Final velocity, $v = 0$ m s^{-1}

Time, $t = 3$ s

$$\frac{v - u}{t} = a,$$

$$\frac{0 - 20}{3} = a \Rightarrow \text{deceleration} = -6.67 \text{ m s}^{-2}$$

86. (i) The velocity of the body is not constant and hence it is moving with variable velocity.

(ii) The velocity of the body is increasing with time. Hence, it is accelerating.

(iii) As the increase in velocity of the body is uniform, or equal increase in velocity in equal time intervals, the acceleration of the body is uniform.

(iv) The change in velocity is 5 m/s for every three second starting from 0 s.

Thus, the acceleration of the body = $\Delta v/\Delta t = 5/3$ m/s^2 = 1.67 m/s^2.

CHAPTER

3

Heat

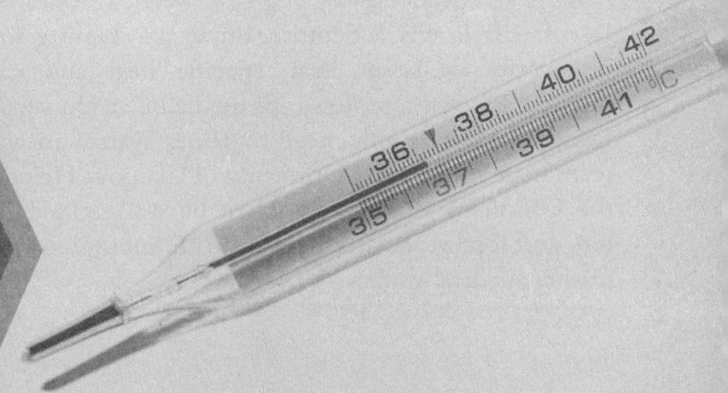

Remember

Before beginning this chapter, you should be able to:

- Define heat and temperature.
- Measure temperature on celsius scale.

Key Ideas

After completing this chapter, you should be able to:

- Identify the differences between heat and temperature and know the measurement of temperature with the help of thermometers.
- Understand transmission of heat and define conduction, convection and radiation.
- Know the working of a thermos flask.
- Understand the expansion of solids, liquids and gases and applications of expansion.
- Explain the change of states of matter due to heating effects.

Scientific Crypt

A Tribute to Joseph Black (1728–1799)

Joseph Black was a Scottish Physician, known for his discoveries of latent heat, specific heat and carbon dioxide. He was a professor of medicine at University of Glasgow. He was influenced by James Watt who was his team mate in the same University of Glasgow. He entered the University of Glasgow when he was eighteen years old, and four years later he went to Edinburgh to persue further medical studies.

Around 1750, Joseph black developed the analytical balance based on light-weight beam balanced on wedge shaped fulcrum. This analytical balance has become an important scientific instrument in most chemistry and physics laboratories.

In 1757, he was appointed as Regius professor of the practice of medicine at the University of Glasgow. The great scientist took his last breath on 6 December 1799.

FUN TIME

CROSSWORD

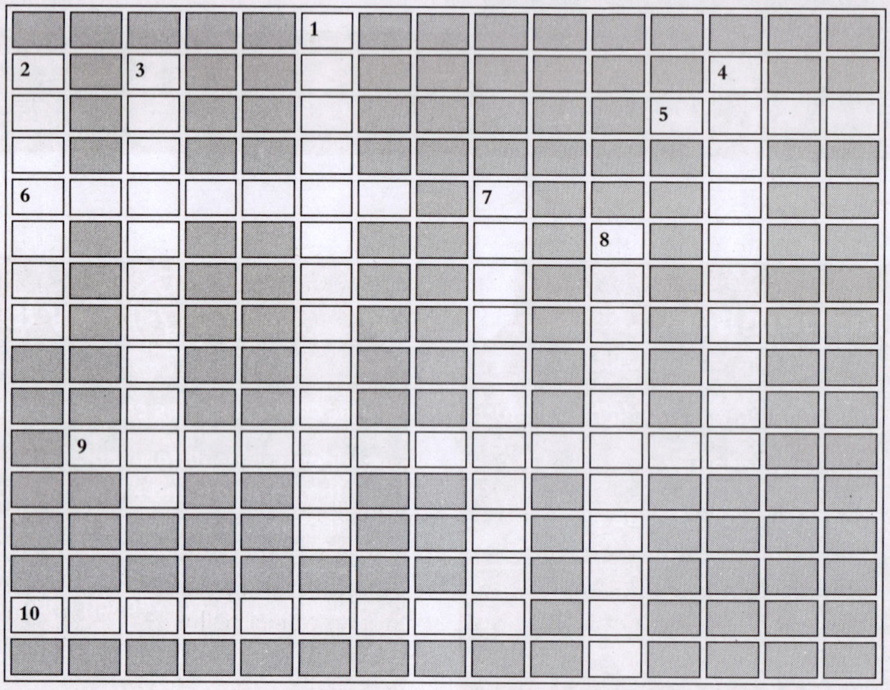

Across

5. The density of water is highest at this temperature measured on Celsius scale.

6. Amount of heat energy required to increase the temperature of 1 g of water by 1°C.

9. This is the process of conversion of substance from gaseous to liquid state.

10. This mode of transition of heat does not require any material medium.

Down

1. Heat energy absorbed by 1 kg of a substance for 1 K raise in temperature.

2. This liquid is preferred as thermometric liquid due to its high specific heat.

3. Due to this the size of a naphthalene ball decreases.

4. This is the mode of transfer of heat energy in which the molecules vibrate at their own position.

7. Due to this process we feel cool when we sit under a rotating fan.

8. It is used to measure the heat energy.

INTRODUCTION

When a pressure cooker is heated on a gas stove, we observe that the water in the pressure cooker gets heated and steam comes out after some time through the nozzle, when the weight over the nozzle is lifted. This proves that work is done on the weight and the capacity to do work is called energy.

Work is done due to the heat supplied to the pressure cooker in this case. Hence, we can conclude that heat is a form of energy.

Heat is an invisible form of energy that can produce the sensation of hot or cold. The property that tells us how hot or cold a particular body is called its temperature, i.e., the degree of hotness or coldness of a body is denoted by its temperature. When heat is supplied to a body, its temperature increases and when heat is taken away from a body, its temperature decreases.

In the ancient times, people used to produce fire by rubbing stones against one another. In an electric iron box, we get heat from electricity. When a candle is lit, the chemical energy stored in the candle generates heat. Thus, heat energy is produced at the expense of some other forms of energy. A steam engine works by converting heat energy into mechanical energy. When a tungsten filament gets intensely hot, it produces light. Thus, heat energy can be transformed to some other forms of energy. So, it is needless to say that heat is a form of energy.

Heat energy can be transformed into other forms of energy, like electrical, mechanical, light, etc., by suitable methods. Heat energy can bring about changes in the physical dimensions, state and the chemical properties of a substance.

Heat is an invisible form of energy that can produce the sensation of hotness or coldness. The property that tells us how hot or cold a particular body, is called its temperature, i.e., the degree of hotness or coldness of a body is determined by its temperature. When heat is supplied to a body, its temperature increases and when heat is taken away from a body, its temperature decreases. The heat energy can be transformed into other forms of energy, like electrical, mechanical, light, etc., by suitable methods. Heat energy can bring about changes in the physical dimensions, state and the chemical properties of a substance.

Temperature

How do we compare the heat energy contained in different bodies. We see that some objects around us are cold while some others are hot. How do we say whether a body is hotter or colder? We often try to know the same by touching them. But is it possible to use the same method always? Then how do we find out how hot an object really is? A reliable method to determine the hotness of an object is measuring its temperature. Temperature is measured in Kelvin (K) in SI system and °C in CGS system.

Konnect

Conversion of temperature from Kelvin scale to Celsius scale is K = (°C + 273)

Heat

When two bodies of different temperatures are in contact, what is the direction of flow of heat? Heat always flows from a body of higher temperature to one of lower temperature.

Table 3.1 Difference between Heat and Temperature

Heat	Temperature
Heat is a form of energy, which causes the sensation of hotness or coldness.	The degree of hotness or coldness of a body is measured in temperature.
Heat energy is the cause.	Temperature is the effect.
It is measured in joule or calorie.	It is measured in kelvin, celsius or Fahrenheit.
Calorimeter is used to measure heat energy.	Thermometer is used to measure temperature.
Heat energy always flows from body at high temperature to body at low temperature.	Temperature depends on the average kinetic energy of the molecules.

Measurement of Temperature

Temperature is measured by a device called thermometer. The property of the expansion and contraction of substances due to heating and cooling is used in thermometers. Generally, mercury is used in the thermometer.

Construction of a Mercury Thermometer

A very thin capillary tube of uniform cross-section, one end of which has a very thin glass bulb and the other end of which is provided with a funnel, is taken. The capillary tube is protected by means of a thick glass stem as shown in Fig. 3.1.

Mercury is poured into the funnel. The mercury slowly drips down into the capillary tube, but in this process some air bubbles may get trapped. The bulb is heated in a water bath, so, that the trapped air escapes through the mercury. This process is repeated several times till the glass bulb and the capillary tube are completely filled with mercury without any air bubbles. Finally, the funnel is cut and the end is sealed.

To mark the scale, the bulb of the thermometer is placed in pure melting ice and the level at which the mercury settles is marked as lower fixed point and taken as 0°C. Now the bulb is held in steam. The level of mercury is now marked as upper fixed point and taken as 100°C on the tube. The distance between the two marks is divided into 100 equal parts. Each part shows 1°C.

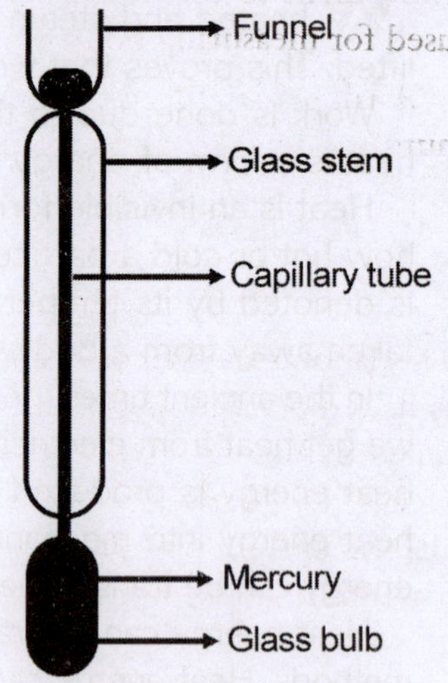

Figure 3.1 Design of a mercury thermometer

Advantages of Mercury as a Thermometric Liquid

1. Its expansion is uniform over a wide range of temperatures.
2. It is a good conductor of heat.
3. It has a low specific heat capacity.
4. It is opaque, shining and clearly visible.
5. It does not wet the glass.
6. It is easily available in pure form.
7. It has a high boiling point and a low melting point.
8. It exerts a very low vapour pressure.

Info Bytes!

Mercury remains liquid over a large temperature range, making it ideal for use in thermometers.

Since the freezing point of mercury is about –40°C, it is not suitable for measuring much low temperatures.

However, there are some disadvantages of mercury as a thermometric liquid. The volume coefficient of mercury is small. Hence, it does not expand by an appreciable volume, thereby making it difficult to record small changes in temperature.

Clinical Thermometer

The thermometer which is used to measure our body temperature is called clinical thermometer.

A clinical thermometer consists of a long, narrow, uniform glass tube. It has a bulb filled with mercury at one end. A constriction is provided, which does not allow mercury to fall back into the bulb.

The clinical thermometer consists of two scales, Celsius scale, indicated by °C and Fahrenheit scale indicated by °F. The normal temperature of human body 37°C or 98.6°F is marked with a red arrow. As the temperature of human body does not go below 35°C or above 43°C, the scale in clinical thermometer is marked from 35°C to 43°C.

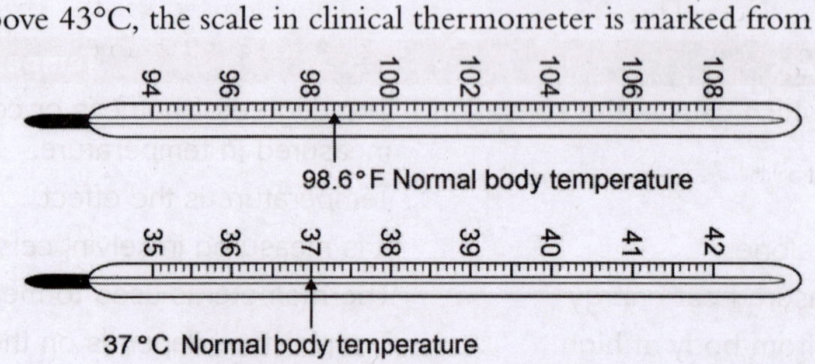

Figure 3.2 A clinical thermometer

Digital and Laboratory Thermometer

Digital thermometers are used for measuring the temperature with the help of an electronic circuit. The information captured is transferred to a microchip that processes it and gets displayed numerically on the digital screen. They are convenient to use, inexpensive, and accurate. Digital thermometers are comparatively advanced thermometers that are used for measuring body temperature.

A laboratory thermometer is used for measuring temperatures, it ranges from -10°C to 110°C which is other than the human body temperature. Laboratory thermometers are used for lab purposes such as checking freezing point, boiling point, or temperature of other substances.

Pyrometer

The laboratory thermometer cannot be used to measure the temperature of a furnace as its temperature is above 1000°C. The thermometer which is used for this purpose is called pyrometer. This thermometer is made by joining together two wires of different metals. Different metals are used on the basis of the temperature to be measured. An electric current passes through this device when one end of it is held in the furnace. The magnitude of electric current is the measure of temperature.

Info Bytes!

Pyrometers are used to measure temperatures in environments too hot for regular thermometers, such as volcanic eruptions and industrial furnaces.

Transmission of Heat

You might have observed that food prepared cools down when kept for a long time. The heat is transferred from the food to the surroundings. So, heat is always transmitted from a hot substance to cold substance. The transmission of heat takes place in three following ways:

1. Conduction
2. Convection
3. Radiation

Let us learn about the different ways of transmission of heat.

Conduction

Some iron nails are fixed on an aluminium rod by means of wax as shown in the Fig. 3.3. The rod is fixed to a stand. The other end of the rod is heated with a spirit lamp. Observe the order in which the nails drop down.

As the heat is transferred from the end of the rod, nearest to the flame to the other end, the nails nearest to the flame fall first.

The process by which heat is transferred from the hotter end to the colder end of an object is known as conduction. In solids generally, the heat is transferred by the process of conduction.

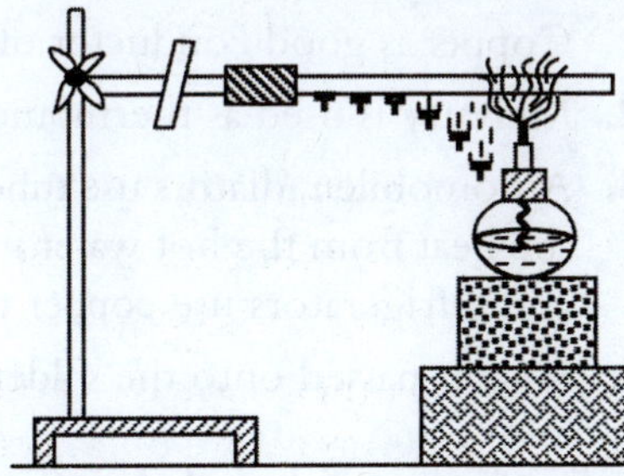

Figure 3.3 Experiment to show the conduction of heat in solids

How does conduction take place? The substances are made-up of many small particles. These particles cannot leave their places, in case of solids, but are able to move a little in their own places. That is they vibrate at their own places. The vibration increases when a particle receives more heat energy and the heat is transferred from one particle to the other particle.

Activity

Fix nails at equal distance by means of wax on two identical rods, one made of copper and the other of aluminium. Heat both the rods by using same spirit lamp as shown in Fig. 3.4. Observe the order in which the nails drop down. The nails on copper rod fall sooner than the aluminium rod. This shows that the heat is transferred faster in the copper rod than in the aluminium rod.

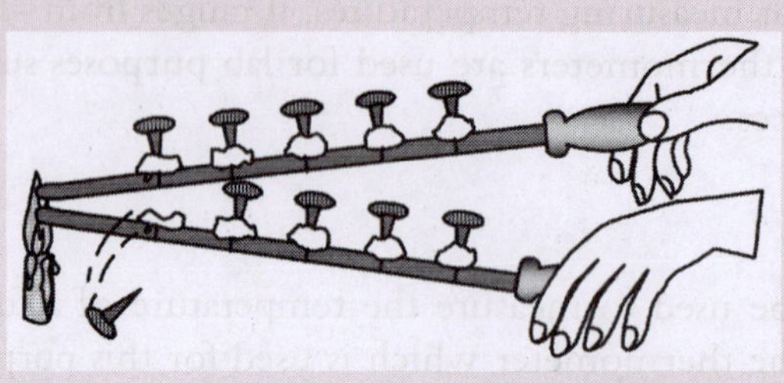

Figure 3.4 Comparison of transfer of heat in copper and aluminium rods

If the particles are closely packed, the conduction becomes faster and if the particles are loosely arranged, the conduction becomes slow. When heat flows through a given material easily, it is said to be a 'conductor' of heat.

Examples: Aluminium, silver, copper, etc

The materials which do not allow heat to pass through them easily are called poor conductors of heat. Poor conductors are also known as 'insulators'.

Examples: Plastic, wood, etc.

We can hold a piece of plastic at one end and burn the other end. Heat does not reach our hand by conduction although there may be very high temperature at the other end. But if you hold one end of a copper rod and heat the other end using a spirit lamp, you cannot hold the other end after a few minutes.

We make use of both conductors and insulators. As heat passes through good conductors fast, they are used to make cooking vessels. These vessels absorb heat fast and transmit it to the food that is to be cooked in them. But the handles of cooking vessels are made-up of insulators.

Applications of Conductors

Good conductors of heat has applications in everyday life. Some of them are listed below.

1. Cooking vessels are made of metals so that heat is conducted through them and passes on to the food being cooked. Copper is good conductor of heat. So, copper-bottom vessels are used to save time and fuel.
2. Mercury is used as thermometric liquid because it is a good conductor of heat.
3. Automobile radiators use tubes made of copper as it is a good conductor of heat. Being a good conductor, it absorbs the heat from the hot water in the engine and transmits it to the surroundings. For the same reason, air conditioners and refrigerators use copper tubes.
4. Heat is passed onto the solder through the tip of the soldering iron which is made of copper.

Applications of Insulators

Bad conductors of heat, such as glass, wool, cotton, felt, asbestos, wood, etc., are called insulators, used widely in various applications, some of which are discussed below.

1. We wear woollen clothes and use blankets in winter as they contain large amount of trapped air which is a bad conductor of heat, and therefore does not allow heat energy to flow outward from our body. Thus, our body stops losing heat and we feel warm. The fur on the body of animals in cold countries keeps the body of the animals warm as it contains

large amount of trapped air. The houses made of mud and thatched roofs are cool in summer and warm in winter as the thatched roof contains large amount of trapped air and also mud is a bad conductor of heat. In summer, the outside heat cannot enter the house and in winter, inside heat cannot flow outside. This keeps the house cool in summer and warm in winter. In cold storage, the air present between double walls prevents the heat energy from flowing in.

2. The gap between double walls of an ice box is filled with glass, wool, which is a bad conductor of heat. It prevents the heat from flowing in so that ice does not melt.
3. The handles of appliances, like pressure cooker, electric iron, electric ovens, etc., are made of bad conductors of heat, such as wood or plastic or ebonite so that while handling them, the heat is not conducted from the hot vessels to our hands.
4. The pipes carrying steam from boiler are covered with asbestos or glass wool to prevent loss of heat due to conduction.

Experiment to Show that Water is a Bad Conductor of Heat

Water is a bad conductor of heat, which can be proved as follows. Take a hard glass tube and drop small pieces of ice, wrapped in copper wire gauze. Pour ice cold water so as to fill the glass tube upto 3/4 of its length. The copper wire gauze prevents the ice from floating. Clamp the test tube as shown in Fig. 3.5.

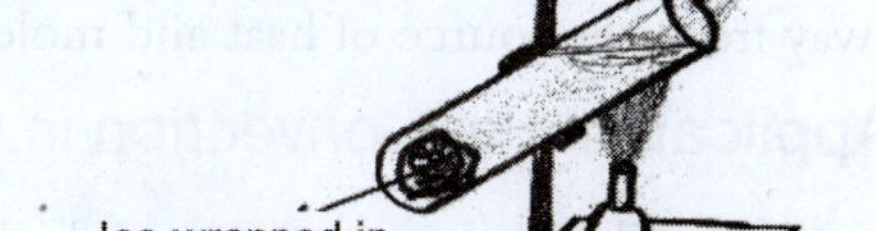

Figure 3.5 Experiment to show that water is a bad conductor of heat

Now, heat the test tube near its mouth with a bunsen burner. It is observed that water near the mouth of the test tube starts boiling but the ice does not melt. This shows that heat is not conducted through water and is a bad conductor of heat.

Experiment to Show that Air is a Bad Conductor of Heat

Air is a bad conductor of heat which can be shown as follows. Drop small pieces of wax in a hard glass tube and close its mouth with a cork. Clamp the glass tube on stand as shown in Fig. 3.6.

Now, heat the glass tube near its mouth. After some time, it is observed that the cork blows away but wax at the bottom does not melt. The air near the mouth gets heated and its pressure increases. The high pressure of air pushes the cork and it blows off but heat is not conducted through the air to the bottom where wax is present. This proves that air is a bad conductor of heat.

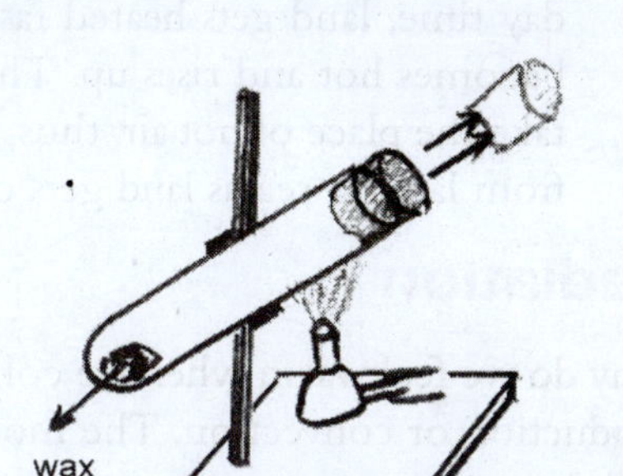

Figure 3.6 Experiment to show that gases are bad conductor(s) of heat.

Convection

Water and air are poor conductors of heat. Let us see how heat transfer takes place in liquids and gases.

Take a beaker and fill it half with water as shown in Fig. 3.7. Add some crystals of potassium permanganate to the water and heat it. Observe the water in the beaker carefully. Streams of coloured water move upwards from the bottom of the beaker and then downwards.

When the water at the bottom gets heated it expands and the density of water becomes less. Hence, water becomes lighter and goes up to the top. At the top the cool water which has more density comes down. Thus, heat is transferred upwards by means of currents. These currents are called convectional currents. This way of heat transfer takes place in liquids and gases, and is called convection.

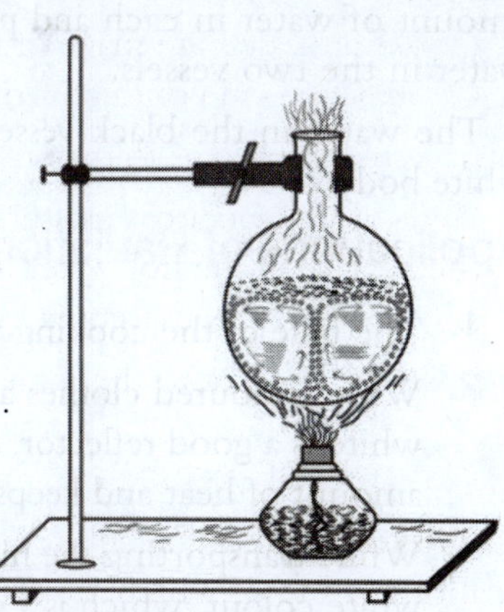

Figure 3.7 Demonstration of convection of heat in liquids

From the above experiment, we can conclude that

1. A medium is necessary for convection.
2. In the process of convection, particles of the medium move from one place to another.

Convection in Gases

Gases are heated by convection. This can be demonstrated as follows.

Take a rectangular wooden box, provided with two glass chimneys, say A and B, and fix them on the top as shown in the Fig. 3.8.

Place a lighted candle below chimney B. Now, when a lighted incense stick is held over chimney A, the smoke given out by it is sucked in through chimney A and comes out through B.

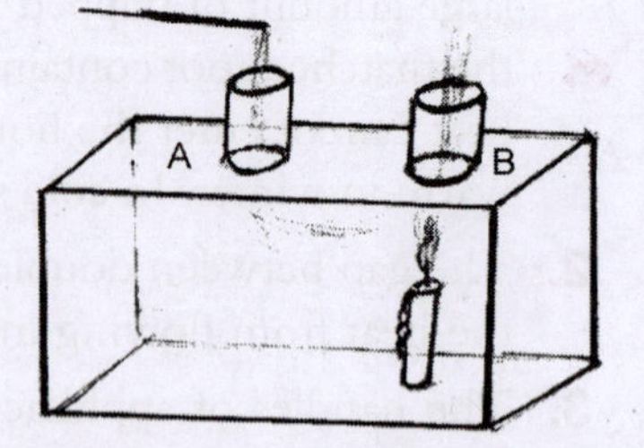

Figure 3.8 Demonstration of convection of heat in gases

The lighted candle heats the air present near chimney B. The hot air, being light, raises up through B, thereby, reducing the air pressure. The cold, heavy air then rushes in through chimney A, sweeping the smoke given out by incense stick. Thus, on absorbing heat, the hot air molecules move away from the source of heat and molecules of cold air move towards the source of heat, forming convection currents.

Applications of Convection in Gases

1. Ventilation is a process by which continuous circulation of air inside the room is maintained due to the formation of convection current. The rooms are provided with a top exit called ventilators through which the hot air and moisture pass. The fresh and cold air then enters the room through windows and doors.
2. Sea and land breezes are formed due to convection currents of air. During the day time, land gets heated faster than sea water. Consequently, the air above land becomes hot and rises up. The cold air above the sea then moves towards land, to take the place of hot air, thus, forming sea breeze. During nights, land breeze flows from land to sea as land gets cooled faster than sea.

Info Bytes!

The Great Red Spot on Jupiter is a giant storm that has been observed for over 350 years. It's a prime example of heat transfer through convection on a massive scale.

Radiation

Why do we feel warm when we come out in the sun? As there is no medium in space, heat cannot be transferred by either conduction or convection. The mode of transfer of heat in the absence of a medium is called radiation.

All hot bodies whether solid, liquid or gas radiate heat in all directions around itself. When thermal radiations falls on a substance, some of it gets reflected and some other of it is absorbed. The temperature of the substance increases when it absorbs the heat radiation.

Take two identical vessels. Paint the outer surface of one vessel with black and of the other with white. Pour equal amount of water in each and place the vessels in the sun for about half an hour and then compare the temperature of water in the two vessels.

The water in the black vessel is warmer than that in the white vessel. Thus, a black body absorbs more heat than a white body.

Applications of Radiation

1. The base of the cooking vessels is coated with mud or painted dull to absorb more heat.
2. White coloured clothes are comfortable in summer and black coloured clothes are comfortable in winter because white is a good reflector, it absorbs less amount of heat. Black is a good absorber and good radiator. It absorbs more amount of heat and keeps our body warm.
3. While transporting the highly inflammable substances, like petrol, LPG, etc., in tankers, the tankers are coated with white colour, which is a good reflector of heat.

Thermos Flask

A thermos flask is an insulating storage vessel which is used to keep a hot liquid hot and a cold liquid cold.

Construction

It consists of a double-walled glass. The air between the two walls is evacuated and sealed. This shinning glass bulb is kept over a rubber cork on a plastic or metal body. The space between the glass and metal is filled with cork which is a bad conductor of heat. The mouth is covered with a plastic cork over which a plastic cover is screwed.
The different forms of heat loss are minimized in a thermos flask, due to the following reasons.

1. **Conduction loss:** Since there is a vacuum, heat cannot be conducted by means of conduction. Further there is a cork and glass wool which are bad conductors of heat.
2. **Convection loss:** Since there is a vacuum, loss due to convection is avoided.
3. **Radiation loss:** Since the glass is shinning, radiation loss is minimized.

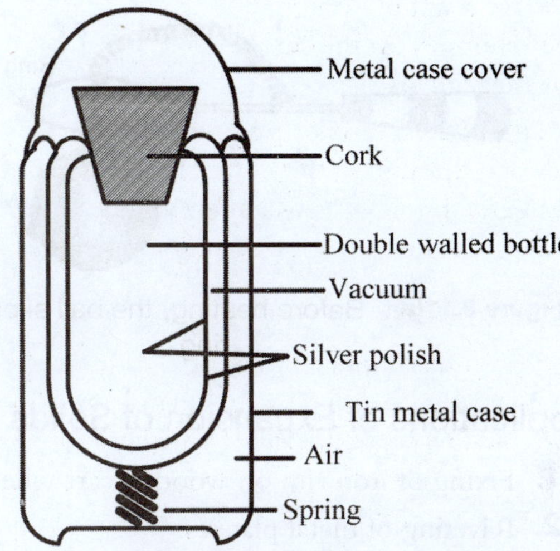

Figure 3.9 Thermos flask

Effects of Heat

When a substance is heated, the following changes take place. In certain cases, the temperature of the substance increases which then undergoes a change in volume. Some substances may undergo a change in state.

Expansion in Solids

Many substances expand when they are heated. They contract when cooled. Take a long aluminium rod clamped at an end as shown in Fig. 3.10. The aluminium rod rolls over a glass rod placed perpendicular to its length on a wooden block. Two weight hangers W_1 and W_2 are attached to the aluminium rod to have a firm contact between the glass rod and the aluminium rod. A light pointer is attached to an end of the glass rod which moves over a paper scale. When the aluminium rod is heated, it expands and rolls over the glass rod and the pointer moves over the scale, confirming the expansion of the aluminium rod.

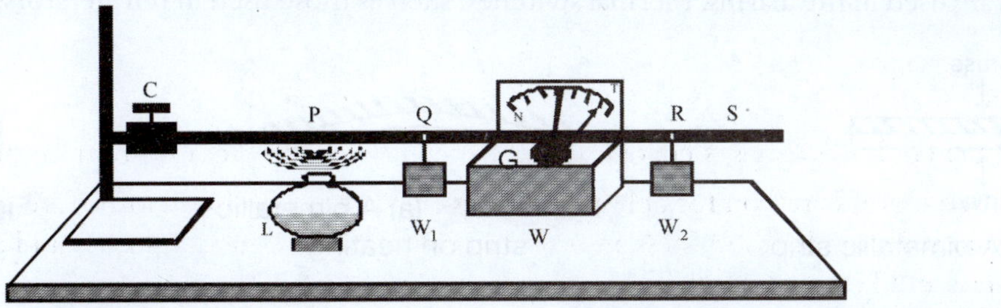

C: Clamp
PQ RS: Aluminium rod
W_1, W_2 : Weights
G: Glass rod
W: Wooden Block
N: Paper pointer
T: Paper scale
L: Spirit lamp

Figure 3.10 Experimental set up of expansion in solids

Gravesand's Ring and Ball Experiment

This apparatus consists of a ring and ball such that the internal diameter of the ring and the external diameter of the ball are equal. When the ball is kept on the ring, it just slips through the ring as shown in Fig. 3.11(a). Now heat the ball with spirit lamp for some time and then keep the ball again on the ring. The ball does not pass through the ring [Fig. 3.11(b)].

From this experiment, it is clear that the solids expand on heating. Now allow the ball to cool to room temperature and place it again on the ring, then the ball passes through the ring easily. This shows that solids contract on cooling.

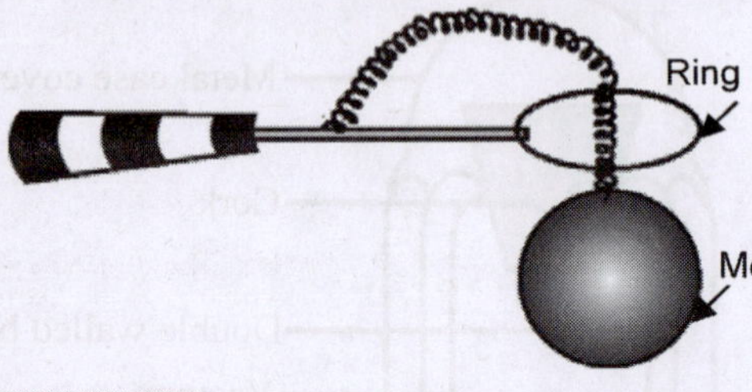

Figure 3.11(a) Before heating, the ball slips through the ring

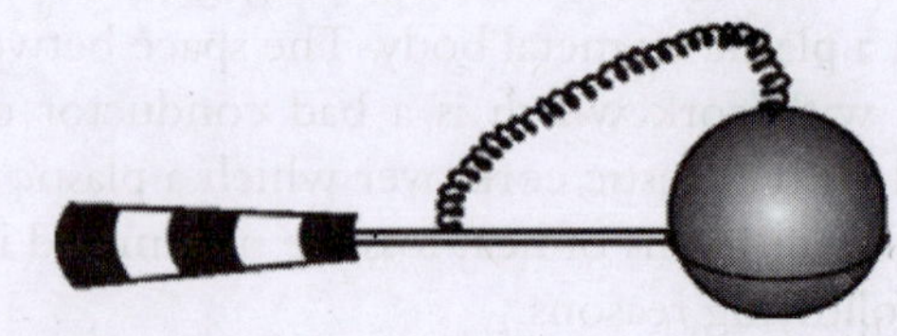

Figure 3.11(b) Upon heating, the ball expands in size and does not pass through the ring

Applications of Expansion of Solids

1. Fixing of iron rim on wooden cart wheels.
2. Riveting of metal plates.
3. A small gap is left while laying rail tracks.
4. Girders are mounted on the rollers by leaving small space.
5. A sag is left, while laying telephone and electric lines.
6. A small gap is left between the blocks, while laying the concrete roads.
7. Special glasses like Borosil or pyrex glasses are used to avoid the breaking of ordinary glass, when hot water is poured.

The Bimetallic Strip

A bimetallic strip is made-up of two different metals joined together by riveting. Take a brass and an invar strip of the same size. Rivet them firmly together as shown in the Fig. 3.12. This is called bimetallic strip. The principle involved is the unequal expansion and contraction of different materials on heating.

When heated brass expands more and its greater length puts it on the outside of the curve as shown in the Fig. 3.13(a). When it is cooled, brass contracts more and its shorter length puts it on the inside of the curve as shown in Fig. 3.13(b).

Bimetallic strips are used in fire alarms, thermal switches, such as those used in refrigerators, bimetallic thermometer, etc.

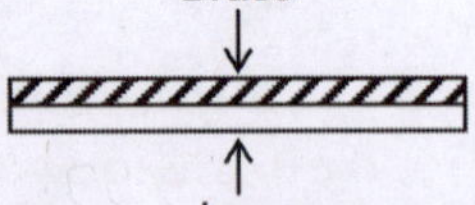

Figure 3.12 A bimetallic strip

Figure 3.13 (a) A bimetallic strip on heating

Figure 3.13 (b) A bimetallic strip on cooling

Expansion of Liquids

Fill a test tube completely with water. Fit a single hole cork on the mouth of the test tube and fix a glass tube in the hole as shown in Fig. 3.14. See that the level of water can be seen above the cork. Note the level of the water in the glass tube.

Observe the level of the water in the glass tube after heating the test tube. It rises slowly. This shows that water expands on heating. When heating is stopped gradually, water goes back to its original level. Thus, liquids expand on heating and contract when cooled.

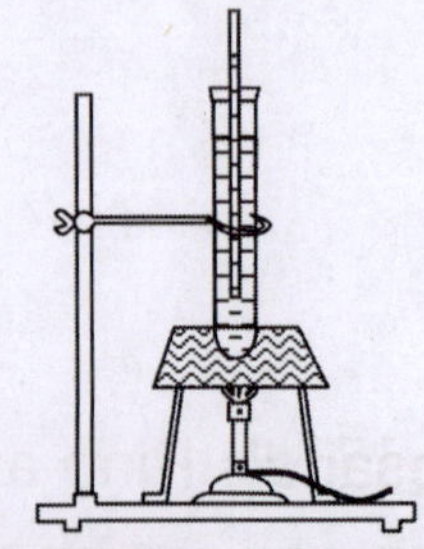

Figure 3.14 Experimental set up of expansion of liquids

Anomalous Expansion of Water

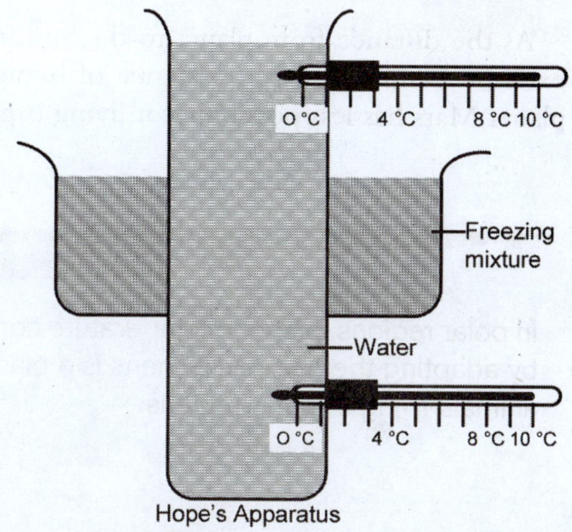

Figure 3.15 Hope's Apparatus

Generally matter expands on heating and contracts on cooling. But water shows a peculiar behaviour. When water at 0°C is heated, it contracts and its volume decreases from 0°C to 4°C. At 4°C water has minimum volume and maximum density. From 4°C onwards, as temperature increases, the volume also increases. This behaviour of water is known as anomalous expansion of water.

The anomalous expansion of water can be demonstrated by Hope's apparatus. It consists of a long cylindrical vessel, surrounded with a cylindrical trough, which is filled with freezing mixture. Freezing mixture contains common salt and ice in the ratio 1 : 3.

Two holes are provided to the long cylindrical vessel one at the top and the other at the bottom. Two thermometers are inserted in these two holes to record the temperature of water (Fig. 3.15). The vessel is filled with water at 10°C. Initially both the thermometers show the same reading.

The temperature of water near the cooling mixture decreases and density increases. When the temperature falls to 4°C, density becomes maximum. Then the water in the central part goes to the lower portion, the lower thermometer shows 4°C and it remains constant. Now the temperature of water in the central portion decreases to 0°C, it moves to upper portion. The upper thermometer shows the reading as 0°C and slowly it freezes to form a thin layer of ice. But the temperature of water in the lower portion shows 4°C. Because of this behaviour of water, aquatic life can survive in frozen ponds in the cold countries.

Expansion of Gases

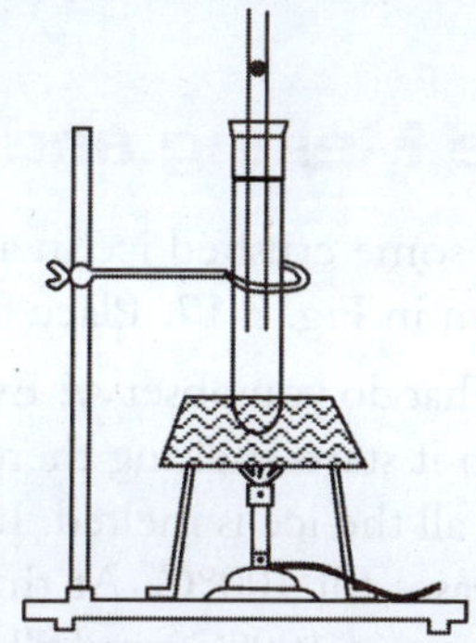

Figure 3.16 Demonstration of expansion of gases

Take an empty test tube and fit its mouth with a cork with a hole as shown in Fig. 3.16. Take a drop of a coloured liquid into a narrow bored glass. Fit this glass tube in the hole in the cork so that the drop of liquid can be seen above the cork.

Now, heat the test tube and carefully observe the coloured drop. We observe that the coloured drop moves upwards.

The air in the test tube expands on heating. Thus, it pushes the drop in the glass tube upwards. The coloured drop falls back to its original place when heating is stopped. Thus, we can conclude that most of the substances in solid, liquid or gaseous state expand when heated and contract when cooled.

Effect of Heat on Living Organisms

The human body functions effectively at 37°C or 98.4°F. All the living beings function properly at fixed temperature. At high temperatures and low temperatures, the functioning of the body varies. Sometimes the behaviour of human beings changes due to sudden increase in temperature.

If temperature of water is increased, then the quantity of dissolved oxygen decreases. It leads to death of animals in water. Even plants cannot survive at extreme hot and cold climatic conditions. For the same reason, we boil the milk and water to kill bacteria. Vegetables and food items are stored in refrigerator to protect from the germs and bacteria.

Only earth has the suitable temperature for the existence of life because of its distance from the Sun. We are in search for the existence of life on other planets.

The closest planet to the Sun is the Mercury, having maximum temperature of about 370°C and minimum temperature of –240°C. The Venus has the maximum temperature about 480°C. In case of the satellite of the Earth that is the moon, has the maximum temperature of 110°C and minimum temperature of –150°C.

As the distance from planet to the Sun increases, the maximum temperature on that planet decreases. Due to these extreme conditions, the existence of living organisms on other planets is very less. Recent research shows that the planet Mars has less possibility of living organisms.

Konnect

In polar regions, extreme temperature conditions exist. Only some plants and animals can live at these conditions by adapting themselves. Lichens is a plant that exists in polar regions and polar bear, polar pig, reindeer are the animals living in polar regions.

Change of State

When water is heated after some time it will begin to boil. It will then turn into vapour. If solid substance like ice is heated, it will reach a certain temperature and is converted into water.

When water is cooled to a certain temperature it is converted to ice. This change of a solid into a liquid or liquid into a solid and a liquid into a gas or a gas into a liquid is called change of state of a substance.

A substance can undergo a change of state, only when heat is either given to it or taken away from it.

$$\text{Solid} \underset{\text{Heat released}}{\overset{\text{Heat absorbed}}{\rightleftharpoons}} \text{Liquid} \underset{\text{Heat released}}{\overset{\text{Heat absorbed}}{\rightleftharpoons}} \text{Gas}$$

The Melting and Boiling Point of a Substance

Take some crushed ice in a beaker. Place a thermometer in the ice and hold it upright as shown in Fig. 3.17. Place the beaker on a stand. Heat the beaker by using a burner.

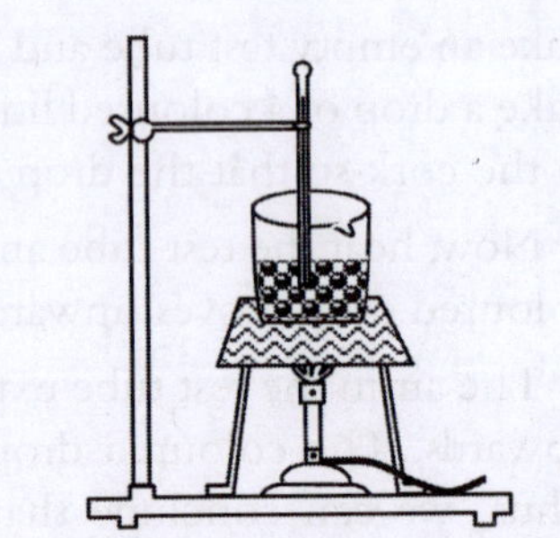

Figure 3.17 Apparatus to determine melting point

What do you observe? Even though heat is being supplied, temperature rises till 0°C and when it starts melting there is no change in the temperature shown by the thermometer until all the ice is melted. It remains at 0°C. On further heating, the temperature of water increases till 100°C. At this temperature, water starts boiling. The temperature remains constant at 100°C until all the water is evaporated.

If we plot a graph by taking time for heat supplied along *X*-axis and temperature along *Y*-axis, a curve as shown in the figure below is obtained.

What happened to the heat supplied? The heat supplied while the ice is changing into water was used up for changing the state. The constant temperature at which a solid substance changes into a liquid is called melting point of the substance.

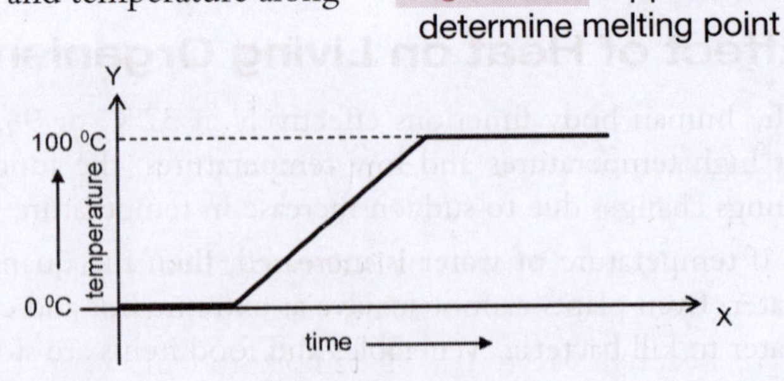

Figure 3.18 Plot between time for heat supplied and temperature

Similarly, the constant temperature at which a liquid substance starts to boil is called 'boiling point' of the substance.

'Freezing point' is the temperature at which a liquid substance changes into a solid when heat is taken away from it. The melting and freezing points of any substance are the same.

The process of changing a substance from gaseous state to liquid state at constant temperature by releasing heat energy is called condensation. That constant temperature at which the substance condenses is known as condensation point.

But some solid substances directly convert into gaseous state without converting into liquid state. The process of converting a solid directly into a gaseous state is called sublimation. That solid substance is called sublimate and the gaseous state of the substance is called sublime.

The process of changing a liquid substance into gaseous state at any temperature below its boiling point is known as evaporation. Evaporation is a slow process. Whereas boiling is a rapid process.

The melting point and boiling point of some substances are given below:

Table 3.2 Melting and boiling point of substances

Substances	Melting point	Boiling point
Water	0°C	100°C
Iron	1535°C	2750°C
Copper	1082°C	2310°C
Lead	327°C	1740°C
Mercury	−39°C	357°C

Absorption of Heat by Different Substances

Take 100 g water and 100 g coconut oil in two beakers A and B, respectively. Measure the initial temperature of water and oil. Now place both on stands and heat them by using identical spirit lamps. Stop heating after 5 minutes and note the temperature of both water and oil.

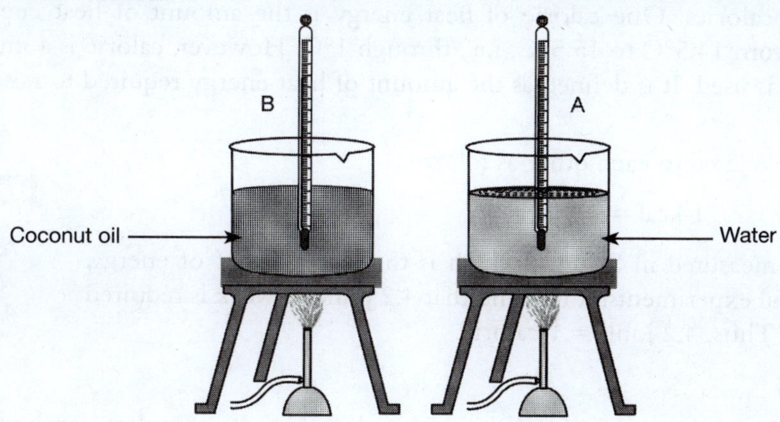

Figure 3.19 Demonstration of absorption of heat by different substances

We find that the rise in the temperature of oil is greater than that of water even though the same amount of heat is given to both the liquids.

When an equal amount of heat is supplied to different substances, the rise in their temperatures is not equal. For equal rise in temperature, the amount of heat absorbed is different.

The heat required to rise the temperature of a certain mass of a substance by 1°C is called heat capacity of that substance.

Specific Heat

The heat capacity of a given material changes with the quantity of the substance taken. Thus, a term known as specific heat capacity which is independent on the quantity of matter is used.

The quantity of heat required to raise the temperature of a unit mass of a substance by 1°C is called specific heat of that substance. Its value remains constant for a given material. The specific heat of water is greater than that of any other substance and its value is 1 cal $g^{-1}°C^{-1}$. Because of high specific heat capacity, water is used as coolant in many applications.

Factors Affecting the Heat Gained or Lost by a Substance

The heat gained or heat lost by a substance depends upon:

1. the mass of the substance, (m)
2. the specific heat of the substance, (s)
3. the change in the temperature of the substance, (Δt)

Konnect

During a phase change (e.g., from solid to liquid), a substance can absorb heat without a change in temperature.

Thus,

$$\text{Heat, } Q = ms\Delta t,\ s = \frac{Q}{m\Delta t}$$

EXAMPLE 3.1 Calculate the amount of heat energy required to increase the temperature of 350 g of water from 15°C to 55°C. (Specific heat capacity of water is 1 cal g^{-1}°C^{-1})

SOLUTION

Given, mass of water = 350 g

Change in temperature, Δt = final temperature - initial temperature = 55°C – 15°C = 40°C

Specific heat capacity of water = 1 cal g^{-1}°C^{-1}

Heat energy supplied; $Q = Ms\Delta t$

$Q = 350 \times 1 \times 40 = 14{,}000$ cal = 14 kcal.

Units of Heat

Heat energy is measured in calories. One calorie of heat energy is the amount of heat energy required to raise the temperature of 1 g of water from 14.5°C to 15.5°C, i.e., through 1°C. However, calorie is a small unit of heat. Instead, a bigger unit called kilocalorie is used. It is defined as the amount of heat energy required to raise the temperature of 1 kg of water through 1°C.

Calorie and kilocalorie are related to each other as follows.

$$1 \text{ kcal} = 1000 \text{ cal.}$$

Now-a-days, heat energy is measured in SI unit, which is the same as that of energy, namely, joule. Through careful experiments, it is found that 4.2 joule of work is required to produce 1 calorie of heat. Thus, 4.2 joule = 1 calorie.

Info Bytes!

As 1 kcal = 1000 cal, we can write 1 kcal = 4200 joule.

Calorific Value of Fuels

Calorific value is defined as the total amount of heat energy produced by the complete combustion of a unit mass of fuel.

$$\text{Calorific value, } C = \frac{Q}{M}$$

Units of calorific value are J kg^{-1} or cal g^{-1}

Generally, gaseous fuels have high calorific values compared to that of solid and liquid fuels.

EXAMPLE 3.2 Find the amount of heat energy produced by 250 g of a fuel with a calorific value of 9500 cal g^{-1}.

SOLUTION

Given calorific value, C = 9500 cal g^{-1}

Mass of the fuel, M = 250 g

Heat energy produced; $Q = C \times M$

$Q = 9500 \times 250 = 23.75 \times 10^5$ cal $= 2.375 \times 10^6$ cal.

Calorimeter

A calorimeter is a highly polished cylindrical copper vessel used to measure the quantity of heat. The copper vessel is placed inside a wooden box. The space between the wooden box and copper vessel is filled with a bad conductor of heat, like cork or sawdust. The wooden box has a lid made of ebonite or a similar bad conductor. It has two holes. A stirrer can be inserted through one hole and thermometer through the other. When two bodies of different temperatures are brought into contact, heat is transferred from the body at a higher temperature to a body at lower temperature. This is the principle used in the measurement of specific heat capacity of a substance by using a calorimeter.

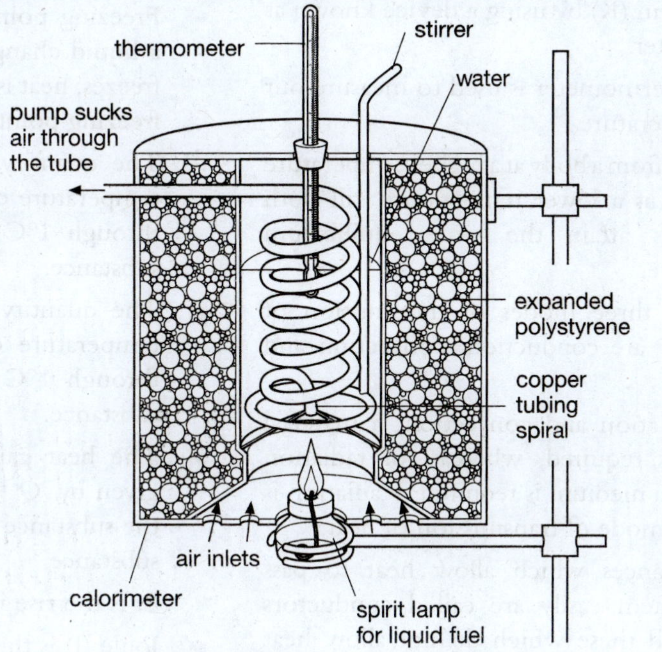

Figure 3.20 A calorimeter

A measured amount of water is taken in the calorimeter and its temperature is noted. The substance whose specific heat is to be determined is heated to a certain temperature and then added to the water in the calorimeter. The water is stirred and the final temperature of the mixture is noted from that. The specific heat of that substance can be calculated.

Konnect

Calorimeters are used in various fields, from food science to measure calorie content, to physics for measuring specific heat capacities.

Newton's Law of Cooling

Newton's law of cooling states that the rate at which an object cools is proportional to the difference in temperature between the object and the object's surroundings.

POINTS TO REMEMBER

- The degree of hotness or coldness of a body is called temperature. It is measured in degree celsius (°C), degree fahrenheit (°F) and in kelvin (K) by using a device known as thermometer.
- Clinical thermometer is used to measure our body temperature.
- Heat flows from a body at a higher temperature to a body at a lower temperature, till both the bodies attain the same equilibrium temperature.
- There are three modes of transmission of heat. They are conduction, convection and radiation.
- For conduction and convection, a material medium is required, whereas for radiation no material medium is required. Radiation is the fastest mode of transmission of heat.
- The substances which allow heat to pass through them easily are called conductors of heat and these which do not allow heat to pass through them easily are called bad conductors of heat.
- Heat energy can bring a change in the physical dimensions (length, area, volume), state and the chemical properties of a substance.
- A bimetallic strip works on the principle of either expansion or contraction of a metal when heat is given or taken out from it.
- A substance undergoes change in its physical state at constant temperature.
- The constant temperature at which a liquid starts boiling is called 'boiling point' of the liquid.
- Freezing point is the temperature at which a liquid changes into a solid. When a liquid freezes, heat is released by it. The melting and freezing point of every substance are equal.
- The quantity of heat required to raise the temperature of a certain mass of a substance through 1°C is called heat capacity of the substance.
- The quantity of heat required to raise the temperature of a unit mass of a substance through 1°C is called specific heat of that substance.
- The heat gained or lost by a substance is given by, $Q = ms\Delta t$, where m is the mass of the substance and s is the specific heat of the substance.

  Δt is the rise in temperature.
- Joule (J) is the unit of heat in SI system.
- Heat energy is also measured in calorie. One calorie of heat energy is required to raise the temperature of 1 g of water through 1°C and 1 calorie = 4.2 J

  1 kcal = 1000 cal = 4200 J
- Heat lost by a body at a higher temperature to a body at a lower temperature is the principle used in the measurement of specific heat capacity of a body. It is measured by using a device called calorimeter.

PRACTICE QUESTIONS CLASSROOM WING

Very Short Answer Type Questions

Directions for questions from 1 to 5: **Fill in the blanks.**

1. Calorific value of fuels is measured in _____ .

2. Most of the amount of heat energy flows from the bottom layers of air to the top in a room fitted with AC through _______.

3. The process of changing a substance from gaseous state to liquid state is called _______.

4. Heat energy produced by 150 g of a fuel of calorific value 8000 cal g^{-1} is _______.

5. When hot water is poured in ordinary glass vessel, it breaks because of ________.

Directions for questions from 6 to 47: **For each of the questions, four choices have been provided. Select the correct alternative.**

6. When two bodies are in thermal contact, the direction of flow of heat is determined by its
(a) Density (b) Temperature
(c) Heat capacity (d) Mass

7. The constant temperature at which a solid substance changes into liquid state is called
(a) Melting point of the substance.
(b) Boiling point of the substance.
(c) Saturation temperature.
(d) Evaporation temperature.

8. Which of the following is incorrect about mercury as a thermometric fluid?
(a) Its expansion is uniform over a wide range of temperatures.
(b) It is a good conductor of heat.
(c) It has a high specific heat capacity.
(d) It is opaque, shining and clearly visible.

9. Temperature is measured in _________.
(a) Degree celsius (b) Kelvin
(c) Degree fahrenheit (d) All the above

10. Normal temperature of the human body is _____.
(a) 87 K (b) 273 K
(c) 37°C (d) 82°F

11. Clinical thermometer is calibrated in _________.
(a) Celsius scale
(b) Fahrenheit scale
(c) Absolute scale
(d) Both (a) and (b)

12. Cooling in a motor car is done by
(a) Conduction (b) Convection
(c) Radiation (d) All of the above

13. The mode of transfer of heat in the absence of a medium is called __________.
(a) Convection (b) Conduction
(c) Radiation (d) All of the above

14. In solids, generally the heat is transferred by
(a) Conduction (b) Convection
(c) Radiation (d) All of the above

15. From the following, choose the correct option that represents the order of the thermal expansions in solids (S), liquids (L) and gases (G) for an equal rise in temperature.
(a) L > S > G (b) S > L > G
(c) G > S > L (d) G > L > S

16. The scale in clinical thermometer is marked from ___°C to ___°C.
(a) 35°C to 43°C (b) 36°C to 44°C
(c) 37°C to 45°C (d) 38°C to 46°C

17. Choose the correct statement: In winter,
(A) a set of double windows is a better insulator.
(B) windows constructed of a single-double thickness glass is a good insulator.
(a) Only A
(b) Only B
(c) Both A and B
(d) Cannot be compared

18. Arrange the following substances in the increasing order of their thermal conductivity.
Copper, iron, glass.
(a) Glass, iron, copper (b) Copper, iron, glass
(c) Iron, glass, copper (d) Iron, copper, glass

19. Mercury has a __________ boiling point and a __________ melting point.

(a) high, low (b) low, high
(c) high, high (d) low, low

20. Choose the correct statement:

(A) When heat energy is given to ice at 0°C, the potential energy of the molecules of ice increases.
(B) Heat added to ice at 0°C does not increase the kinetic energy, and hence, there is no rise of temperature.

(a) Only A (b) Only B
(c) Both A and B (d) None of these

21. Choose the correct statement:

(A) Boiling of a given substance takes place at all temperatures.
(B) Evaporation of a substance takes place at a constant temperature.
(C) Boiling takes place at every part of the liquid.
(D) Evaporation takes place only on the surface of liquid.

(a) Both A and C
(b) B, C and D
(c) Both C and D
(d) All of the above

22. Choose the correct statement:

(A) Solids undergo linear, arial and cubical expansions.
(B) Liquids and gases undergo cubical expansion.

(a) Only A (b) Only B
(c) Both A and B (d) None of these

23. In solids generally, the heat is transferred by the process of __________.

(a) Conduction (b) Convection
(c) Radiation (d) Evaporation

24. Which of the following statements is/are wrong?

(a) Normally, solids expand on melting.
(b) Normally, a liquid contract on freezing.
(c) There is no effect on volume during cooling or heating a gas.
(d) All of the above

25. Which of the following is a poor conductor of heat?

(a) Plastic (b) Aluminium
(c) Silver (d) Copper

***Directions for questions from 26 and 27:* The heating curve of a particular substance in solid state is as shown in the figure. Choose the correct alternative.**

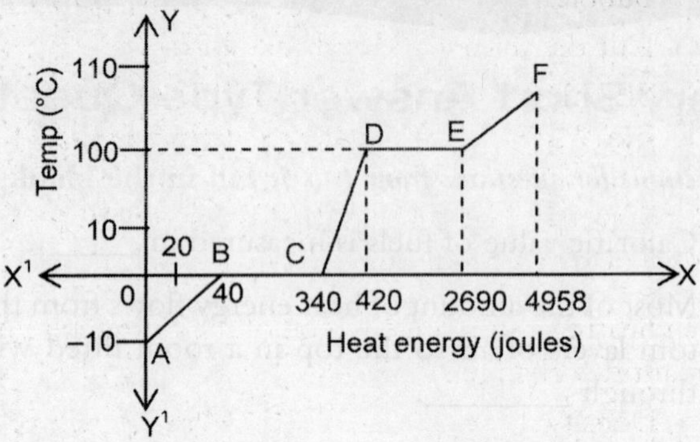

26. If mass of the substance is 20 g, then the heat energy required to melt 1 g of the substance is ______ J.

(a) 300 (b) 15
(c) 113, 50 (d) 2270

27. The change of state in the graph is represented by ______ part.

(a) AB (b) BC
(c) DE (d) Both (b) and (c)

28. Arrange the following steps in a sequential order to explain the formation of convectional currents through ventilation.

(A) The cold air enters into the room through windows from high pressure to low pressure region.
(B) Hot air in the room is less denser and it raises up.
(C) The rooms are provided with ventilators at the top.
(D) Hot air passes out through the ventilators it creates low pressure region in the rooms.

(a) CADB (b) CDAB
(c) BADC (d) CBDA

29. Arrange the following steps in sequential order to construct a celsius thermometer.

(A) Lower fixing point is marked by placing the bulb of the thermometer in pure melting ice.
(B) A thin capillary tube, covered with a thick glass stem and providing a funnel is taken.
(C) The distance between upper fixing point and lower fixing point is divided into 100 equal parts and calibrated.
(D) Upper fixing point is marked by placing the bulb of the thermometer in boiling water.

(E) While pouring the mercury in the tube, place the mercury bulb in hot water bath to remove air bubbles.

(F) Cut the funnel and seal that end.

(a) BEFADC (b) BEADCF
(c) BFECAD (d) BEFCAD

***Directions for questions from 30 to 37:* Select the correct alternative from the given choices.**

30. On heating a substance which of the following physical quantities change(s)?

(a) Density (b) Mass
(c) Volume (d) Both (a) and (c)

31. Bimetallic strip works on the principle of ______.

(a) Unequal expansion of solids
(b) Unequal contraction of solids
(c) Equal expansion of solids
(d) Both (a) and (b)

32. SI unit of specific heat capacity is ______.

(a) $J\ kg^{-1}°C^{-1}$ (b) $cal\ g^{-1}°C^{-1}$
(c) $J\ kg^{-1}\ K^{-1}$ (d) All of the above

33. A thermometer works on the principle of

(a) Linear expansion of solid.
(b) Cubical expansion of solid.
(c) Uniform expansion of volume of liquid or gas with temperature.
(d) Both (b) and (c)

34. In case of an incense stick or an *agarbati*, the smoke at the lighted end of stick moves in upward direction, it is because

(a) The cool air below the lighted end moves to take the place of hot air above the lighted end.
(b) The air at the hot end is more dense.
(c) It is natural for the smoke to move up.
(d) The smoke is repelled by the gravity of earth.

35. Arrange the following steps in a sequential order to demonstrate the expansion of gases.

(A) Heat the test tube and observe the position of coloured drop in the narrow glass tube.

(B) Take a drop of coloured liquid into a narrow glass tube.

(C) Take an empty test tube, fit its mouth with one-holed-cork stopper.

(D) Fit the narrow glass tube through the cork so that the level of the coloured drop is just above the cork.

(E) The air in the tube expands and pushes the coloured drop in the narrow tube upwards.

(a) BCADE (b) CBDAE
(c) BADCE (d) CADEB

36. If Q cal of heat energy is supplied to '*m*' kg of a substance, its temperature changes from t_1°C to t_2°C. Arrange the following steps in a sequential order to calculate the specific heat capacity of the substance in SI system.

(A) Note down the mass of the substance as '*m*' kg, heat energy as Q cal and the temperatures as t_1°C and t_2°C.

(B) Write the formula for the amount of heat energy lost or gained by a body as, $Q = ms\Delta t$.

(C) Convert the heat energy and temperatures, into SI system.

(D) Substitute the values in the formula, and calculate the specific heat capacity of the substance.

(E) Find the change in temperature of the substance.

(a) ACEDB (b) CDAEB
(c) ACEBD (d) CEABD

37. The mode of transfer of heat in the absence of a medium is called ______.

(a) Conduction (b) Convection
(c) Radiation (d) None of these

***Directions for questions from 38 to 40:* The heating curve of a particular substance in solid state is as shown in the figure: Choose the correct alternative.**

38. The base of the cooking vessels is coated with ______ to absorb more heat.

(a) mud (b) Painted dull
(c) Both (a) and (b) (d) None of these

39. Which of the following statements is incorrect?

(a) White is a good reflector.
(b) White absorbs less amount of heat.
(c) Black is a good absorber and good radiator.
(d) White keeps our body warm.

40. Which of the following colours is good reflector of heat?

(a) Black (b) White
(c) Grey (d) None of these

***Directions for questions from 41 to 47:* Select the correct alternative from the given choices.**

41. **Assertion (A):** The volume of a given mass of water is more at 0°C when compared to water at 4°C.

Reason (R): Water expands when its temperature is increased from 0°C to 4°C.

(a) Both A and R are true and R is the correct explanation of A.
(b) Both A and R are true, but R is not the correct explanation of A.
(c) A is true but R is false.
(d) Both A and R are false.

42. **Assertion (A):** We prefer to wear white clothes in winter.

Reason (R): White clothes are good reflectors of heat.

(a) Both A and R are true and R is the correct explanation of A.
(b) Both A and R are true, but R is not the correct explanation of A.
(c) A is true but R is false.
(d) A is false but R is true.

43. When one takes a hot shower Fog is formed on the bathroom mirror but this does not happen during a cold shower because______

(a) Evaporation of water is more at higher temperature.
(b) Formation of fog on the mirror does not depend on amount of vapour.
(c) Formation of fog on mirror is not concerned with temperature of water.
(d) Both (a) and (b)

44. **Assertion (A):** The temperature of a body can be increased by applying an external force.

Reason (R): Heat is a form of energy.

(a) Both A and R are true and R is the correct explanation of A.
(b) Both A and R are true, but R is not the correct explanation of A.
(c) A is true but R is false.
(d) Both A and R are false.

45. **Assertion (A):** The heat energy reaches the surface of earth travelling through vacuum.

Reason (R): Heat radiations are electromagnetic radiations.

(a) Both A and R are true and R is the correct explanation of A.
(b) Both A and R are true, but R is not the correct explanation of A.
(c) A is true but R is false.
(d) Both A and R are false.

46. Freezing mixture contains common salt and ice in the ratio

(a) 1 : 3. (b) 3: 1
(c) 1: 1 (d) 2: 1

47. The ______ has a maximum temperature of about 480°C.

(a) Mercury (b) Venus
(c) Earth (d) Jupiter

***Directions for questions from 48 to 51:* Match the entries given in Column A with the appropriate ones in Column B.**

48. Match the following

	Column A		Column B
A.	Expansion of metals	a.	Medium is required
B.	Conduction	b.	Medium is not required
C.	Radiation	c.	Freezing point
D.	Melting point	d.	Absorption of heat energy

49.

	Column A		Column B
A.	Specific heat capacity	a.	Maximum
B.	Density of water at 4°C	b.	cal g^{-1}
C.	Calorific value	c.	Minimum
D.	Heat capacity	d.	Boling point of water
E.	Volume of water at 4°C	e.	cal g^{-1}°C^{-1}
F.	Upper fixing point	f.	cal°C^{-1}

50.

	Column A		Column B
A.	Thermometric liquid	a.	Double walled
B.	Rotating paper pinwheel	b.	Solid state to gaseous state directly
C.	Evaporation	c.	Common salt and ice
D.	Thermos flask	d.	Convectional currents
E.	Freezing mixture	e.	Mercury
F.	Sublimation	f.	Liquid to gas, below its boiling point

51.

Column A	Column B
A. Heat	a. Medium is necessary
B. Thermometer	b. Aluminium
C. Conduction	c. Used to find specific heat
D. Insulator	d. Energy
E. Calorimeter	e. Device to measure temperature
F. Calorie	f. Summer
G. Conductor	g. Unit of heat
H. Dark coloured clothes	h. Glass
I. Light coloured clothes	i. Winter

***Directions for questions from 52 to 72:* Answer the following questions.**

52. Why white clothes are comfortable in summer?
53. What is the temperature of steam at normal atmospheric pressure?
54. Define temperature.
55. Define melting and boiling points.
56. What is specific heat capacity?
57. Give three examples each of a good and bad conductor of heat.
58. Why do we cover our bodies with blankets at night in winter?
59. When two bodies are in thermal equilibrium, what can be said about their temperatures and heat loss?
60. Which among the following temperatures (70° C, 500° C, –273° C) can be measured using a mercury thermometer?
61. A substance undergoes a change in state. Which among temperature, internal energy or mass does/do not change?
62. What is the thermometer used to measure the temperature of a furnace?
63. What is the physical quantity that decides the flow of heat energy?
64. What is the principle of thermometer?
65. Why is the handle of a kettle covered with plastic?
66. When a metallic sphere is dropped from a certain height, what happens to the potential energy of the body?
67. What is the unit of measurement for heat?
68. What are the animals and plants living in polar region?
69. The temperature of a substance taken in a closed container has to be maintained uniform. Which container (Wooden/Metal, painted with white/black outside) is most suitable for this purpose?
70. What is the range of temperatures, that can be measured using clinical thermometer in Fahrenheit scale?
71. What is the specific heat capacity of water in different system of units?
72. Two iron spheres of equal mass having temperatures 20°C and 48°C are brought into contact with each other. What is the equilibrium temperature? Assume there is no heat loss to surroundings.

Short Answer Type Questions

73. Distinguish between heat and temperature.
74. What are the applications of expansion of solids?
75. Describe about clinical thermometer.
76. Write the applications of good conductors of heat.
77. Find the heat energy required to raise the temperature of 5 kg of water at 80°C to 100°C. (Specific heat of water is 1 cal $g^{-1}°C^{-1}$)
78. Explain how land and sea breezes occur.
79. Why is mercury used in thermometers?
80. Define conduction, convection and radiation.
81. If 0.5 cal g^{-1} $°C^{-1}$ is the specific heat capacity of a substance of mass 50 g, calculate the amount of heat energy required to change the temperature of a substance from –5° C to 10° C.
82. Why is an iron tyre heated before fitting it on a cart wheel?

83. What are the factors affecting the heat lost or gained by a body?

84. Write the applications of radiation.

85. What is the function of a thermos flask, how does it reduce heat loss?

86. Arrange the following in the increasing order of temperature when the following substances are kept open in sun light for the same period of time.

(A) 2 kg of ice at 0° C

(B) 2 kg of water at 0° C

(C) 2 kg of iron at 0° C

Essay Type Questions

87. The heat energy produced by the complete combustion of 25 g of a fuel is supplied to 500 g of water to increase the value of temperature from 35°C to 55°C. Find the calorific value of the fuel. (Specific heat capacity of water = 1 cal $g^{-1}°C^{-1}$)

88. Describe an experiment to determine the melting point and boiling point of water..

89. Describe the construction of mercury thermometer.

90. Describe an experiment to show that water is a bad conductor of heat.

91. Describe the construction of calorimeter.

92. Describe an experiment to show that the solids expand on heating.

93. Explain the anomalous expansion of water with Hope's apparatus.

94. (a) Write the relation between heat capacity and specific heat capacity.

(b) 7000 J of heat energy is supplied to a copper sphere of mass 90 g. What is the rise in temperature of the sphere?

(Specific heat capacity of copper = 0.09 cal $g^{-1}°C^{-1}$)

PRACTICE QUESTIONS COMPETITION WING

Level 1: Apply your Concepts

***Directions for questions from 1 to 15:* Fill in the blanks.**

1. Heat flows from one end of a steel spoon to the other end by ________.
2. If heat energy is given to a substance and its temperature remains constant, then the substance undergoes a change in ________.
3. The temperature at which a liquid converts to gaseous state is called ________ of a liquid.
4. The unit of specific heat capacity is________.
5. The transfer of heat which takes place due to the vibration of particles is ________.
6. Water is a ________ conductor of heat.
7. If temperature of a substance increases, the average kinetic energy of molecules of the substance ________.
8. Fastest mode of transmission of heat is ________.
9. Calorific value of ________ fuels is high.
10. The substances which do not allow heat to travel through them easily are said to be ________ of heat.
11. Change in temperature of a body is 57°C. The equivalent change in temperature in Kelvin scale is ________.
12. During sublimation, the solid substance, which is converting to gaseous state is called ________.
13. Heat capacity of 250 g of water is ________.
14. 100 g of ice at 0°C is mixed with 0.25 kg of water at 0°C. The net transfer of heat is ________.
15. Condensation point of a substance is numerically equal to ________.

***Directions for questions from 16 to 25:* State whether the following statements are true or false.**

16. The whole amount of heat energy from the sun reaches the earth by conduction.
17. For a substance to undergo a change of state, heat must be either given to it or taken away from it.
18. The heat required to raise the temperature of 1 kg of water by 1°C is called one calorie.
19. The heat absorbed by a substance decreases with increase in temperature.
20. The temperature of boiling water can be measured by a clinical thermometer.
21. Heat lost by radiation depends upon whether the outer surface of the body is black or polished.
22. On heating, iron expands more than copper for an equal rise in temperature.
23. To transmit heat from one object to another by conduction, the two objects should be in contact.
24. During day time, the temperature of water and sand is same.
25. When two bodies at the same temperature are in contact, no heat flows from one body to another.

***Directions for questions from 26 to 44:* For each of the questions, four choices have been provided. Select the correct alternative.**

26. The physical state of a substance can be changed by
    (a) Maintaining its temperature.
    (b) Removing heat energy from the substance.
    (c) Giving heat energy to the substance.
    (d) Both (b) and (c)
27. By heating, ________ of substances can be changed.
    (a) Size (b) Temperature
    (c) State (d) All of the above
28. Heat flow from one body to another body stops when both bodies attain equal ________.
    (a) Temperature (b) Heat energy
    (c) Mass (d) Volume
29. An iron ball at 40°C is dropped in a mug containing oil at 40°C. Then
    (a) Heat flows from iron ball to oil.
    (b) Heat flows from oil to iron ball.
    (c) Heat does not flow between oil and iron.
    (d) Temperature of oil increases and temperature of iron ball decreases.

30. In the steam engine, most of the heat energy is converted into ________.
(a) Electrical energy (b) Light energy
(c) Sound energy (d) Mechanical energy

31. The range of temperature that can be measured by using a clinical thermometer is
(a) 35°C to 43°C (b) 35°F to 43°F
(c) 35 K to 43 K (d) All of the above

32. Which of the following is true in case of mode of transmission of heat?
(a) Convection is possible only in case of liquids and gases.
(b) Radiation is the fastest mode of heat transfer.
(c) Conduction is possible only in case of solids.
(d) All of the above

33. Sea breeze and land breeze are formed due to ________.
(a) Conduction (b) Convection
(c) Radiation (d) All of the above

34. Woollen clothes keep us warm during winter because ________.
(a) Wool is a poor conductor of heat.
(b) Wool is a good conductor of heat.
(c) Air trapped in between the fibres prevents the heat flow.
(d) Both (a) and (c)

35. In a thermos flask, the loss of heat energy due to the following method is minimized.
(a) Conduction
(b) Convection
(c) Radiation
(d) All of the above

36. Heat energy brings about ________.
(a) Chemical changes in matter
(b) Change in dimensions
(c) Change in temperature
(d) All of the above

37. The heat gained or heat lost by a substance depends upon:
(a) the mass of the substance, (m)
(b) the specific heat of the substance, (s)
(c) the change in the temperature of the substance, (Δt)
(d) All of these

38. Which of the following is a poor conductor of heat?
(a) Wood (b) Water
(c) Air (d) All of the above

39. Which of the following statements is/are true?
(a) Celsius (°C) is the general unit of temperature.
(b) 30°C = 303 K.
(c) When heat energy flows from one body to another, the change in temperature of bodies need not be equal.
(d) All of the above

40. Choose the correct statement:
(A) During boiling, a liquid changes into gaseous state at constant temperature with absorption of heat energy.
(B) During solidification, a liquid changes into solid state at constant temperature with release of heat energy.
(a) Only A (b) Only B
(c) Both A and B (d) None of these

41. Fog is formed on the bathroom mirror when one takes a hot shower but does not during a cold shower, because
(a) Evaporation of water is more at higher temperature.
(b) Formation of fog on the mirror does not depend on amount of vapour.
(c) Formation of fog on mirror is not concerned with temperature of water.
(d) Both (a) and (b)

42. Which of the following statements is (are) true in case of change of state?
(a) Every substance on absorbing heat, undergoes change in state from solid to liquid and liquid to gas at any temperature.
(b) All substances do not undergo change in state from solid to liquid and liquid to gas on absorbing heat at any temperature.
(c) During change of state there is no change in temperature.
(d) Both (b) and (c)

43. A bimetallic strip made-up of copper and brass as shown below. Which among the following statements is/are true about the bimetallic strip? (Expansion of brass is more than expansion of copper).

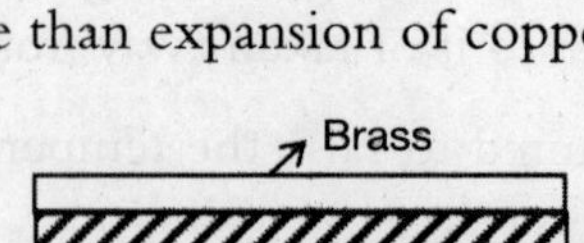

(a) If this bimetallic strip is heated, brass takes outer edge of the bend and copper takes the inner edge of the bend.

(b) If this bimetallic strip is cooled, brass takes inner edge of the bend and copper takes the outer edge of the bend.

(c) Heating and cooling do not affect the bimetallic strip.

(d) Both (a) and (b)

44. A metallic rod is bent in the form of a rectangle as shown in the given figure and heated. Then the gap between the ends P and Q ________.

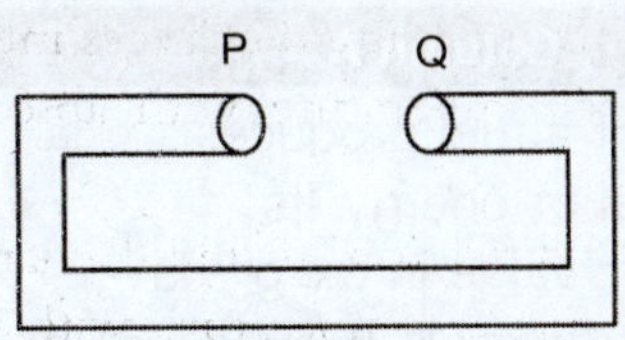

(a) Increases (b) Decreases

(c) Remains same (d) Cannot be determined

***Directions for questions from 45 to 47:* The heating curve of a particular substance in solid state is as shown in the figure. Choose the correct alternative.**

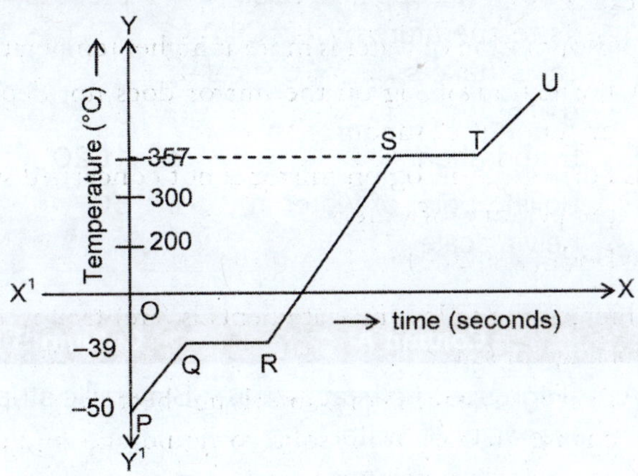

45. What is the boiling point of the substance?

(a) –39 (b) 300

(c) 357 (d) Cannot be determined

46. What does the portion QR of the graph indicates?

(a) No change in heat energy.

(b) Change in temperature.

(c) Change of state.

(d) Both (b) and (c)

47. What does the RS part of the graph indicates?

(a) Solid (b) Liquid

(c) Gaseous (d) Cannot be determined

48. Arrange the following steps in sequential order to show that the conduction of heat is different in different conductors.

(A) Take two identical rods one is copper and the other is iron.

(B) The ends of the two rods are heated with the same spirit lamp.

(C) Fix some nails on the rods with the help of wax at equal distances.

(D) The nails near to the flame falls first from the copper rod and then from the iron rod.

(a) ACDB (b) ABCD

(c) ACBD (d) ADBC

49. If '*m*' g of fuel is completely burned and that heat energy is supplied to '*M*' g of water to raise its temperature by Δt°C, then arrange the following steps in a sequence to calculate the calorific value of the fuel.

(A) Determine the heat energy absorbed by water.

(B) Determine the calorific value by dividing heat energy produced with mass of the fuel.

(C) Note down the mass of water, specific heat capacity and change in temperature of water.

(D) Heat energy absorbed by water is equal to heat given by the fuel after complete combustion.

(a) ACBD (b) ADCB

(c) CADB (d) CDBA

***Directions for questions 50 and 52:* For each of the questions, four choices have been provided. Select the correct alternative.**

50. Choose the correct statement.

(a) Specific heat capacity of a body in all its states is constant.

(b) Specific heat capacity of a body is different in different states.

(c) Specific heat capacity is a characteristic property of a material and it is different for different materials.

(d) Both (b) and (c)

51. **Assertion (A):** Temperature of a body can be increased by passing sound waves through it.

Reason (R): Heat and sound are different forms of energy.

(a) Both A and R are true and R is the correct explanation of A.

(b) Both A and R are true, but R is not the correct explanation of A.

(c) A is true but R is false.

(d) Both A and R are false.

52. Assertion: Convection is the process of transfer of heat energy in metals.

Reason: The atoms in metals are not free to move from one place to another.

(a) Both A and R are true and R is the correct explanation of A.

(b) Both A and R are true, but R is not the correct explanation of A.

(c) A is true but R is false.

(d) Both A and R are false.

Directions for question 53: **The heating curve of a particular substance in solid state is as shown in the figure: Choose the correct alternative.**

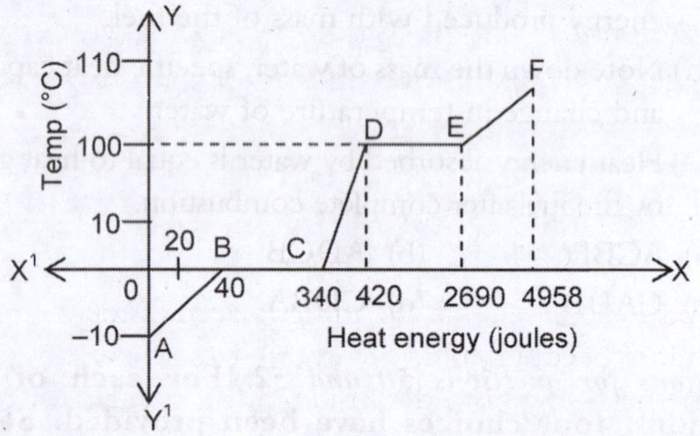

53. The amount of heat energy absorbed by the substance to change completely from liquid at its boiling point to gaseous state is ______ J.

(a) 4618 (b) 2270

(c) 4538 (d) 4958

Directions for questions from 54 to 56: **Match the entries given in Column A with the appropriate ones in Column B.**

54.

	Column A		Column B
A.	Thermometric liquid	a.	−240°C
B.	Lower fixing point	b.	Anomalous behaviour of water
C.	Survival of aquatic life	c.	310 K
D.	Maximum temperature on the moon	d.	Low vapour pressure
E.	Minimum temperature on the planet Mercury	e.	Freezing point of water
F.	Normal human body temperature	f.	110°C

55.

	Column A		Column B
A.	50 g of a fuel produces 25 kcal of energy. Its calorific value in cal g^{-1} is	a.	373
B.	400 cal of heat is supplied to 50 g of water to raise its temperature by 8°C. Heat capacity in cal $°C^{-1}$	b.	Slow process
C.	Boiling	c.	500
D.	Heat energy supplied to 150 g of copper to raise its temperature by 12°C in cal is (take $s_{copper} = 0.9$ cal $g^{-1}°C^{-1}$)	d.	Quick process
E.	Evaporation	e.	1620
F.	Boiling point of water in Kelvin scale	f.	50

56.

	Column A		Column B
A.	High specific heat capacity of water	a.	Bimetallic strip
B.	Human body temperature	b.	Six's maximum and minimum thermometer
C.	Boiling point of mercury	c.	357°C
D.	Thermal switches	d.	273 K
E.	Maximum and minimum temperature of a day	e.	Clinical thermomter
F.	Freezing point of water	f.	Coolant

Level 2: Review your Concepts

57. The kinetic energy of a body of mass 'm' moving with a speed 'v' is given by $\frac{1}{2}mv^2$. A bullet fired from gun moves with a speed of 50 m s^{-1} strikes target. If 50 per cent of the kinetic energy is absorbed by the bullet as heat energy, calculate the change in temperature of the bullet. The specific heat capacity of the material of the bullet is 42 J kg^{-1} °C^{-1}.

58. A graph is drawn by taking the rise in temperature on Y-axis and heat supplied on X-axis. Find out the melting point and boiling point of that substance.

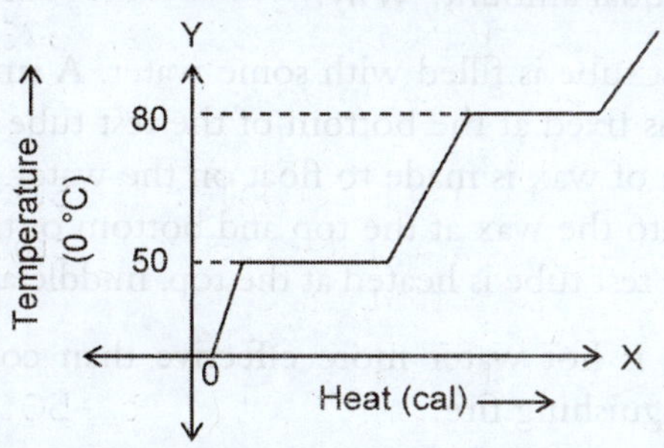

59. A physics student performed an experiment by taking a beaker with 1 ℓ of water at 30°C and dropping an iron sphere with temperature 90°C in it. After sometime, student measured their equilibrium temperature as 48°C. If the density of iron sphere is 7870 kg m^{-3}, then find the volume of the iron sphere. Specific heat of iron is 0.110 cal g^{-1}°C^{-1}.

60. A science student in a science fair demonstrated the existence of water and ice in same container at 0°C and water and steam in a same closed container at 100°C. Explain how is it possible to have two different states of matter at the same temperature.

61. Thermometer 'A' of length 20 cm has the tempera ture range 32 °A – 212 °A and thermometer 'B' of the same length has the temperature range 37 °B – 157 °B. Choose the one which can measure an accurate temperature of the body.

62. Ramu took four identical iron balls of temperatures 6°C, 10°C, 20°C and 32°C. He kept them in physical (thermal) contact with one another. After some time, he measured the equilibrium temperature attained by these four balls. What is the value of the equilibrium temperature?

63. Five per cent kinetic energy of a bullet fired from a gun is converted into heat energy. If the specific heat of the bullet is 490 J kg^{-1}°C^{-1} and the change in temperature of the bullet is 1°C, then the speed of the bullet is ______ ms^{-1}.

64. Rajesh took two identical glasses containing the same amount of hot milk, at the same temperature. He kept one glass undisturbed. While the other one, he continuously stirred using a spoon. Then, among them, milk in which glass cools faster? Why?

65. A physics student took a tumbler full of dry ice with a thermometer placed in it. He started supplying heat energy at constant rate by placing it on a heating device. The student observed no change in the thermometer reading even after 90% of ice melted. Explain what happened to the heat energy supplied.

66. A new thermometer calibrated as x °U to (x + 100) °U, then find the reading on this scale which is equal to 300 K temperature on the absolute scale.

67. Water at 10°C is in liquid form but iron at 10°C is in solid form. What is the reason?

68. Ram took equal masses of cooking oil and water, respectively, in two different identical beakers and placed them on identical heat engines and supplied same amount of heat to them. With the help of thermometer, he noted their temperatures. Which one of them would be hotter. Why?

69. Akbar observed that the things placed inside the refrigerator become cold. He wanted to know how does the heat flow from the inside of the refrigerator to the outside of the refrigerator. Explain.

70. If a uniform metal plate with a hole in it is heated, then explain how the size of the hole gets affected?

71. Raju was trying very hard to unscrew the metal cap of a bottle. Then he heated the cap slightly and was able to unscrew it easily. Explain.

72. Why does a blacksmith heat the iron block before hammering it to change its shape?

73. If we touch a piece of steel and wood on a winter day, we feel that the steel is colder than wood. If we touch the steel and the wood on a summer day, we feel that steel is hotter than wood. Why?

Level 3: Assess Your Concepts

74. Is it possible to raise the temperature of water by heating it in a container made-up of paper? [Temperature required to burn the paper is more than 100°C]

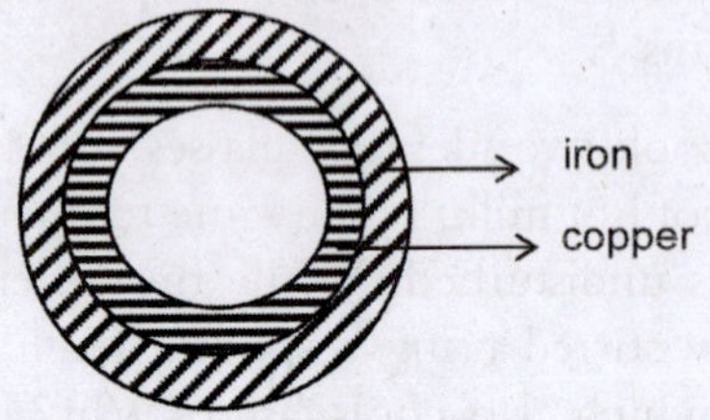

75. Rings made-up of copper and iron are fixed as shown in the figure. On heating the rings, explain what happens to them, if the thickness of the rings are negligible.

76. 20 g of water at 50°C is mixed with 10 g of water at 15°C, then find the equilibrium temperature of the mixture.

77. Explain why a clinical thermometer is exclusively used to measure the human body temperature and a laboratory thermometer is used to measure the temperatures of different substances but not to measure the human body temperature.

78. Two beakers A and B contain water at different temperatures. When 1 litre of water from beaker A is mixed with 2 litre of water from beaker B, the equilibrium temperature is 16°C and when 2 litre of water from beaker A is mixed with 2 litre of water from beaker B, then the equilibrium temperature is 14°C. Determine the temperature of water in the beakers A and B.

79. Two beakers contain hot water of the same temperature. One beaker is placed in another beaker containing cold water and the other beaker in front of a rotating fan. It is observed that the beaker placed in front the fan cools faster. Explain the reason.

80. When the same amount of heat is supplied to the different materials, will they increase their temperature by the equal amount? Why?

81. A test tube is filled with some water. A small piece of wax is fixed at the bottom of the test tube and a small piece of wax is made to float on the water. What happens to the wax at the top and bottom of the test tube if the test tube is heated at the top, middle and bottom?

82. Why is hot water more effective than cold water in extinguishing fire?

83. Rajini is heating her metal scale of length 15 cm; she found that the length of the metal scale is increased by 1 cm. Then find the length of a single division on the scale after heating and find the difference between the smallest division before and after heating the scale.

AT

ANSWER KEYS

Crossword

Across

5. Four 6. Calorie 9. Condensation 10. Radiation

Down

1. Specific heat 2. Mercury 3. Sublimation 4. Conduction 7. Evaporation
8. Calorimeter

Classroom Wing

Very Short Answer Type Questions

1. cal g^{-1} 2. convection 3. condensation 4. 12×10^5 cal
5. uneven expansion 6. (b) 7. (a) 8. (c) 9. (d)
10. (c) 11. (d) 12. (b) 13. (c) 14. (a)
15. (d) 16. (a) 17. (a) 18. (a) 19. (a)
20. (c) 21. (c) 22. (a) 23. (a) 24. (c)
25. (a) 26. (b) 27. (d) 28. (d) 29. (a)
30. (d) 31. (d) 32. (c) 33. (c) 34. (a)
35. (b) 36. (c) 37. (c) 38. (c) 39. (d)
40. (b) 41. (c) 42. (d) 43. (a) 44. (a)
45. (a) 46. (a) 47. (a)
48. A → d, B → a, C → b, D → c 49. A → e, B → a, C → b, D → f, E → c, F → d
50. A → e, B → d, C → f, D → a, E → c, F → b
51. A → d, B → e, C → a, b, D → h, E → c, F → g, G → b, H → i, I → f 53. 100°C
60. 70 °C 61. Temperature and mass of a body remain constant 67. Calorie
69. Wooden Container 71. 4200 J kg^{-1} K^{-1} 72. 34°C

Short Answer Type Questions

77. 100 kcal 81. 375 cal 86. CBA

Essay Type Questions

87. 400 cal g^{-1} 94. $C = ms$; 205.8°C

Competition Wing

Level 1: Apply your Concepts

1. Conduction 2. state 3. boiling point
4. cal g^{-1} $°C^{-1}$, Joule g^{-1} $°C^{-1}$ and Joule kg^{-1} K^{-1} 5. conduction
6. bad 7. increases 8. radiation 9. gaseous 10. bad conductors
11. 57 K 12. sublimate 13. 250 cal$°C^{-1}$ 14. zero 15. boiling point
16. False 17. True 18. False 19. False 20. False

21. True	22. False	23. True	24. False	25. True
26. (d)	27. (d)	28. (a)	29. (c)	30. (d)
31. (a)	32. (d)	33. (b)	34. (d)	35. (d)
36. (d)	37. (d)	38. (d)	39. (d)	40. (c)
41. (a)	42. (d)	43. (d)	44. (a)	45. (c)
46. (c)	47. (b)	48. (c)	49. (c)	50. (d)
51. (a)	52. (c)	53. (b)		

54. A → d, B → e, C → b, D → f, E → a, F → c

55. A → c, B → f, C → d, D → e, E → b, F → a

56. A → f, B → e, C → c, D → a, E → b, F → d

Level 2: Review your Concepts

57. $\Delta t = 14.8$ °C   59. 4.95×10^{-4} m^3 62. 17°C   63. 140 m s^{-1}

66. $R = (27 + X)$ °U

Level 3: Assess Your Concepts

76. T = 38.33 °C   78. 20°C   83. 0.06 mm

Hints and Explanations

Classroom Wing

Very Short Answer Type Questions

1. Calorific value of fuels is measured in cal g^{-1}.

2. In a room fitted with AC, heat flows by the process of convection.

3. (condensation)
The process of changing a substance from gaseous state to liquid state is called condensation.

4. (12×10^5 cal)
Calorific; $c = \dfrac{Q}{m}$
$c = 8000$ cal g^{-1}
$m = 150$ g
Heat energy produced; $Q = mc$
$= 150 \times 8000 = 120 \times 10^4$ cal
$= 12 \times 10^5$ cal

5. (uneven expansion)
When hot water is poured in ordinary glass vessel, it breaks because of uneven expansion of the glass.

6. (b)
Heat flows from a body at higher temperature to a body at lower temperature.

7. (a)
The temperature at which a solid substance changes into a liquid is called the melting point of the substance.

8. (c)
Mercury has low specific heat capacity.

9. (d)
Temperature is measured in degree celsius, kelvin or degree fahrenheit.

10. (c)
Normal temperature of the human body is 37°C.

11. (d)
In a clinical thermometer, both Celsius scale and Fahrenheit scale readings are marked.

12. (b)
Cooling in a motor car is done by convection.

13. (c)
The mode of transfer of heat in the absence of a medium is called radiation.

14. (a)
In solids generally the heat is transferred by conduction.

15. (d)
On increase in temperature, expansion of gas > expansion of liquid > expansion of solid.

16. (a)
The scale in clinical thermometer is marked from 35°C to 43°C.

17. (a)
In winter a set of double windows is a better insulator, because the gap between double window contains trapped air, which acts as an insulator and does not allow the heat from the room to flow out.

18. (a)
The increasing order of thermal conductivity of given substances is glass, iron, copper.

19. (a)
Mercury has a high boiling point and a low melting point.

20. (c)
Heat added to ice at 0°C, increases the potential energy component of the internal energy of ice, but does not increase the kinetic energy component and hence there is no rise of temperature.

21. (c)
(1) Boiling takes place only at constant temperature.
(2) Evaporation takes place at all temperatures.
(3) Boiling takes place at every part of the liquid.
(4) Evaporation takes place on the surface.

22. (a)
Fluids do not have specific length and area, but have definite volume. Thus the only expansion in fluids is volume expansion. Whereas solids undergo linear, arial, and cubical expansion due to their definite length, area and volume.

23. (c)
In solids generally, the heat is transferred by the process of conduction.

24. (c)
Normally, solids expand on heating, whereas liquids contract on cooling.

25. (a)
The materials which do not allow heat to pass through them easily are called poor conductors of heat. Poor conductors are also known as 'insulators'.
Examples: Plastic, wood, etc.

26. (b)
The substance melts by absorbing 340 – 40 = 300 J of energy i.e., 20 g of substance absorbs 300 J of energy and melts.

∴ Unit mass (1 g) of substance absorbs of energy and melts without rise in temperature. $\frac{300}{20} = 15$ J

27. (d)
The horizontal portion of graph, where temperature is constant represents change of state.

28. (d)
The rooms are provided with ventilators at the top. The hot air in the room is less denser, it raises up. This hot air passes through the ventilators and creates low pressure region inside the room. Then the cold air, which is more denser it enters into the room through windows and door from high pressure region to low pressure region. Thus the convectional currents are developed.

29. (a)
Take a thin capillary tube which is covered with a thick glass stem. Fill the bulb of thermometer with mercury, while filling with mercury, air bubble may trapped. To remove the air bubbles, place the thermometer bulb in hot water bath. Then cut the funnel and that end is sealed. Now mark the lower fixing point, by placing bulb in pure melting ice. Mark the upper fixing point by placing the bulb in boiling water. The distance between the two fixed points is divided into 100 equal parts and calibrated.

30. On heating, substances either expand or contract, i.e., their volume (either change in length or change in area) changes, and hence, density changes. But mass remains the same.

31. Bimetallic strip works on the principle of unequal expansion (or contraction) of metallic strips with which it is made of.

32. Amount of heat energy required to raise the temperature of unit mass of a substance through 1°C is called specific heat capacity.
∴ Its SI unit is J kg^{-1} K^{-1}

33. Thermometer works on the principle of cubical expansion of liquid or gas. And this expansion should be uniform throughout the material.

34. In case of an incense stick, the air at the lighted end is hot, and hence, volume increases and density decreases, so, it rises up (moves up).
(or)
The air at the hot end is at a higher temperature, so, its density is less and this lesser dense air rises up and more dense air occupies this place, so, it is due to convection of gases.

35. Take an empty test tube, fit its mouth with one holed cork stopper. Take a drop of coloured liquid into a narrow glass tube. Fit the narrow glass tube through the cork so that the level of the coloured drop is just above the cork. Heat the test tube and observe the position of coloured drop in the narrow glass tube. The trapped air in the test tube expands and it pushes the coloured drop upwards.

36. Note down the given values, that is mass of the substance as m kg, heat energy as Q cal and the temperatures of the substance as t_1°C. Convert the heat energy and temperatures into SI system. Find the change in temperature of the substance. Write the formula for heat energy gained or lost by a body, $Q = ms\Delta t$. Calculate the specific heat capacity of the substance.

37. The mode of transfer of heat in the absence of a medium is called radiation.

38. The base of the cooking vessels is coated with mud or painted dull to absorb more heat.

39. Black is a good absorber and good radiator. It absorbs more amount of heat and keeps our body warm.

40. White is a good reflector, it absorbs less amount of heat. Black is a good absorber and good radiator.

41. At 4°C, water has minimum volume and maximum density, which is explained as anomalous expansion of water. So, A is correct. As the temperature of water is increased from 0°C to 4°C, it contracts and from 4°C to 0°C, it expands. This is known as anomalous expansion of water. Hence, water will occupy more volume at 0°C than that of 4°C.

42. We prefer to wear dark clothes in winter because they absorb the heat and keep the body warm. However, white clothes are good reflectors of heat and are worn in summer.

43. Fog is formed on the bathroom mirror when we take a hot shower. Because the evaporation of water molecules is more at higher temperature.

44. Work can be done by applying an external force and this can be converted into heat energy and hence, the temperature can be increased.
Hence, the correct option is (a).

45. Heat energy reaches the surface of earth travelling through vacuum as the heat radiations are electromagnetic in nature.
Hence, the correct option is (a).

46. Freezing mixture contains common salt and ice in the ratio 1 : 3.

47. The Venus has the maximum temperature about 480°C.

48. A → d Expansion of a metal takes by absorbing heat.
B → a For the process of conduction medium is required.
C → b Medium is not required for radiation.
D → c Melting point is equal to freezing point.

49. A → e Specific heat capacity $s = \dfrac{Q}{M\Delta t}$
Its unit is cal g^{-1} °C^{-1}
B → a Density of water at 4°C is maximum.
C → b Calorific value is defined as the amount of heat energy produced by the complete combustion per unit mass of a fuel. Its unit is cal g^{-1}.
D → f Heat capacity is the amount of heat energy required to change the temperature by 1°C. Its unit is cal°C^{-1}
E → c Volume of water at 4°C is minimum.
F → d The upper fixing point in the thermometer is marked at boiling point of water.

50. A → e Liquid used in thermometers is called thermometric liquid. Mercury is used as thermometric liquid.
B → d Paper pinwheel rotates due to the flow of air, that is convectional currents.
C → f The process of changing a liquid into gaseous state, below its boiling point is called evaporation.
D → a Thermos flask is a double walled container filled with air in the gap to reduce the loss of heat.
E → c Freezing mixture is the mixture of common salt and ice, to produce low temperatures.
F → b The process of converting a solid, directly into gaseous state is called sublimination.

51. A → d Heat is a form of energy.
B → e Thermometer is used for measuring temperature.
C → a, b For heat transfer by conduction, a medium is necessary. In aluminium heat is transferred by conduction.
D → h A substance which does not allow the passage of heat through it is known as an insulator. Glass is an insulator.
E → c Calorimeter is used to find the specific heat of a substance.
F → g CGS unit of heat energy is calorie.
G → b A substance which allows heat to pass through it is known as a conductor. Aluminium is a good conductor.
H → I Dark colour clothes are good absorbers of heat energy. So they are preferred in winter.
I → f Light coloured clothes are good reflectors and emitters of heat energy. So, they are preferred in summer.

52. White colour is good reflector of heat. It absorbs minimum heat energy.

53. Steam can exist at a temperature 100° C.

54. The degree of hotness or coldness of a body is called temperature. It depends on the kinetic energy of molecules of the body.

55. The constant temperature at which a solid substance changes into a liquid is called the 'melting point' of the substance.
Similarly, the constant temperature at which a liquid substance starts to boil is called the 'boiling point' of the substance.

56. The amount of heat energy required to raise the temperature of unit mass of a substance by 1°C is known as specific heat capacity of the substance.

$$s = \frac{Q}{m\Delta t}$$

57. Examples of good conductors of heat are aluminium copper, silver, iron etc. Examples of bad conductors of heat are wood, plastic, glass, cotton, etc.

58. Blanket does not allow heat energy to flow outward from our body. Because it contains large amount of trapped air, which is a bad conductor of heat.

59. When two bodies are in thermal contact, their temperature is same and the heat lost by one body is equal to that gained by other body.

60. Mercury can exist in liquid state only at 70 °C from the given choices.

61. During the change of state, the temperature and mass of a body remain constant.

62. The thermometer used to measure the temperature of a furnace above 1000°C is called pyrometer.

63. Temperature decides the direction of flow of heat energy. Always heat energy flows from high temperature body to low temperature body.

64. The principle of thermometer is the property of expansion or contraction of a substance on heating or cooling.

65. Plastic is bad conductor of heat. When we are handling that kettle, heat will not be transferred to our hand, through the plastic.

66. The potential energy of the body dropped gets converted to heat energy and hence its temperature increases.

67. Calorie is the unit of heat energy.

68. The plant that exists in polar region is Lichens. The animals living in polar region are polar bear, polar pig and reindeer.

69. A wooden container painted white outside is most suitable.

70. The range of temperatures that can be measured using thermometer is 95°F to 110°F (or) 35°C to 43°C.

71. Specific heat capacity of water = 1 cal $g^{-1}°C^{-1}$

$$= \frac{4.2\ J}{\frac{1}{1000}\ kg\ 1\ K} = 4200\ J\ kg^{-1}\ K^{-1}$$

72. No heat loss to the surrounding

Temperature of first sphere; $t_1 = 20°C$.

Temperature of second sphere; $t_2 = 48°C$.

When the two spheres are kept in contact

Equilibrium temperature $= \frac{t_1 + t_2}{2} = \frac{20 + 48}{2} = \frac{68}{2} =$ 34°C.

Short Answer Type Questions

73.

	Heat	Temperature
1.	Heat is a form of energy, which causes the sensation of hotness or coldness.	The degree of hotness or coldness of a body is measured in temperature.
2.	Heat energy is the cause.	Temperature is the effect.
3.	It is measured in joule or calorie.	It is measured in kelvin or celsius or fahrenheit.
4.	Calorimeter is used to measure heat energy.	Thermometer is used to measure temperature.
5.	Heat energy always flows from body at high temperature to body at low temperature.	Temperature depends on the average kinetic energy of the molecules.

74. Applications of expansion of solids:

(i) Fixing of iron rim on wooden cart wheels.

(ii) Riveting of metal plates.

(iii) A small gap is left while laying rail tracks.

(iv) Girders are mounted on the rollers by leaving small space.

(v) A sag is left, while laying telephone and electric lines.

(vi) A small gap is left between the blocks, while laying the concrete roads.

(vii) Special glasses like borosil or pyrex glasses are used to avoid the breaking of ordinary glass, when hot water is poured.

75. Clinical thermometer: The thermometer which is used to measure our body temperature is called a 'clinical thermometer'.

A clinical thermometer consists of a long, narrow, uniform glass tube. It has a bulb filled with mercury at one end. A constriction is provided, which does not allow mercury to fall back into the bulb.

The clinical thermometer consists of two scales, Celsius scale, indicated by °C and Fahrenheit scale indicated by °F. The normal temperature of human body 37°C or 98.4°F is marked with a red arrow.

As the temperature of human body does not go below 35°C or above 43°C, the scale in clinical thermometer is marked from 35°C to 43°C.

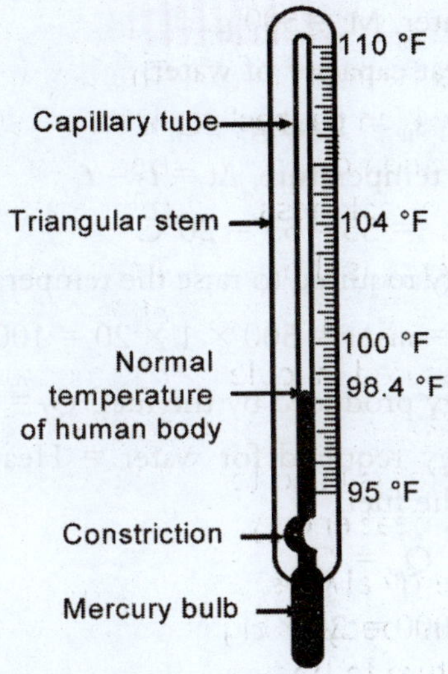

76. Applications of good conductors: Good conductors of heat find applications in daily life. Some of them are listed below.

(i) Cooking vessels are made of metals so that heat is conducted through them and passes onto the food, being cooked. Copper is good conductor of heat. So, copper-bottom vessels are used to save time and fuel.

(ii) Mercury is used as thermometric liquid because it is a good conductor of heat.

(iii) Automobile radiators use tubes made of copper as it is a good conductor of heat. Being a good conductor, it absorbs the heat from the hot water from the engine and transmit it to the surroundings. For the same reason, air conditioners and refrigerators use copper tubes.

(iv) Heat is passed onto the solder through the tip of the soldering iron which is made of copper.

77. Mass of water; m = 5 kg = 5000 g

Initial temperature; t_1 = 80°C

Final temperature; t_2 = 100°C

Change in temperature, $\Delta t = t_2 - t_1$ = 20°C

Specific heat capacity of water; s = 1 cal g^{-1}°C^{-1}

Heat energy supplied; $Q = ms\Delta t$

= 5000 × 1 × 20 = 10 × 10^4 cal

= 100 × 10^3 cal = 100 kcal

78. Sea and land breezes are formed due to convection currents of air. During the day time land gets heated faster than sea water. Consequently, the air above land becomes hot and rises up. The cold air above the sea then moves towards land, to take the place of hot air, thus forming sea breeze. During nights, land breeze flows from land to sea as land gets cooled faster than sea.

79. (i) Its expansion is uniform over a wide range of temperatures.

(ii) It is a good conductor of heat.

(iii) It has a low specific heat capacity.

(iv) It is opaque, shining and clearly visible.

(v) It does not wet the glass.

(vi) It is easily available in pure form.

(vii) It has a high boiling point and a low melting point.

(viii) It exerts a very low vapour pressure.

80. **Conduction:** The process of transmission of heat energy from one place to another place without the actual movement of the molecules is called conduction. In case of conduction, heat energy is transmitted by the vibration of molecules.

Convection: The process of transmission of heat energy by the motion of the molecules of the medium from one place to another place is called convection. Generally convection takes place in liquids and gases.

Radiation: The process of transmission of heat in the absence of medium is called radiation. In this process, heat energy is transmitted in the form of electromagnetic waves.

81. $Q = ms\,\Delta t = 50 \times 0.5 \times (10 - (-5)) = 25(15) = 375$ cal.

82. While fixing an iron rim to a wooden cart wheel, the iron rim with diameter slightly less than the diameter of wooden cart wheel is taken. The iron rim is heated to expand. It is fixed over the wooden cart wheel. Cool the iron rim. So, that it contracts and holds the wooden wheel tightly.

83. (i) Heat lost or gained by a body is directly proportional to the mass of the body.

$$Q \propto m \quad (1)$$

(ii) Heat lost or gained by a body is directly proportional to change in temperature of the body.

$$Q \propto \Delta t \quad (2)$$

(iii) It also depends on the nature of the body. From (1) and (2)

$$Q \propto m\Delta t \Rightarrow Q = ms\Delta t.$$

Where, '*s*' is the specific heat capacity, its depends on nature of the body.

84. Applications of Radiation:

(i) The base of the cooking vessels are coated with mud or painted dull to absorb more heat.

(ii) White coloured clothes are comfortable in summer and black coloured clothes are comfortable in winter because white is good reflector, it absorbs less amount of heat. Black is good absorber and good radiator. It absorbs more amount of heat and keeps our body warm.

(iii) While transporting the highly inflammable substance like petrol and LPG etc., in tankers, the tankers are coated with white colour, which is a good reflector of heat.

85. A thermos flask is used to keep a hot liquid hot and a cold liquid cold.

Construction: It consists of a double walled glass. The air between the two walls is evacuated and sealed. This shining glass bulb is kept over a rubber cork on a plastic or metal body. The space between the glass and metal is filled with cork which is a bad conductor of heat. The mouth is covered with a plastic cork over which a plastic cover is screwed.

The different forms of heat loss are minimized in a thermos flask, due to the following reasons.

(i) **Conduction loss:** Since there is a vacuum, heat cannot be conducted by means of conduction. Further there is a cork and glass wool which are bad conductors of heat.

(ii) **Convection loss:** Since there is a vacuum, loss due to convection is avoided.

(iii) **Radiation loss:** Since the glass is shining, radiation loss is minimized.

86. As the specific heat capacity of iron is less than that of water, the temperature of iron will be high among the given substances.
Ice at 0 °C will show the least final temperature as it has to melt before its temperature starts to increase. Hence, the correct order is CBA.

Essay Type Questions

87. Mass of fuel, $m_f = 25$ g.
Calorific value, c =?
Mass of water, M = 500 g.
Specific heat capacity of water,

$$s_w = 1 \text{ cal g}^{-1}\,{}^0\text{C}^{-1}.$$

Change in temperature, $\Delta t = t_2 - t_1$

$$= 55 - 35 = 20°\text{C}.$$

Heat energy required to raise the temperature of water,

$$Q_w = ms\Delta t = 500 \times 1 \times 20 = 10000 \text{ cal}.$$

Heat energy produced by the fuel, $Q_f = m_f c$

Heat energy required for water = Heat energy produced by the fuel,

$$Q_w = Q_f.$$

$$10000 = 25 \times c$$

$$c = \frac{10000}{25} = 400 \text{ cal g}^{-1}$$

88. The melting and boiling points of a substance: Take some crushed ice in a beaker. Place a thermometer in the ice and hold it upright as shown in figure. Place the beaker on a stand. Heat the beaker by using a burner. It is observed that, even though heat is being supplied temperature rises till 0°C and when it starts melting there is no change in the temperature shown by the thermometer until all the ice is melted. It remains at 0°C. On further heating the temperature of water increases till 100°C. At this temperature water starts boiling. The temperature remains constant at 100°C until all the water is evaporated.

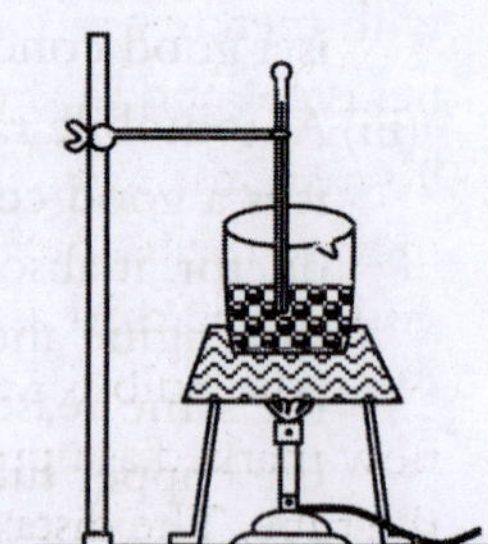

If we plot a graph by taking heat supplied along X-axis and temperature along Y-axis, a curve as shown in the figure below is obtained.

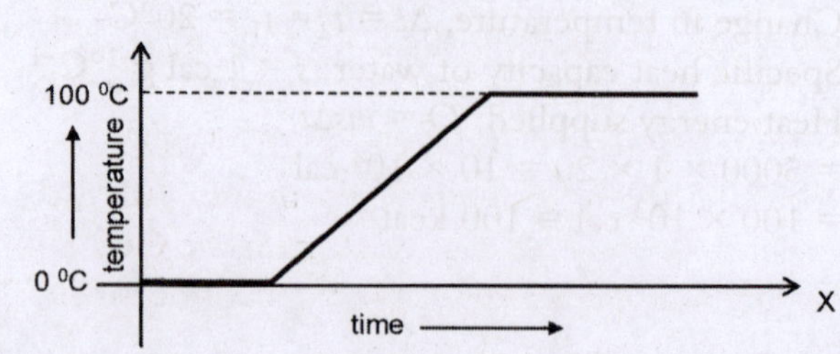

Thus, the melting of ice is 0°C and boiling point of water is 100°C.

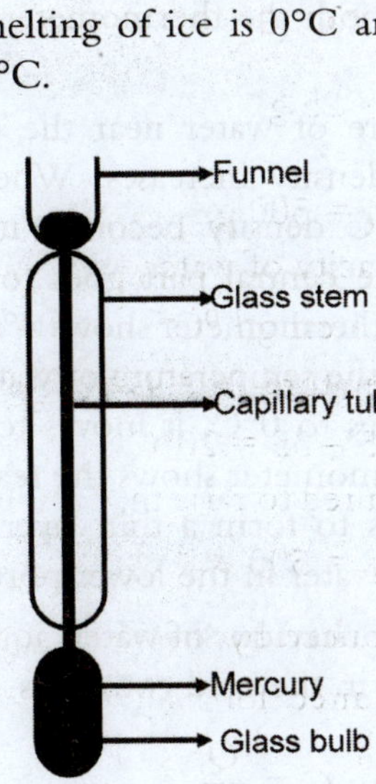

89. **Construction of a mercury thermometer:** A very thin capillary tube of uniform cross-section, one end of which has a very thin glass bulb and the other end of which is provided with a funnel is taken. The capillary tube is protected by means of a thick glass stem as shown in the figure.

    Mercury is poured into the funnel. The mercury slowly drips down into the capillary tube, but in this process some air bubbles may get trapped. The bulb is heated in a water bath, so that the trapped air escapes through the mercury. This process is repeated several times till the glass bulb and the capillary tube are completely filled with mercury without any air bubbles. Finally, the funnel is cut and the end is sealed.

    To mark the scale, the bulb of the thermometer is placed in pure melting ice and the level at which the mercury settles is marked as lower fixed point and taken as 0°C. Now the bulb is held in steam. The level of mercury is now marked as upper fixed point and taken as 100°C on the tube. The distance between the two marks is divided into 100 equal parts. Each part shows 1°C.

90. Experiment to show that water is a bad conductor of heat: Water is a bad conductor of heat, which can be proved as follows. Take a hard glass tube and drop small pieces of ice, wrapped in copper wire gauze. Pour ice cold water so as to fill the glass tube upto 3/4 of its length. The copper wire gauze prevents the ice from floating. Clamp the test tube as shown in figure.

    Now, heat the test tube near its mouth with a bunsen burner. It is observed that water near the mouth of the test tube starts boiling but the ice does not melt. This shows that heat is not conducted through water and that water is a bad conductor of heat.

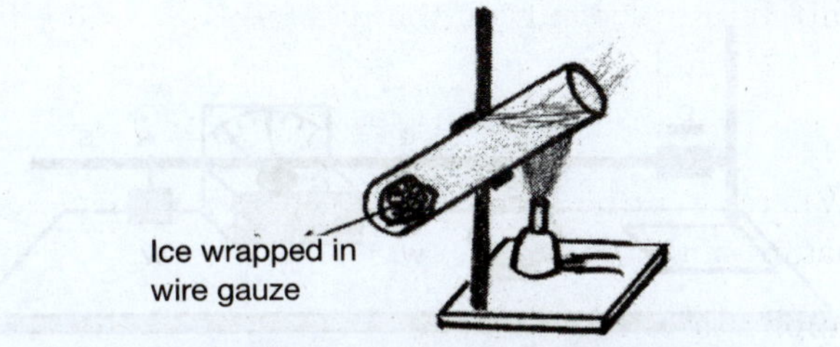

Experiment to show that water is a bad conductor of heat

91. Calorimeter: A calorimeter is a highly polished cylindrical copper vessel used to measure the quantity of heat. The copper vessel is placed inside a wooden box. The space between the wooden box and copper vessel is filled with a bad conductor of heat like cork or sawdust. The wooden box has a lid made of ebonite or a similar bad conductor. It has two holes. A stirrer can be inserted through one hole and thermometer through the other. When two bodies of different temperatures are brought into contact heat is transferred from the body at a higher temperature to a body at a lower temperature. This is the principle used in the measurement of specific heat capacity of a substance by using a calorimeter.

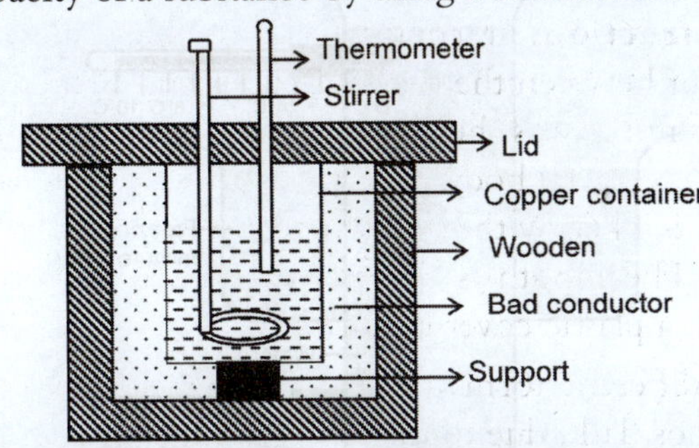

A measured amount of water is taken in the calorimeter and its temperature is noted. The substance whose specific heat is to be determined is heated to a certain temperature and then added to the water in the calorimeter. The water is stirred and the final temperature of the mixture is noted from that. The specific heat of that substance can be calculated.

92. Expansion in solids: Take a long aluminium rod clamped at an end as shown in figure. The aluminium rod rolls over a glass rod placed perpendicular to its length on a wooden block. Two weight hangers W_1 and W_2 are attached to the aluminium rod to have a firm contact between the glass rod and the aluminium rod. A light pointer is attached to an end of the glass rod which moves over a paper scale. When the aluminium rod is heated, it expands and rolls over the glass rod and the pointer moves over the scale, confirming the expansion of the aluminium rod.

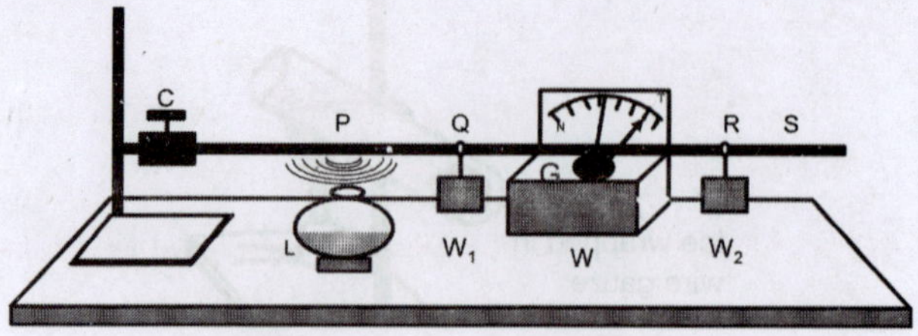

93. Anomalous expansion of water: Generally matter expands on heating and contracts on cooling. But water shows a peculiar behaviour. When water at 0°C is heated, it contracts and its volume decreases from to 0°C at 4°C. Water has minimum volume and maximum density at 4°C. From 4°C onwards, as temperature increases, its volume also increases. This behaviour of water is known as anomalous expansion of water.

So the anomalous expansion of water can be demonstrated by hope's apparatus.

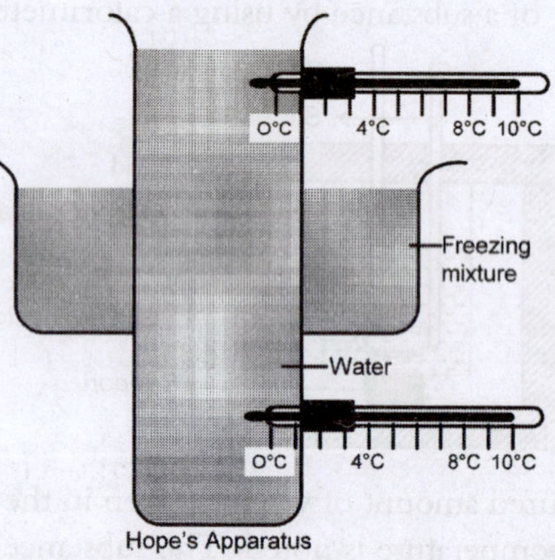

Hope's Apparatus

It consists of a long cylindrical vessel. Surrounded with a cylindrical trough, which is filled with freezing mixture. Freezing mixture contains common salt and ice in the ratio 1 : 3.

Two holes are provided to the long cylindrical vessel one at the top and the other at the bottom. Two thermometers are inserted in these two holes to record the temperature of water. The vessel is filled with water at 10°C. Initially both the thermometers show the same reading.

The temperature of water near the cooling mixture decreases and density increases. When the temperature falls to 4°C density becomes maximum. Then the water in the central part goes to the lower portion, the lower thermometer shows 4°C and it remains constant. Now the temperature of water in the central portion decreases to 0°C, it moves to upper portion. The upper thermometer shows the reading as 0°C and slowly it freezes to form a thin layer of ice. But the temperature of water in the lower portion shows 4°C.

Because of this behaviour of water, aquatic life survives in frozen ponds in the cold countries.

94. (a) Heat capacity $C = \dfrac{Q}{\Delta t}$ (1)

Specific heat capacity, $s = \dfrac{Q}{m\Delta t}$ (2)

From equation (2); $s = \dfrac{Q}{m\Delta t} \Rightarrow Q = ms\Delta t$

Substitute this in eq (1)

$$C = \frac{Q}{\Delta t} = \frac{ms\Delta t}{\Delta t}$$

$$\therefore C = ms$$

(b) Heat energy supplied, $Q = 7000\text{ J} = \dfrac{7000}{4.2}$ cal.

Mass of copper sphere, $m = 90$ g.

Specific heat capacity of copper, $s_{cu} = 0.09$ cal g^{-1}°C^{-1}

Change in temperature $\Delta t = ?$

We know that heat energy gained or lost, $Q = ms\Delta t$.

$$\therefore 7000 \times \frac{1}{4.2} = 90 \times 0.09 \times \Delta t$$

$$\Delta t = \frac{7000}{4.2 \times 90 \times 0.09} = \frac{700}{4.2 \times 9 \times 0.09}$$

$$\Delta t = \frac{100}{9 \times 0.54} = 205.8°C$$

Competition Wing

Level 1: Apply your Concepts

1. In case of metals, the heat flows by the process of conduction.
2. (state)
The temperature of a body remains constant if the substance undergoes a change in state.
3. (boiling point)
The temperature at which a liquid substance changes into gaseous state is called the boiling point of the substance.
4. The unit of specific heat capacity is cal g^{-1} $°C^{-1}$, Joule g^{-1} $°C^{-1}$ and Joule kg^{-1} K^{-1}.
5. (conduction)
The transfer of heat from one place to another by the vibration of particles is called conduction.
6. Water is a bad conductor of heat.
7. Temperature is directly proportional to the average kinetic energy of molecules. As temperature increases, average kinetic energy also increases.
8. Radiation is the fastest mode of transmission of heat.
9. Gaseous fuels have high calorific value, compared to solid fuels and liquid fuels.
10. The materials which do not allow heat to travel through them easily are called bad conductors of heat.
11. Change in temperature in Kelvin scale is equal to the change in temperature in Celsius scale.
Change in temperature = 57°C = 57 K.
12. During sublimation, the solid substance, which is converting to its gaseous state is called sublimate.
13. Heat capacity, $C = ms$
$C = 250 \times 1 = 250$ cal $°C^{-1}$
14. When 100 g of ice at 0°C is mixed with 250 g of water at 0°C, the net transfer of heat energy is zero. Because, both are at same temperature.
15. Condensation point of a substance is numerically equal to the boiling point of the substance.
16. False.
The heat energy from the sun reaches us in the form of electromagnetic radiation.
17. For a substance to undergo a change of state, heat must either be given to it or taken away from it.
18. The heat required to raise the temperature of 1 kg of water by 1°C is called one kilocalorie.
19. Heat absorbed by a substance increases with the increase in temperature.
20. The maximum temperature that can be measured by using a clinical thermometer is less than the boiling point of water.
21. Heat transfer by radiation depends upon whether the outer surface of the body is black or polished.
22. On heating copper expands more than iron for an equal rise in temperature.
23. To transmit heat from one object to another by conduction, the two objects should have a physical contact between them.
24. False.
During day time, the temperature of land is more than that of water.
25. True.
When two bodies of different temperature are in contact, heat flows from the body at higher temperature to the body at lower temperature.
26. Change of state of a substance is due to the change in heat energy.
27. On heating substances will undergo change in size, temperature and state.
28. Heat flow from one body to another body stops, when both the bodies reach equal temperature.
29. There is no net heat flow, because temperature is same.
30. In a steam engine most of the heat energy is converted into mechanical energy.
31. The range of a clinical thermometer is from 35°C to 43°C.
32. The molecules of a solid are held strongly due to strong intermolecular forces. As these molecules cannot travel to the source of heat energy, therefore, convection is not possible in case of solids, but transformation of heat takes place from one molecule to another molecule which is side by it, i.e., conduction takes place.

Radiation is the fastest mode of heat transfer from hot body to cold body.

33. Sea breeze and land breeze are formed due to convection.

34. Woollen clothes keep us warm during winter because wool is a poor conductor of heat and at the same time air trapped in-between the fibres minimizes heat flow. Here air acts as a thermal insulator.

35. In a thermos flask, the loss of heat energy is minimized due to conduction, convection and radiation.

36. Heat energy brings about change in the dimensions of a substance (object), chemical composition of substance and also change in its temperature.

37. The heat gained or heat lost by a substance depends upon:

1. the mass of the substance, (m)
2. the specific heat of the substance, (s)
3. the change in the temperature of the substance, (Δt)

38. Among the given options, all are poor conductors of heat.

39. (i) General unit of temperature is degree Celsius (°C).

(ii) 30° C = (30 + 273) K = 303 K.

(iii) When heat energy flows from one body to another, the change in temperature of the bodies need not be equal.

40. Both the given statements are true.

41. Fog is formed on the bathroom mirror when we take a hot shower. Because the evaporation of water molecules is more at higher temperature.

42. When a substance is undergoing change of state, the temperature remains constant. But all substances do not undergo changes in their states at any temperature on absorbing or losing heat.

43. When the given bimetallic strip is heated, due to more expansion of brass than copper brass takes outer edge of the bend and copper takes inner edge. If it is cooled, due to more contraction of brass than copper, copper takes the outer edge of the bend and brass takes the inner edge.

44. When the rod is heated, the distance between any adjacent molecules increases, hence, the perimeter of the rectangle and the gap between P and Q increases.

45. From the graph the substance which is in liquid state at 357°C converts into gaseous state at the same temperature, which is represented by $\overline{ST}$ in the graph.

∴ Boiling point of the substance = 357°C

46. The portion QR of the graph indicates change of state.

47. The substance is in solid state from −50°C to −39°C and it changes its state at −39°C, i.e., converts into liquid state. Therefore, it will be in liquid state from −39°C to 357°C. Hence, $\overline{RS}$ part of the graph indicates liquid state.

48. Take two identical rods, one is copper and the other is iron. Fix some nails to the rods with the help of wax at equal distances. Heat the two rods with same spirit lamp at one end by holding at the other ends. Now the nails near to the flame fall, first from the copper rod and then from the iron rod. This happens because the conduction of heat in copper is faster than that in iron.

49. Note down the mass, specific heat capacity and change in temperature of water. Determine the heat absorbed by water using $Q = MS\Delta t$. This heat energy absorbed is equal to the heat produced by 'm' g of fuel after complete combustion. Then determine the calorific value by using $c = Q/m$.

50. Specific heat capacity of a body is the amount of heat energy required to raise the temperature of unit mass of substance through 1°C. It is the characteristic property of a body and it remains constant in a given state. But changes from state to state for a given substance.

51. Sound and heat are different forms of energy. Hence, temperature can be increased by passing sound waves through a medium.
Hence, the correct option is (a).

52. In metals heat is transferred by conduction as molecules are not free to move in a metal.
Hence, the correct option is (c).

53. The substance in liquid state changes to gaseous state by absorbing energy of 2690 − 420 = 2270 J.

54.

A → d	Thermometric liquid should exert a very low vapour pressure.
B → e	Freezing point of water is marked as lower fixing point on the thermometer.
C → b	Because of anomalous behaviour of water, aquatic life can exist at the bottom even the top surface of the ponds freeze.
D → f	Maximum temperature on the Moon is about 110°C
E → a	Minimum temperature on the Mercury is about −240°C.

F → c Normal human body temperature is 37°C $= 273 + 37 = 310$ K.

55. A → c Calorific value $= \frac{Q}{M} = \frac{25000 \text{ cal}}{50 \text{ g}}$

$= 500 \text{ cal g}^{-1}$

B → f Heat capacity; $C = \frac{Q}{\Delta t} = \frac{400}{8}$

$= 50 \text{ cal°C}^{-1}$

C → d Boiling takes place at a constant temperature and it is a quick process.

D → e Heat energy supplied; $Q = ms\Delta t$

$Q = 150 \times 0.9 \times 12 = 1620$ cal

E → b Evaporation takes place at any temperature, below its boiling point. It is a slow process

F → a Boiling point of water is 100°C = (100 + 273) K = 373 K

56. A → f Because of high specific heat capacity of water, water is used as coolant.

B → e Clinical thermometer is used to measure the temperature of human body.

C → c Boling point of mercury is 357°C.

D → a Thermal switch works on the principle of bimetallic strip.

E → b Six's maximum and minimum thermometer is used to determine the maximum and minimum temperature of a day.

F → d Freezing point of water is 0°C. This is equal to 273 K ; because K = C + 273.

Level 2: Review your Concepts

57. Given $k = \frac{1}{2} mv^2$

According to the problem,

$\frac{1}{2}(\frac{1}{2} mv^2) = \text{Heat}$

$\frac{1}{2}(\frac{1}{2} mv^2) = ms\,\Delta t$

$\frac{(50)^2}{4} = \Delta t \times 42$

$\Delta t = 14.8$ °C

58. Melting point = 50°C

Boiling point = 80°C

59. Mass of 1 ℓ of water = 1 kg;

$(\Delta t)_w = 48 - 30 = 18°\text{C}$;

$(\Delta t)_{\text{iron}} = 90 - 48 = 42°\text{C}$

Heat absorbed by water = Heat lost (removed) from iron.

$(ms\Delta t)_w = (ms\Delta t)_{\text{iron}}$

$$m_i = \frac{(ms\Delta t)_W}{(s\Delta t)_{iron}}\left(\frac{1000 \times 1 \times 18}{0.110 \times 42}\right) = 3.896 \text{ kg}$$

$$\text{Density} = \frac{\text{mass}}{V}$$

$$V = \frac{m}{d} = \frac{3.896}{7870} = 4.95 \times 10^{-4} \text{ m}^3$$

60. When we supply heat energy to ice, its temperature increases till it reaches 0°C but continues to be ice only. On further supply of heat energy, there is no rise in temperature but ice converts into water at same 0°C temperature. Heat supplied is used for phase transformation (state change) only. Similarly, water at 100°C on supplying heat energy converts into steam without any change in temperature. The heat absorbed is utilized only to change the state of matter from liquid state to gaseous state. Hence, ice and water exist in contact at 0°C and water and steam exist in contact at 100°C.

61. Thermometer 'A' has the number of divisions (212 – 32) = 180 and thermometer 'B' has (157 – 37) = 120 divisions. So, the single division value on scale A is smaller than 'B' scale.

So, thermometer 'A' measures the temperature more accurately than 'B'.

62. As the four bodies are identical, the equilibrium temperature is the average of the temperatures.

That is, $t = \frac{t_1 + t_2 + t_3 + t_4}{4}$

$= \frac{6 + 10 + 20 + 32}{4} = 17°\text{C}$

63. According to the problem,

$\frac{5}{100}\left[\frac{1}{2} mv^2\right] = m \times s \times \Delta t$

$\frac{5v^2}{200} = 490 \times 1$

$v^2 = 490 \times 40 = v = 140 \text{ m s}^{-1}$

64. The milk in glass which is stirred by a spoon cools first. When we stir using a spoon, it will increase the movement of molecules. The cold molecules on the surface will settle at the bottom and hot molecules from bottom reach the top. Thus, stirring increase the heat transfer rate by convection.

65. When ice at 0°C is changed into water at 0°C, the energy is used to increase the intermolecular spacing and to change into the liquid state. The heat energy supplied is not used to increase the temperature of the substance.

66. New thermometer $LFP = X\ °U$ and $UFP = (X + 100)\ °U$

Reading on kelvin scale is 300 K that means

$C = K - 273 = 300 - 273 = 27\ °C$

Let 'R' be the reading on the new thermometer.

$$\left(\frac{R - LFP}{UFP - LFP}\right)_{\text{new scale}} = \left(\frac{C - 0}{100 - 0}\right)_{°C}$$

$$\frac{R - X}{(X + 100) - X} = \frac{C}{100}$$

$$\frac{R - X}{100} = \frac{27}{100}$$

$R - X = 27$

$R = (27 + X)\ °U$

67. In water the intermolecular force of attraction is less when compared to that in iron. So, iron required more amount of energy than water to convert from a solid state to a liquid state. Thus, iron exists in solid state whereas water exists in liquid state at 10°C.

68. The oil becomes hotter than water because the specific heat capacity of oil is less compared to that of water (1 cal $g^{-1}°C^{-1}$). The quantity of heat required to raise the temperature of 1 g of a substance by 1°C is called specific heat of the substance. Low specific heat means, for the same amount of heat supplied, the change in temperature is more.

69. In a refrigerator, the refrigerant (the liquid used for refrigeration) is in the liquid state and is evaporated suddenly. Because of this, there is a reduction in temperature and it is used to remove the temperature inside the refrigerator.

70. The size of the hole will increase, due to thermal expansion. When it is heated, the distance between any two molecules increases. Thus, the size of the hole increases.

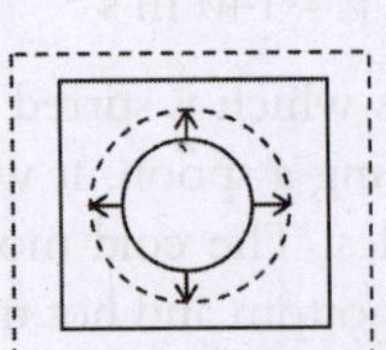

71. When the cap is heated, it expand more than bottle. Thus, we can easily unscrew the cap.

72. When an iron block is heated, the molecules try to move apart and the force of attraction between the molecules reduce. So, we can easily change dimensions of the iron block

73. On a winter day if we touch steel and wood, we feel that the steel is colder than wood because steel is a good conductor and wood is a bad conductor. Heat flows from our body to the steel surface is more or heat transfer rate is high. But the heat transfer rate from our body to wood is less, so, we feel that steel is colder than wood. When we touch steel and wood on a summer day, we feel that the steel is hotter than the wood due to the same reason. Here the rate of heat flow from steel to our body is more than the heat flow from wood to our body.

Level 3: Assess Your Concepts

74. Yes, it is possible to a raise the temperature of water by placing it in a paper container. The temperature required to burn the paper is more than 100°C. As the paper and the water is in thermal contact, the temperature of both water and the paper remains the same and the heat supplied to the paper container is also absorbed by the water present in it.

75. When heated the metal rings expand. But the thermal expansion of copper is more than the thermal expansion of iron. Thus, the iron ring breaks.

76. Given, Mass of water (m_1) = 20 g

Initial temperature of water (T_1) = 50 °C

Mass of water (m_2) = 10 g

Initial temperature of water (T_2) = 15 °C

Specific heat capacity of water = 1 cal $g^{-1}\ °C^{-1}$

Let T be the resultant temperature.

From principle of method of mixtures,

Heat energy given by 20 g of water = Heat energy taken by 10 g of water

$m_1\ s\ (T_1 - T) = m_2\ s\ (T - T_2)$

$20 \times 1 \times (50 - T) = 10 \times 1 \times (T - 15)$

$20\ (50 - T) = 10\ (T - 15)$

$1000 - 20\ T = 10\ T - 150$

$30\ T = 1150$

$T = 38.33\ °C$

77. The clinical thermometer is designed to measure the temperature of the human body only. The temperature of human body normally does not go below 35°C and above 42°C. It means that the range is from 35°C to 42°C. So, it is not used for measuring the temperature of any object other than human body.

Normal thermometer or laboratory thermometer is generally from –10°C to 110°C and value of each small division is 1°C. Thus, small variations in body temperature cannot be measured accurately by using a laboratory thermometer. So, we cannot use this thermometer to find out the temperature of the human body.

78. Heat lost = Heat gained

When 1 litre of water from A is mixed with 2 litres of water from B, then the equilibrium temperature attained is 16°C.

$Q = ms\Delta t$. Let t_A and t_B be the initial temperatures of water present in beaker A and B and let temperature of A be less than temperature of B.

$1 \times S \times (16 - t_A) = 2 \times S \times (t_B - 16)$

$(16 - t_A) = 2(t_B - 16)$

$2t_B + t_A = 48$ – (1)

When 2 litres of water from A is mixed with 2 litres of water from B, then the equilibrium temperature of the mixture is 14°C.

$2 \times S \times (14 - t_A) = 2 \times S \times (t_B - 14)$

$(14 - t_A) = (t_B - 14)$

$t_B + t_A = 28$ – (2)

$2t_B + t_A = 48$ – (1)

$2t_B + 2t_A = 56$ – (3)

(3) – (1) $\Rightarrow t_A = 8°C$

$(t_B) + (t_A) = 28$

$t_B = 28 - t_A = 28 - 8 = 20°C$

79. The beaker which is placed in front of a rotating fan will cool first. When the beaker is in water, the cold water absorbs heat. But when it is in front of a rotating fan, the heat transfer is due to forced convection of air.

Heat transfer rate is more in forced convection, so, the beaker placed in front of a rotating fan cools faster.

80. No, because of that the specific heat capacity is different for different materials, so the quantity of heat taken by the material is different for different materials for an equal rise in temperature.

81. By heating the test tube at its top, the wax present at top surface will only melt but the wax present at the bottom of the test tube in water does not melt as there is no transfer of heat in the downward direction by convection. So, the temperature of water at the bottom of the test tube remains constant and there is no change in the state of wax present at the bottom.

By heating the test tube at the middle, the wax at the top surface will melt but the wax present at the bottom surface remains same because heat convection takes place in upward direction only. By heating the test tube at bottom, both the wax present at top and bottom melt because heat gets transferred from bottom to top due to convection.

82. Hot water requires less amount of heat energy to convert into vapour when compared to cold water. The vapour formed above the fire will displace the oxygen and the oxygen supply to the fire. Thus, hot water is more effective than cold water to extinguish fire.

83. Initial length of meter scale is $L_1 = 15$ cm = 150 mm

Final length of meter scale after heating is, $L_2 = 15 + 1 = 16$ cm = 160 mm

In 15 cm length 150 divisions, each of 1 mm, are there and for 16 cm length also 150 divisions are available.

Therefore, the length of each division on the scale before heating is 150 mm /150 = 1.00 mm

Therefore, the length of each division on the scale after heating is 160 mm /150 = 1.06 mm

∴ Single division length on the scale after heating is 1.06 mm

Increase in the scale division due to expansion = 1.06 – 1 =0.06 mm

(3) − (1) ⇒ $t_A = 8°C$

(2) ⇒ $t_B + t_A = 28$

CHAPTER

4

Light

Remember

Before beginning this chapter, you should be able to:

- Familiarize with light, darkness and natural sources of light
- Describe human eye and functions

Key Ideas

After completing this chapter, you should be able to:

- Know luminous bodies, non-luminous bodies, homogeneous and heterogeneous bodies
- Understand rectilinear propagation of light: occurrence of eclipse, working of pin hole camera
- Learn about laws of reflection and their verification
- Use ray diagrams for images formed by plane mirror and spherical mirrors
- Understand dispersion of light and its application

Scientific Crypt

A Tribute to Sir Isaac Newton (1643–1727)

Who discovered the concept of universal law of gravitation and laws of motion? Who invented the first practical reflecting telescope? Who along with Gottfried Leibniz was responsible for the development of calculus? Who gave the generalized binomial theorem? Surely all of us must have got it right, it is none other than Sir Issac Newton. He was a mathematician, physicist and an astronomer. He was also an alchemist and theologian. His work "Mathematical Principles of Natural Philosophy", published in 1687, laid the foundation for most of the classical mechanics that we know today. In Physics, Newton contributed to classical mechanics, built the first practical reflecting telescope, formulated an empirical law to study the speed of sound. In mathematics, he was instrumental in the development of the concept of calculus and also contributed to the study of power series. The epitaph written by the English poet Alexander Pope is a true tribute to Newton's accomplishments, the epitaph reads: Nature and nature's laws lay hid in night; God said "Let Newton be" and all was light. While the humble Newton remarked "I do not know what I may appear to the world, but to myself I seem to have been only like a boy playing on the sea-shore, and diverting myself in now and then finding a smoother pebble or a prettier shell than ordinary, whilst the great ocean of truth lay all undiscovered before me".

FUN TIME

CROSSWORD

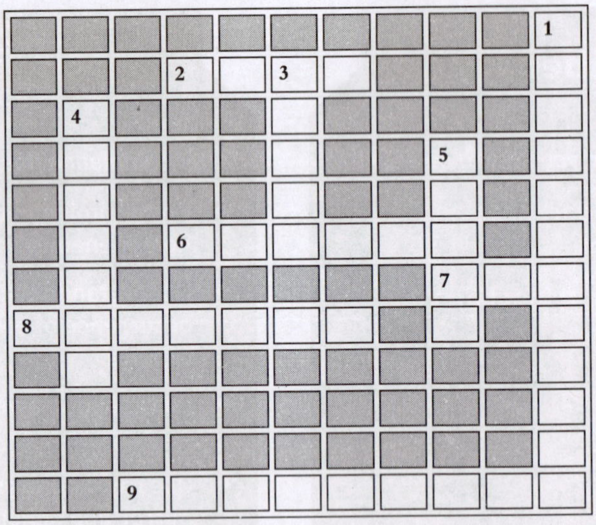

Across

2. A light ray passing along the principle axis will meet at this point on a concave mirror.
6. A mirror which can form diminished virtual image.
7. Minimum number of light rays required for drawing a ray diagram.
8. This is formed due to the dispersion of light.
9. The device used for tracing the enemy's position during wars.

Down

1. The multiple reflection of light is the principle used in the construction of this device.
3. The unit of luminous intensity.
4. This is the nature of image formed by a convex mirror.
5. The angle in degrees between two plane mirrors when 5 images are formed.

INTRODUCTION

Eyes are the most valuable sense organ. We wonder at the wonders created by nature and enjoy the beauty of nature man by viewing them through our eyes.

Light helps us to view the beautiful world. It is impossible to see the surroundings in the darkness. We are able to see an object when light that comes from the object enters our eye. Light can be understood as a form of energy that produces the sensation of vision. In day time, light given out by the sun falls on different objects and the reflected light from the object enters our eye and enables us to view the objects.

Let us understand this concept by considering some more examples. While playing cricket, how are we able to see the ball? How are we able to read this text? We are able to see the cricket ball or this text because light falling on both comes back and enters our eyes.

Can we say that all bodies that we are able to see emit light on their own? No, most of the objects which are seen do not emit light on their own.

A body that emits its own light is called luminous body and the bodies which do not emit light on their own are known as non-luminous bodies. Luminous bodies also mean self-luminous bodies. The sun and other stars are luminous bodies. Certain organisms, like glow-worm, firefly and some kinds of fish also emit light and the light given by them is called bioluminescence.

If non-luminous bodies do not emit light, then how do we see them? The light falling on a non-luminous body is sent in all directions because of different phenomena, like reflection of light or scattering of light. This reflected or scattered light from the non-luminous body helps us to view the body. We are able to see stars as they are luminous and we are able to see non-luminous bodies, like the moon and other planets when they reflect the light falling on them.

An object or a system of objects that gives out light is called source of light. The sun, a burning candle, a glowing electric bulb, all are examples of 'sources of light'. Some of these sources, like the sun, other stars, a glow-worm and certain types of fish are natural sources of light, while certain other sources of light, like an electric bulb, a lamp are called artificial sources of light as they are man made.

Can a body be luminous at some point of time and non-luminous at certain other time? A candle is non-luminous when it is not burning but becomes luminous when it is lit.

Medium

Matter of any type is normally called medium. When light falls on them, different media react differently. Any thing through which light energy can partially or wholly pass is called an optical medium.

Types of Media

An optical medium which has a uniform composition through out is called homogeneous medium. An optical medium which has different composition at different points is called heterogeneous medium.

Examples: Air, pure water, etc.

A medium that allows light to pass through is called transparent medium. Air, glass, pure water are some examples of transparent medium. The medium through which light rays cannot pass is called opaque medium.

Examples: Wood, metal, etc.

There are certain media, like fog, oil paper which allow light to partially pass through them, they are called translucent media.

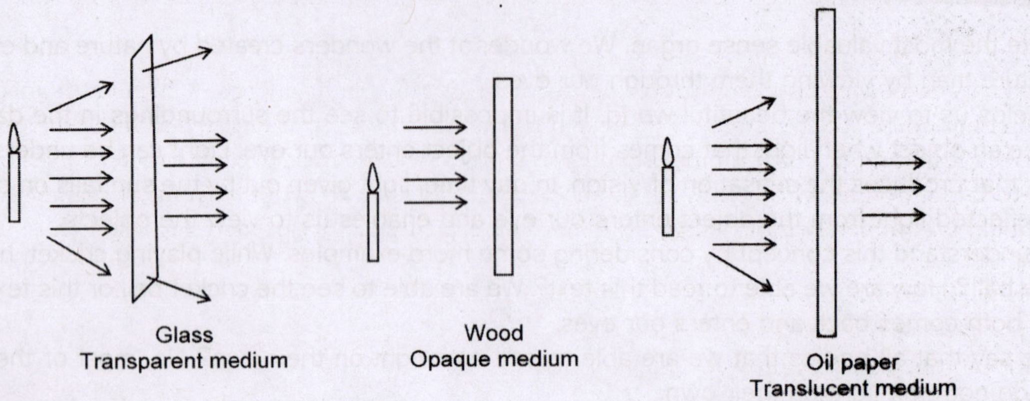

Figure 4.1 Different types of media on the basis of extent to which light is passed through

Source of Light

Depending on its size, a source of light can be a point source or an extended source.

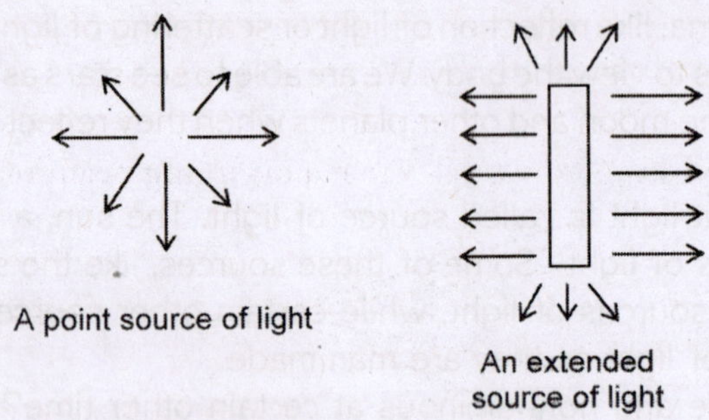

Figure 4.2 Sources of light

> **Info Bytes!**
>
> The sun, our primary natural source of light, emits an estimated 3.8 10^{26} watts of energy per second!

- **Point source of light:** A source of light that is of the size of pin head of a pin, is called point source of light.
- **Extended source of light:** A source of light which is bigger than the point source of light is called an extended source of light. (E.g., a glowing tube light, a burning candle, etc.)

Some sources of light emit light only when they are very hot and are called hot sources of light.

Examples: The sun, a candle, a filament bulb, etc.

Certain other sources of light emit light even when they are cool and they are called cold sources of light.

Examples: Glow-worm.

A particular source of light is either hot or cold depending on the method by which light is produced in it.

Hurricane Lamp

In olden days, people used oil lamps in which oil from seeds was used to light lamps. A more sophisticated oil lamp is Hurricane lamp.

This consists of a small kerosene tank at the bottom to which a burner is fixed. One end of a wick, which is passing through the burner, is put inside the kerosene in the tank. A glass chimney is provided to prevent wind from putting off the flame and also to distribute the light evenly in all directions.

When the wick is lit, kerosene flows up through the fine hole in the wick due to capillary action. The holes provided to the burner helps cool air to come in and the holes provided at the top helps the hot air to leave the lamp.

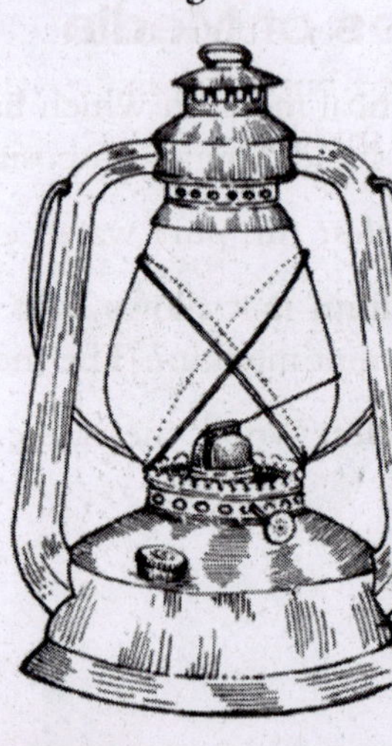

Figure 4.3 A Hurricane lamp

The Electric Bulb

The most widely used source of light is electric bulb, which was invented by Thomas Alva Edison. It converts electrical energy into light energy.

When electricity is allowed to pass through the filament, it emits light energy. A filament is made up of a substance having high melting point (like tungsten). The heated filament is the source of light, and if the melting point of filament's substance is low,it might melt. For this purpose, the two ends of the filament fixed to two terminals of the bulb which are attached to two copper wires whose ends are connected to a battery. To avoid burning of filament at high temperature, the air in the bulb is completely removed and is filled with a small quantity of inert gas, like helium and is sealed then.

Nature of Light

How to understand the nature of light? The best way is to observe different phenomena where light is involved and then try to understand, its nature by explaining the different phenomena. For a better understanding, we take the path along which light travels is a 'ray of light'. A line segment represents a light ray with an arrow indicating the direction of propagation of the light.

We call a group of adjacent light rays as a beam of light rays. If the light rays are parallel to each other, then it is called parallel beam of light rays.

In general, rays coming from a distant source are parallel rays. If all light rays appear to meet at a point, then they are called converging beam of light.

When the light rays appear to be coming out of a point, then we call them a diverging beam of light.

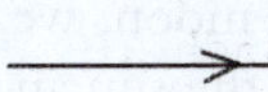

A light ray

Figure 4.4

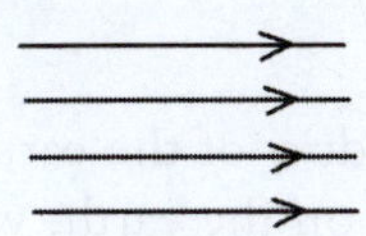

Parallel beam of light

Figure 4.5

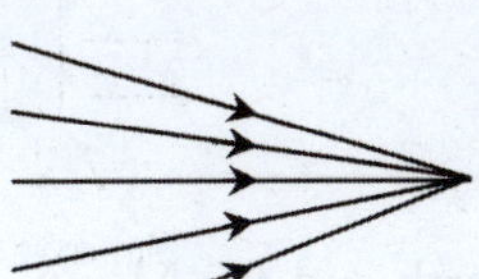

Convergent beam of light

Figure 4.6

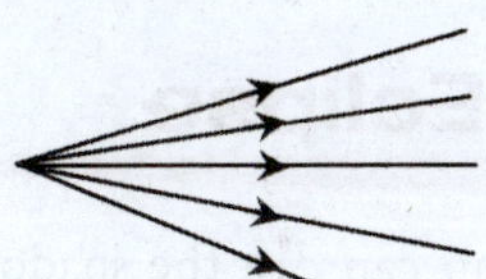

Divergent beam of light

Figure 4.7

Rectilinear Propagation of Light

Why have we represented a ray of light with a straight line? Why can't it be a curved line? This is because light travels in straight line. In a homogeneous medium, light travels along a straight line path and this is known as rectilinear propagation of light. This is because light always tries to travel between two points in the shortest possible time.

Let us verify this nature of light. Take three identical cardboards with holes at the centre. Place them on a table in such a way that all the holes are along a straight line. When a burning candle is placed on one side, it can be viewed from the other side. If the middle cardboard is moved side ways or disturbed, we will not be able to see the candle. This is because of the rectilinear propagation of light.

Konnect

We can see objects through a straight hollow tube. But when it is bent, we will not be able to view these objects. This is also because of the rectilinear propagation of light. Formation of shadows and occurrence of eclipse can be explained with the help of the rectilinear propagation of light.

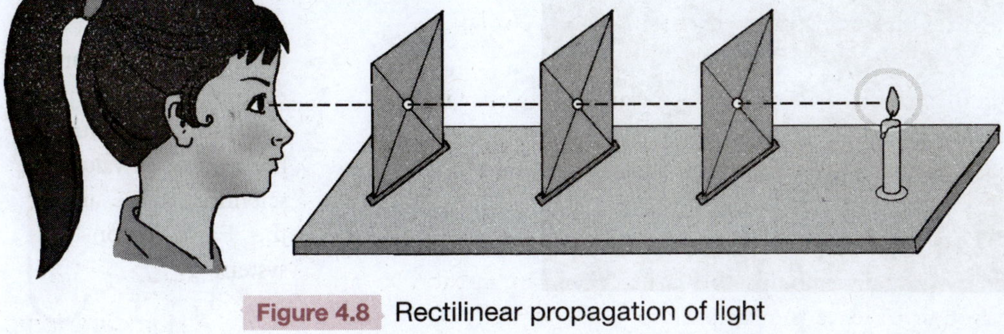

Figure 4.8 Rectilinear propagation of light

Speed of Light

When light travels in straight line path, with what speed does it travel? In fact light travels with great speed, it travels 3,00,000 kilometre in one second in air or vacuum. Its speed decreases when it enters another medium from air or vacuum.

Shadow

What is a shadow? How is it formed? Shadow is the dark region formed behind an opaque body when it is placed in the path of light. Shadows are formed due to the rectilinear propagation of light.

In the diagram, we can see the shadow (SH) of an opaque object (OJ) formed on a screen (AB) when it is placed in front of a point source '*P*'. Imagine what happens if the path of the light is not a straight line? What happens if we place an opaque object in front of an extended source of light?

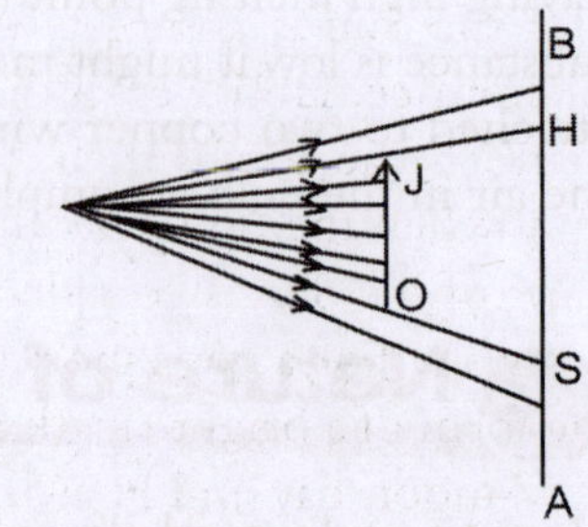

Figure 4.9 Formation of shadow

Now the shadow has two different regions, one is a complete dark region (SH) and two partial dark regions (HH^1 and SS^1). The complete dark region is called umbra and the partial dark region is called Penumbra.

Umbra and Penumbra are formed only when an opaque object is placed in front of an extended source of light. The size of the umbra and the penumbra depends on the size of the source, size of the object and the distance between the source and the object and also on the distance between the object and the screen.

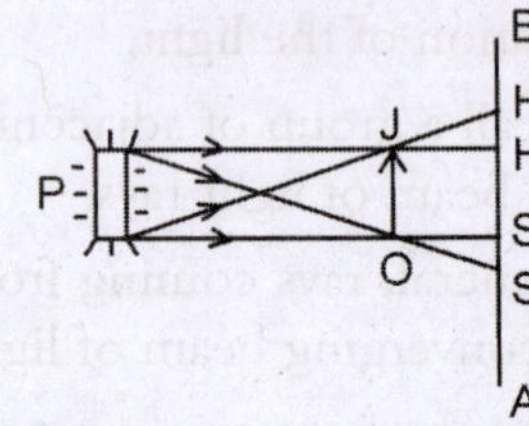

Figure 4.10 Formation of Umbra and Penumbra

Eclipse

The Sun can cast the shadow of the Earth and the Moon. When the shadow of the earth falls on the moon, we cannot see the moon and this is called lunar eclipse. If the shadow of moon falls on the earth, we cannot see the sun and this is called solar eclipse.

Lunar Eclipse

On a full moon night the Sun and the Moon are on the opposite sides of the Earth. In any full moon night, the Sun, the Moon and the Earth happen to come in a straight line, a part or whole of the Moon is not visible to us for some time from some parts of the Earth. Then we say that lunar eclipse has occurred. Lunar eclipse where the Moon is partially not visible because of the Earth's shadow, and this is called partial lunar eclipse. When the Moon is completely not visible from the Earth, we call it 'total lunar eclipse'. Lunar eclipse always occurs on a full moon night.

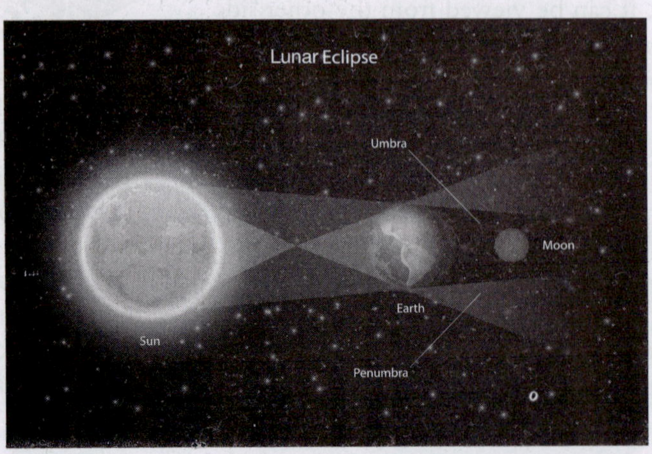

Info Bytes!

- A shadow is not an absence of light but actually a lesser concentration of light.
- Solar and lunar eclipses are not just beautiful to witness but also offer valuable scientific data about the Earth-Moon-Sun system.

Solar Eclipse

On a new moon day, the Moon lies in between the Earth and the Sun. During the course of their motion, if the Sun, the Moon and the Earth happen to fall in a straight line, then the shadow of the Moon falls on the Earth and causes solar eclipse. Solar eclipse occurs only on new moon days.

Info Bytes!

Solar eclipse should never be viewed directly with naked eyes. To view a solar eclipse partial or total, one must take precautions by using proper protective visual aids.

If the Sun is completely blocked by the Moon, then we say 'total solar eclipse' has taken place. However, if the Sun is partially visible and if some amount of light happens to reach the Earth, then 'partial solar eclipse' occurs. An 'annular solar eclipse' occurs only when the tip of the umbra of the Moon falls on the Earth. In such a situation, the view of the Sun is completely blocked by the Moon and only the outer rim of the Sun is visible. For a very short period, people of that region view the corona of the Sun in the form of a bright ring known as 'diamond ring'. Solar eclipse does not occur on every new-moon day and lunar eclipse does not occur on every full moon day. The plane of the Earth's orbit around the Sun and the plane of the Moon's orbit around the Earth are tilted with respect to each other. The centres of the Sun, the Earth and the Moon do not lie on a straight line on every new moon or full moon day.

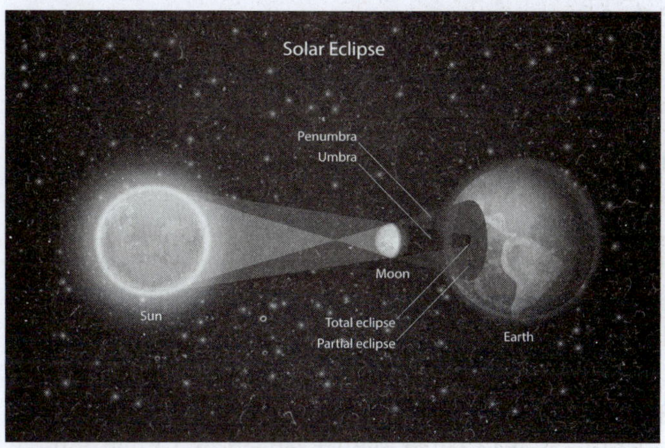

Pinhole Camera

This is a device which forms a photograph like image of a stationary bright object on a screen. This works on the principle of rectilinear propagation of light.

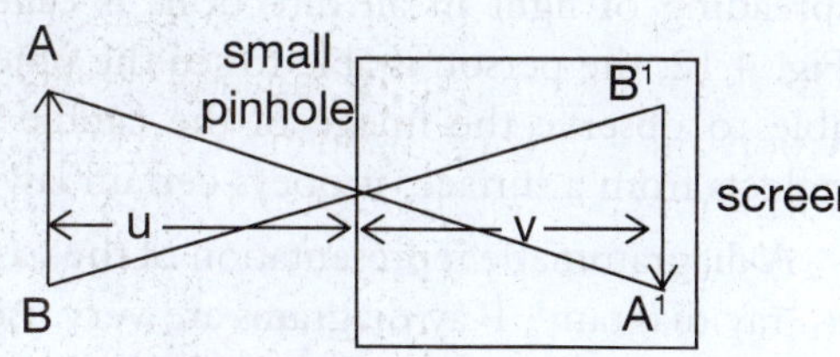

Figure 4.11 A pinhole camera

A pinhole camera consists of a cubical or cylindrical empty cardboard box with a fine hole on one side and with a paper or glass on the opposite side that acts as a screen. The box is blackened from inside so that any light which falls on its walls directly or indirectly is absorbed. When a stationary bright object (AB) is placed in front of a pinhole camera, an inverted impression (A^1B^1) can be seen on the screen. To take actual photograph, the pinhole camera is covered with thick black cloth and screen is replaced by a photographic film. The camera is faced towards the objects to be photographed and black cloth is removed only from the side of the pinhole. The film gets exposed to the light coming from the object through the pin hole. The film is developed and printed in studio. The size of the image formed by a pinhole camera depends on the distance of the object in front of the pinhole and the distance of the screen or film behind the pinhole. To compare the size of the image with the size of the object, we define magnification.

$$\text{Magnification } (m) = \frac{\text{size of image } (i)}{\text{size of object } (o)} = \frac{\text{distance of image } (v)}{\text{distance of object } (u)}$$

$$= \frac{\text{width of the pinhole camera}}{\text{object distance}}$$

EXAMPLE 4.1 A pencil of height 10 cm is placed at 3 cm distance from the pinhole camera. If the width of the camera is 5 cm, find the magnification and size of the image.

SOLUTION

Given that size of object, $o = 10$ cm

Distance of object, $u = 3$ cm

Distance of image, $v = 5$ cm

We know, $m = \frac{o}{i} = \frac{u}{v}$

$\therefore$ magnification $m = \frac{u \times v}{o} = 3 \times 5 = 15$

Given $m = \frac{o}{i}$; $i = o \times m$

$\therefore$ image size, $i = 10 \times 1.5 = 15$ cm

Info Bytes!

Normally we use 'u' to represent object distance and 'v' to represent image distance and both are measured from the optical instrument.

Reflection

In the Fig. 4.12, a lighted candle is placed in front of an object (OJ) and a screen (MN) is placed behind the object. What does a person looking at the object and screen observe? He can see a shadow of the object on the screen. Since the object spreads out all the light that falls on it, that object is visible to the person. What happens if the object has a polished surface like that of a mirror. The person observes the image of the candle also. This is because of a phenomenon known as reflection of light.

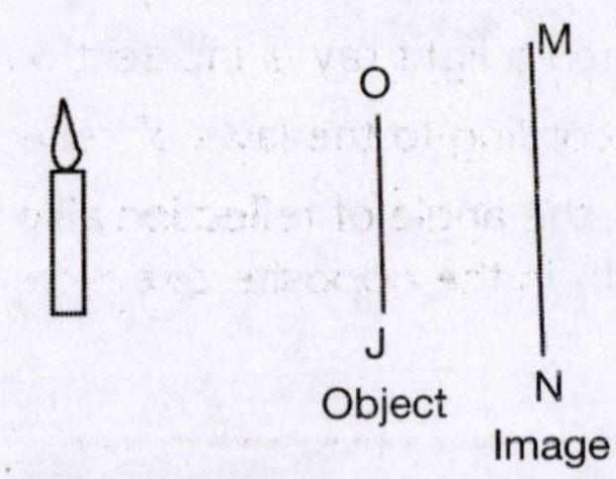

Figure 4.12 Formation of image of the object and candle

When light falls on a polished or smooth surface, it bounces back from the surface in a well defined direction. This phenomenon is called regular reflection. Other non-polished surfaces also reflect light. But it is in different directions. This type of spreading of light in all directions is called diffused reflection. That means in the Fig. 4.12, the person is able to see the object because of 'diffused reflection' and he is able to observe the image of the candle because of regular reflection. When light reflects from a surface, it obeys certain laws known as 'laws of reflection'.

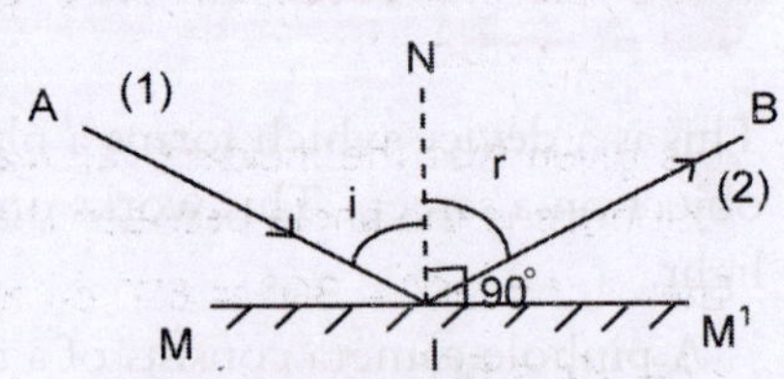

Figure 4.13 Reflection of light (Regular reflection)

A diagrammatic representation of the passage of light by treating it as a 'ray' is known as 'ray diagram'. Ray diagrams are very useful in understanding image formations.

The ray diagram in the Fig. 4.13, shows a light ray (1) incident on a mirror (MM^1) at a point (I) and reflected ray (2) into the same optical medium. A light ray from a source of light reaching a given reflecting surface is called incident ray (AI).

The point at which the incident ray strikes the reflecting surface is called 'point of incidence' (I). The light ray which bounces from the reflecting surface and travels in the same optical medium is called reflected ray (IB).

The perpendicular to the reflecting surface, drawn at the point of incidence is called normal at the point of incidence (IN). The angle between the normal and the incident ray is called angle of incidence ($\angle$AIN). The angle between the normal and reflected ray is called angle of reflection ($\angle$NIB).

Laws of Reflection

1. The incident ray, the normal at the point of incidence and the reflected ray all lie in the same plane.
2. The angle of reflection is equal to the angle of incidence, $\angle i = \angle r$.

Verification of Laws of Reflection

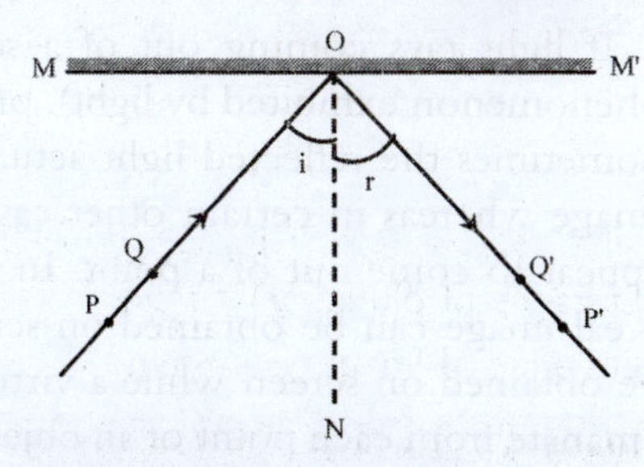

Figure 4.14 Verification of Laws of Reflection

1. Spread a white sheet of paper on a table.
2. Draw a straight line and fix a plane mirror (MM^1) vertically along this line.
3. Fix two pins, P and Q, in front of the mirror.
4. Looking from the position shown in the Fig. 4.14, fix two more pins P^1 and Q^1, such that these pins and images of P and Q are in the same straight line.
5. Remove the mirror and pins. Join QP and Q^1 P^1 and produce them to meet the mirror at point 'O' on the line.
6. Draw a perpendicular (ON) to the line at 'O'.
7. It is observed that QP, ON and P^1 Q^1 all lie in the same plane. Since QP and Q^1P^1 represent incident and reflected rays, we can conclude that incident ray, reflected ray and the normal at the point of incidence all lie in the same plane.
8. When $\angle QON$ and $\angle Q^1ON$ are measured, it is observed that they are equal. So, angle of incidence is equal to the angle of reflection.

EXAMPLE 4.2 What happens to a light ray that is incident on a plane mirror normally?

SOLUTION

When a light ray is incident on a plane mirror normally, the angle of incidence $\angle i = 0$.

According to the laws of reflection, $\angle i = \angle r$.

So, the angle of reflection also must be zero. The reflected ray must travel along the same path in the opposite direction.

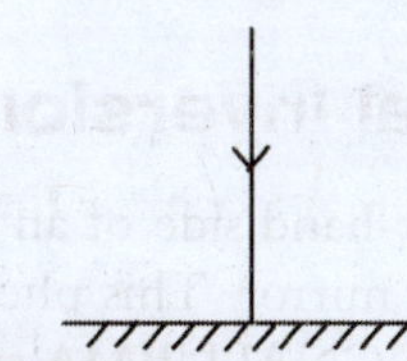

Figure 4.15 Light ray incident normally to plane mirror surface

EXAMPLE 4.3 If a light ray incident on a plane mirror makes an angle 30° with it, find the angle of incidence and angle of reflection.

SOLUTION

It is given that the incident ray makes an angle 30° with the mirror. But the angle of incidence is the angle between the incident ray and the normal.

Then, $\angle i = 90° - 30° = 60°$ on applying laws of reflection,

$\angle i = \angle r = 60°$.

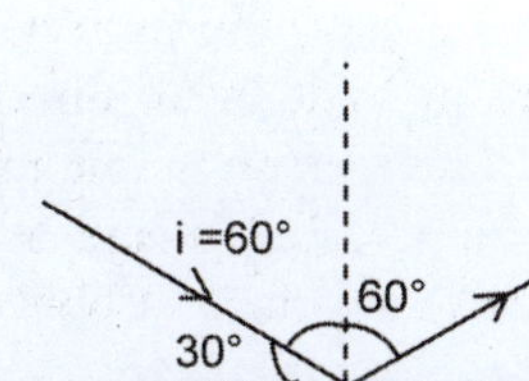

Figure 4.16 Light ray making angle 30° with plane mirror

Image Formed by a Plane Mirror

We can use ray diagrams to identify the position and nature of the image formed by a plane mirror. If a point source is placed in front of a mirror, light rays travel from the source in all direction. When any two light rays (OA and OB) are observed, we see that they form a divergent beam of light (AC and BD).

This divergent beam, appears to come from a point O' behind the mirror. In fact, this O' is the meeting point of two divergent rays AC and BD when they are extended in the backward direction as shown in the Fig. 4.17. This point O' represents the image of the point source O.

Likewise, we can get the image of an extended source of light with the help of ray diagrams.

If light rays coming out of a source, either after reflection or refraction (one more phenomenon exhibited by light), once again meet, then they form the image of the source. Sometimes the reflected light actually meet to form the image. Such image is called real image whereas in certain other cases, the reflected light rays form a diverging beam and appear to come out of a point. In such cases, the image formed is called a virtual image. Real image can be obtained on screen while a virtual image cannot be. Real image can be obtained on screen while a virtual image cannot be. It is to be noted that rays of light emanate from each point of an object in all directions. These rays when they strike a mirror get reflected in the manner described above and the mirror forms the image of each point of the object. Since for every point on the object there is a corresponding image point, we see the image of the whole object in the mirror.

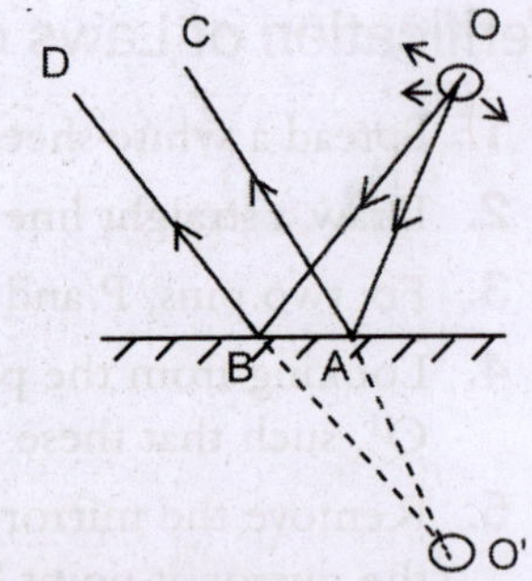

Figure 4.17 Formation of image of a point source

Characteristics of Image Formed by a Plane Mirror

1. Size of the image is the same as the size of the object.
2. The distance of the object in front of the mirror is equal to the distance of the image behind the mirror.
3. A virtual and erect image is formed.
4. The image formed by a mirror is laterally inverted.

Konnect

Your reflection in a plane mirror is actually a virtual image located as far behind the mirror as you are in front of it.

Lateral Inversion

The right-hand side of an object placed in front of a plane mirror appears as the left-hand side in the image formed by the plane mirror. This phenomenon is called lateral inversion. That is why the letters in AMBULANCE are written in inverted ECNALUBMA so that in the rear view mirror of car, one can read it correctly.

Figure 4.18 Lateral inversion

Activity

Take a piece of thermocol and cut it in the form of letter P as shown in the Fig. 4.18. Place this in front of a plane mirror and view by the image formed in the mirror. The image appears to be laterally inverted as shown in the Fig. 4.18.

Uses of Plane Mirrors

1. Plane mirrors are used as looking glasses.
2. Plane mirrors are used by opticians to maintain the standard distance of the chart required for testing eyesight.
3. Plane mirrors are used for providing false dimensions in some shops.

4. Plane mirrors are used in solar cookers as a reflectors of sunlight.
5. Plane mirrors are used in making kaleidoscopes and reflecting periscopes.

Mirrors Placed at an Angle

How many images are observed by two plane mirrors placed at an angle? Imagine yourself positioned between two mirrors placed parallel to each other. How many images are observed?

The number of images observed by two plane mirrors depend on the angle between them. If two plane mirrors are placed at an angle θ, then the number of images observed (n) is given by,

$$n = \frac{360^\circ}{\theta}; \text{ if } \frac{360^\circ}{\theta} \text{ is odd or } n = \frac{360^\circ}{\theta} - 1; \text{ if } \frac{360^\circ}{\theta} \text{ is even.}$$

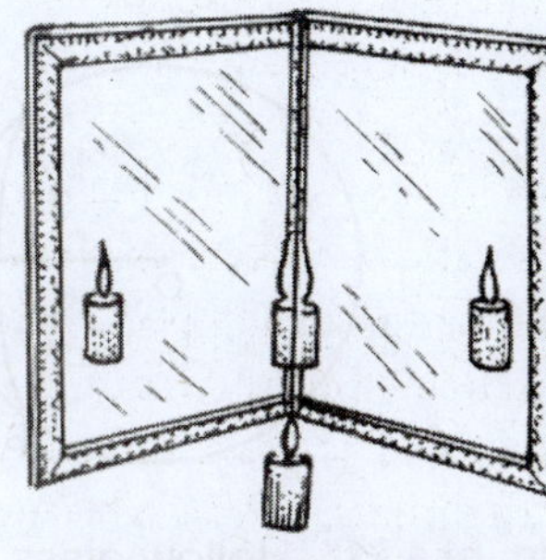

Figure 4.19 Mirrors placed at angle

It is to be noted that the number of images observed by two plane mirrors placed at an angle is always 'odd'.

This phenomenon is 'multiple reflection of light'.

Kaleidoscope

This works on the principle of multiple reflections in inclined plane mirrors. Three plane mirrors inclined at an angle of 60° to each other fixed inside a cylindrical box is called kaleidoscope. A few pieces of coloured glasses are placed inside the box and when viewed from the other end beautiful patterns could be seen due to the multiple images of glass pieces formed by the mirrors.

Periscope

Periscope is a device used to see objects, which are not in the direct line of sight. This is used by soldiers to see enemy's movements. A reflecting periscope consists of a tube bent twice at right angles. It is provided with two openings, and two plane mirrors are fixed at the bends of the tube such that they make an angle of 45° with the frame of the tube.

The rays of light from the object enter the periscope from the upper tube, get reflected twice and enters the eye of the person looking through the periscope. In certain periscopes instead of mirrors, prisms are used. These periscopes work on the principle of total internal reflection (which you will learn in higher classes).

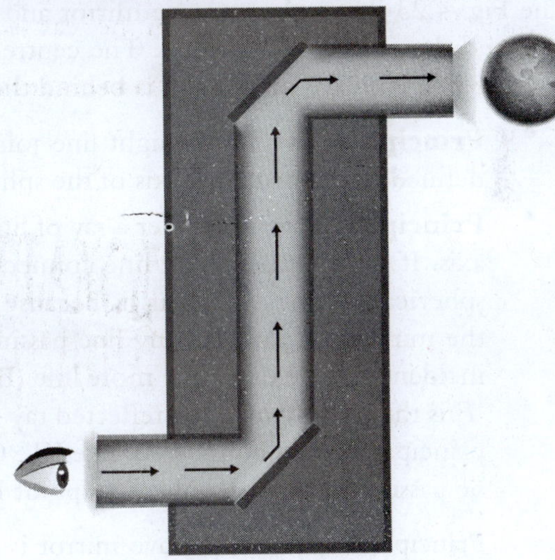

Figure 4.20 A periscope

Spherical Mirrors

A mirror need not always be plane, we have spherical mirrors also. Have you ever seen your image in a large spoon? You would have observed that the two sides of a spoon forms two different types of images and both are different from the image formed by a plane mirror.

Here we study the images formed by spherical mirrors.

Spherical mirror can be considered as a part of a sphere. Consider a hollow glass sphere and cut a piece of the sphere as shown in the Fig. 4.21. The inner face of the spherical mirror is called concave and the outer face is called convex.

If the convex surface is silvered and the inner surface is smooth and polished, then the mirror is 'concave mirror'. If the concave surface is silvered and convex surface is smooth and polished, then it is called convex mirror. Convex mirror is also called 'diverging mirror' whereas, concave mirror is called 'converging mirror'.

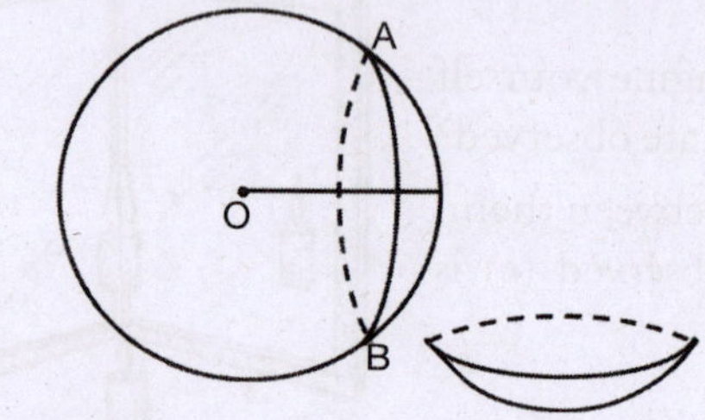

Figure 4.21 Hollow glass sphere and a section of it

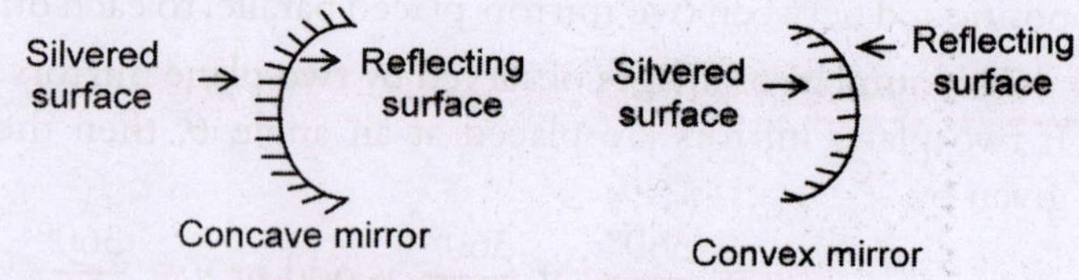

Figure 4.22 Spherical mirrors

To understand the formation of images by spherical mirrors, we must first be familiar with some terms used with spherical mirrors.

- **Pole (P):** The geometric centre of the mirror is called pole of the mirror.

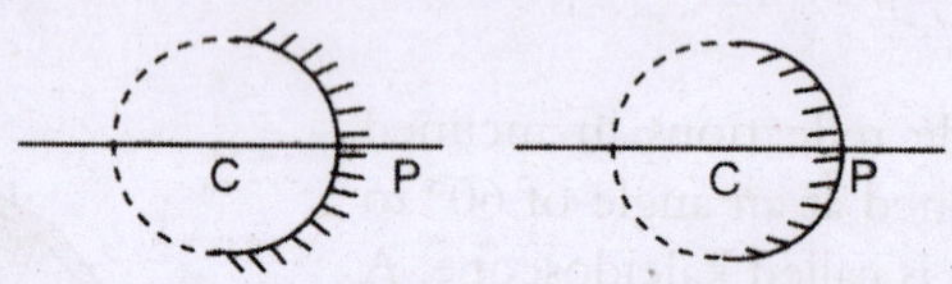

- **Centre of curvature (C) and radius of curvature (R):** The centre of the sphere of which the given spherical mirror is a part is called its centre of curvature. The radius of the sphere is called radius of curvature of the mirror.

The Fig. 4.23 shows the concave mirror and convex mirror with the positions of the pole and the centre of curvature. The centre of curvature is in front of the mirror in the case of a concave mirror and is behind the mirror in the case of a convex mirror.

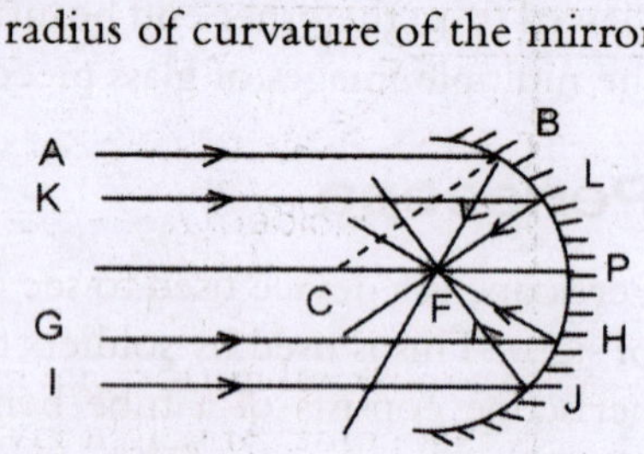

Figure 4.23 A concave mirror

- **Principal axis:** The straight line joining the pole and centre of curvature is defined as the principal axis of the spherical mirror.
- **Principal focus:** Consider a ray of light, AB, which is parallel to the principal axis. If we draw a straight line connecting B and C, this will be normal to the spherical mirror at B. This is because C is the centre of the sphere of which the mirror is a part and any line passing through 'C' will be a normal to the sphere. Now, $\angle ABC$ is the angle of incidence. If we draw one more line (BF) such that $\angle ABC = \angle CBF$, then that line represents a reflected ray of AB. '*F*' is the point where the reflected ray intersects the principal axis. If some more light rays which are parallel to the principal axis are considered, like KL, GH and IJ, after reflection from the concave mirror they are also observed to be passing through F only. This point F on the principal axis is defined as the principal focus.

  Principal focus of a concave mirror is defined as a point on the principal axis where a beam of light rays initially parallel to the principal axis meet after reflection from the concave mirror. We can find a similar point in the case of a convex mirror also.

  Principal focus of a convex mirror is defined as a point on the principal axis where a beam of light rays travelling parallel to the principal axis appears to diverge from it after reflection.

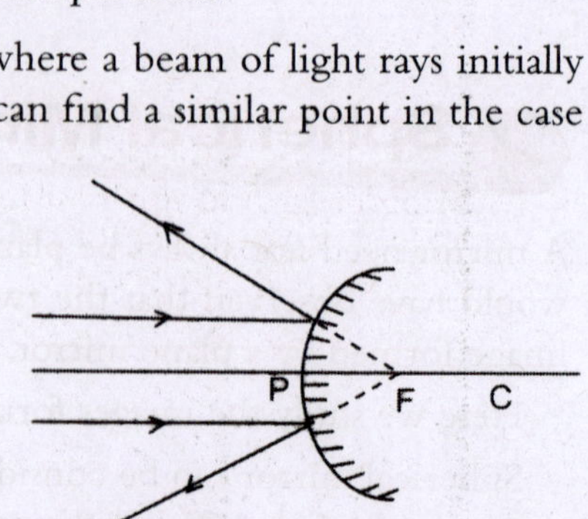

Figure 4.24 A convex mirror

- **Focal length:** The distance between pole and principal focus of a spherical mirror is called focal length. This is normally represented with a letter '*f*'.

  In general, focal length $= \dfrac{\text{radius of curvature}}{2}$

- **Aperture:** The diameter of the reflecting surface of spherical mirror is called its aperture.

EXAMPLE 4.4 A convex mirror has a radius of curvature of 40 cm. Find its focal length.

SOLUTION

$$\text{Focal length } f = \frac{\text{Radius of curvature}}{2} = \frac{40}{2}$$

$\therefore f = 20$ cm

Rules for Drawing Ray Diagrams

We can understand the formation of images with the help of ray diagrams.

1. From the definition of principal focus, if any ray of light, travelling parallel to the principal axis, after reflection either passes through or appears to diverge from the principal focus.
2. If any ray of light initially passes through (concave mirror) or appears to pass through (convex mirror) the principal focus of the spherical mirror, after reflection, travels parallel to principal axis.

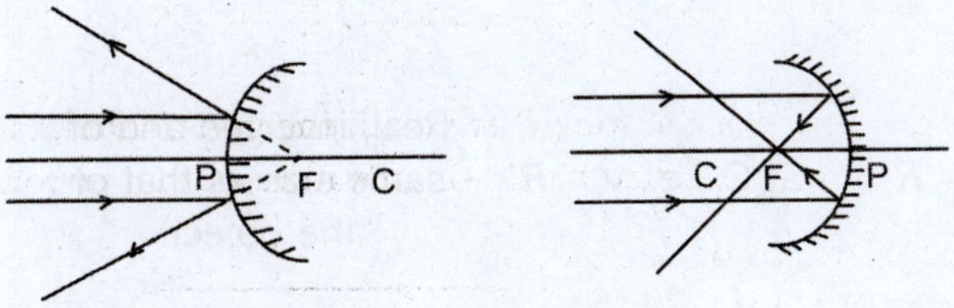

Figure 4.25 Incident ray is parallel to the principal axis

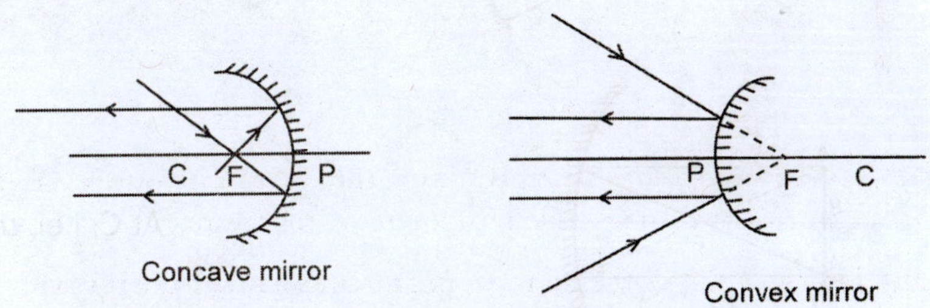

Figure 4.26 Incident ray passes through the principal focus

3. In a spherical mirror, any line that joins the centre of curvature C with a point on the mirror is normal to its surface at that point. Any light ray incident normally on a mirror gets reflected normally and retraces its path.

   As such, any light ray passing through the centre of curvature of the spherical mirror returns along the same path after reflection from the mirror.

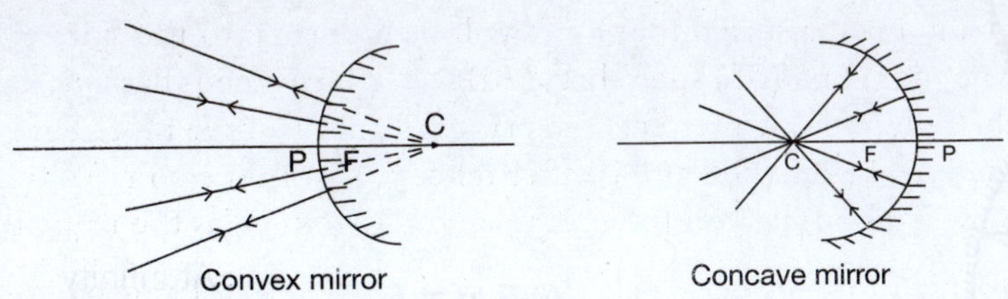

Figure 4.27 Incident ray passing through the centre of curvature

In order to find the position of the image of a point source formed by a spherical mirror, we use any two rules discussed above.

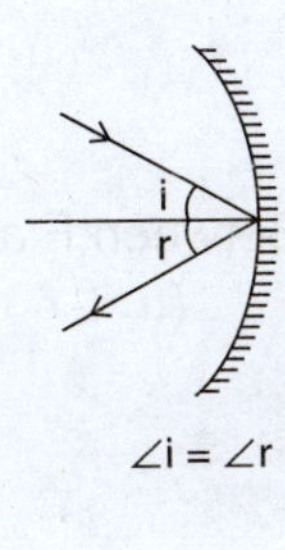

$\angle i = \angle r$

Formation of Images in Concave Mirror

Table 4.1 Nature of images Formed by Concave Mirror

Diagram	Object distance	Image distance	Nature of the image
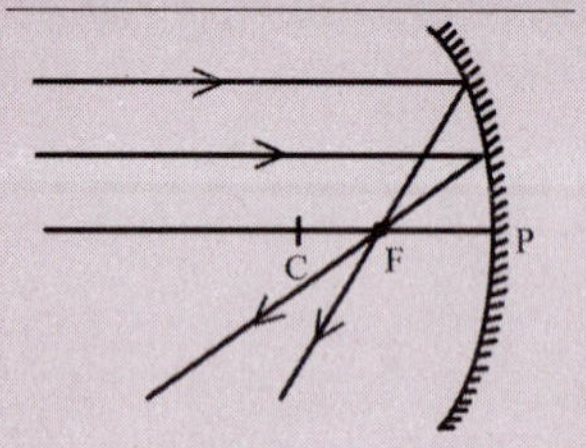	Infinity, i.e., $u = \infty$	Image distance = focal length, i.e., on principal focus	Real, inverted and highly diminished
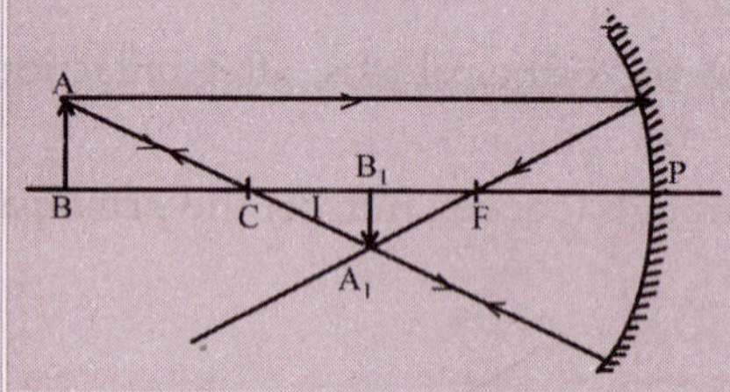	Beyond C but not at ∞ ($\infty > u > R$)	Image lies between F and C	Real, inverted and diminished
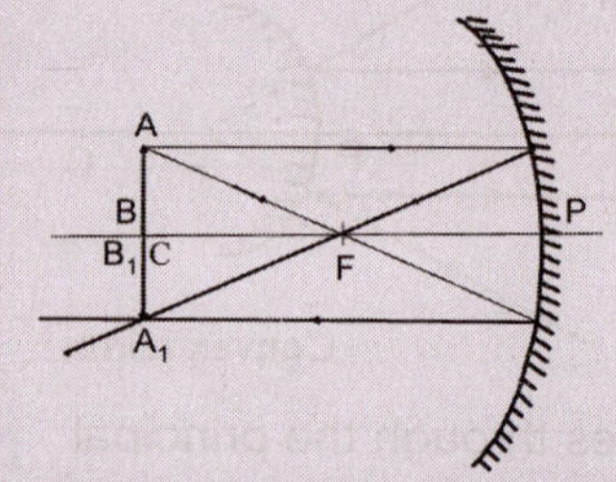	At C, i.e., $u = R$	at C, i.e., $v = R$	Real, inverted and of same size as that of the object.
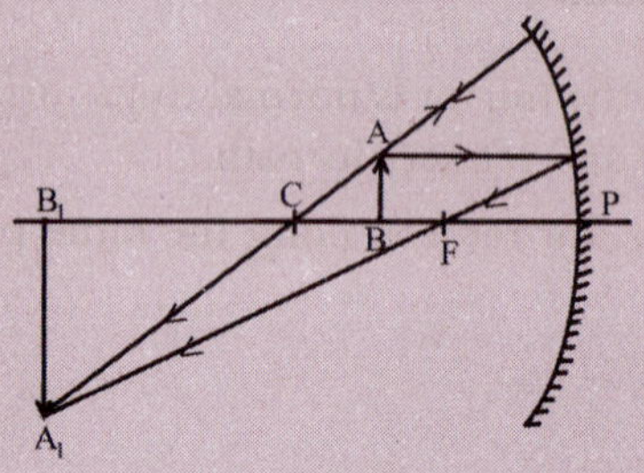	Between C and F ($R > u > f$)	Beyond C ($v > R$)	Real, inverted and magnified
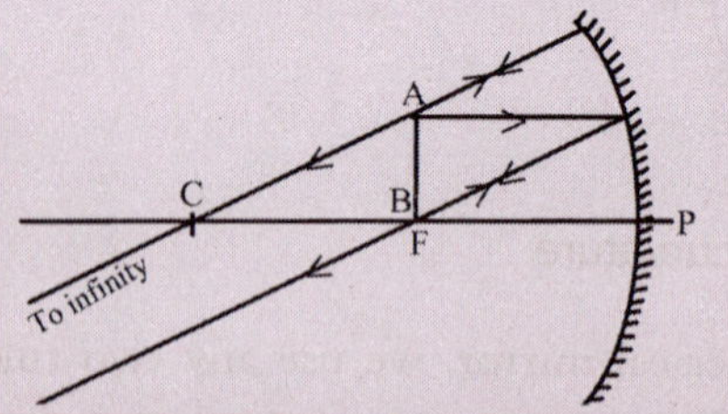	At F, $u = f$	At infinity ($v = \infty$)	Real, inverted and highly magnified
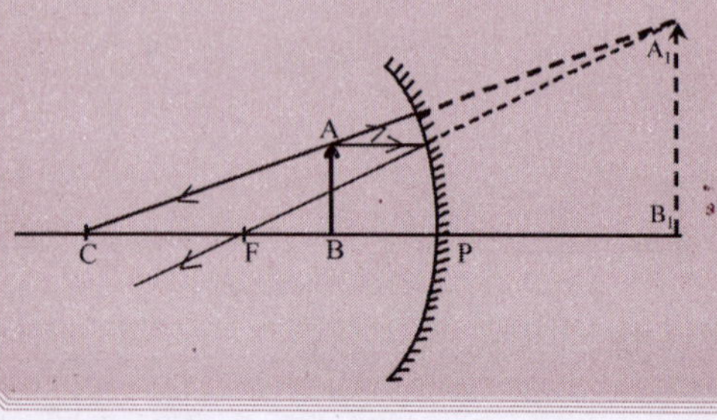	Between F and P ($u < f$)	Beyond the mirror	Virtual, erect and magnified and formed on the opposite side of the mirror as that of the object.

Uses of Concave Mirrors

1. Concave mirrors are used in torches and searchlights as reflectors to spread light over longer distances.
2. They are used by dentists to see the cavities of the teeth.
3. They are used as a shaving mirror.

Formation of Images by Convex Mirror

Table 4.2 Nature of Images Formed by Convex Mirror

Diagram	Object distance	Image distance	Nature of the image
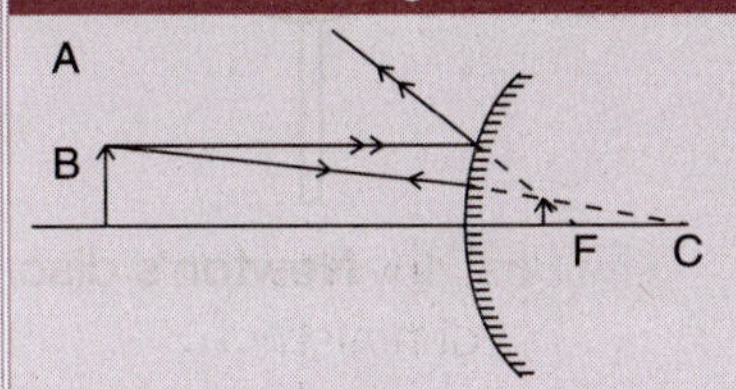	Infinity, i.e., $u = \infty$	At the principal focus.	Erect, virtual and diminished.
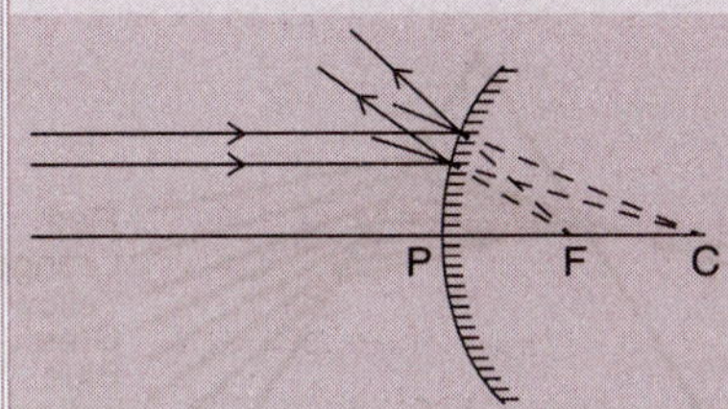	At any other position	Between the principal focus and the pole of the mirror	Smaller than compared to that of the object

When the object is at infinity, or it is nearer to the convex mirror, the nature of the image is almost similar. Wherever, the object is placed, the image formed by a convex mirror is always erect, virtual and diminished. The only difference is, when the object is at infinity, the image is highly diminished and formed at the principal focus. When the object is placed at any other position, the position of the image lies between the principal focus and the pole of the mirror as shown in the Fig. 4.28.

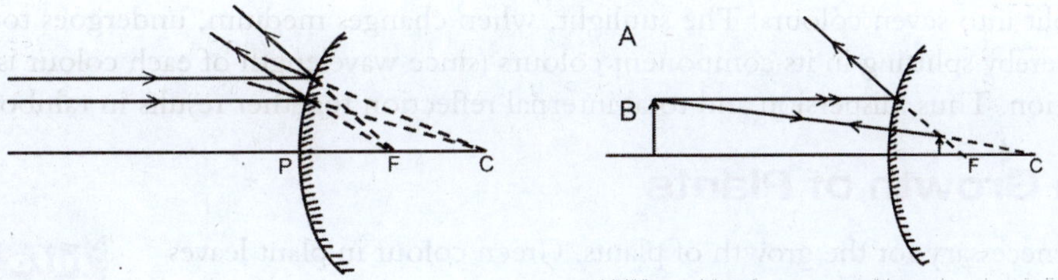

Object is at infinity

Object is at any other point other than infinity

Figure 4.28 Formation of images by convex mirror

Uses of Convex Mirrors

1. Convex mirrors are used as a side view mirrors in vehicles.
2. They are used as street light reflectors.

Important Points to Note About the Images Formed by a Spherical Mirror

1. Only concave mirror forms a real image.
2. Virtual images can be formed by all mirrors, i.e., plane, concave and convex. Plane mirrors always form a virtual image of the same size as that of the object. Virtual images formed by concave mirrors are always magnified. Convex mirrors always form a diminished virtual image.

3. A real image is inverted whereas a virtual image is always erect.
4. In the case of concave mirror, as the object is moved towards the mirror the real image formed moves away from the mirror. If the object is placed at C, then the object and the image sizes are the same.

Dispersion of Light

The world would not have been so beautiful without the colorful world. To understand about colours, let us do the following experiment. A circular cardboard with seven equal portions marked on it is to be taken. Colour those seven portions with violet, indigo, blue, green, yellow, orange and red. Make a small hole at the centre and fix this circular disc to a rod. When the disc is made to rotate with the help of the rod. In the beginning when the motion of disc is slow, we are able to distinguish all the seven colours separately. But when the disc reaches a certain speed, the disc appear to be white and we no longer see those seven colours separately. This experiment was first conducted by Sir Isaac Newton and the disc described above is known as Newton's disc.

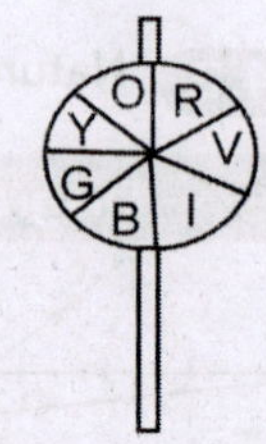

Figure 4.29 Newton's disc

A prism is a transparent material bounded by two triangular and three rectangular surfaces. When white light is allowed to pass through the prism, we can observe seven different colours on a screen placed on the other side of the prism.

From the experiment explained above, we come to know that seven different colours can be combined to form white light and white light can be split into seven different colours. This phenomenon of splitting of white light into seven different colours is known as dispersion of light. Have you ever wondered what a rainbow is and how it is formed? Rainbow is formed when white light passes through raindrops under certain conditions and split into seven colours. The sunlight, when changes medium, undergoes total internal reflection through these droplets thereby splitting in its component colours (since wavelength of each colour is different) and hence results in rainbow formation. Thus, dispersion and total internal reflection together results in rainbow formation.

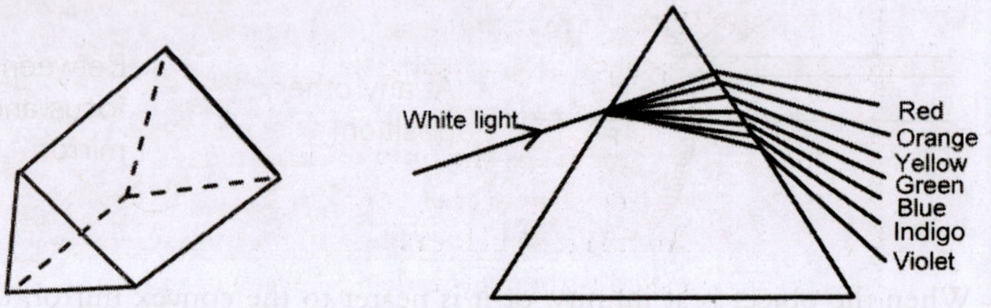

Figure 4.30 Dispersion of white light through prism

Role of Light in Growth of Plants

We all know that light is necessary for the growth of plants. Green colour in plant leaves is due to 'chlorophyll'. Chlorophyll helps to convert light energy into chemical energy. This process of conversion of light energy into chemical energy is called photosynthesis. During the process of photosynthesis the atmospheric CO_2 combines with water and is converts into glucose and releases oxygen. This chemical energy is stored in plants in the form of food.

> **Info Bytes!**
>
> Plants primarily use the blue and red wavelengths of light for photosynthesis.

Intensity of Light

We see objects of different brightness around us. The difference in the brightness of objects is due to the difference in the amount of light entering our eye or due to the difference in the intensity of light.

The intensity of light emitted by different sources is measured by comparing the amount of light emitted from a unit area in a given time of the source with that of a standard source. The luminous intensity of light emitted by a source is compared with that of a standard candle and is expressed in candle power. The SI unit of luminous intensity is candela. If the intensity of a source of light is 50 candle power, the intensity of the light emitted by it is 50 times brighter than that of the standard candle.

Lumen is a derived unit of candela and lux is a derived unit of lumen.

$$1 \text{ Lumen} = 12.56; \text{ candle power} = \frac{1}{683} \text{ watt.}$$

POINTS TO REMEMBER

- Light is a form of energy which causes the sensation of vision. Its speed in air is 3×10^8 m s^{-1}. The medium through which light passes is called an optical medium.
- Formation of shadows and eclipses are due to rectilinear propagation of light.
- Laws of reflection:
  (i) Angle of incidence = angle of reflection.
  (ii) The incident ray, the reflected ray and the normal at the point of incidence all lie in the same plane.
- An image which can be caught on a screen is called real image and an image which cannot be caught on a screen is called virtual image. The real images of all real objects are always inverted and virtual images are always erect.
- A plane mirror always forms a virtual and erect image. But, it laterally inverts the image of the object.
- For small aperture spherical mirrors:

  $$\text{Focal length} = \frac{\text{radius of curvature}}{2}$$

- The number of images 'n' observed by plane mirrors which are inclined at a certain angle 'θ' is given by,

  $$n = \frac{360°}{\theta} - 1, \text{ if } \frac{360°}{\theta} \text{ is even.}$$

  $$n = \frac{360°}{\theta} \text{ if } \frac{360°}{\theta} \text{ is odd.}$$

- A convex mirror always forms virtual, erect and a diminished image. This is used as a rear view mirror in vehicles.
- A concave mirror forms a virtual, magnified, erect image of an object, when it is placed very close to the pole of the mirror (i.e., at a distance less than the focal length of the mirror). And in all the remaining cases it forms a real, inverted image of the same size or different size when compared with the object depending on the position of the object in front of it.
- (i) Concave mirrors are used in torches, searching lights, as shaving mirrors and also used by dentists.
  (ii) Convex mirrors are used in street light reflector and also used as rear view mirrors.
- The phenomenon of splitting of white light into seven different colours is known as dispersion of light. Rainbow is formed due to the dispersion of light through raindrops.
- (i) The intensity of light produced by a source of light is compared with that of a standard candle and it is expressed in 'candle power'.
  (ii) The modern unit of intensity of light is lumen.
  1 lumen = 12.56 candle power.
  683 lumen = 1 watt.
- (i) The intensity of light at any place is measured in terms of lumen present on a unit area. This unit is called foot candle.
  (ii) Lux is the modern unit.
  1 foot candle = 10.76 lux.

PRACTICE QUESTIONS CLASSROOM WING

Very Short Answer Type Questions

***Directions for questions from 1 to 4:* Fill in the blanks.**

1. If a parallel beam of light ray is incident on a convex mirror. Then, after reflection the light rays appear to diverge from _________.
2. The image of an object formed by the inner surface of a spoon, when it is placed very close to it is _______ and _______.
3. The distance between the principal focus and centre of curvature of the convex mirror is equal to _______.
4. Two plane mirrors are inclined at an angle of 30°, the number of images observed are _________.

***Directions for questions from 5 to 42:* For each of the questions, four choices have been provided. Select the correct alternative.**

5. Which of the following is opaque?
   (a) Water (b) Glass
   (c) Mirror (d) Prism
6. When the Earth comes into the umbra and penumbra of the Moon, _______ is formed.
   (a) lunar eclipse (b) solar eclipse
   (c) partial lunar eclipse (d) None of the above.
7. A light ray is incident on a plane mirror placed in a horizontal plane, making an angle of 30° with the vertical, then the angle between the reflected ray and the normal is _________.
   (a) 35° (b) 60°
   (c) 90° (d) 30°
8. The direction of light can be changed by ________.
   (a) A plane mirror (b) A piece of paper
   (c) A stone (d) All of the above
9. The size of an image formed by a plane mirror is ______
   (a) Larger than the size of the object.
   (b) Smaller than the size of the object.
   (c) Equal to the size of the object.
   (d) Cannot be determined.
10. The image of an object formed on the outer surface of a spoon is always _______.
    (a) Erect (b) Virtual
    (c) Inverted (d) Both (a) and (b)
11. A magnified virtual image can be formed by a _______.
    (a) Plane mirror (b) Concave mirror
    (c) Convex mirror (d) All of the above
12. When a ray of light passes through a prism,
    (a) The deviation of red light is maximum.
    (b) The deviation of violet light is maximum.
    (c) The deviation of blue light is maximum.
    (d) All rays deviate equally.
13. Image formed by a convex mirror is ________.
    (a) Virtual
    (b) Erect
    (c) Smaller in size than the object
    (d) All of the above
14. The modern unit of intensity of light is ________.
    (a) Lumen (b) Candle power
    (c) Lux (d) All of the above
15. Read the following statements and choose the correct option.
    (A) Planets are not luminous bodies.
    (B) The sun is the nearest star to us from which the earth receives most of the light.
    (a) Only A is true
    (b) Only B is true
    (c) Both A and B are true
    (d) Both A and B are false
16. Which of the following is (are) natural source(s) of light?
    (a) Planets (b) Glow-worm
    (c) Stars (d) Both (b) and (c)
17. Read the following statements and choose the correct option.
    (A) Only a point source forms a complete umbra.

(B) An extended source of light forms both umbra and penumbra.

(a) Only A is true
(b) Only B is true
(c) Both A and B are true
(d) Both A and B are false

18. The line joining the centre of curvature and pole of the mirror is called _______.

(a) The principal axis
(b) *y*–axis
(c) The centre axis
(d) None of these

19. Which of the following is (are) converging mirror(s)?

(a) Convex mirror
(b) Concave mirror
(c) Plane mirror
(d) Both (a) and (b)

20. The image distance in case of a convex mirror can be

(a) Greater than focal length
(b) Less than focal length
(c) Equal to focal length
(d) Both (b) and (c)

21. According to the laws of reflection,

(a) The angle of incidence (*i*) = the angle of reflection (*r*).
(b) The incident ray, the reflected ray and the normal lie in the same plane.
(c) The incident ray and the reflected ray lie on either side of the normal.
(d) All of the above

22. One lumen = _______ candle power.

(a) 10.76
(b) 12.56
(c) 700
(d) None of these

23. An object is placed in front of a mirror. Arrange the following steps in sequential order to determine the nature of the mirror.

(A) Check whether the image formed is virtual or real.
(B) Check whether the virtual image formed is dimished, magnified or same size as that of the object.
(C) If the image formed is real, the mirror used is concave.
(D) If a magnified virtual image is formed, the mirror is concave; if a diminished virtual image is formed, the mirror is convex and if the size of the image is equal to the size of the object, plane mirror is used.

(a) ACBD
(b) BDCA
(c) ACDB
(d) BADC

24. Write the following steps in sequential order to verify the laws of reflection.

(A) Draw a normal at the point where the two lines PQ and $P_1 Q_1$ meet.
(B) Remove the pins and the mirror and join P, Q similarly join P_1,Q_1.
(C) View the image of P and Q and fix two more pins P_1 and Q_1 such that the images of pins P, Q and P_1, Q_1 are along the same line.
(D) Draw a straight line on a white paper spread on the table and fix a plane mirror on the line.
(E) Fix two pins P and Q in front of the mirror.
(F) Measure the angle of incidence and angle of reflection and compare them to verify the law reflection.

(a) DABECF
(b) ACDBFE
(c) DECBAF
(d) DBACEF

25. **Assertion (A):** A rainbow is formed when white light is incident on raindrops.

Reason (R): White light contains seven colours and it undergoes dispersion inside a raindrop.

(a) Both A and R are correct, and R is the correct explanation of A.
(b) Both A and R are correct, but R is not the correct explanation of A.
(c) A is correct but R is incorrect.
(d) Both A and R are incorrect.

26. Which of the following is an example(s) of heterogenous medium?

(a) Air
(b) Pure water
(c) Both (a) and (b)
(d) None of these

27. Read the following statements and choose the correct option.

(A) Planets are not luminous bodies.
(B) The sun is the nearest star to us from which the earth receives most of the light.

(a) Only A is true
(b) Only B is true
(c) Both A and B are true
(d) Both A and B are false

28. Which of the following is (are) natural source(s) of light?

(a) Planets
(b) Glow-worm
(c) Stars
(d) Both (b) and (c)

29. Which of the following is/are hot sources of light?

(a) Sun
(b) Candle
(c) Filament of a bulb
(d) All of these

30. A ray of light is incident on a plane mirror, making an angle 'q' with the surface of the mirror. Arrange the following steps in sequential order to calculate the angle between the incident light ray and the reflected light ray.

(A) Draw a normal line on the plane mirror at the point of incidence of the light ray.

(B) Note down the angle between the plane mirror and the incident light ray.

(C) The sum of the angle of incidence and the angle between the plane mirror and the incident ray is 90°. Determine the angle of incidence.

(D) From the laws of reflection, the angle of incidence is equal to the angle of reflection. Then the sum of the angle of incidence and the angle of reflection gives the angle between the incident light ray and the reflected light ray.

(a) DACB (b) CDAB
(c) BACD (d) DBAC

31. Write the following steps in sequential order to determine the nature of the image formed by a concave mirror when an object is placed between the pole and the principal focus of the mirror, with the help of a ray diagram.

(A) Draw two incident light rays, one parallel to the principal axis and the other coming from the centre of curvature and draw the paths of the reflected light rays.

(B) The reflected light rays are diverging. So, draw the extended lines till they intersect.

(C) Draw a concave mirror and mark the pole, the principal focus, the centre of curvature of the mirror.

(D) Mark the image at the point of intersection of the extended light rays and write the nature of the image.

(E) Draw the principal axis and mark the position of the object on the principal axis between the pole and the principal focus.

(a) CADBE (b) ECBAD
(c) CBAED (d) CEABD

32. The length of the straight line joining the centre of curvature and any point on the surface of a spherical mirror is the _____ of the mirror.

(a) Focal length (b) Principal axis
(c) Radius of curvature (d) Optic axis

33. When electricity is allowed to pass through the filament, it emits _________ energy.

(a) Light (b) Electric
(c) Chemical (d) Sound

34. The angle of deviation of a light ray reflected by a plane mirror is 150°. The angle of reflection is _____.

(a) 30° (b) 60°
(c) 15° (d) 10°

35. The number of images of an object placed between two plane mirrors placed parallel to each other is _____.

(a) Two (b) One
(c) Infinite (d) Cannot be determined

36. Choose the correct statement from the following.

(a) Light is the only form of energy which causes the sensation of vision.
(b) The sensation of heat is due to the presence of infrared radiation.
(c) Light travels in a straight line.
(d) All of the above

37. When the light rays appear to be coming out of a point, then we call them a _________ beam of light.

(a) Convergent (b) Divergent
(c) Parallel (d) None of these

38. Read the following statements and choose the correct option.

(A) Shadows are formed due to rectilinear propagation of light.

(B) When the position of the earth is between the sun and the moon, lunar eclipse is formed.

(a) Only A is true
(b) Only B is true
(c) Both A and B are true
(d) Both A and B are false

39. **Assertion (A):** A convex mirror always forms a diminished and virtual image.

Reason (R): The laws of reflection are not applicable in the case of spherical mirrors.

(a) Both A and R are correct and R is the correct explanation of A.
(b) Both A and R are correct but R is not the correct explanation of A.
(c) A is correct and R is incorrect.
(d) Both A and R are incorrect.

40. **Assertion (A):** Photosynthesis takes place only during the day.

Reason (R): Light energy is required for the process of photosynthesis.

(a) Both A and R are correct and R is the correct explanation of A.
(b) Both A and R are correct but R is not the correct explanation of A.

(c) A is correct and R is incorrect.
(d) Both A and R are incorrect.

41. **Assertion (A):** Convex mirrors are used as rear view mirrors in vehicles.
Reason (R): The field view of convex mirrors is maximum and they form diminished images.
(a) A and R are true and R is the correct explanation of A.
(b) A and R are true, but R is not the correct explanation of A.
(c) A is true but R is false.
(d) Both A and R are false.

42. **Assertion (A):** A rainbow is formed when white light is incident on raindrops.
Reason (R): White light contains seven colours and it undergoes dispersion inside a raindrop.
(a) A and R are true and R is the correct explanation of A.
(b) A and R are true, but R is not the correct explanation of A.
(c) A is true but R is false.
(d) Both A and R are false.

Directions for questions from 43 to 47: Match the entries given in Column A with the appropriate ones in Column B.

43.

Column A		Column B	
A.	Laterally inverted image	a.	Convex mirror
B.	Light rays emitted from a candle	b.	Parallel beam of light rays
C.	Concave mirror	c.	Convergent light rays
D.	Reflected light rays from a concave mirror, when the object is at the centre of curvature of the mirror	d.	Plane mirror
		e.	Inverted and real image
		f.	Divergent light rays

44.

Column A		Column B	
A.	When a light ray incidents normally on a plane mirror, the angle of deviation is	a.	New moon day
B.	Chlorophyll	b.	120°
C.	Solar eclipse	c.	Green colour
D.	Lunar eclipse	d.	180°
E.	When a light ray incidents with an angle of incidence as 30° on a plane mirror, the angle of deviation is	e.	Full moon night
		f.	White colour

45.

Column A		Column B	
A.	A plane mirror	a.	Luminous source
B.	Virtual image formed by a concave mirror	b.	Can be caught on a screen.
C.	Reflection of light	c.	Magnified
D.	The Sun	d.	Real
E.	Real image	e.	Vacuum
F.	Prism	f.	Image distance is equal to object distance.
G.	Image on the retina	g.	Dispersion
H.	Velocity of light is maximum	h.	Periscope

46.

Column A		Column B	
A	Shadow	a.	Glow worm
B.	Cold source of light	b.	Solar eclipse
C.	Magnification of the pin hole camera	c.	Erect, virtual and diminished
D.	Convex mirror	d.	$\frac{\text{Size of the image}}{\text{Size of the object}}$

47.

Column A		Column B	
A.	Intensity of light	a.	Plane mirror
B.	Rainbow	b.	Shadow
C.	Looking glass	c.	Hot source
D.	Eclipse	d.	Lumen
E.	Filament bulb	e.	Dispersion

***Directions for questions from 48 to 67:* Answer the following questions.**

48. Distinguish between luminous and non-luminous bodies.

49. Which among Moon, Sun, Fire Fly is/are natural source(s) of light?

50. What are point source and extended source of light?

51. What is rectilinear propagation of light?

52. What is a lunar eclipse?

53. What is reflection?

54. What is a real image?

55. Write the mathematical expression to calculate the number of image observed by two plane mirrors placed at an angle 'θ'.

56. Define centre of curvature.

57. How many colours does white light consist of and what are they?

58. What are hot and cold sources of light?

59. An opaque object is moved away from a point source of light and the screen. Then, what happens the size of the umbra?

60. An opaque object is placed between a point source of light and the screen. If the point source of light moves towards the opaque object, then what happens to the size of the umbra?

61. What is diffused reflection?

62. What is a virtual image?

63. An object is placed between two plane mirrors which are inclined to each other at 30°. What is the number of images formed by the two mirrors?

64. A light ray is made to incident on a wooden surface as shown in the below figure. What is the angle of deviation?

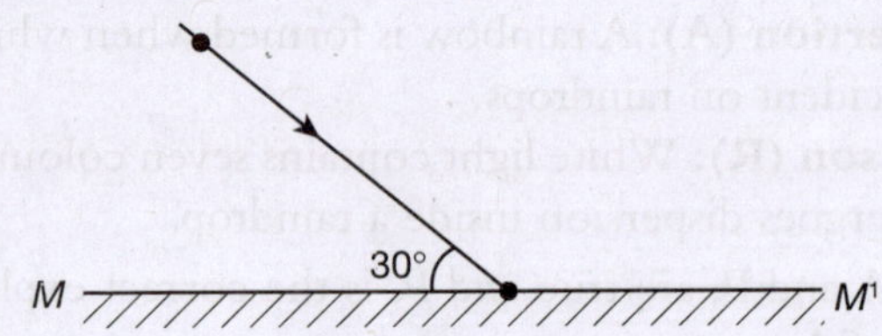

65. Write the relationship between focal length and radius of curvature.

66. A light is made to incident on a reflecting surface as shown in the below figure. What is the angle of deviation?

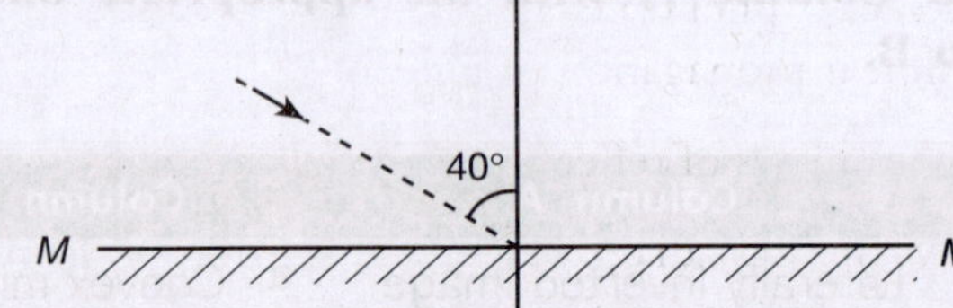

67. What is the distance between the pole and the centre of curvature of a concave mirror of focal length 'f' and radius of curvature R?

Short Answer Type Questions

68. Define transparent, translucent and opaque optical media with examples.

69. Describe pinhole camera. Write an expression for the magnification of image formed by a pinhole camera.

70. (a) What are the characteristics of an image formed by a plane mirror?

(b) Write few uses of plane mirror.

71. A light ray from an object 'O' is reflected from a mirror as shown in the below figure. What is the angle of deviation?

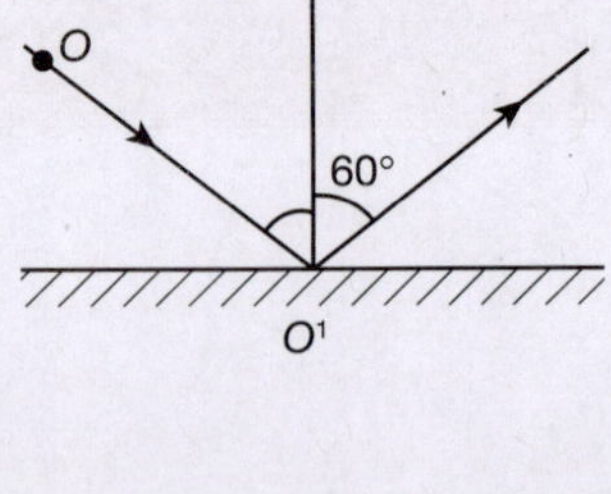

72. What are the three rays we consider to draw ray diagrams in order to show the formation of images by spherical mirrors? How do they propagate after reflection?

73. Explain how an opaque paper can be made translucent.

74. Describe ray of light, beam of light, parallel beam of light, converging beam of light and diverging beam of light.

75. (a) Sate laws of reflection.

(b) Draw a ray diagram to represent formation of an image of a point source by a plane mirror.

76. Determine the radius of curvature of a convex mirror shown below.

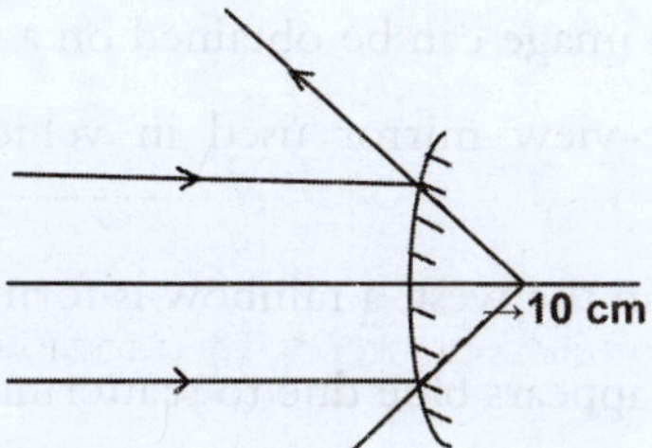

77. Which property of light is involved in the formation of shadow? Explain in which case you will not get penumbra at all.

78. Why is the light from the moon called cool light and the light from the sun called hot light?

79. During lightning and thundering, why is the lightning seen first and then the thunder heard? Explain.

80. (i) Distinguish between concave and convex mirrors.

(ii) Write few uses of spherical mirror.

81. What are cold and hot sources of light? Give examples for each.

82. Explain how light helps in the growth of plants.

Essay Type Questions

83. Write two phenomena which can be understood by rectilinear propagation of light.

84. How can laws of reflection be experimentally verified?

85. Draw the ray diagrams to represent the formation of image when object is at infinity and any distance between infinity and pole of a convex mirror.

86. Describe few sources of light briefly.

87. Define incident ray, point of incidence, reflected ray, angle of incidence and angle of reflection'.

88. Describe the working of a 'kaleidoscope' and a 'periscope'.

89. Explain the formation of images by a concave mirror with the help of a ray diagram.

PRACTICE QUESTIONS COMPETITION WING

Level 1: Apply your Concepts

***Directions for questions from 1 to 15:* Fill in the blanks.**

1. The line joining the pole of the concave mirror and centre of curvature is called _____

2. When the Moon comes into the umbra and penumbra of the Earth, __________ is formed.

3. The phenomenon of light involved in the formation of shadow is __________.

4. Periscope works on the principle of ________ of light.

5. The image formed by a plane mirror is _______ in nature.

6. Oil paper is an example of _______ medium of light.

7. An electric bulb converts ________ energy to ________ energy.

8. Real images are formed by _________ beam of light.

9. Virtual images are formed by _________ beam of light.

10. ________ helps to convert light energy into chemical energy.

11. When the Moon is not completely visible from the Earth, we call it ________ eclipse.

12. A concave mirror is formed from a sphere of radius 20 cm. The image of an object at an infinite distance is formed at a distance of ________ cm from the mirror.

13. The light rays incident on a convex mirror are directed towards the principal focus. Then, the reflected light rays are parallel to __________.

14. A point object is placed between two parallel plane mirrors. Then, the number of images formed by the two mirrors is ________.

15. A light ray from an object 'O', reflected from a mirror is as shown in the below figure. Then, the angle of incidence is equal to _____.

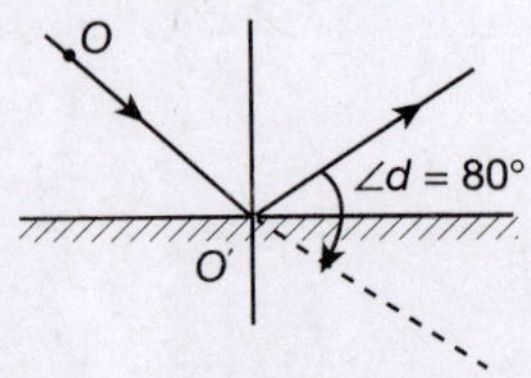

***Directions for questions from 16 to 23:* State whether the following statements are true or false.**

16. Pure water is a transparent medium.

17. Eclipses are formed due to rectilinear propagation of light.

18. The path of light is straight line.

19. Sunlight is not necessary for the growth of plants.

20. A virtual image can be obtained on a screen.

21. The rare-view mirror used in vehicles is a convex mirror.

22. If sun is in the west, a rainbow is formed in the east.

23. The sky appears blue due to scattering of light.

***Directions for questions from 24 to 54:* For each of the questions, four choices have been provided. Select the correct alternative.**

24. The difference in the brightness of objects is due to difference in the __________ of light entering into our eyes.

(a) Intensity (b) Colour of light
(c) Speed (d) None of these

25. The image of an object placed in front of a concave mirror found to coincide with object itself. The position of the object is __________.

(a) At C
(b) Between C and F
(c) Between F and pole
(d) At F

26. The image of an object is formed at infinite distance from a concave mirror. The position of the object is __________.

(a) At C (b) Between C and F
(c) At F (d) Between pole and F

27. A magnified image can be formed by __________ mirror.

(a) Concave (b) Plane
(c) Convex (d) Centre of curvature

28. Geometric centre of a mirror is called _______.
(a) Pole (b) Principal focus
(c) Optic centre (d) Centre of curvature

29. An incident ray passes through the centre of curvature of a concave mirror. After reflection the ray _______.
(a) Passes through the principal focus
(b) Retraces its path
(c) Passes along the principal focus
(d) None of these

30. The phenomenon of light which is responsible for vision is _______.
(a) Refraction (b) Irregular reflection
(c) Dispersion (d) Both (b) and (c)

31. Which of the following is (are) true in the case of a plane mirror?
(a) Object distance = image distance.
(b) Object size = image size.
(c) The image formed is virtual.
(d) All of the above

32. Two plane mirrors are arranged such that their reflecting surfaces are parallel and face each other. When an object is placed between them, the number of images formed are _______.
(a) 2 (b) Infinite
(c) 3 (d) 4

33. The intensity of light _______, when the distance from the source increases.
(a) Increases
(b) Decreases
(c) First increases and then decreases
(d) Remains same

34. The image formed by a plane mirror is _______.
(a) Virtual (b) Real
(c) Inverted (d) Highly magnified

35. Read the following statements and choose the correct option.
(A) Moon is a luminous source of light.
(B) A glow-worm is a natural source of light.
(a) Only A is true
(b) Only B is true
(c) Both A and B are true
(d) Both A and B are false

36. Which of the following is (are) man-made sources of light?
(a) Incandescent lamp
(b) Fluorescent lamp
(c) Hurricane lamp
(d) All of the above

37. Read the following statements and choose the correct option.
(A) Shadows are formed due to rectilinear propagation of light.
(B) When the position of the earth is between sun and moon, lunar eclipse is formed.
(a) Only A is true
(b) Only B is true
(c) Both A and B are true
(d) Both A and B are false

38. The image formed by a pinhole camera is _______.
(a) Real
(b) Inverted
(c) The nature of image depends on the shape of pinhole
(d) Both (a) and (b)

39. The length of the straight line joining the centre of curvature and any point on the surface of a spherical mirror is the _______ of the mirror.
(a) Focal length
(b) Principal axis
(c) Radius of curvature
(d) Optic axis

40. The image formed by a concave mirror can be _______.
(a) Real
(b) Virtual
(c) Magnified
(d) All of the above

41. A light ray which is incident along the principal axis of a mirror after reflection _______.
(a) Retraces its path
(b) Passes through centre of curvature
(c) Makes zero angle with the normal
(d) All the above

42. The rear view mirrors used in vehicles are _______.
(a) Plane (b) Concave
(c) Convex (d) None of the above

43. Choose the correct statement from the following.
(a) Light causes sensation of vision.
(b) The sensation of heat is due to the presence of infrared radiation.
(c) Light travels in a straight line.
(d) All the above

44. One foot candle = _____ lux.
(a) 12.56 (b) 10.76
(c) 700 (d) None of these

45. A student focused a distant object on a spherical mirror and found the distance between the mirror and the screen to be 40 cm. Write the following steps in a sequential order to find the radius of curvature of the spherical mirror.
(A) The focal length (f) of the mirror is equal to the distance between the mirror and the screen.
(B) Note the distance between the mirror and the screen from the given data.
(C) The radius of curvature of the spherical mirror, $R = 2f$.
(D) Substitute the value of 'f' and obtain R.
(a) BACD (b) ACBD
(c) ABCD (d) DBCA

46. Write the following steps in sequential order to determine the radius of curvature of a given concave mirror.
(A) The radius of the curvature of a concave mirror is equal to twice its focal length.
(B) Take a concave mirror and mount it on a stand.
(C) Take a screen and adjust it before the mirror to catch the inverted, real and diminished image of the object.
(D) Focus the mirror on a distant object like a tree or a building.
(E) The distance between the mirror and the screen is equal to the focal length of the mirror.
(a) BACED (b) BDCEA
(c) ABCDE (d) ACBDE

47. The light rays from a point object placed at the focus of a concave mirror, after reflection
(a) Emerge perpendicular to the principal axis.
(b) Emerge parallel to the principal axis.
(c) Form real image.
(d) Both (b) and (c)

48. An object is placed between two mirrors which make an angle of 45° with each other, then the number of images observed are _____.
(a) 8 (b) 7
(c) 2 (d) Infinite

49. A light ray from an object 'P' is reflected from a mirror as shown in the figure, then

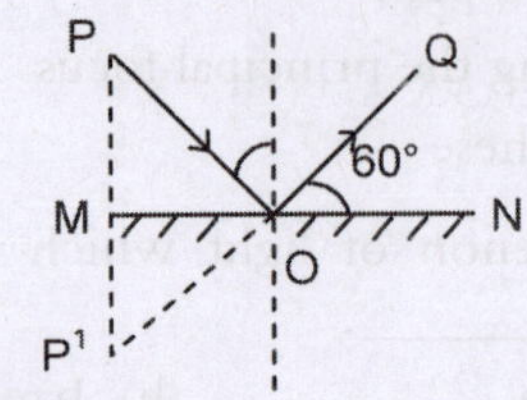

(a) Angle of incidence is 30°
(b) $PM = MP^1$
(c) $\angle PON = 120°$
(d) All of the above

50. Choose the correct statement(s) from the following.
(a) In a glow-worm the energy produced during a chemical reaction in its body is released in the form of light only.
(b) An electric bulb glows, when the filament attains very high temperature due to the passage of current.
(c) Due to the powerful reactions taking place in the sun, the energy produced by the sun consists of light and heat.
(d) All of the above

51. The number of images of an object placed between two plane parallel mirrors is ____.
(a) Two
(b) One
(c) Infinite
(d) Cannot be determined

52. The image distance of an object which is placed at an infinite distance is equal to
(a) The radius of curvature of the spherical mirror.
(b) The focal length of the spherical mirror.
(c) Infinity, in case of plane mirror.
(d) Both (b) and (c)

53. **Assertion (A):** A convex mirror always forms a diminished and virtual image.
Reason (R): The laws of reflection are not applicable in the case of spherical mirrors.
(a) A and R are true and R is the correct explanation of A.

(b) A and R are true, but R is not the correct explanation of A.
(c) A is true but R is false.
(d) Both A and R are false.

54. Assertion (A): Photosynthesis takes place only during the day.
Reason (R): Light energy is required for the process of photosynthesis.
(a) A and R are true and R is the correct explanation of A.
(b) A and R are true, but R is not the correct explanation of A.
(c) A is true but R is false.
(d) Both A and R are false.

Directions for questions from 55 to 57: **Match the entries given in Column A with the appropriate ones in Column B.**

55.

Column A	Column B
A Convex mirror	a. Dispersion of light
B. Concave mirror	b. Dentists
C. Plane mirror	c. Kaleidoscope
D. Prism	d. Street light reflectors

56.

Column A	Column B
A When a light incident normally on a reflecting surface, the angle of reflection is	a. Dispersion of light
B. Rectilinear propagation of light	b. 0°
C. Prism	c. Lunar eclipse
D. Non-luminous body	d. A burning candle
	e. Moon

57.

Column A	Column B
A. Pinhole camera	a. Extended source
B. Kaleidoscope	b. Multiple reflection
C. Distance from pole to the centre of a mirror	c. Rectilinear propagation
D. Distance from the pole of the mirror to the principal focus.	d. Focal length
E. Tube light	e. Radius of curvature.

Level 2: Review your Concepts

58. *A*, *B*, *C* and *D* are four transparent sheets of equal thickness and made of material of refractive indices μ_A, μ_B, μ_C, and μ_D. If a light ray propagates through them as shown in the figure, compare their refractive indices and find if any of them have the same refractive index.

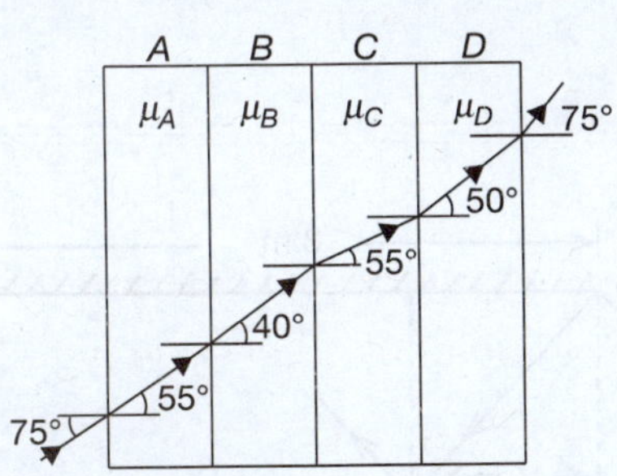

59. Why does not an aeroplane or a bird cast a shadow when they are at greater heights?

60. Why cannot a mirror whose surface is rough produce a clear image?

61. A clever student has used the concept of formation of shadow to determine the height of a long pole (OA). There was an electric bulb at the top of the vertical pole. The student placed an object of length 1 m at a height of 2 m from the ground as shown in the figure. The size of the shadow formed on the ground is 2 m. Determine the length of the pole.

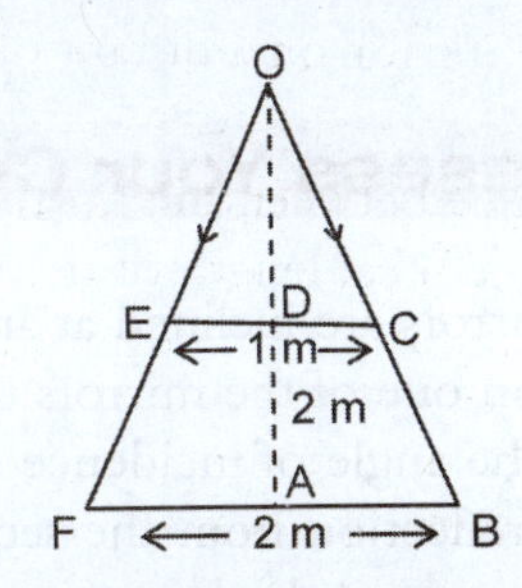

[**Hint:** In triangle OAB and ΔODC

$$\frac{OA}{OD} = \frac{AB}{DC},\ DC = \frac{1}{2}\ EC \text{ and } AB = \frac{1}{2}\ FB]$$

62. When the object is displaced towards a spherical mirror, then what are the changes that occur in the formed image?

63. A pinhole camera of width 1 m is focussed to an object at a distance 30 m from it. If the height of the object is 3 m, what is the height of the image?

64. Jim determined the number of images formed by two plane mirrors inclined at certain angle from a ray diagram shown below. Can you determine the number of images formed by two plane mirrors in the arrangement shown below?

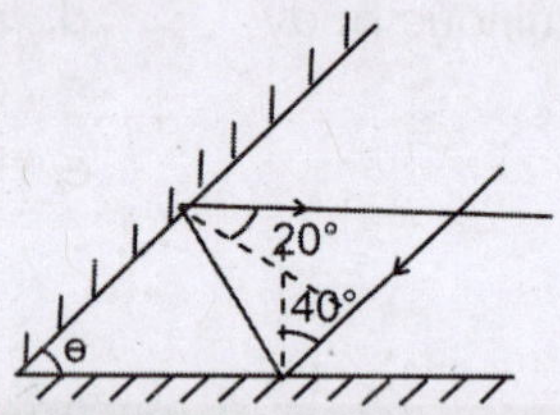

65. Rama watched in discovery channel that in outer space, at greater heights above the surface of the Earth where atmosphere does not exist appears completely dark. Explain what would be the reason for this?

66. Determine the velocity and the angle of refraction of a light wave passing through a window glass of 6 mm thickness when incident normally. ($\mu_{glass} = 2$)

67. Express 100 W in candle power.

68. A physics teacher asked a student to find how much time does the light take to reach the earth if the distance between the sun and the earth is 150×10^6 km? Teacher also gives an extra input that velocity of light is 3×10^8 m s^{-1}. What would be the answer of the student?

69. Why is a convex mirror used as a rear-view mirror in vehicles? Explain.

70. A physics student proved that, 'sunlight consists of different colours' and even gives two examples to support this. Explain.

71. Explain the formation of real and virtual images. Discuss what kind of images are formed in plane, convex and concave mirrors.

72. In the headlights of a car, what kind of mirrors are used? What is the use of mirror in the car headlights? Explain.

73. (A) Vishal wrote the word 'LIGHT' on a paper and placed it in front of a plane mirror (as shown in figure) and noticed how the letters of the word appear in the mirror. Write down what he noticed in the mirror

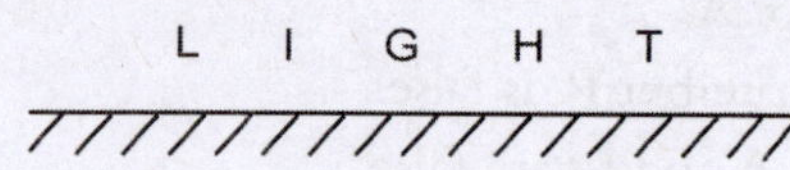

(B) What is his observation about the nature of the image? And through what angle did the image get inverted when compared to the object?

74. A bus driver is observing the image of a car in his rear view (side) mirror. How does the size of the image change when the car approaches the bus?

75. How can we get an infinite number of images of the given object?

76. When the physics teacher has given a task to determine the focal length of a concave mirror, a clever boy in the class focussed the mirror to a distant object. He moved the screen in front of the mirror and caught a real image on a screen at a distance of 20 cm from the mirror and he determined the focal length. Where should the object be place so that the object and the image are formed at the same position?

Level 3: Assess Your Concepts

77. Two plane mirrors are inclined at an angle 'θ'. A light ray incident on one of the mirrors undergoes multiple reflections. The angle of incidence on the first mirror is 15°. After reflection from the second mirror, if the light ray retraces its path, determine the value of θ.

78. Two identical mirrors are placed in a hollow cylindrical tube as shown in the figure. A light ray incident on one of the mirrors undergoes multiple reflections. If the length of each mirror is 3 m, and the velocity of light is 3×10^8 m s^{-1}, then find the time taken by the light ray incident on the mirror to come out of the hollow cylinder.

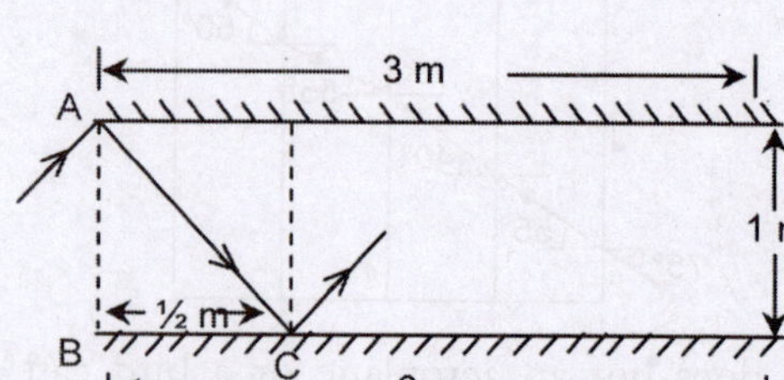

79. A student constructed a periscope by joining different periscopes P, Q, R, S and T as shown in the figure. Then,

(i) how many times does the incident light ray undergo reflection.

(ii) when he observes the image of an object using only one periscope what kind of variation can be observed in the image, when compared with the image formed by the periscope shown in the figure?

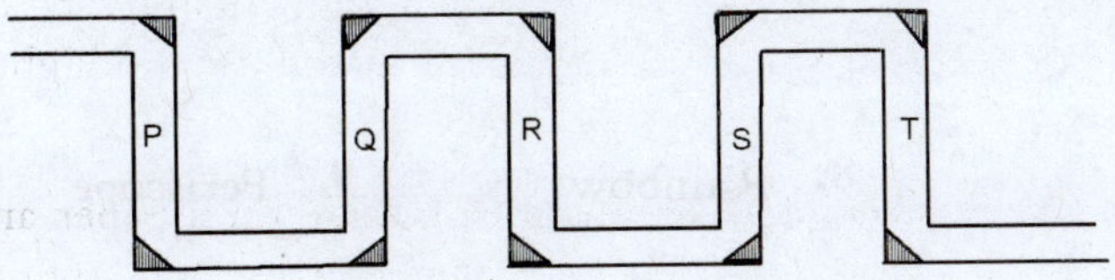

80. In the figure, AB is an object and A^1B^1 is the image formed when a spherical mirror is placed at point P. Identify the type of mirror and describe the nature of image. (Where *F* and *C* are focus and centre of curvature of the mirror)

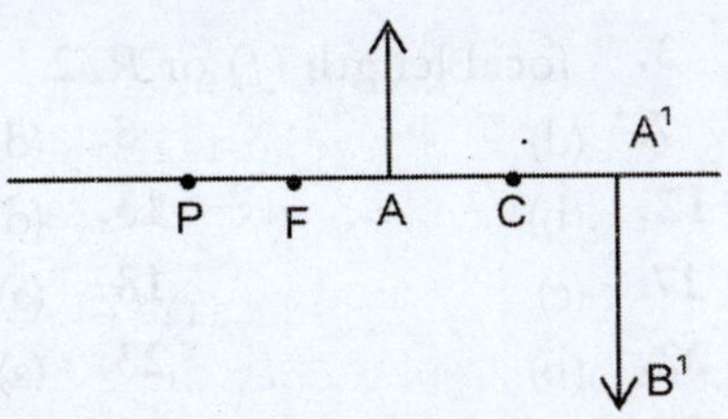

81. A laser source placed between two concave mirrors sends light rays as shown in the figure.

If PQ and RS are parallel to the principal axis, determine the focal lengths and radius of curvatures of both the mirrors.

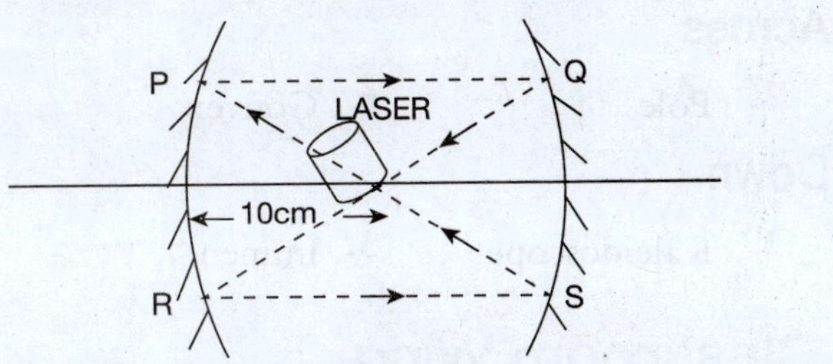

82. If the object is placed at 2f distance from a concave mirror, then find its image distance and the nature of the image with the help of a ray diagram.

AT

ANSWER KEYS

Crossword

Across

2. Pole 6. Convex 7. Two 8. Rainbow 9. Periscope

Down

1. Kaleidoscope 3. Lumen 4. Virtual 5. Sixty

Classroom Wing

Very Short Answer Type Questions

1. principal focus of the convex mirror 2. virtual and erect 3. focal length (f) or $R/2$
4. 11 5. (c) 6. (b) 7. (d) 8. (d)
9. (c) 10. (d) 11. (b) 12. (b) 13. (d)
14. (c) 15. (c) 16. (d) 17. (c) 18. (a)
19. (b) 20. (d) 21. (d) 22. (b) 23. (a)
24. (c) 25. (a) 26. (c) 27. (c) 28. (d)
29. (d) 30. (c) 31. (d) 32. (c) 33. (a)
34. (c) 35. (c) 36. (d) 37. (b) 38. (c)
39. (c) 40. (a) 41. (a) 42. (a)
43. A → d, B → f, C → e, D → c
44. A → d, B → c, C → a, D → e, E → b 45. A → f, B → c, C → h, D → a, E → b, F → g, G → d, H → e
46. A → b, B → a, C → d, D → c 47. A → d, B → e, C → a, D → b, E → c
59. decreases 60. increases 63. 11 64. 60° 66. 80°
67. Equal to R 71. 60°

Competition Wing

Level 1: Apply your Concepts

1. principal axis 2. lunar eclipse 3. rectilinear propagation 4. reflection
5. virtual 6. translucent 7. electrical, light 8. convergent 9. divergent
10. chlorophyll 11. total lunar eclipse 12. 10 cm 13. principal axis 14. infinite
15. $i = 50°$ 16. True 17. True 18. True 19. False
20. False 21. True 22. True 23. True 24. (a)
25. (a) 26. (c) 27. (a) 28. (a) 29. (b)
30. (b) 31. (d) 32. (b) 33. (b) 34. (a)
35. (b) 36. (d) 37. (c) 38. (d) 39. (c)
40. (d) 41. (d) 42. (c) 43. (d) 44. (b)
45. BACD 46. BDCEA 47. (d) 48. (b) 49. (d)
50. (d) 51. (c) 52. (d) 53. (c) 54. (a)
55. A → d, B → b, C → c, D → a 56. A → b, B → c, C → a, D → e
57. A → c, B → b, C → e, D → d, E → a

Level 2: Review your Concepts

61. 4 m **63.** 1/10 **64.** 5 **66.** 1.5×10^8 m/s
67. 8,57,848 candle power **68.** 8.33 minute **76.** 40 cm

Level 3: Assess Your Concepts

77. 15° **78.** 2.24×10^{-8} s.

Hints and Explanations

Classroom Wing

Very Short Answer Type Questions

1. The reflected light rays appear to emerge from the principal focus of the convex mirror.
2. (virtual and erect.)
   The image of an object formed by the inner surface of a spoon, when it is placed very close to it is virtual and erect. The inner surface of the spoon acts like a concave mirror.
3. The distance between the principal focus and centre of curvature of the convex mirror is equal to focal length (f) or $R/2$.
4. (11)
   $$n = \frac{360}{\theta} - 1 = \frac{360}{30} - 1 = 12 - 1 = 11$$
5. (c)
   A mirror does not allow light rays to pass through it.
6. (b)
   When the Earth comes into the umbra and penumbra of the Moon a solar eclipse takes place.
7. (d)
   According to laws of reflection, angle of incidence = angle of reflection.
   ∴ The ray emerges (reflects back) at the same angle i.e., 30°.
8. (d)
   Direction of light can be changed by a plane mirror, a piece of paper and a stone.
9. (c)
   The size of the image formed by a plane mirror is equal to the size of the object.
10. (d)
    The image of an object formed by a convex mirror (the outer side of spoon) is always erect and virtual in nature.
11. (b)
    A magnified virtual image is formed by a concave mirror.
12. (b)
    When ray of light passes through a prism the violet light bends more towards its base.
13. (d)
    Image formed by a convex mirror is virtual, diminished and erect.
14. (c)
    Intensity of light at any place is expressed by a modern unit called lux.
15. (c)
    Planets are not luminous, the sun is the nearest star to our planet (earth) from which it receives most of the light.
16. (d)
    Stars and glow-worm are natural sources of light.
17. (c)
    Only a point source of light forms a complete dark patch on a screen i.e., umbra.
    An extended source of light forms both umbra and penumbra.
18. (a)
    The line joining the centre of curvature and pole of the mirror is called the principal axis of the mirror.
19. (b)
    The light rays, after reflection from concave mirror, meet at one point. Hence concave mirror is a converging mirror.
20. (d)
    (i) The position of an image in case of convex mirror is between pole and the focus of mirror.
    (ii) If an object is at an infinite distance the image will be formed at focus.
21. (d)
    According to the laws of reflection:
    (1) The angle of incidence (i) = the angle of reflection (r),
    (2) the incident ray, the reflected ray and the normal lie in the same plane and

(3) the incident and the reflected rays lie on either side of the normal.

22. (b)

One lumen = 12.56 candle power.

23. (a)

Initially, the nature of the image is determined (virtual or real) (a). If the image formed is real the mirror used is concave mirror, as real images can be formed by only concave mirror (c).

If the image formed is virtual check whether the image is magnified, diminished or same size as that of the object (b).

If the virtual image is magnified concave mirror is used. If the virtual image is diminished, convex mirror is used and if the size of the image is equal to the size of the object a plane mirror is used (d).

24. (c)

Initially a line is drawn on the paper spread on the table. Place a plane mirror on the line (d) and fix two pins P and Q in front of the mirror (e). View the image of P and Q and fix two more pins P_1 and Q_1 such that the images of P and Q and the pins P_1 and Q_1 are along the same line (c).

Remove the pins and the mirror and join the line P Q and P_1 Q_1 (b). Draw a normal (a) and measure the angle of incidence and angle of reflection. See that the angle of incidence [i] is equal to angle of reflection [r] (f).

25. White light contains all the seven colours of light. When it passes through light raindrops, under certain conditions, it undergoes dispersion and forms a rainbow. So, A and R are correct and R is the correct explanation of A.

26. An optical medium which has diff erent composition at diff erent points is called heterogeneous medium.

Examples: Air, pure water, etc.

27. Planets are not luminous, the sun is the nearest star to our planet (earth) from which it receives most of the light.

28. Stars and glow-worm are natural sources of light.

29. Some sources of light emit light only when they are very hot and are called hot sources of light.

Examples: The sun, a candle, a filament bulb, etc.

30. Note down the given angle, i.e., the angle between the incident light ray and the plane mirror. Draw a normal line on the plane mirror at the point of incidence. The sum of the angle between the normal and the incident light ray and the angle between the plane mirror and the incident light ray is 90°. From this, determine the angle of incidence. From the laws of reflection the angle of incidence is equal to the angle of reflection. Then the sum of the angle of incidence and the angle of reflection gives the angle between the incident light ray and the reflected light ray.

31. Draw a concave mirror and mark the pole, the principal focus and the centre of curvature of the mirror. Draw the principal axis of the mirror and mark the position of the object between the principal focus and pole of the mirror. Draw two incident light rays from the object, one parallel to the principal axis and the other coming from the centre of curvature, and draw the corresponding reflected rays. These reflecting light rays are diverging. So, draw the extended lines till they intersect. Mark the image at a point where the extended light rays intersect and write the nature of the image.

32. The length of the straight line joining the centre of curvature and any point on the surface of a spherical mirror is the radius of curvature of the mirror (R).

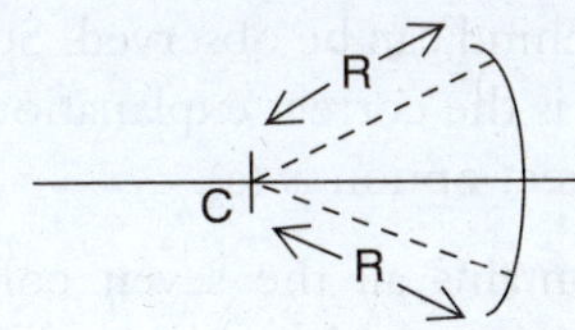

33. When electricity is allowed to pass through the filament, it emits light energy.

34. The angle of deviation $d = 180 - 2i = 180 - 2r$

$150 = 180 - 2r$

$2r = 30°$ $r = 15°$.

35. When two mirrors are placed parallel to each other, the image of an object formed by one mirror acts, like virtual object for another mirror, and its virtual image acts, like virtual object for previous one and this process continues and an infinite number of images are formed by the two mirrors.

(or)

$$n = \frac{360°}{\theta} - 1$$

$$\theta = 0$$

$$\Rightarrow n = \frac{360°}{0} - 1$$

$$n = \infty - 1 = \text{infinite}$$

36. (i) Light causes sensation of vision.

(ii) The sensation of heat is due to the presence of infrared radiation.

(iii) Light travels in a straight line.

37. When the light rays appear to be coming out of a point, then we call them a diverging beam of light.

38. (i) Light casts shadows of objects in its path due to its rectilinear propagation property.

(ii) Lunar eclipse is formed, when earth comes between the sun and the moon.

39. In the case of a convex mirror, the nature of the image formed is always diminished and it is a virtual and erect image. So, A is correct but R is incorrect because the laws of reflection are applicable in all types of mirrors including spherical mirrors.

40. Light energy is required for the process of photosynthesis. The light energy is converted into chemical energy with the help of chlorophyll present in the leaves of plants. So, A and R are correct and R is the correct explanation of A.

41. Convex mirrors are used as rear view mirrors in vehicles because the field view of a convex mirror is large and it forms a diminished image so that the vehicles coming from behind can be observed. So, A and R are correct and 'R' is the correct explanation of A.

Hence, the correct option is (a).

42. White light contains all the seven colours of light. When white light passes through raindrops under certain conditions it undergoes dispersion and forms a rainbow. So, A and R is correct and R is the correct explanation of A.

Hence, the correct option is (a).

43. A → d The nature of the image formed by a plane mirror is laterally inverted, virtual and of the same size as that of the object.

B → f The light rays emitted from a candle are divergent light rays.

C → e An inverted real image is formed only in a concave mirror.

D → c The reflected light rays from a concave mirror, when the object is placed at the centre of curvature, converge at the same point. These are convergent light rays.

44. A → d When a light ray incidents normally on a plane mirror, it retraces its own path. Then the angle of deviation is 180°.

B → c The green colour in plants is due to the chlorophyll present in them.

C → a Solar eclipse occurs only on new moon days.

D → e Lunar eclipse occurs only on full moon nights.

E → b The angle of deviation is = 180° – 60° = 120°.

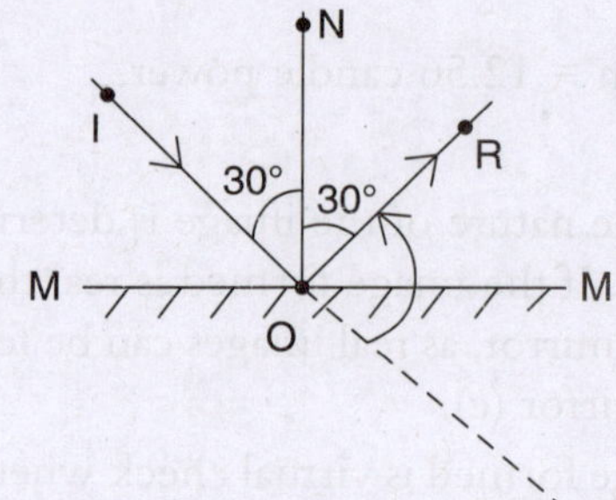

45. A → f In case of plane mirror, object distance is equal to image distance.

B → c Virtual image formed by a concave mirror is magnified.

C → h Periscope works on the principle of reflection of light.

D → a Sun is a self luminous body.

E → b Real images can be caught on the screen.

F → g When white light passes through a prism it splits into seven colours, which is known as dispersion of light.

G → d The image formed on the retina is real.

H → e Velocity of light is maximum in vacuum.

46. (A) → b A solar eclipse occurs when the moon casts its shadow on the earth.

(B) → a Glow worm is a cold source of light.

(C) → d Magnification in pinhole camera

$$M = \frac{\text{Width of the pinhole}}{\text{Distance of the object}} = \frac{\text{Size of the image } (i)}{\text{Size of the object } (o)}$$

(D) → c A convex mirror forms an erect, virtual and diminished image.

47. A → d Intensity of light is measured in lumen.

B → e Dispersion of light is responsible for the formation of rainbow.

C → a A plane mirror is used as looking glass.

D → b Eclipse is the shadow of the Earth or the Moon.

E → c Filament bulb is an example of hot source.

48. A body that emits its own light is called "luminous body" and the bodies which do not emit light on their own are known as "non-luminous body".

49. Moon is the natural satellite of the earth. It only reflects the sunlight falling on it.

50. Point source of light: A source of light that is of the size of pin head of a pin, is called a point source of light.

Extended source of light: A source of light which is bigger than the point source of light is called an extended source of light.

51. In a homogeneous medium, light travels along a straight line path and this is known as rectilinear propagation of light.

52. In any full moon night, the sun, the moon and the earth happen to come in a straight line, a part or whole of the moon is not visible to us for some time from some parts of the earth. Then we say that lunar eclipse has occurred.

53. When light incident on the surface of a opaque body it bounces back. This phenomenon is called reflection.

54. The reflected light actually meet to form the image. Such image is called a "real image"

55. If two plane mirrors are placed at an angle 'θ', then the number of images formed(n) is given by $n = \frac{360}{\theta}$ if $\frac{360}{\theta}$ is odd or $n = \frac{360}{\theta} - 1$ if $\frac{360}{\theta}$ is even.

56. The centre of the sphere of which the given spherical mirror is a part is called its centre of curvature.

57. White light consists of seven colours they are violet, indigo, blue, green, yellow, orange and red.

58. Some sources of light emit light only when they are very hot and are called "hot sources of light".

Example: The sun, a candle, a filament bulb, etc.

Certain other sources of light emit light even when they are cool and they are called "cold sources of light".

Example: Glow-worm.

59.

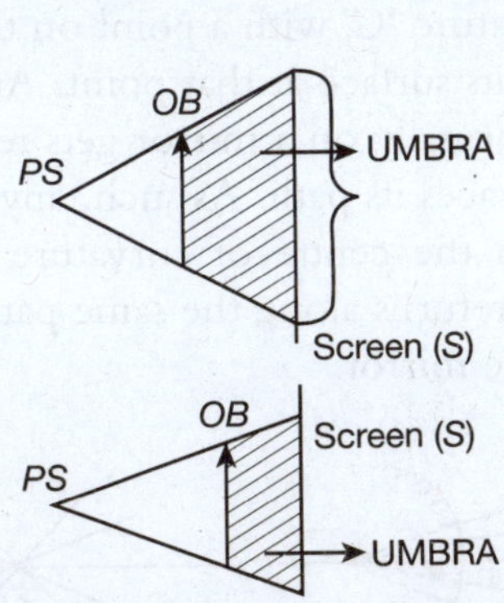

The size of umbra on screen (S) decreases when only the opaque object (OB) is moving towards the screen and away from the point source of light.

60. When point source moves towards the opaque object, the size of the umbra increases.

61. When light incident on a non-polished surface it reflects in different direction. This phenomenon is known as diffuse reflection.

62. The reflected light rays form a diverging beam and appear to come out of a point. In such cases, the image formed is called a virtual image.

63. Given: $\theta = 30°$

The number of image (n) formed is,

$$n = \frac{360°}{30°} = 12 \text{ (it is an even number)}$$

So,

$$n = \frac{360°}{30°} - 1 = 12 - 1 = 11 \text{ (odd number)}.$$

64.

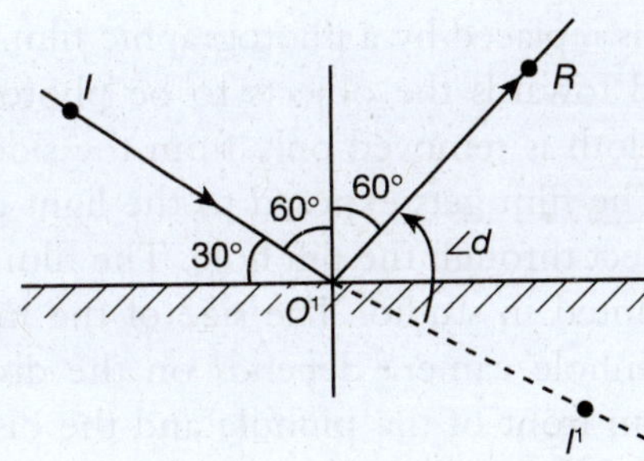

$\angle d = 180°\ \angle IOR$

$= 180° - 120°$

$= 60°$

65. In general, focal length $= \frac{\text{radius of curvature}}{2}$

66. $\angle d = 180° - (2i)$

$= 180° - 100° = 80°$

67. The distance from pole to the centre of curvature of concave mirror is equal to R.

Short Answer Type Questions

68. A medium that allows light to pass through it is called transparent medium. Air, glass, pure water are some examples of transparent medium.

The medium through which light rays cannot pass at all is called an opaque medium.

Wood, metal, etc. are some example of opaque medium.

There are certain media like fog, oil paper which allow light partially to pass through them are called translucent media

69. Pinhole camera: This is a device which forms a photograph like image of a stationary bright object on a screen. This works on the rectilinear propagation of light.

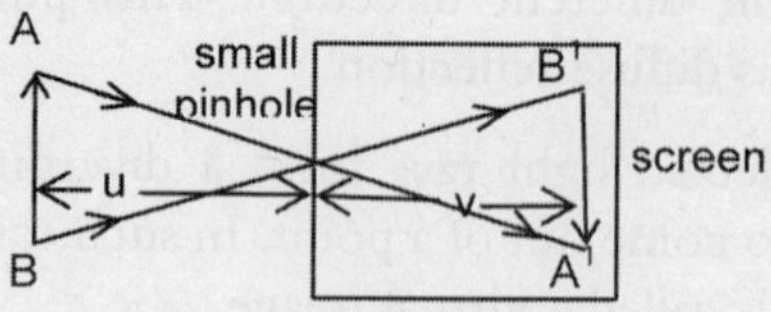

A pinhole camera consists of a cubical or cylindrical empty cardboard box with a fine hole on one side and with a paper or glass on the opposite side that acts as a screen. The box is blackened from inside so that any light which falls on its walls directly or indirectly is absorbed. When a stationary bright object (AB) is placed in front of a pinhole camera, an inverted impression (A^1B^1) can be seen on the screen. To take actual photograph, the pinhole camera is covered with thick black cloth and screen is replaced by a photographic film. The camera is faced towards the objects to be photographed and black cloth is removed only from the side of the pinhole. The film gets exposed to the light coming from the object through the pin hole. The film is developed and printed in studio. The size of the image formed by a pinhole camera depends on the distance of the object in front of the pinhole and the distance of the screen or film behind the pinhole. To compare the size of the image with the size of the object, we define magnification.

$$\text{Magnification } (m) = \frac{\text{size of image}(i)}{\text{size of object}(o)}$$

$$= \frac{\text{distance of image}(v)}{\text{distance of object}(u)}$$

$$= \frac{\text{width of the pinhole camera}}{\text{object distance}}$$

70. (a) Characteristics of image formed by a plane mirror.

(1) Size of the image is same as the size of the object.

(2) The distance of the object in front of the mirror is equal to the distance of the image behind the mirror.

(3) A virtual and erect image is formed.

(4) The image formed by a mirror is laterally inverted.

(b) Uses of plane mirrors:

(1) Plane mirrors are used as looking glasses.

(2) Plane mirrors are used by opticians to maintain the standard distance of the chart required for testing eye sight.

(3) Plane mirrors are used for providing false dimensions in some shops.

(4) Plane mirrors are used in solar cookers as a reflectors of sun light.

(5) Plane mirrors are used in making kaleidoscopes and reflecting periscopes.

71. Here, $\angle i = \angle r$

$2\angle i + \angle d = 180°$

$\angle d = 180° - 2\angle i = 180° - 2(60°)$

$= 180° - 120° = 60°$

72. (i) From the definition of principal focus, if any ray of light, travelling parallel to the principal axis, after reflection either passes through or appears to diverge from the principal focus.

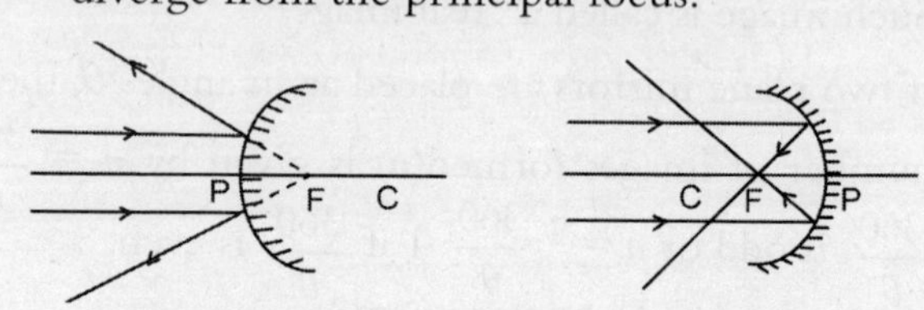

(ii) If any ray of light initially passes through (concave mirror) or appears to pass through (convex mirror) the principal focus of the spherical mirror, after reflection, travels parallel to principal axis.

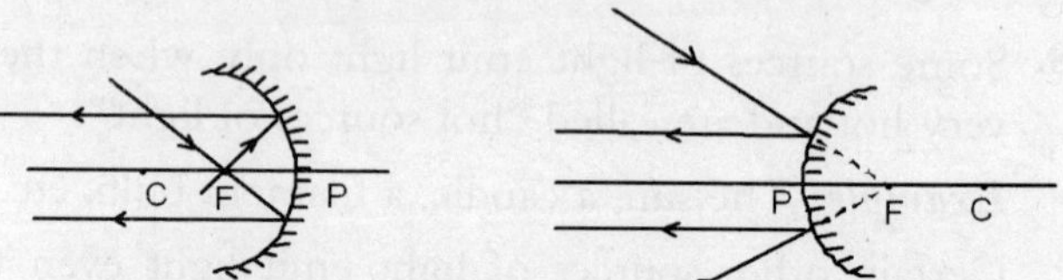

Concave mirror

Convex mirror

(iii) In a spherical mirror, any line that joins the centre of curvature 'C' with a point on the mirror is normal to its surface at that point. Any light ray incident normally on a mirror gets reflected normally and retraces its path. As such, any light ray passing through the centre of curvature of the spherical mirror returns along the same path after reflection from the mirror.

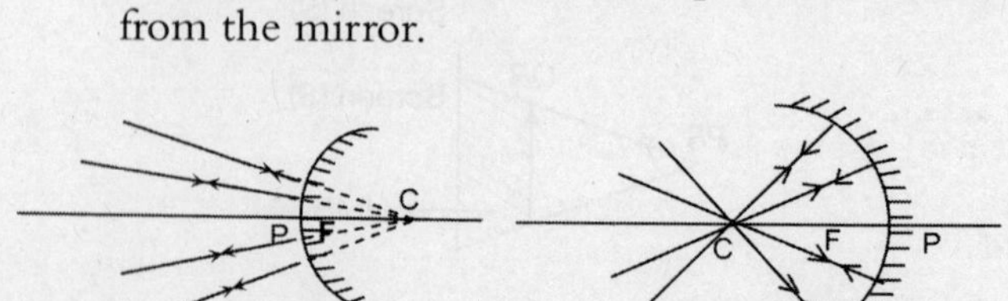

Convex mirror

Concave mirror

In order to find the position of the image of a point source formed by a spherical mirror, we use any two of the three rays discussed above.

73. An oiled opaque paper is a translucent medium of light. The pores of an opaque paper do not allow any light to get transmitted as some part of it get either absorbed or reflected. On oiling it, the pores get filled with oil and hence some part of light can be transmitted while remaining light gets reflected or absorbed. Hence oiled paper behaves as a translucent object.

74. The path along which light travels is a "ray of light". A line segment represents a light ray with an arrow indicating the direction of propagation of the light.

A light ray

We call a group of adjacent light rays as a beam of light rays. If the light rays are parallel to each other then it is called parallel beam of light ray.

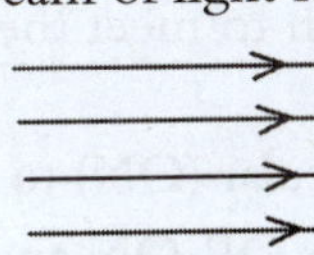

Parallel beam of light

In general rays coming from a distant source are parallel rays. If all light rays appear to meet at a point then they are called a converging beam of light.

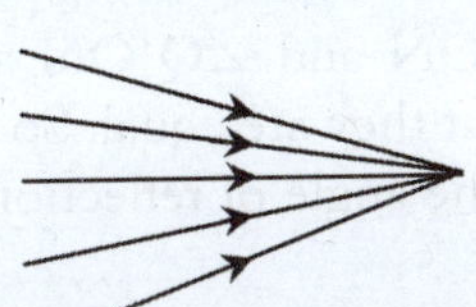

Convergent beam of light

When the light rays appear to be coming out of a point, then we call them a diverging beam of light.

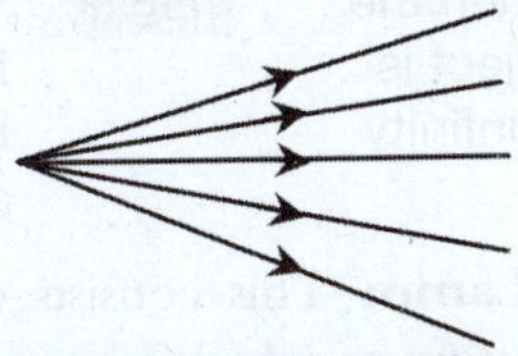

Divergent beam of light

75. **(i) Laws of reflection**

(1) The incident ray, the normal at the point of incidence and the reflected ray all lie in the same plane.

(2) The angle of incidence is equal to the angle of reflection, $i = r$.

(ii)

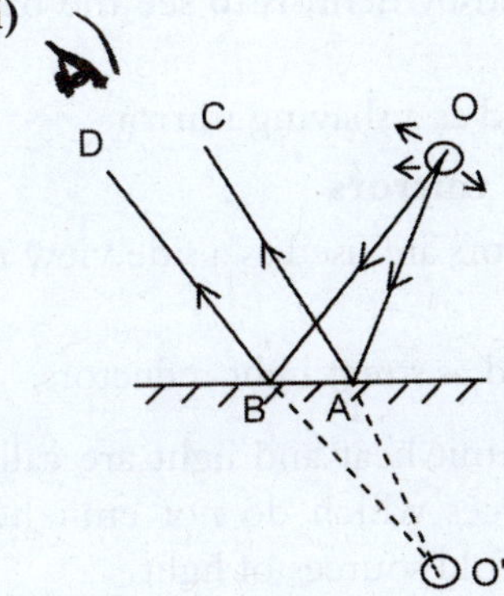

76. From the figure, as the beam of light which is incident on the mirror is a parallel beam of light, the reflected rays appear to come from the principal focus. Hence the focal length of the mirror = 10 cm.

But radius of curvature $R = 2f$

$= 2 \times 10 = 20$ cm

77. The formation of shadows takes place due to the rectilinear propagation of light. When the source is a point source, the region on the screen is completely dark, that is, only umbra is formed.

78. The light from the moon is cool, because it is not directly emitted by the moon. The light from the sun, after reflection from the surface of the moon, reaches the earth. During the reflection from the moon, most of the infrared radiation is absorbed by the moon. Some part of the infrared radiation is again absorbed by atmosphere. Hence the light from the moon is called as cold light. But the light from the sun is hot, because the radiations coming from the sun contains infrared radiations along with the visible light. These infrared radiations causes heating effect. Hence, the light from the sun is called hot.

79. The velocity of light in air is 3×10^8 m s^{-1}. Whereas, the velocity of sound in air at room temperature is around 340 m s^{-1}. The velocity of light is many times more than the velocity of sound in a given medium. Hence the lightning is seen first and then thunder is heard.

80. If the convex (outer) surface is silvered and the concave (inner) surface is smoothened by polishing then the mirror is "concave mirror". If the concave (inner) surface is silvered and convex (outer) surface is smoothened and polished then it is called convex mirror.

(i) Uses of concave mirrors

(1) Concave mirrors are used in torches and searchlights as reflectors to spread light over longer distances.

(2) They are used by dentists to see the back part of the teeth.

(3) They are used as a shaving mirror.

(ii) Uses of convex mirrors

(1) Convex mirrors are used as a side view mirrors in vehicles.

(2) They are used as street light reflectors.

81. The sources which emit heat and light are called hot sources and the sources which do not emit heat but only light are called cold sources of light.

e.g., Cold source of light – glow-worm.

Hot source of light – sun, incandescent lamp, candle, etc.

82. We all know that light is necessary for the growth of plants. Green colour in plant leaves is due to "Chlorophyll". Chlorophyll helps to convert light energy into chemical energy. This process of conversion of light energy into chemical energy is called as photosynthesis. During the process of photosynthesis the atmospheric CO_2 combines with water and is converted into glucose and releases oxygen. This chemical energy is stored in plants in the form of food. It is also observed that different colours of light have different effects on the growth of plants.

Essay Type Questions

83. Why we have represented a ray of light with a straight line? Why it cannot be a curved line? This is because light travels in a straight line. In a homogeneous medium, light travels along a straight line path and this is known as rectilinear propagation of light. This is because light always tries to travel between two points in the shortest possible time.

Let us verify this nature of light. Take three identical cardboards with holes at the centre. Place them on a table in such a way that all the holes are along a straight line. When a burning candle is placed on one side, it can be viewed from the other side. If the middle cardboard is moved sideways or disturbed, we will not be able to see the candle. This is because of the rectilinear propagation of light.

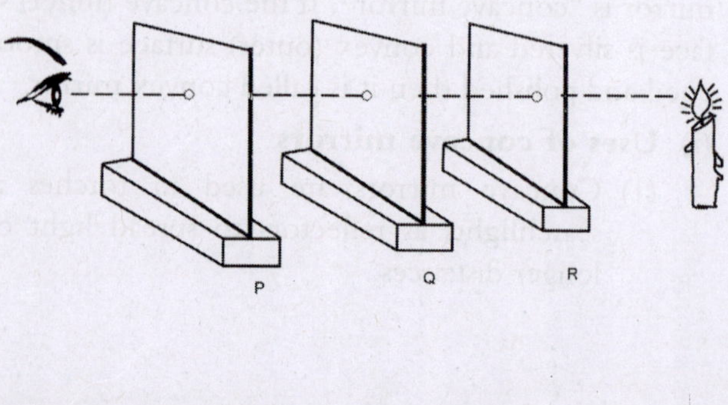

84. Verification of laws of reflection

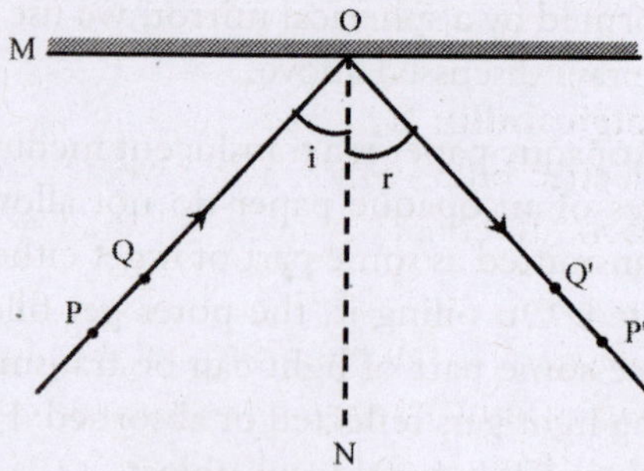

(1) Spread a white sheet of paper on a table.

(2) Draw a straight line and fix a plane mirror (MM^1) vertically along this line.

(3) Fix two pins, P and Q, in front of the mirror.

(4) Looking from the position shown in the figure, fix two more pins P^1 and Q^1, such that these pins and images of P and Q are in the same straight line.

(5) Remove the mirror and pins. Join QP and $Q^1 P^1$ and produce them to meet the mirror at point 'O' on the line.

(6) Draw a perpendicular (ON) to the line at 'O'.

(7) It is observed that QP, ON and $P^1 Q^1$ all lie in the same plane. Since QP and Q^1P^1 represent incident and reflected rays, we can conclude that incident ray, reflected ray and the normal at the point of incidence all lie in the same plane.

(8) When $\angle QON$ and $\angle Q^1ON$ are measured, it is observed that they are equal. So angle of incidence is equal to the angle of reflection.

85.

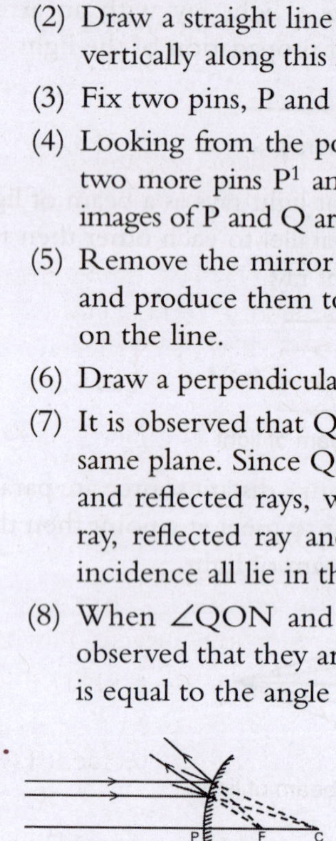

Fig (i) When the object is at infinity

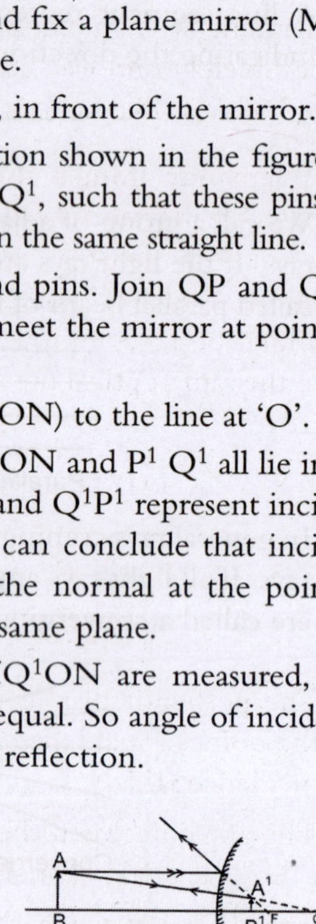

Fig (ii) When the object is at any distance between infinity and pole

86. Hurricane Lamp: This consists of a small kerosene tank at the bottom to which a burner is fixed. One end of a wick, which is passing through the burner, is put inside the kerosene in the tank. A glass chimney is provided to prevent wind from putting off the flame and also to distribute the light evenly in all directions.

When the wick is lit, kerosene flows up through the fine hole in the wick due to capillary action. The holes provided to the burner helps cool air to come in and the holes provided at the top helps the hot air to leave the lamp.

The electric bulb: The most widely used source of light is electric bulb, which was invented by Thomas Alva Edison. It converts electrical energy into light energy.

When electricity is allowed to pass through the filament it emits light energy. For this purpose, the two ends of the filament are fixed to two terminals of the bulb, which are attached to two copper wires whose ends are connected to a battery. To avoid burning of filament at high temperature, the air in the bulb is completely removed and is filled with a small quantity of inert gas like helium and sealed.

87. A light ray from a source of light reaching a given reflecting surface is called the "incident ray" (AI). The point at which the incident ray strikes the reflecting surface is called "point of incidence" (I). The light ray which bounces from the reflecting surface and travels in the same optical medium is called the "reflected ray" (IB).

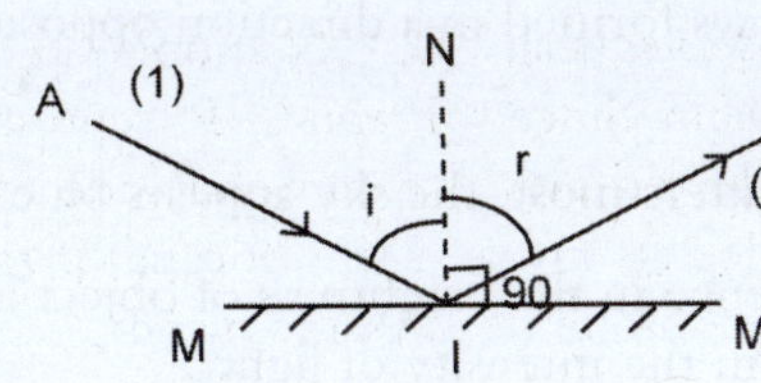

The perpendicular to the reflecting surface, drawn at the point of incidence is called 'normal' at the point of incidence (IN).

The angle between the normal and the incident ray is called the angle of incidence (∠AIN)

The angle between the normal and reflected ray is called the angle of reflection (∠NIB).

88. Kaleidoscope: This works on the principle of multiple reflections in inclined plane mirrors.

Three plane mirrors inclined at an angle of 60° to each other fixed inside a cylindrical box constitute a kaleidoscope. A few pieces of coloured glasses are placed inside the box and when viewed from the other end, beautiful patterns could be seen due to the multiple images of glass pieces formed by the mirrors.

Periscope: Periscope is a device used to see objects, which are not in the direct line of sight.

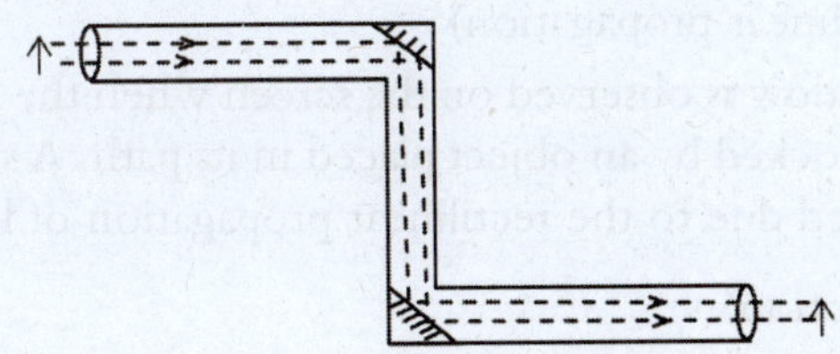

This is used by soldiers to see enemy's movements. A reflecting periscope consists of a tube bent twice at right angles. It is provided with two openings, and two plane mirrors are fixed at the bends of the tube such that they make an angle of 45° with the frame of the tube.

The rays of light from the object enter the periscope from the upper tube, get reflected twice and enter the eye of the person looking through the periscope.

In certain periscopes instead of mirrors, prisms are used. These periscopes work on the principle of total internal reflection (which you will learn in higher classes).

89. Refer to the Table given on Page no. 4.14 for the formation of image in concave mirror

Competition Wing

Level 1: Apply your Concepts

1. The line joining the pole of the mirror and the centre of curvature is called principal axis and every line is parallel to itself.
2. (lunar eclipse)

   When the Moon comes into the umbra and the penumbra of the Earth, lunar eclipse takes place.
3. (rectilinear propagation)

   A shadow is observed on the screen when the light rays are blocked by an object placed in its path. A shadow is formed due to the rectilinear propagation of light.
4. (reflection)

   Periscope works on the principle of reflection of light.
5. (virtual)

   The image formed by a plane mirror cannot be caught on the screen. So it is virtual in nature.
6. Oil paper is an example of translucent medium of light.
7. An electric bulb converts electrical energy to light energy.
8. Real images are formed by convergent beam of light.
9. Virtual images are formed by divergent beam of light.
10. Chlorophyll in the plant leaves helps to convert light energy into chemical energy.
11. When the Moon is not completely visible from the Earth, we call it as total lunar eclipse.
12. When the object is placed at infinite distance, the image is formed at the principal focus. Radius of curvature, $(R) = 20$ cm.

    Focal length $= \frac{R}{2} = \frac{20}{2} = 10$ cm
13. 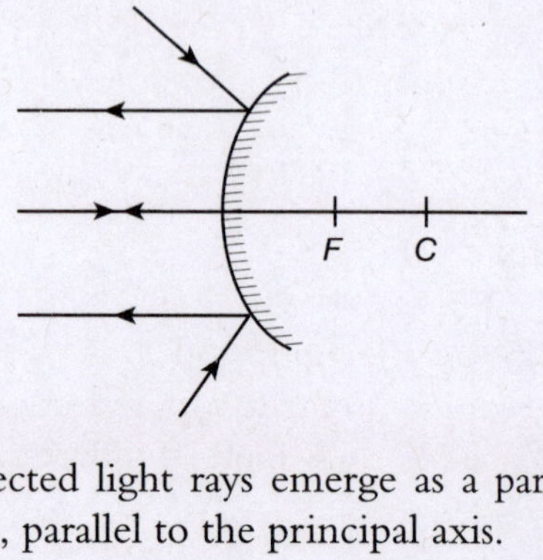

    The reflected light rays emerge as a parallel beam of light rays, parallel to the principal axis.
14. The number of images formed by two parallel mirrors is infinite.
15. $\angle i = \angle r$

    $2\angle i + \angle d = 180°$

    $2\angle i = 180° - 80° = 100°$

    $\angle i = 50°$
16. True. Pure water is a transparent medium.
17. Eclipses (shadows) are formed due to rectilinear propagation of light.
18. Light travels in straight lines.
19. Photosynthesis takes place in the presence of sunlight.
20. The image which cannot be caught on a screen is called virtual image.
21. The mirror which is used in vehicles as rear viewer is a convex mirror.
22. Sun rays fall on water drops and forms rainbow. A rainbow is always formed in a direction opposite to that of the sun.
23. As light scatters most, the sky appears blue.
24. The difference in the brightness of object is due to the difference in the intensity of light.
25. When the object is place at centre of curvature (C), the image is also formed at the same position.
26. When the object is placed at the principal focus (F), the image is formed at infinite distance.
27. Only concave mirrors form magnified images.
28. Geometric centre of a mirror is called pole of the mirror.
29. An incident ray passing through the centre of curvature retraces its path.
30. The phenomenon which is responsible for vision is irregular reflection.
31. All the three statements are true according to the laws of reflection.
32. When two plane mirrors are placed parallel to each other, and when an object is placed between them, then the image of the object formed by any one of the mirror will act like virtual object for other mirror. This process continues and infinite number of images are formed. (or)

$\theta = 0°$, $n = \frac{360°}{\theta} - 1 = \frac{360°}{0} - 1 = \infty - 1 = \infty$

Where n = number of images formed.

θ = angle between the mirrors.

33. The intensity of light decreases, when the distance from the source increases.

34. (1) The image formed by a plane mirror is virtual as the image cannot be caught on a screen.
(2) It is an erect image.
(3) The height of the image is the same as that of the object.

35. The moon is not a luminous source of light; it simply reflects the light which is incident on it. A glow-worm is a natural source of light.

36. Among the given options, all the given sources of light are man-made.

37. (1) Light casts shadows of objects in its path due to its rectilinear propagation property.
(2) Lunar eclipse is formed, when earth comes between the sun and the moon.

38. The image formed by a pinhole camera is real, inverted and the nature of the image does not depend on the shape of the pinhole.

39. The length of the straight line joining the centre of curvature and any point on the surface of a spherical mirror is the radius of curvature of the mirror (R).

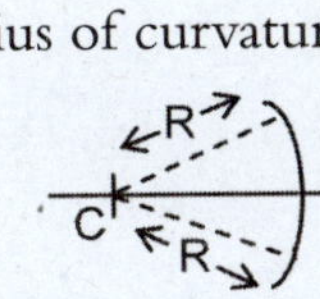

40. The image formed by a concave mirror is real or virtual depending on the position of the object in front of the mirror. It is inverted or erect and magnified or diminished depending on the position of the object in front of the mirror.

41. The light ray which is incident along the principal axis of a mirror falls normally on the mirror, and hence, it retraces its path.

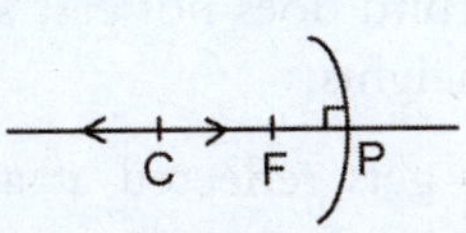

From the figure, it is clear that it passes through the centre of curvature.

As the line passing through the centre of curvature is perpendicular to the mirror, the angle made by the light ray with the normal is zero.

42. The mirror which is used as a rear viewer in vehicles is a convex mirror.

43. (1) Light causes sensation of vision.
(2) The sensation of heat is due to the presence of infrared radiation.
(3) Light travels in a straight line.

44. One foot candle = 10.76 lux

45. **(a)** Note the distance between the mirror and the screen from the given data – (B)
The focal length, f = 40 cm – (A)
Use, $R = 2f$ – (C)
=> R = 2 × 40 = 80 cm – (D)
Hence, the correct order is BACD.

46. (b) Take a concave mirror and mount it on a stand – (B). Focus the mirror on a distant object like a tree or a building – (D). Take a screen and adjust it before the mirror to catch the inverted, real and diminished image of the object – (C)
The distance between the mirror and the screen is equal to the focal length of the mirror – (E)
Then, the radius of curvature of concave mirror is equal to twice the focal length of the mirror – (A).
Hence, the correct order is BDCEA.

47. When light rays pass through the focus of a concave mirror, the reflected rays emerge parallel to the principal axis.

48. The number of images formed

$$(n) = \frac{360}{\theta} - 1$$
$$= \frac{360}{45} - 1$$
$$= 8 - 1$$
$$= 7$$

49.

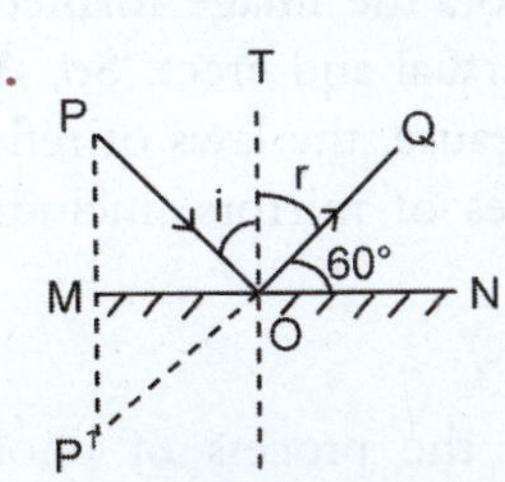

(i) From figure
$\angle TON = 90°$
$\therefore \angle TOQ = \angle r = 90° - 60° = 30°$
$\therefore$ angle of reflection = 30°.
But according to the laws of reflection, the angle of incidence (i) = the angle of reflection (r).
$\therefore i = 30°$

(ii) In case of a plane mirror, object distance = image distance.

(iii) $\angle PON = \angle POQ + \angle QON$

$= \angle POT + \angle TOQ + \angle QON$

$= 30° + 30° + 60°$

$= 120°$

50. (1) In a glow-worm the energy produced during a chemical reaction in its body is released in the form of light only.

(2) An electric bulb glows, when the filament attains very high temperature due to the passage of current.

(3) Due to the powerful reactions taking place in the sun, the energy produced by the sun consists light and heat.

51. When two mirrors are placed parallel to each other. The image of an object formed by one mirror acts like virtual object for another mirror, and its virtual image acts like virtual object for previous one and this process continues and an infinite number of images are formed by the two mirrors.

(or)

$$n = \frac{360}{\theta} - 1$$

$\theta = 0°$

$$\Rightarrow n = \frac{360}{0} - 1$$

$n = \infty - 1 = \infty =$ infinite

52. The image of an object which is placed at an infinite distance will be formed at the focus in case of convex and concave mirrors whereas, it is equal to infinity in the case of a plane mirror.

53. In the case of a convex mirror, the image formed is always diminished and it is virtual and erect. So, A is correct but R is incorrect because, the laws of reflection are applicable in all types of mirrors, including spherical mirrors.
Hence, the correct option is (c).

54. Light energy is required for the process of photosynthesis. The light energy is converted into chemical energy with the help of chlorophyll present in the leaves of plants. So, A and R are correct and R is the correct explanation of A.
Hence, the correct option is (a).

55. A → d Convex mirror is used as street light reflector.

B → b A concave mirror is used by dentist.

C → c Plane mirror is used in kaleidoscope.

D → a Prism is used to observe the dispersion of light.

56. (A) → b When a light incidents normally on a reflecting surface, the angle of reflection is 0°.

(B) → c Lunar eclipse forms due to rectilinear propagation of light.

(C) → a When a white light passes through a prism it produces 'dispersion of light'.

(D) → e Moon is a non-luminous body.

57. A → c Pinhole camera works on the principle of rectilinear propagation.

B → b Kaleidoscope works on the principle of multiple reflection.

C → e Distance between the pole of the mirror and centre of curvature is called radius of curvature.

D → d Distance between the pole of the mirror and principal focus is called focal length.

E → a A glowing tube light is an example of extended source of light.

Level 2: Review your Concepts

58. Let us represent angles of incidence and angles of refraction in A, B, C, D as i_A, i_B, i_c, i_D, r_A, r_B, r_C and r_D respectively.

$r_B < i_A \Rightarrow \mu_B > \mu_A$

$r_C > i_B \Rightarrow \mu_B > \mu_C$

$r_C = r_A \Rightarrow \mu_C = \mu_A$

$r_D < i_c \Rightarrow \mu_D > \mu_C$

$r_B < r_D \Rightarrow \mu_B > \mu_D$

$\Rightarrow \mu_A = \mu_C < \mu_D < \mu_B$

59. If we consider the sun as source and aeroplane as object and the earth as a screen, the aeroplane will cast its shadow on the earth when it is at a lower height. But as the aeroplane moves up the distance of screen from the object increases. As the aeroplane moves further and further away, the umbra becomes smaller and smaller and finally it completely disappears. Thus, an aeroplane or a bird does not cast a shadow when they are at greater heights.

60. The light that gets reflected at a rough and uneven surface goes in different direction, due to irregular reflection. This is the reason why a mirror whose surface is rough cannot produce clear image. Any surface that is smooth can produce a clear image because of regular reflection that takes place at its surfaces.

61. $DC = \frac{1}{2}\ EC = \frac{1}{2} \times 1 = 0.5$ m

$AB = \frac{1}{2}\ FB = \frac{1}{2} \times 2 = 1$ m

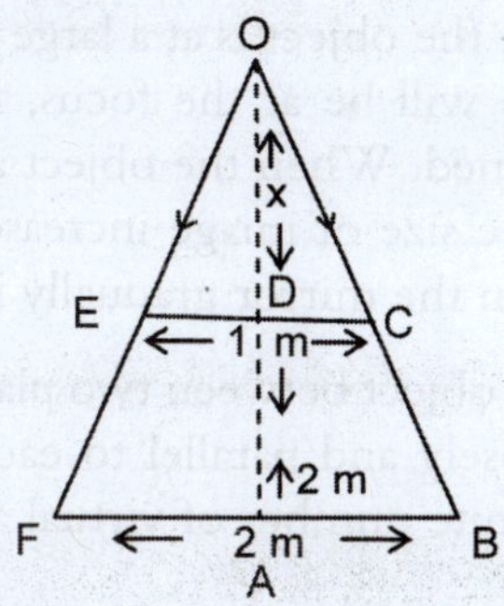

$$\frac{OA}{OD} = \frac{AB}{DC}$$

$$\frac{x+2}{x} = \frac{1}{1/2}$$

$$\frac{x+2}{x} = 2$$

$$2x = x+2$$

$$x = 2\ m$$

$\therefore$ OA = 2 + 2 = 4 m

62. When the object is moved towards the concave mirror, then the image is displaced in the opposite direction, and it gets magnified gradually. (Refer to the ray diagrams given as formation of image by concave mirror.) When the object is moved towards the convex mirror, then its image is shifted towards the pole of the convex mirror and its size increases but not more than the actual size of the object.

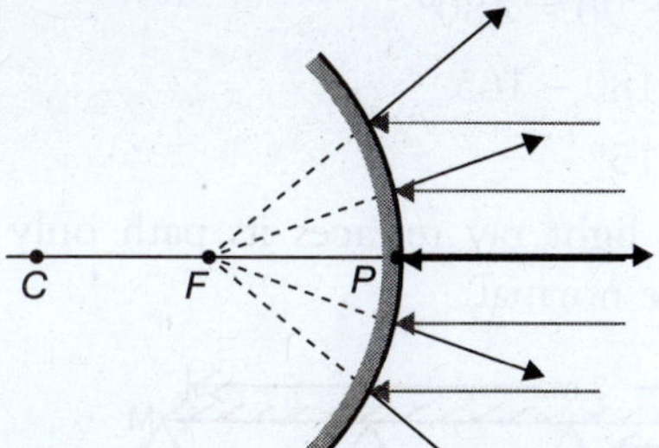

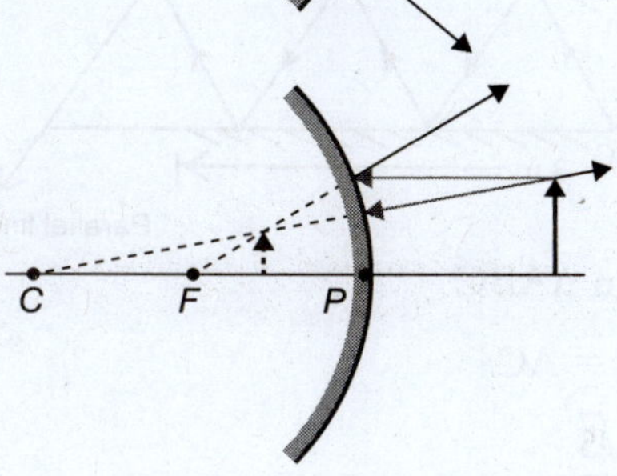

63. Magnification $= \frac{h_i}{h_o} = \frac{v}{u}$

$$\frac{h_i}{3} = \frac{1}{30}$$

$$h_i = \frac{3}{30} = \frac{1}{10} = 0.1 \text{ m}$$

64.

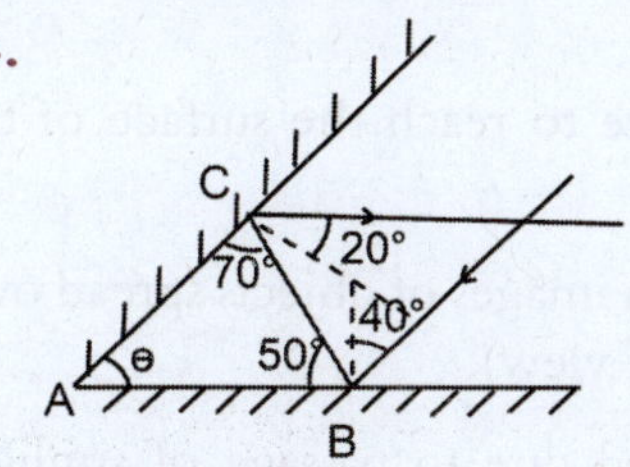

In Δ ABC

$\angle ABC = 50°$

$\angle ACB = 70°$

But $\angle ACB + \angle ABC + \angle CAB = 180°$

$70 + 50 + \angle CAB = 180°$

$\angle CAB = 180 \quad 120 = 60°$

$$n = \frac{360°}{\theta} - 1 = \frac{360°}{60°} - 1 = 6 - 1 = 5$$

65. At greater heights above the surface of the earth it appears complete dark, as there exist no scattering particles (dust or moisture).

66. Given, refractive index of the glass, $\mu_{glass} = 2$

Velocity of light in air/vacuum, $c = 3 \times 10^8$ m/s.

When the angle of incidence of the light ray in air is zero, then the angle of refraction of the light ray in the glass is also zero.

Refractive index, $\mu_{glass} = \frac{c}{v}$, where 'c' is the velocity of light in air and v is the velocity of light in glass.

$$\therefore v = \frac{c}{\mu_{glass}} = \frac{3\times10^8}{2} = 1.5\times10^8 \text{ m/s}$$

67. Power of the bulb = 100 W

1 W = 683 lumen and 1 lumen

= 12.56 candle power.

$\therefore$ 100 W = 100 × 683 lumen

= 100 × 683 × 12.56 candle power

= 8,57,848 candle power.

$\therefore$ The intensity of bulb is 8,57,848 times more than the brightness (intensity) of a candle.

68. Velocity of light, $c = 3 \times 10^8$ m s^{-1}.

Distance of the sun from the earth,

$d = 150 \times 10^6$ km.

$= 150 \times 10^6 \times 10^3$ m

$= 150 \times 10^9$ m

$\therefore$ Velocity $= \dfrac{\text{distance } (d)}{\text{time } (t)}$

$t = \dfrac{150 \times 10^9 \text{ m}}{3 \times 10^8 \text{ m s}^{-1}} = 500$ s

$= 8.33$ minute

$\therefore$ light takes 8.33 minute to reach the surface of the earth from the sun.

69. Convex mirrors can form images of objects spread over a large area (large field of view).

70. (i) The rainbow formed due to passage of sunlight (white coloured light) through water droplets contains seven colours.

(ii) When we blow a soap-bubble we can see different colours.

(iii) When white light (sunlight) reflects from the surface of compact disk, we see many colours.

(iv) When light is allowed to pass through a prism, we see a band of seven colours.

$\therefore$ From the above facts he concluded that the light from the sun is a mixture of colours.

71. The image which cannot be caught on a screen is called virtual image and which can be caught on the screen is called real image. Real images are formed by a convergent beam of light rays, and virtual images are formed by a divergent beam of light rays.

(i) The image formed by a plane mirror is virtual in nature and always erect but laterally inverted and same in size as that of object.

(ii) The image formed by convex mirror is always erect, virtual in nature but smaller in size than that of object.

(iii) The image formed by concave mirror is either real or virtual and it may be inverted or erect, depending on the position of object in front of it.

72. The mirrors used in car headlights are concave mirrors. They reflect the light from the bulb which is placed at the focus. These light rays travel parallel and travel longer distances.

73. (a) As the image formed by a plane mirror is laterally inverted, the image of letters LIGHT appears as shown in figure.

(b) Image formed is laterally inverted and it is virtual, i.e., it cannot be caught on a screen.

The image is inverted through an angle of 180°.

74. The mirror used in vehicles as rear view mirror is convex. So, when the object is at a large distance from the mirror, image will be at the focus, i.e., a diminished image is obtained. When the object approaches nearer and nearer, the size of image increases. So, size of the image of car in the mirror gradually increases.

75. If we place an object between two plane mirrors which are placed closely and parallel to each other, then we obtain an infinite number of virtual and erect images.

76. The light rays coming from an object at infinity after reflection focus at the principal focus.

Hence, focal length $f = 20$ cm

The image is formed at the same position as that of the object, when the object is placed at the centre of curvature.

$\therefore$ Radius of curvature $= 2f = 2 \times 20 = 40$ cm

Level 3: Assess Your Concepts

77. $\angle OAB = 90 - 15 = 75°$

($\because$ angle of incidence = angle of reflection)

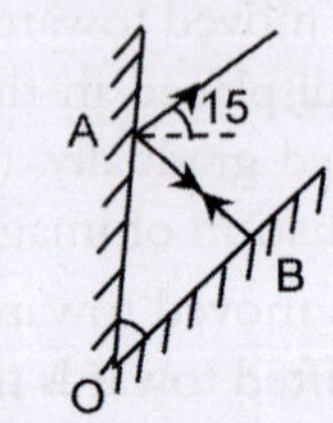

In ΔOAB, $\angle OAB + \angle AOB + \angle ABO = 180°$.

$75 + \theta + 90 = 180°$

$\Rightarrow \theta = 180 - 165$

$= 15°$

($\because$ The light ray retraces its path only if it incident along the normal)

78.

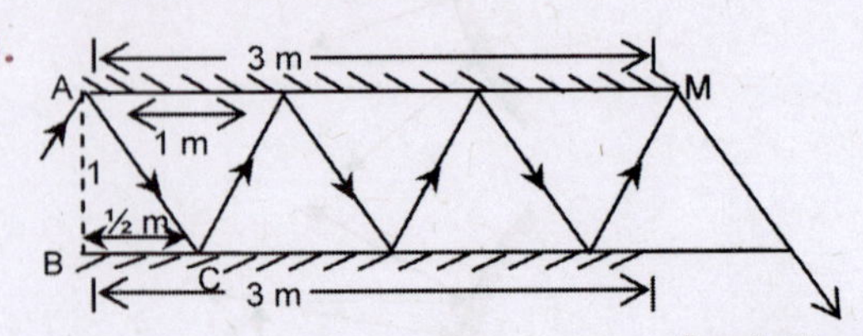

$\therefore$ From ΔABC

$1^2 + ½^2 = AC^2$

$AC = \dfrac{\sqrt{5}}{2}$

∴ Distance travelled by the light ray,

$$d = 6 \times \frac{\sqrt{5}}{2} \text{ m}$$

$$\therefore \text{ Time taken} = \frac{d}{v} = \frac{\frac{6\sqrt{5}}{2}}{3\times10^{8}} = \frac{6\sqrt{5}\times10^{-8}}{6} \text{ s}$$

∴ Time taken by light ray to reach point M is = $\sqrt{5}\times10^{-8}$ s.

79. (i) From the figure, the light rays from the object undergo reflection at each mirror surface and emerges out. Therefore, the light ray undergoes 10 reflections.

(ii) When the student views the object through periscope '*P*', the image will be bright. Whereas, the intensity of image observed through the periscope formed by joining a number of periscopes is less due to large number of reflections at mirror surfaces.

80. An inverted image will be formed only by concave mirror.

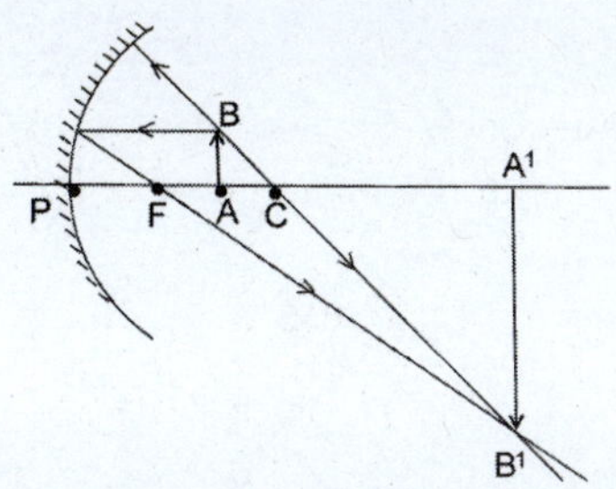

∴ The spherical mirror used is concave mirror.

Nature of image: (1) inverted (2) magnified (larger in size) (3) real image.

81. As the light ray after reflection from the first mirror travels parallel to the principal axis, it is placed at the principal focus of first mirror. The reflected ray from the second mirror travel through the focus of the first mirror. Therefore, the source is also placed at the focus of second mirror.

So, focal length f = 10 cm and radius of curvature $R = 2 \times f = 2 \times 10 = 20$ cm

82. AB is the object placed at 2f distance from the pole of the concave mirror. A[1]B[1] is the image formed by the concave mirror at 2f distance from its pole. It is a real, inverted image of size the same as that of the object.

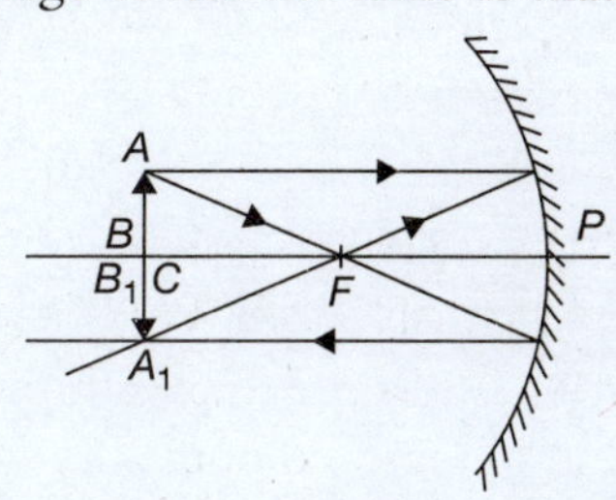

CHAPTER

5

Sound

Remember

Before beginning this chapter, you should be able to:

- Define sound
- Distinguish different sources of sound

Key Ideas

After completing this chapter, you should be able to:

- Understand sound as a form of energy
- Know the ultrasonic and infrasonic sound
- Understand propagation of sound
- Expalin reflection of sound and understand the concept of echo
- Imply practical applications of reflection of sound

Scientific Crypt

A Tribute to Heinrich Rudolf Hertz (1857–1894)

Heinrich Hertz was born on 22nd February 1857, in Hamburg, Germany. His father Gustav Hertz, was head of the judiciary in the city of Hamburg and his mother's name was Elizabeth Pfefferkorn Hertz. From his childhood days itself, he started showing unusual talent in science, mathematics, manual skills and languages. As a teenager, he constructed a spectrometer and a galvanometer which he used during his university studies also. Hertz did his graduation from the gymnasium in Hamburg in 1875 and completed his regular engineering studies from the University of Munich in 1877. During this time he developed a preference for physics to engineering. This lead to the remarkable combination of theoretical and experimental work, and he received the degree of Magna Cum Laude for "Induction in Rotating Spheres".

This German physicist also discovered the photoelectric effect and gave the first experimental proof of the existence of radio waves. With his acumenship, he experimentally produced and studied electromagnetic waves (also known as Hertzian waves). He studied electric charge in rarefied gases and also produced the great works "Electric Waves" and "Principles of Mechanics". In his honour, the unit of frequency is named "hertz". This great physicist left the world on January 1st, 1894 but not before leaving a huge impact in the field of science.

FUN TIME

CROSSWORD

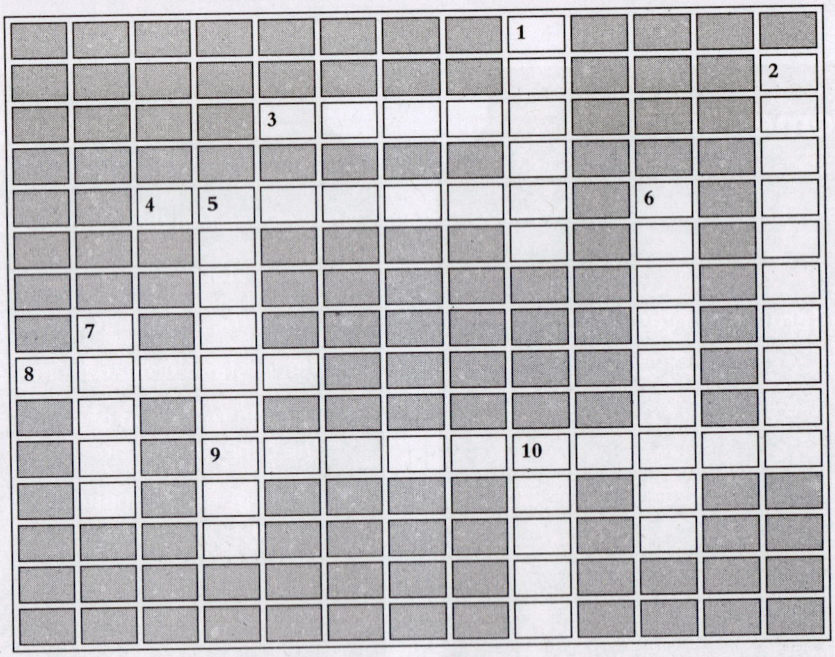

Across

3. The technique used to calculated depth of ocean beds.
4. An example for reed instrument.
8. The sound travels faster in ______ state of matter.
9. The type of sound that can be used to homogenise milk.

Down

1. The organ which helps the birds to produce sound.
2. Oscillating simple pendulum produces ______ types of vibrations.
5. Loudness of sound depends on ______.
6. Number of vibrations made in a unit time.
7. The gender which produces high frequency of sound.
10. Every vibrating body produces.

INTRODUCTION

We hear a lot of sounds in our surroundings; the rattling sound produced by the vehicles, sound produced by television, musical sound produced from a music player. These are all non-living things which produces sound. Similarly, sound is also produced by living beings.

For instance, a roaring lion, a barking dog, and people talking to each other. Such objects which produce sound are known as sources of sound. Is energy spent in all these cases to produce sound? Is the sound produced by all these sources similar? How is the sound produced by one source different from the other? Let us discuss certain terms which are useful in comparing the sounds produced by different sources, and the differences in their propagation through different media, and the way sounds are produced by different sources.

Production of Sound

Let us understand the production of sound with the help of certain activities.

Activity 1

Stretch a rubber band tightly between two fixed ends. Pluck it at the centre with your finger. You will be able to hear the sound produced by the rubber band. You will also observe the vibratory motion of the rubber band.

Activity 2

Tuning fork is a U-shaped steel rod with a steel handle. The handle is called stem and the two arms are called prongs.

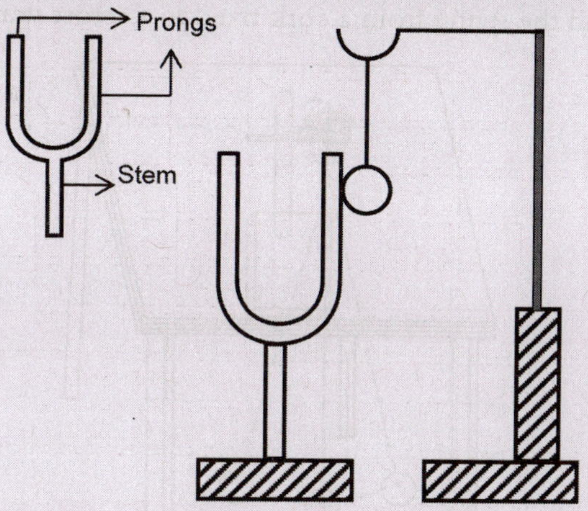

Figure 5.1 Activity for production of sound

Suspend a pith ball from a stand and strike the tuning fork with a hammer. Place the vibrating tuning fork in contact with the pith ball. We can observe the pith ball flying away. This is due to the vibration of tuning fork. You will be able to hear the sound if you place your ear near to the tuning fork. Thus, we can conclude that sound is produced by vibrating bodies.

What is vibratory motion? In Activity 1, sound is produced by a vibrating rubber band. What kind of motion did the rubber band exhibit? The rubber band makes a to and fro motion.

In Activity 2, what kind of motion do the prongs of tuning fork make? The prongs also make a to and fro motion. To and fro motion about a mean position or equilibrium position is called oscillatory or vibratory motion. Let us understand certain terms used in explaining oscillatory motion of a body.

Oscillation, Time Period, Frequency, and Amplitude of a Sound

One to and fro motion of a vibrating or oscillating body is called one **vibration** or one **oscillation**. The time taken for one vibration or one oscillation is known as the **time period**. It is usually denoted by a letter T and measured in second (s). Number of oscillations or number of vibrations made in a unit time is known as the **frequency**.

Thus,

$$\text{frequency} = \frac{\text{Number of oscillations}}{\text{Time taken}}$$

If we consider one oscillation, the time taken to complete one oscillation is its **time period (*T*)**.

Therefore,

$$\text{frequency} = \frac{1}{\text{Time period }(T)}$$

It is measured in s^{-1} or hertz.

Kilohertz (kHz), megahertz (MHz) are the bigger units of frequency.

$$1 \text{ kHz} = 1000 \text{ Hz}.$$

$$1 \text{ MHz} = 10^6 \text{ Hz}.$$

Info Bytes!

The smallest oscillation your ear can detect is about the diameter of a hydrogen molecule!

The maximum displacement a vibrating or oscillating body moved in one direction from its rest position is known as the **amplitude**. It is measured in cm or m.

Experiment to Determine the Frequency of Oscillation

A simple pendulum consists of a mass, called bob, suspended from a rigid support with the help of an unstretchable massless string. Practically, a simple pendulum consists of a metallic bob suspended from an unstretchable thread. Tie a metallic ball by using a string. Suspend the string from a cork fixed to a retort stand as shown in the Fig. 5.2.

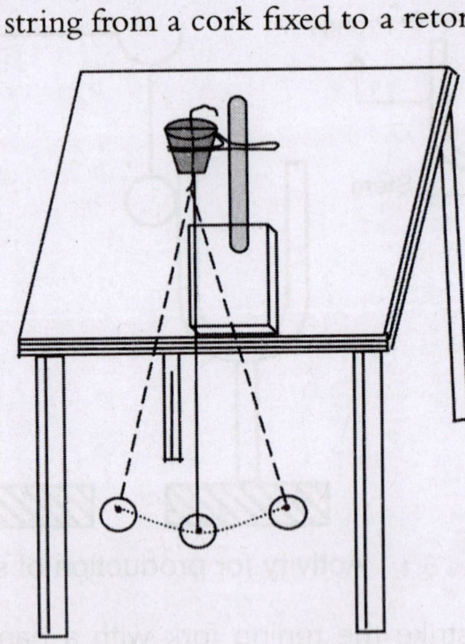

Figure 5.2 Determination of frequency of oscillation

Keep a stopwatch ready and pull the metallic ball from its initial position of rest and release. When the bob reaches the extreme position on the other side, start the stopwatch. Count the number of oscillations. At the end of 20 oscillations, stop the stopwatch and determine the time taken to complete 20 oscillations (t_1). Repeat the experiment and determine the time taken for 20 oscillations (t_2).

Determine the average of t_1 and t_2 as $t = \frac{t_1 + t_2}{2}$.

Now the time period (T) of the oscillation can be determined as

$$T = \frac{t}{20}$$

The frequency of oscillation, $f = \frac{1}{T}$.

Tabulate the observations as follows:

Observation Table

Time for 20 oscillations			Time period	Frequency
t_1	t_2	$t = \frac{t_1 + t_2}{2}$	$T = \frac{t}{20}$	$f = \frac{1}{T}$

Ultrasonic and Infrasonic Sound

It has been proved that the human ear is not sensitive to sounds of all frequencies. If the frequency of vibration of a body is less than 20 Hz, the vibrations are known as subsonic or **infrasonic vibrations**. Human ear is not sensitive to infrasonic vibrations. Similarly, human ear is not sensitive to the vibrations of frequency greater than 20,000 Hz; such vibrations are known as **ultrasonic vibrations**. Some of the animals, like dogs and bats, are sensitive to ultrasonic sounds. Hence, to hear the sound produced by any vibration, the source has to complete more than 20 vibrations and less than 20,000 vibrations in one second.

In the experiment of oscillating simple pendulum, does the pendulum produce sound? As the simple pendulum cannot complete 20 oscillations in one second, its oscillations are not perceived by the human ear.

The vibrations of frequency between 20 Hz and 20,000 Hz is perceived by the human ear and such vibrations are known as sonic vibrations or sound vibrations.

Applications of Ultrasonic Vibrations

1. Bats produce ultrasonic sounds in the frequency range from 50 Hz to 80,000 Hz when they fly. When these sounds strike the insects, they get reflected. They can locate their prey by receiving the reflected sound. Dolphins also locate their prey in a similar manner. This is called echolocation.
2. Ultrasonic sounds are used in sonar to find the depth of ocean bed.
3. For imaging the internal organs of human body, ultrasonic sound is used. The system of ultrasound scanning is used in sonography, where the condition of foetus inside the womb can be found out.
4. Milk can be homogenized by using ultrasonic sound.
5. Ultrasonic sounds are used to detect flaws inside a metal.
6. Dogs are sensitive to the frequency of about 40,000 Hz. So, they are trained specially to respond to a whistle called Galton whistle, which produces ultrasonic vibrations and this cannot be heard by humans.

Info Bytes!

Ultrasonic vibrations are used in medicine to break down kidney stones, a procedure called lithotripsy!

Propagation of Sound

Propagation of Sound Through Solids

Propagation of sound through solids can be explained through the activities below:

Activity

Ask your friend to hit one end of table in the class by using a metallic scale. Place your ear on the table. You will be able to hear the sound, which is propagated through the table. This shows that sound propagates through solids.

Activity

Take a long metallic rod. Place one end of the metallic rod near your ear. Ask your friend to hit the other end. You will be able to hear two distinct sounds; one propagated through the metallic rod and the other propagated through air. Thus, sound can propagate through both solids and gases. You can also observe that the sound which is propagated through the rod reaches you first. Thus, the speed of the sound through solids is greater than the speed of the sound through gas. You will also find that the sound propagated through air is much louder and clear.

Propagation of Sound Through Liquids

Experiment to prove that sound travels through liquids is explained below:

Take a metallic container and fill it with water. Take two coins and hit one on the other inside water. You will be able to hear a sound. Now place your ear against the side of the container and again hit one coin on the other inside the water. You will hear a louder and clear sound than the sound heard in the first case. Thus, sound also travels through liquids.

We know, sound is produced by vibrating objects. When an object vibrates, it moves back and forth about its mean position. When it moves forward, it pushes the air in front of it and compresses the air, creating a region of high pressure. This region is called compression (C), as shown in Fig 5.3. This compression moves away from the vibrating object. When the vibrating object moves backwards, it creates a region of low pressure called rarefaction (R), as shown in Fig 5.3. Hence, when the object moves back and forth rapidly, a series of compressions and rarefactions are created in the medium. These make the sound wave propagate through the medium. As sound waves propagate through air, the air molecules vibrate back and forth parallel to the direction of motion of the wave. Hence, sound waves are longitudinal in nature.

Compression is the region of high pressure and rarefaction is the region of low pressure. Pressure is related to the density of the medium. More density of the medium gives more pressure and vice versa. Thus, propagation of sound can be visualized as propagation of pressure variations, i.e., compressions and rarefactions or density variations in the medium.

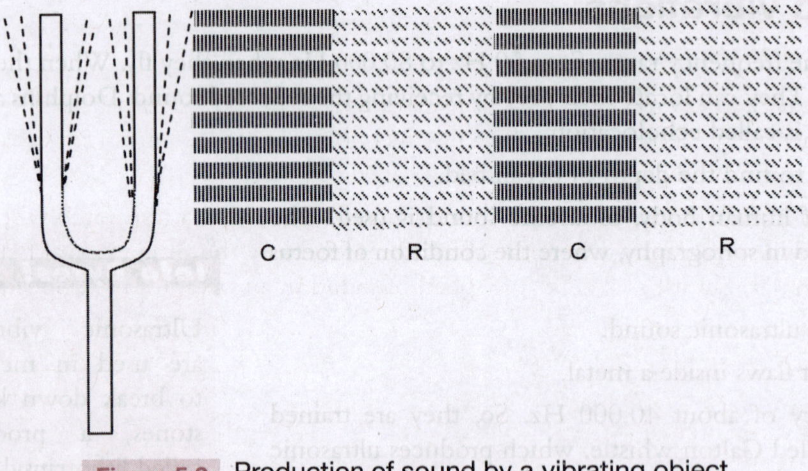

Figure 5.3 Production of sound by a vibrating object

Info Bytes!

- The speed of sound varies depending on the medium; it's faster in water than in air.
- Whales use the unique properties of sound in water to communicate over long distances!

Propagation of Sound Through Vacuum

From the above activities you have learnt that sound travels through solid, liquid, and gas.

Activity

Consider a glass jar with an outlet at the bottom as shown in the Fig. 5.4. Switch on the electric bell. We will be able to hear the sound produced by the bell. Connect a vacuum pump to the outlet of the jar and remove the air inside the jar. As the air is gradually removed from the jar, the intensity of sound decreases and finally we do not hear the sound. When the air is removed a vacuum is created, hence, we are unable to hear the sound. This shows that a medium is required for the propagation of sound.

Experiment to Determine the Speed of Sound in Air

Select an open place such that two persons P_1 and P_2 are separated by a distance say 1 km, but can see each other. The apparatus required for the experiment are a cracker, a stopwatch, and a survey chain. The person P_1 will fire the cracker. As soon as the person P_2 sees the light, he will start the stopwatch. The person P_2 will switch off the stopwatch when he hears the sound of the cracker. Note down the time interval that corresponds, to the time taken by sound to travel from P_1 and P_2. Measure the distance between the two places by using the survey chain.

We know that, speed $= \dfrac{\text{distance}}{\text{time}}$

The speed of the sound in air $= \dfrac{\text{distance between the two places}}{\text{time interval}}$

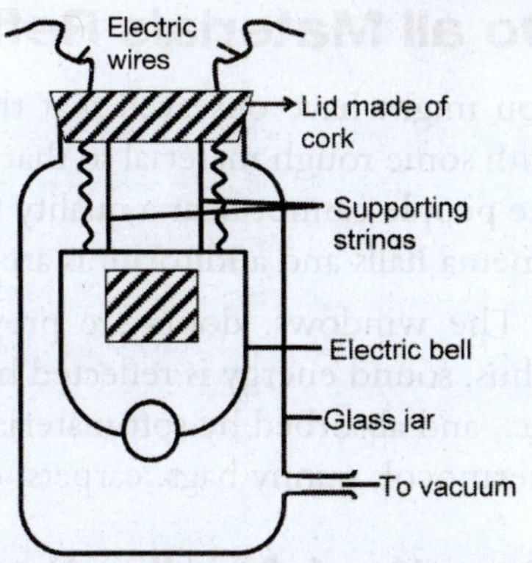

Figure 5.4 Bell jar experiment

Konnect

In the above experiment, the time taken by the light to reach the person P_2 is neglected as the speed of the light (3×10^8 m s^{-1}) is very high compared to the speed of sound. In the above activity, both sound and light are produced at the same instant of time. But first the light reaches the person then the sound. This is due to a very high speed of light (3×10^8 m s^{-1}) compared with the speed of sound (330 m s^{-1}). Due to the same reason, the thunder is heard after the flash of light is seen.

Formation of Thunder

During lightning, nearly 75% of its electrical energy is used in heating the gases present in and around the flash. Due to this, the temperature of the surrounding region increases to about 10,000 K in a few seconds. As a result, a pressure wave is created giving rise to compressions and rarefactions and producing a violent sound called thunder.

Distance of the cloud from the surface of the earth can be measured as discussed below. Start a stopwatch when you see the flash of lightning. Stop the stopwatch when you hear the sound of the thunder. Note the time interval between the flash of lightning and the sound of the thunder. Let it be 't' s. Let the speed of sound in air be 330 m s^{-1}. Speed of sound

$= \dfrac{\text{height of the cloud}}{\text{time interval } (t)}$

Height of the cloud = speed of sound × time interval = $(330 \times t)$ m.

Reflection of Sound

Let us understand this concept with the help of the following activity:

Activity

Mount a smooth and hard wooden plank ABCD vertically on the surface of a table as shown in the Fig. 5.5. Clamp two pipes P and Q inclined at certain angles on the table. Place a ticking clock S closer is to the pipe P. The ticking sound produced by the clock travels through the pipe and directed towards the wooden plank. Now keep your ear to the open end of Q and adjust the position of Q to listen to the ticking sound. The sound which travels through the pipe gets reflected from the wooden plank to reach you. Measure the angle made by the two pipes with the normal. The pipes P and Q make equal angle with the normal. Thus, the sound which is incident and reflected from the wooden plank makes equal angle with the normal. This phenomenon of sound is known as reflection of sound.

Do all Materials Reflect Sound?

You might have observed that the walls of cinema halls and auditoria are coated with some rough material so that the sound is absorbed. If the sound gets reflected, the people cannot hear a quality sound. For the same reason, the stairs and seats of cinema halls and auditoriums are covered with sound absorbing materials.

The windows, doors are provided with thick curtains to absorb the sound. Thus, sound energy is reflected by hard surfaces, like metal sheets, walls, plywood, etc., and absorbed by soft materials with loose texture, like cloth, porous material, thermocol, gunny bags, carpets, etc.

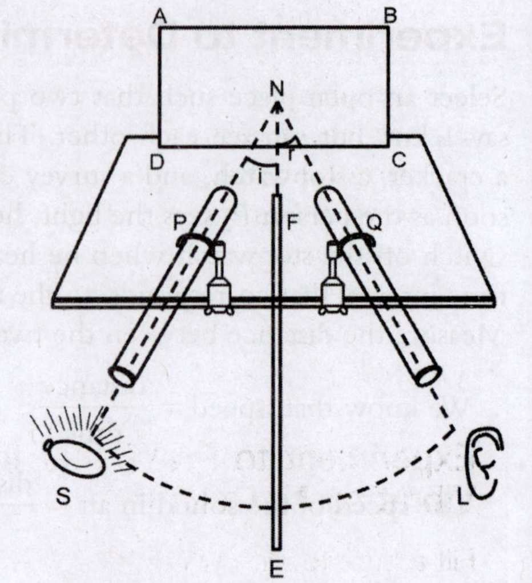

Figure 5.5 Reflection of Sound

Practical Applications of Reflection of Sound

- **Mega phone:** It consists of a horn-shaped tube. Sound proceeds at the narrow end undergoes multiple reflections and comes out of the tube. It can travel longer distances.
- **Sonar (Sound Navigation and Ranging):** It is a technique used in ships to calculate the depth of ocean beds. Ultrasonic sound is sent to the ocean beds from the ship. This ultrasonic sound gets reflected from the ocean beds. The reflected sound is received by a suitable detector in the ship. The time taken to receive the sound is measured. Let 't' be the time taken, 'v' be the velocity of sound in water, and 'd' be the depth of the ocean bed.

  Then, $v = 2d/t$ or $d = vt/2$.
- **Toy telephone:** Take a long piece of thread. Fix two plastic or paper cups at the ends of the thread. Let the two ends be held by two different persons. Let one person speak at one end, and hold the other cup nearer to the ear of the other person. He will be able to hear the sound which is propagated through the thread.
- **Different kinds of sound:** We can easily make out the sound produced by different vibrating objects. For example, one can easily distinguish the sound produced by a girl and a boy. The sound produced by a flute is different from the sound produced by a violin. The sound of a cat is different from the sound of a dog. The frequencies of vibration or the pitch of the sounds produced by different sources are different. This helps us to distinguish different sounds.
- **Loudness or intensity of sound:** It is the property that distinguishes a feeble sound from a louder one. The loudness of sound increases with the amplitude of vibration of a vibrating body. The amplitude of vibration depends upon the energy. More the energy spent to set a body into vibration the more is the amplitude of vibration. Thus, the loudness of sound increases with increase in amplitude or energy and vice versa. Loudness is a characteristic of sound which differentiates a soft and loud sound.
- **Measurement of loudness of sound:** Loudness of sound is measured in a unit called decibel and it is denoted as dB. Humans are sensitive to sound of loudness from 10 dB to 180 dB. The sound of loudness more than 90 dB is painful to humans and causes various health problems. The sound of loudness from 50 dB to 60 dB is considered as normal.
- **Factors affecting the loudness of sound:** Loudness of sound depends upon the surface area of the vibrating body. For example, the loudness of sound produced from a table of larger surface area is greater than the loudness of sound produced by a table of smaller surface area. Thus, loudness of sound increases as the surface area of the vibrating body increases.
- **Loudness of sound decreases with increase in distance:** As you move away from a source of sound, the intensity of sound decreases. For example, if you sit on the first bench in your class, the loudness of the sound heard will be more. But if you sit on the last bench in your classroom, the loudness of the sound heard by you will be less.
- **Pitch:** The shrillness of sound depends on the pitch of the sound. The voice of a woman is shriller than the voice of a man. This is due to the higher pitch of the sound of a woman than the pitch of the sound of a man. The pitch

of a sound depends on the frequency. Higher the frequency of sound, greater is the pitch. For example, a flute can produce the sound of different pitch. The pitch of the sound produced can be varied by changing the length of the vibrating body. In the case of the musical instruments, like violin, the pitch of the sound is varied by changing the length of the vibrating part of the string. The frequency of vibration depends on the length of the vibrating part of the string. Thus, the pitch of a sound does not depend on the amount of energy spent in making the body to vibrate or the amplitude of vibration, but it is the effect produced in the brain by the sound of some particular frequency.

Activity

Experiment to Prove that the Pitch of the Sound Decreases with Increase in Length of a Vibrating Air Column

Fill a burette with water nearly $\frac{3}{4}$th of the length. Blow air into the burette. A high pitched sound is produced.

Now reduce the quantity of water in the burette by releasing the tap at the bottom of the burette. Blow air into the burette once again. A sound of low pitch is produced in this case. Repeat the experiment by reducing the quantity of water in the burette. You will observe that as the length of the air column in the burette increases the pitch of the sound decreases. This is due to the decrease in frequency of vibrating air column as the length of the air column increases.

- **Quality of sound or timbre:** Voice of a person can be distinguished from the voice of another person even though the vocal cords of two persons are of the same length and thickness. This is due to the difference in characteristic property known as quality of sound or timbre. Similarly, the notes produced by two musical instruments, like violin and sitar are different even if the length and the thickness of the strings in both the instruments are same, due to the difference in the quality of sound.

Info Bytes!

Quality of a sound is a characteristic property which distinguishes two sounds of equal pitch and loudness.

- **Sound produced by animals and human beings:** In humans, the sound is produced by the vibration of vocal cords. The vocal cords are stretched across the larynx and it leaves a gap between them for the passage of air. The air from the lungs is forced through the slit and the vocal cords vibrate to produce sound. The frequency of sound produced depends on the thickness and the tension of vocal cords. When the vocal cords are tight and thin a high frequency sound (shrill sound) is produced and when the vocal cords are loose and thick, they produce sound of low frequency. The pitch of the sound produced depends on the muscles attached to the vocal cords. Take a rubber band and cut it into two pieces of equal lengths. Place the two pieces one above the other. Stretch them and blow air between them. Observe the pitch of the sound produced. Now stretch the rubber bands further and blow air between them and once again observe the pitch of the sound produced. It is observed that when the rubber bands are stretched further there is an increase in the pitch of the sound. Now take a thin rubber band and cut it into two pieces. Blow air between them after stretching them. It is observed that the pitch of the sound produced is very high when a thin rubber band is used.
- **Sound produced by animals:** The sound produced by mammals is due to the vibration of vocal cords. Birds produce sound with the help of ring of cartilage called **syrinx**, which is fixed at the beginning of the wind pipe. Some birds can produce sound of two different notes as they have two parts in the syrinx. The sound produced by flapping of the wings by the insects, such as mosquitoes, houseflies are audiable as the frequency of flapping is more than 20 Hz.
- **Hearing:** The vibrations of air in the form of compressions and rarefactions produced by the source of sound reach the ear and they cause vibrations on the ear drum. These vibrations make the ear drum to vibrate and they are picked-up by the auditory nerves which are sent as impulses to the centre of hearing in the brain.

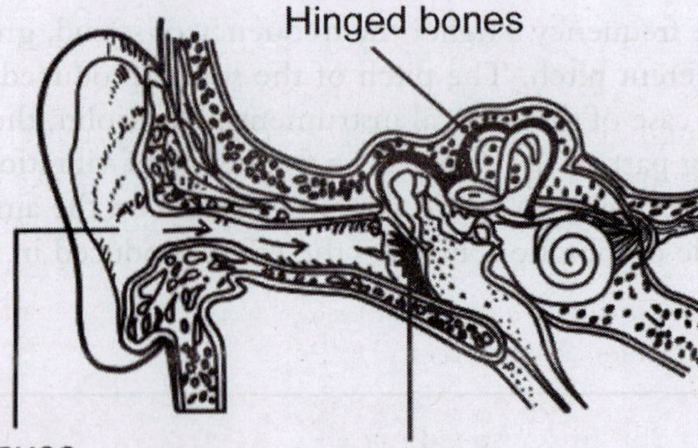

Figure 5.6 Human ear

- **Music and noise:** The sound that produces a pleasant effect on our ears is called **music** and the sound that produces an unpleasant effect on our ears is called **noise**.

Konnect

It is difficult to classify a given sound as music or noise as they produce a pleasant effect on one person and produce an unpleasant effect on another person.

Musical Instruments

Musical instruments are of the following types:

1. **Stringed instruments:** These instruments have stretched strings mounted on wooden frames. These strings produce musical sounds when vibrated. The pitch of the sound can be changed by changing the length, tension, and thickness of the vibrating string. Veena, Sitar, Guitar, Violin, etc., are examples of stringed instruments.
2. **Wind or reed instruments:** These instruments are made of long and hollow pipes with a certain number of holes on the sides. The air column in the tube is made to vibrate by blowing air into it. This vibrating air column produces musical sound. Flute, bassoon, oboes are examples of wind instruments.
3. **Percussion instruments (Drum instruments):** These instruments have stretched membranes made-up of leather. Vibration of these membranes produce musical sound. Different musical sounds can be produced by exciting these membranes at different tensions. Drums, mridangam, tabla, etc., are examples of percussion instruments.
   Some instruments are just struck or beaten in a rhythm to produce music. They are called Ghana vadya.
   Examples: manjira, the ghatam, jal tarang, etc.
4. **Noise pollution:** The undesirable, loud, and harsh sounds produced in the environment by different sources is called noise pollution. Nowadays, the dependence on various kinds of machines at home, workplace, and factories has increased. This leads to an increase in noise pollution. The noise pollution can be determined by loudness of sound and duration of sound at a particular place. Use of a television, a radio, a vacuum cleaner, exploding crackers, publicity announcements made by trading companies, noise produced in factories and noise produced by vehicles are examples of sources of noise pollution. Noise pollution results in loss of hearing, loss of work efficiency, and tension in humans.

The following measures must be taken to prevent and control noise pollution.

1. Silencers should be provided in automobiles.
2. Usage of loudspeakers should be reduced.
3. Factories should be located away from the residential areas.
4. T.V., radio, and music players should be played at a lower volume.

Echo

If you stand in front of a huge building at a distance greater than 17 m, and clap, you will be able to hear the clap sound twice. When sound strikes a smooth and hard surface, it is reflected back to the listener and repetition of the sound, a short time after it is produced is called an echo. Why should we stand at a minimum distance of 17 m to hear the echo? The sound heard by a human ear will persist in his brain for 0.1 s. This is known as persistence of hearing. Thus, to hear the echo distinctly, the time gap between the two sounds must be 0.1 s. Let the distance between the listener and the reflecting surface be d. The total distance travelled by the sound = $2d$.

The speed of sound in air, $V = 330$ m s^{-1}, speed $s = \dfrac{2d}{t}$.

$$330 = \frac{2d}{0.1}$$

Thus,

$$d = \frac{0.1 \times 330}{2} = 16.5 \text{ m.}$$

Thus, the minimum distance between the listener and the reflecting surface to hear the echo in air is 16.5 m (when the velocity of sound through air is 330 m s^{-1}).

POINTS TO REMEMBER

- ✔ Sound is a form of energy which is produced by vibrating bodies.
- ✔ The number of vibrations produced by a vibrating body in a unit time is called frequency of vibration.
- ✔ The time taken by an oscillating body to complete one oscillation is called time period (T).
- ✔ Frequency, $f = \dfrac{1}{\text{Time period } (T)}$
- ✔ The maximum displacement a vibrating body from its rest position is called amplitude.
- ✔ The S.I. unit of frequency is hertz (Hz).
- ✔ If the frequency of vibration is less than 20 Hz, it is known as infrasonic vibration.
- ✔ If the frequency of vibrations is more than 20,000 Hz, it is known as ultrasonic vibration.
- ✔ The velocity of sound through solids (V_s) > velocity of sound through liquids (V_ℓ) > velocity of sound through gases (V_g).
- ✔ Velocity of sound = $\dfrac{\text{distance travelled by the sound}}{\text{time taken}}$.
- ✔ When sound strikes a surface, it is reflected back to the listener and repetition of sound a short time after it is produced is called an echo.
- ✔ The loudness of sound increases with the increase in amplitude of vibration of a vibrating body.
- ✔ The shrillness of sound depends on the pitch of the sound.
- ✔ Quality of sound is a characteristic property which distinguishes two sounds of same frequency and loudness.
- ✔ The loudness of sound is measured in decibel.

PRACTICE QUESTIONS CLASSROOM WING

Very Short Answer Type Questions

***Directions for questions from 1 to 5:* Fill in the blanks.**

1. The sounds of frequencies greater than ________ are called ultrasonic sounds.

2. Sound travels much ________ than light in a given medium.

3. In general, the voice of a woman has a ________ than that of a man.

4. ________ is used in medical diagnosis.

5. Loudness of sound decreases with increase in ________.

***Directions for questions from 6 to 42:* For each of the questions, four choices have been provided. Select the correct alternative.**

6. The vibrations of a turning fork are ________ in nature.

(a) Oscillatory (b) Periodic
(c) Both (a) and (b) (d) None of these

7. The frequency of sound waves which can be heard by humans is ________.

(a) Less than 20 Hz
(b) Greater than 20 kHz
(c) Between 20 Hz and 20 kHz
(d) None of these

8. If the time period of a simple pendulum is 10 seconds, then its frequency is ________ Hz.

(a) 10 (b) 5
(c) 0.1 (d) 1

9. A string is stretched over two rigid supports and a weight of 1 kgwt is suspended from one of its free ends and then it is plucked. If the length of string over two rigid supports is decreased and plucked again, then the frequency of sound produced

(a) In the first case is more.
(b) In the second case is more.
(c) In both the cases is equal.
(d) Cannot be determined

10. The principle of reflection of sound is used ________.

(a) In hearing echos
(b) To locate shoals of fish under the sea bed
(c) In the detection of insects by bats
(d) All of the above

11. The velocity of sound is maximum in ________.

(a) Liquids (b) Solids
(c) Gases (d) Cannot be determined

12. Sound cannot travel in ________.

(a) Air (b) Glass
(c) Iron (d) Vacuum

13. Bats make use of ________ waves.

(a) Ultrasonic sound (b) Infrasonic sound
(c) Audible range sound (d) All of the above

14. The frequency of vibration ________ with the increase in time period.

(a) Increase (b) Decreases
(c) Remains same (d) Cannot be determined

15. The order of magnitude of velocity of sound in solids, liquids and gases is ________. (V_s = velocity in solids, V_ℓ = velocity in liquids and V_g = velocity in gases)

(a) $V_g > V_\ell > V_s$ (b) $V_s > V_g > V_\ell$
(c) $V_g < V_\ell < V_s$ (d) $V_s = V_g = V_\ell$

16. 1 kHz = ________ Hz.

(a) 100 (b) 1000
(c) 10000 (d) 100000

17. As the simple pendulum cannot complete ________ oscillations in one second, its oscillations are not perceived by the human ear.

(a) 10 (b) 20
(c) 30 (d) 40

18. Which of the following statements is correct?

(a) All vibrations produce sound.
(b) Vibrations of frequency more than 20 Hz only produce sound.

(c) Vibrations of frequency more than 20 Hz only produce sound.

(d) Vibrations of frequency between 20 Hz and 20,000 Hz only produce sound.

19. The loudness of sound depends upon

(a) Its amplitude (b) Its frequency

(c) Its velocity (d) All of the above

20. Harmonium is an example of ______.

(a) A stringed instrument (b) A wind instrument

(c) A percussion instrument (d) None of these

21. 1 decibel = ______ bell.

(a) 10 (b) 1/10

(c) 100 (d) 1/100

22. The sound of loudness of sound in the range of 15 *B*-16 *B* is:

(a) Not audible (b) Just audible

(c) Moderate (d) Painful to the ear

23. Arrange the following steps of an experiment in a sequential order to determine the frequency of a simple pendulum.

(A) Start the stopwatch when the bob reaches the extreme position and count the number of oscillations.

(B) Suspend a simple pendulum from a cork fixed to a stand.

(C) Repeat the experiment and determine the time taken for 20 oscillations. (t_2)

(D) Pull the bob of the simple pendulum from its initial position of rest and release.

(E) Stop the stopwatch at the end of 20 oscillations and determine the time taken to complete 20 oscillations (t_1).

(F) Determine the average of t_1 and t_2 as t.

(G) The time period of the oscillation is found using, $T = \frac{t}{20}$ and frequency using, $f = \frac{1}{T}$.

(a) ADBCEFG (b) AFEDBCG

(c) BDAECFG (d) BDEFCAG

24. Arrange the following steps of an experiment in a sequential order to determine the speed of sound in air.

(A) Let two persons P_1 and P_2 are separated by a distance of 1 km in an open place.

(B) The person P_1 will fire the cracker and person P_2 will start the stopwatch as soon as he sees the light.

(C) Note the time taken by the sound to travel from P_1 to P_2.

(D) The person P_2 will stop the stopwatch as soon as he hears the sound of the cracker.

(E) The speed of the sound in air is the ratio of the distance between the two places to the time interval.

(F) Measure the distance between the two places by using the survey chain.

(a) ABCDEF (b) ABDCFE

(c) ADBFCE (d) BCADEF

25. Which of the following statements is correct?

(a) All vibrations produce sound.

(b) Vibrations of frequency less than 20 Hz only produce sound.

(c) Vibrations of frequency more than 20 Hz only produce sound.

(d) Vibrations of frequency between 20 Hz and 20,000 Hz only produce sound.

26. The maximum possible displacement of a vibrating body from its mean position during its motion is equal to:

(a) Its amplitude. (b) Half its amplitude.

(c) Twice its amplitude. (d) Its frequency.

27. In which instrument does the vibrating air column produced by blowing air into the tube produce musical sound?

(a) Oboes (b) Veena

(c) Mridangam (d) Violin

28. Three persons P_1, P_2, and P_3 are at three different points A, B and C as shown in the figure. P_1 and P_2 clap at the same time. For P_3 to hear two distinct claps, the minimum distance between P_1 and P_2 should be ______ m. (The velocity of sound in air is 330 m s^{-1})

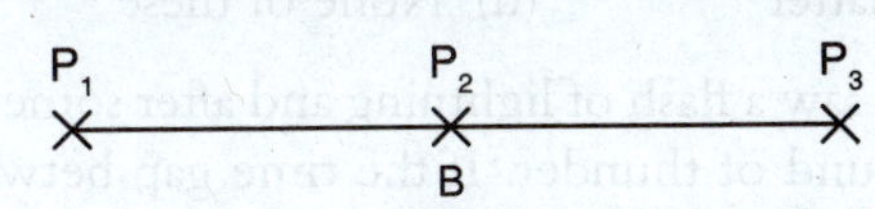

(a) 33 (b) 330

(c) 363 (d) 660

29. Which of the following statements is correct?

(a) The pitch of sound decreases with a decrease in the length of a vibrating air column.

(b) The pitch of sound increases with a decrease in the thickness of a vibrating string.

(c) The pitch of sound decreases with a decrease in the length of the vibrating string.

(d) The pitch of sound depends upon the amplitude of a vibrating body.

30. **Assertion (A):** Rama Raju loves listening to Carnatic music played on Mridangam whereas his daughter Neeta gets irritated by it.
Reason (R): The sound that produces pleasant effect on our ears is called music and the sound that produces an unpleasant effect on our ears is called noise.
(a) Both A and R are correct and R is the correct explanation of A.
(b) Both A and R are correct but R is not the correct explanation of A.
(c) A is correct and R is incorrect.
(d) Both A and R are incorrect.

31. **Assertion (A):** The pitch of the sound produced by the vibrating string can be changed.
Reason (R): The pitch of the sound can be changed by changing the length, tension and thickness of the vibrating string.
(a) Both A and R are correct and R is the correct explanation of A.
(b) Both A and R are correct but R is not the correct explanation of A.
(c) A is correct and R is incorrect.
(d) Both A and R are incorrect.

32. Which of the following is/are practical application(s) of reflection of sound?
(a) Mega phone (b) Sonar
(c) Toy telephone (d) All of these

33. The sound that produces a pleasant effect on our ears is called ______.
(a) Music (b) Noise
(c) Clatter (d) None of these

34. Ratan saw a flash of lightning and after sometime heard the sound of thunder. If the time gap between seeing and hearing is 3 s, then write the following steps in sequence to find the height from the ground where the lightning is produced.
(A) Consider the velocity of sound (v) as 330 m s^{-1}.
(B) Note the time gap (t) between seeing and hearing.
(C) From the formula, speed = $\frac{\text{distance}}{\text{time taken}}$, height at which lightning was produced = speed of sound × time interval.
(D) Substitute the values in the equation (1) and find the value of the height of the lightning from the ground.
(a) BACD (b) BCAD
(c) CBDA (d) DABC

35. Which of the following statements is right?
(a) The pitch varies with change in amplitude.
(b) The frequency of vibration identifies the pitch of any sound.
(c) The voice of a woman has low pitch when compared to that of a man.
(d) A tabla produces high pitch sound when compared to that of a flute.

36. Write the following steps in sequence to prove that sound travels through liquids.
(A) Place the ear against the side of the container and repeat the activity of hitting one coin with the other inside the water.
(B) Take a metallic container and fill it with water.
(C) Place two coins inside the water. Hit one on the other and observe the sound produced.
(D) Now, a clear and louder sound is heard proving that sound also travels through liquids.
(a) ABDC (b) CABD
(c) BCAD (d) DABC

37. Loudness of sound ______ with ______ in distance.
(a) decreases, increase (b) increases, decrease
(c) increases, increase (d) decreases, decrease

38. Which of the following is/are example(s) of stringed instruments?
(a) Veena (b) Sitar
(c) Guitar (d) All of these

39. If more energy is spent to set a body into vibration, then
(a) The amplitude of vibrating body is more.
(b) The amplitude of vibrating body is less.
(c) The amplitude of vibrating body always remains same even after setting it into vibration.
(d) Both (b) and (c).

40. Jal tarang is an example of
(a) Percussion instrument
(b) Stringed instrument
(c) Wind instrument
(d) Reed instrument

41. The instruments made of long and hollow pipes with a certain number of holes on the sides are
(a) Wind or reed instruments.
(b) Stringed instruments.
(c) Drum instruments.
(d) All of the above

42. Noise pollution results in
(a) loss of hearing
(b) loss of work efficiency
(c) tension in humans
(d) All of these

***Directions for questions from 43 to 46:* Match the entries given in Column A with the appropriate ones in Column B.**

43.

Column A	Column B
A. Height of the cloud	a. Gunny bags
B. Frequency, $n = 10$ Hz	b. Painful to humans
C. Sound absorption	c. Time Period $T = 0.1$s
D. More than 90 dB	d. Speed of sound × time interval
E. Syrinx	e. Ring of cartilage

44.

Column A	Column B
A. Sound	a. Percussion instrument
B. Depth of ocean bed	b. Sound needs a medium
C. Maximum displacement	c. SONAR
D. Tabla	d. Amplitude
E. Bell jar experiment	e. Vibrating body

45.

Column A	Column B
A. 1 MHz	a. 10^6 Hz
B. 340 m s^{-1}	b. Decibel
C. Music	c. Velocity of sound in air at 20 °C
D. Loudness of sound	d. 50 Hz to 80,000 Hz
E. Bats	e. Pleasant sensation of hearing

46.

Column A	Column B
A. Bell jar experiment	a. 0.1 s
B. Bats	b. 10 Hz
C. Persistence of hearing	c. Sound can not travel in vacuum
D. Infrasonic	d. 50 Hz to 80,000 Hz

***Directions for questions from 47 to 66:* Answer the following questions.**

47. What is the ratio of frequency to time period of a seconds' pendulum?

48. If a body vibrates 40 times in 4 seconds, then calculate its frequency.

49. What is the length of a simple pendulum?

50. What is frequency of oscillation?

51. What is meant by one oscillation of a simple pendulum?

52. A thunder is heard by a girl in 6 seconds after the lightning is seen and the speed of sound in air is 330 m s^{-1}. What is the distance from the girl to where lightning occurred?

53. What is reflection of sound?

54. What is an echo?

55. What is the frequency of infrasonic sound?

56. What is the velocity of sound in vacuum?

57. What is the product of frequency and time period of a seconds pendulum?

58. What is quality of sound?

59. What is noise pollution?

60. Why the oscillations of a simple pendulum are not perceived by the human ear?

61. What is the persistence of hearing?

62. What is the minimum distance between the reflector and the listener to hear the echo, when the speed of sound in air is 330 m s^{-1}?

63. What is the principle on which megaphone works?

64. What happens to the pitch of the sound when the length of the vibrating column is increased?

65. A body completes 50 oscillations in 20 s. What is the frequency?

66. The time period of a vibrating body is 0.1 s. Find its frequency.

Short Answer Type Questions

67. Describe an experiment to show that sound travels through liquids.

68. When two drums A and B, having frequencies of 500 Hz and 216 Hz, respectively are vibrated simultaneously, then the shrillness of sound produced by drum A will be more /less/equal to drum B?

69. Explain the formation of thunder.

70. A thunder is heard 2 s after a flash of lightning is seen. If the velocity of sound in air is 330 m s^{-1}, how far away from you has lightning occurred?

71. What are the differences between music and noise?

72. Why is the sound produced at one end of a metallic pipe heard twice at the other end?

73. An observer stands at a distance of 6600 m from a cliff and fires a gun. If the speed of sound in air is 330 m s^{-1}, then the time taken by him to hear an echo is ________.

74. State some sources of noise pollution.

75. What are the factors which affect the loudness of sound?

76. What are the factors which affect the pitch of sound?

77. Time period of a pendulum is given by, $T = 2\pi\sqrt{\frac{\ell}{g}}$. If the length of the pendulum is increased by four times, then the time period is ________.

78. Give two practical applications of reflection of sound.

79. What is the minimum distance required to hear an echo, when the speed of sound in air is 340 m s^{-1}?

80. Describe an experiment to prove that the pitch of the sound is dependent on the length of a vibrating air column.

81. The time period of a simple pendulum of length 'ℓ' on the Earth is 'T'. If it is taken to the moon, then time period of pendulum on the moon is ________. (take $g_e = 6\ g_m$)

Essay Type Questions

82. Explain how the sound produced by a source reaches the ear with a neat diagram.

83. Explain how sound is produced in humans.

84. What are the different measures to be taken to reduce noise pollution?

85. Describe an activity to show that pitch depends on the thickness of the vibrating body.

86. Explain the propagation of sound in air.

87. What are wind and percussion instruments? Give examples.

88. (a) What is sonography?
(b) How do bats and whales make use of ultrasonic sounds?
(c) What are the harmful effects of noise pollution?

89. (a) What are the higher units of frequency?
(b) How is noise pollution determined at a given place?
(c) Name some sound absorbing materials.

90. Describe an experiment to show that sound cannot propagate in vacuum.

PRACTICE QUESTIONS COMPETITION WING

Level 1: Apply your Concepts

***Directions for questions from 1 to 15:* Fill in the blanks.**

1. If a body vibrates 20 times in 2 seconds, then its time period is ______.
2. The velocity of sound is minimum in ______.
3. The time taken to perform 45 vibrations is ______ times the time taken for a single vibration.
4. If a body vibrates 50 times in a second, then its frequency is ______.
5. ______ principle is used to locate shoals of fish under the seabed.
6. 1 kHz = ______ Hz.
7. ______ property distinguishes two sounds of the same frequency and loudness.
8. The time period of a simple pendulum is independent of ______ of oscillation.
9. The loudness of sound is determined by its ______.
10. ______ sound is used as a diagnostic tool in medical science.
11. The ______ of sound is determined by its frequency.
12. Mala heard a thunder 4 s after lightning is seen. If the distance of that lightning spot from him is 1320 m, then the speed of sound in air would be ______.
13. The sound produced by a company horn reaches a person on the road at a distance of 990 m in the time of ______ s. Consider the velocity of sound in air as 330 m s^{-1}.
14. Propagation of sound can be visualized as propagation of ______ in the medium.
15. A frequency of 1 Hz means ______ oscillations per second.

***Directions for questions from 16 to 25:* State whether the following statements are true or false.**

16. The to and fro motion of an object is called vibration.
17. The maximum displacement of a bob from its mean position is called its amplitude.
18. The unit of frequency is second.
19. The time taken to perform 30 vibrations is 30 times the time taken for a single vibration.
20. If a body vibrates 20 times in a second, then its frequency is 20 Hz.
21. Sitar, veena, and guitar are some percussion instruments.
22. The sounds of frequencies greater than 20 kHz are called ultrasonic sounds.
23. Sound travels much faster than light in a given medium.
24. The velocity of sound is more in vacuum than in any other medium.
25. In general, the voice of a woman has a higher frequency than that of a man.

***Directions for questions from 26 to 59:* For each of the questions, four choices have been provided. Select the correct alternative.**

26. Ultrasonic sound waves are used in ______.
    (a) Dishwashers
    (b) Medical diagnostics
    (c) Detection of flaws in materials
    (d) All of the above
27. The sound produced by a siren given by a company reaches a person on the road at a distance of 110 m in ______s. (Velocity of sound in air is 330 m s^{-1})
    (a) 3 (b) 4
    (c) 1/3 (d) 0.5
28. The velocity of a wave is 220 m s^{-1}, the distance travelled by the wave in 2s is ______ m
    (a) 440 (b) 247.5
    (c) 330 (d) 880
29. An echo of sound produced by a person, is heard from a distant tower after an interval of 1.5 s. If the speed of sound in air is 330 m s^{-1}, then the distance of the tower from the person is ______ m.
    (a) 495 (b) 247.5
    (c) 330 (d) 500

30. The flash of lightening is seen much before we hear the thunder because
(a) The speed of light is more than the speed of sound.
(b) The speed of sound is more than the speed of light.
(c) The speed of light is equal to the speed of sound.
(d) The speed of sound is more in vacuum than in air.

31. Which of the following materials is the best absorber of sound?
(a) Metallic sheet (b) Plywood
(c) Cork (d) Shining water surface

32. The pitch of sound is determined by the ______ of vibration.
(a) Frequency (b) Amplitude
(c) Velocity (d) None of these

33. When two tuning forks A and B, having frequencies 512 Hz and 212 Hz, respectively, are vibrated simultaneously, the pitch of sound produced
(a) By 'A' will be more.
(b) By 'B' will be more.
(c) By A and B will be equal.
(d) Cannot be determined

34. The time period of a seconds pendulum is ______ s.
(a) 1 (b) 2
(c) 4 (d) 6

35. The frequency of a vibrating body is 100 Hz. Its time period is ______.
(a) 0.01 s (b) 100 s
(c) 0.01 s^{-1} (d) 100 s^{-1}

36. The velocity of sound in vacuum is ______ m s^{-1}.
(a) 332 (b) 330
(c) 3×10^8 (d) Zero

37. The time taken to displace a vibrating body from its mean position to maximum displacement is______.
(a) Time period (b) $\frac{\text{time period}}{2}$
(c) 2 time period (d) $\frac{\text{time period}}{4}$

38. Which of the following statements is wrong?
(a) Galton Whistle produces frequency more than 20,000 Hz.
(b) Infrasonic vibrations are used for homogenizing milk.
(c) Dolphins use ultrasonic sound to locate their prey.
(d) None of the above

39. As the amplitude of a vibrating body increases, the loudness of the sound produced ______.
(a) Increases (b) Decreases
(c) Remains same (d) None of these

40. Tabla is an example of ______.
(a) Stringed instrument (b) Wind instrument
(c) Percussion instrument (d) Ghana vadya

41. The loudness of sound is measured in ______.
(a) Seconds (b) Metre
(c) Decibels (d) Hertz

42. Loudness of a sound in the range of 5 dB – 8 dB is ______.
(a) Not audiable
(b) Loud sound
(c) Uncomfortable loud sound
(d) Painful sound

43. When the length of the pendulum increases, the time period of the pendulum ______.
(a) Increases (b) Decreases
(c) Remains same (d) None of these.

44. Arrange the following steps of an experiment in a sequential order to determine the time period of a simple pendulum.
(A) Pull the bob of the simple pendulum from its initial position of rest and release.
(B) Determine the average of t_1 and t_2 which is denoted as 't'.
(C) Start the stopwatch when the bob reaches the extreme position and count the number of oscillations.
(D) Suspend a single pendulum from a rigid support.
(E) Stop the stop watch at the end of 20 oscillations and determine the time taken to complete 20 oscillations (t_1).
(F) Repeat the experiment and determine the time taken for 20 oscillations (t_2).
(G) The time period of the oscillation is found using, $T = \frac{t}{20}$.
(a) DACEFBG (b) DCAFEBG
(c) ABCDFEG (d) DBADGEF

45. Arrange the following steps in sequential order to find the depth of the ocean bed using SONAR.
(A) The ultrasonic sound reflected from the ocean bed is received by a detector in the ship.

(B) The velocity of sound in water, $v = \frac{2d}{t}$.

(C) From the transmitter, ultrasonic sound is sent to the ocean bed at depth 'd'.

(D) The time taken t to receive the sound is measured.

(E) Calculate the depth of ocean bed, $d = \frac{Vt}{2}$.

(a) ADCBE
(b) CADEB
(c) CADBE
(d) ADCEB

46. If the time taken for the reflected sound to reach the sonar is 2 s, the depth of the sea is ______ m. (velocity of sound in water is 1500 m s^{-1})

(a) 1500 (b) 3000
(c) 750 (d) 500

47. Which of the following statements is correct?

(a) The pitch changes with change in amplitude.
(b) The frequency of vibration determines the pitch of any sound.
(c) The voice of woman has low pitch when compared to that of a man.
(d) A tabla produces high pitch sound when compared to that of a flute.

48. The direction of an incident sound wave makes an angle of 30° with the normal of a reflecting surface. The reflected sound wave makes an angle of ______ with the normal.

(a) 60° (b) 30°
(c) 90° (d) 120°

49. A sound wave makes an angle 30^0 with the reflecting surface. The angle of reflection is ______

(a) 30° (b) 60°
(c) 90° (d) 120°

50. Which of the following statements is correct?

(a) The pitch of sound decreases with a decrease in the length of a vibrating air column.
(b) The pitch of sound increases with a decrease in the thickness of a vibrating string.
(c) The pitch of sound decreases with a decrease in the length of the vibrating string.
(d) The pitch of sound depends upon the amplitude of a vibrating body.

51. If the depth of the sea is 1.125 km, the time taken for the reflected sound to reach the sonar is ______ s. (velocity of sound in water is 1500 m s^{-1})

(a) 1 (b) 1.5
(c) 2 (d) 2.5

52. A man is standing not exactly at the centre of two walls. He fires a gun and hears the first echo after 1 s and the second echo after 2 s. If the speed of the sound is 330 m s^{-1}, what is the distance between the walls?

(a) 330 m (b) 360 m
(c) 420 m (d) 495 m

53. Three persons P_1, P_2, and P_3 are at different points A, B, and C, respectively, as shown in the figure. Two persons P_1 and P_3 clap at the same time. Which among the following can be the minimum distance between P_2 and P_3 to hear the clap sound distinctly? (Take the velocity of sound in air as 330 m s^{-1})

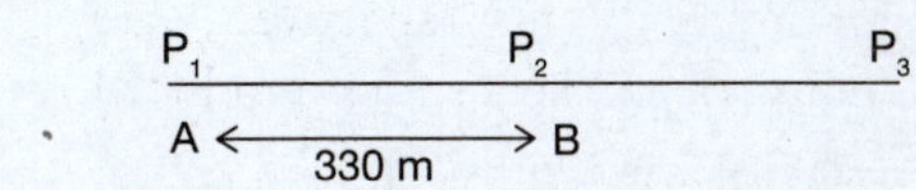

(a) 330 m (b) 384 m
(c) 363 m (d) 660 m

54. The frequency of a vibrating body is 10 Hz. The time taken by it to complete 5 vibrations is ______ s.

(a) 0.5 (b) 5
(c) 2 (d) 10

55. A person hears the sound of the explosion of a bomb after 5 s and another person hears the sound after 6 s. The ratio of minimum and maximum possible distance between the persons is ______. (velocity of sound in air is 330 m s^{-1})

(a) 1:1 (b) 1:2
(c) 1:11 (d) 5:6

56. A person hears the sound of explosion of a bomb after 5 s. If the velocity of sound in air is 330 m s^{-1}, the distance between the bomb and the person is ______ km.

(a) 1 (b) 1.65
(c) 2.35 (d) 330

57. If a vibrating body produces 20 vibrations in 10 second, then its frequency is ______ Hz.

(a) 1 (b) 2
(c) 0.5 (d) 20

58. Higher the frequency of sound, ______ is the pitch.

(a) greater (b) lesser
(c) lower (d) None

59. How can we distinguish between both the sounds, when two boys of same age scream at once with the same pitch and loudness?

***Directions for questions from 60 to 62:* Match the entries given in Column A with the appropriate ones in Column B.**

60.

Column A	Column B
A. $\angle i = \angle r$	a. 0.1 s
B. Persistence of hearing	b. Infrasonic
C. Dolphins	c. Law of reflection of sound
D. Carpets	d. Echoes
E. 10 Hz	e. Reduce noise pollution

61.

Column A	Column B
A. SONAR	a. Percussion instrument
B. Velocity of sound in air at 20°C	b. Reflection of sound
C. *Mridangam*	c. Ghana vadya
D. *Jal tarang*	d. 340 m s^{-1}
	e. 320 m s^{-1}

62.

Column A	Column B
A. Compressions and rarefactions	a. Birds
B. Syrinx	b. Sound wave
C. Internal organs	c. Noise
D. Sound of thunder	d. Surface area of vibrating body
E. Intensity	e. Ultrasonic sounds

Level 2: Review your Concepts

63. A person standing at a distance of 170 m from the wall blows a whistle. He hears an echo in the time interval of 1 s. What is the speed of sound in air?

64. A person stands in between two parallel cliffs which are 132 m apart. If he blows a whistle and hears two successive echoes after 0.4 s and 0.8 s. Then, the distance of the person from the nearer cliff is ______.

65. Chanukya was eager to know the time taken by sound to travel the same distance in water and air. So, he set a body on vibration with a frequency of 250 Hz in air and the sound produced by this is heard at a distance of 175 m. Now if the body is vibrated in water, what is the difference in the time taken by the sound to travel the same distance in water and air? (The velocity of sound in air and water is 350 m s^{-1} and 1400 m s^{-1}, respectively).

66. Give suitable reasons, as to why sound cannot be heard in the following cases:

(i) A simple pendulum executing 10 oscillations in one second.

(ii) The sound produced by a Galton whistle

(iii) Music played in a fully evacuated room

(iv) A 5 dB whisper

67. The velocity of sound in air, in water and in a given solid is, 330 m s^{-1}, 1350 m s^{-1} and 1500 m s^{-1}, respectively. If a vibrating tuning fork of frequency 150 Hz is placed in each of these media, then find the distance covered by the sound in air, water and solid, respectively, at the end of 50 vibrations.

68. Dinesh, who is fond of music, vibrates a glass with a spoon. If he fills the glass with water, will there be any change in any of the characteristics of the sound produced? Explain.

69. Raju stands in between two buildings which are parallel to each other. The distance from Raju to the first building is 100 m. He dropped a heavy block to the ground and hears two successive echoes after 0.2 s and 0.4 s. What is the total distance between the two buildings?

70. Two astronauts who land on the moon cannot talk with each other. What could be the reason for this? Suggest a method for them to talk each other.

71. The time period of a simple pendulum is given by the formula, $T = 2\pi\sqrt{\frac{\ell}{g}}$, where T = time period, l = length of pendulum and g = acceleration due to gravity.

If the length of the pendulum is decreased to 1/4 of its initial value, then what happens to its frequency of oscillations?

72. Standing between two hills, a researcher makes a loud sound. She hears two echoes at the end of 3 s and 4 s. Using the survey map, she notes that the distance between the hills is 1190 m. What will be the speed of sound at that place?

73. A police targets a thief, who is at rest at point Q. He fires a bullet from a point P which is at a distance of 990 m from Q and it reaches the point Q in 3 s. When the bullet is fired at P it produced a sound, which was heard by the thief. What is the difference in time taken by the sound and the bullet to reach point Q. Will the thief be able to escape from the bullet fired by police? Take the velocity of sound in air as 330 m s^{-1}.

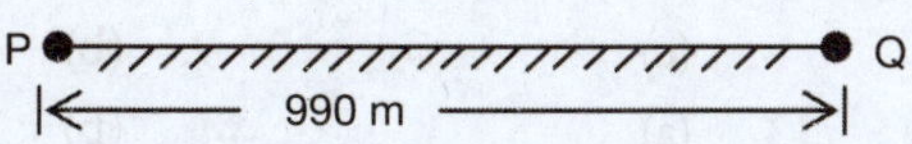

74. Why the sound is made to undergo multiple reflection in a mega phone?

75. The flash of lightning, produced at a distance of 10 km above the ground level is seen much before hearing the thunder bolt. Find the time gap between the two events observed by a person on the ground if the time taken by the lightning to reach the surface of earth is negligible.
(velocity of sound = 330 m s^{-1} and velocity of light = 3×10^8 m s^{-1}).

76. Why is the voice of children more shrill than that of adults'? Explain.

77. List the following persons in ascending order, according to the shrillness in their voice.

(a) A woman of age 40 (b) A man of age 40
(c) A 5th class girl (d) An infant baby

78. A ship at rest is sending ultrasonic sound waves to detect a shoal of fish. If the time gap between the signal sent from the ship and received (reflected) signal is 0.5 s, then find the distance of the shoal of fish from the ship. (Velocity of sound in water is 1400 m s^{-1})

79. Why are the walls, roof, seats, and steps, of a cinema theatre or auditorium covered with special material?

80. Why are concave reflectors used in big auditoria?

Level 3: Assess Your Concepts

81. The audible range of frequency is 20 Hz to 20,000 Hz. Determine the corresponding range of time periods of vibrations.

82. A bat entering into a well finds it difficult to come out of it. Explain the reason.

83. Ramu and Numu are celebrating Diwali with crackers when Ramu fired a cracker after looking at the lighting Numu started counting seconds hand movement in his watch at 8:00 pm and he stopped counting when he heard the cracker sound at 08:00:02 pm. Find the distance between Ramu and Numu if the speed of the sound is 310 m s^{-1}.

84. A student breaks a fused bulb, and then hears a sound of explosion. What could be the reason for this? Explain.

85. How are dogs made alert by the crime department? Explain.

86. Three boys Ravi, John, and Asif stand in a straight line as shown in the figure. Ravi and Asif fire crackers at the same instant of time. John hears the first sound after 2 s and the second sound after 2.5 s. Determine the distance between Ravi and Asif. The velocity of sound in air is 330 m s^{-1}.

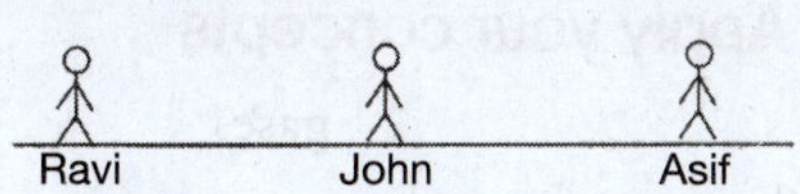

87. A child pushed his cradle for play and started learning numbers by counting the oscillations of his cradle. He counted one number per one oscillation starting from 1, then find the number of numbers the child learned and cradle frequency of oscillations for the total time of 60 second, if the time period of the cradle is 2.5 s.

ANSWER KEYS

Crossword

Across

3. SONAR 4. Bassoon 8. Solid 9. Ultrasonic

Down

1. Syrinx 2. Infrasonic 5. Amplitude 6. Frequency 7. Women
10. Sound

Classroom Wing

Very Short Answer Type Questions

1. 20 kHz 2. slower 3. higher frequency 4. Ultrasonic
5. distance 6. (c) 7. (c) 8. (c) 9. (b)
10. (d) 11. (b) 12. (d) 13. (a) 14. (b)
15. (c) 16. (b) 17. (b) 18. (a) 19. (a)
20. (b) 21. (b) 22. (d) 23. (c) 24. (b)
25. (a) 26. (a) 27. (a) 28. (a) 29. (b)
30. (b) 31. (a) 32. (d) 33. (a) 34. (a)
35. (b) 36. (c) 37. (a) 38. (d) 39. (a)
40. (a) 41. (a) 42. (d)
43. A → d, B → c, C → a, D → b, E → e 44. A → e, B → c, C → d, D → a, E → b
45. A → a, B → c, C → e, D → b, E → d 46. A → c, B → d, C → a, D → b 47. 1/4
48. 10 Hz 52. 1980 m 57. 1 65. 2.5 Hz 66. 10 Hz

Competition Wing

Level 1: Apply your concepts

1. 0.1 s 2. gases 3. 45 4. 500 Hz
5. Reflection of sound 6. 1000 7. Quality 8. amplitude
9. amplitude 10. ultrasound 11. pitch 12. 330 m s^{-1} 13. 3 s
14. pressure variations 15. one 16. True 17. True
18. False 19. True 20. True 21. False 22. True
23. False 24. False 25. True 26. (d) 27. (c)
28. (a) 29. (b) 30. (a) 31. (c) 32. (a)
33. (a) 34. (b) 35. (a) 36. (d) 37. (d)
38. (b) 39. (a) 40. (c) 41. (c) 42. (a)
43. (a) 44. (a) 45. (c) 46. (a) 47. (b)
48. (b) 49. (b) 50. (b) 51. (b) 52. (d)
53. (c) 54. (a) 55. (c) 56. (b) 57. (b)
58. (a) 59. timbre or quality of sound 60. A → c, B → a, C → d, D → e, E → b
61. A → b, B → d, C → a, D → c 62. A → b, B → a, C → e, D → c, E → d

Level 2: Review your Concepts

63. 340 m s^{-1} **64.** 44 m **65.** 3/8 s **66.** 5 dB

67. 110 m in air, 450 m in water, 500 m in solid. **69.** 300 m **71.** 1/2(T)

72. 340 m/s **73.** 330 m s^{-1} **75.** 30.30 s **78.** 350 m

Level 3: Assess Your Concepts

81. 5×10^{-2} s to 5×10^{-5} s **83.** 620 m **86.** 1485 m **87.** 0.4 Hz

Hints and Explanations

Classroom Wing

Very Short Answer Type Questions

1. (20 kHz)
The sounds with frequencies greater than 20 kHz are called ultrasounds.

2. (slower)
Velocity of light is more than the velocity of sound in a given medium i.e., light travels faster than sound in a given medium.

3. (higher frequency)
The frequency of vibration determines the shrillness or pitch of any sound. If the frequency of vibration is low we say that the sound has low pitch. If the frequency of vibration is high, we say that the sound has a high pitch. In the case of women, the sound produced is high pitched. So voice of women has a higher frequency than that of men.

4. Ultrasonic sound is used in medical diagnosis.

5. Loudness decreases with distance.

6. (c)
The vibrations of a turning fork are oscillatory and periodic in nature.

7. (c)
The audible range of frequency is 20 Hz to 20 kHz.

8. (c)
Time period (T) = 10 s.
Frequency (n) = $1/T = \frac{1}{10\,\text{s}} = 0.1\ \text{s}^{-1} = 0.1$ Hz. (or)
Number of oscillations in 10 s is one.
$\therefore$ No. of oscillations in 1 s = $1/10 = 0.1$ Hz

9. (b)
When the length of string between the rigid supports decreases the number of vibrations completed in 1 second increases and hence frequency increases.

10. (d)
The reflection of sound is used in
(1) hearing the echo.
(2) to locate the shoal of fish under the sea bed.
(3) detection of insects by bats.

11. (b)
Velocity of sound is maximum in solids, lesser in liquids and least in gases.

12. (d)
Sound cannot travel through vacuum.

13. (a)
Bats make use of ultrasonic sound waves.

14. (b)
Frequency $f = \frac{1}{\text{Time period}}$. Therefore, as the time period increases the frequency decreases.

15. (c)
The velocity of sound is more in solids, less in liquids and least in gases.
$\therefore V_S > V_l > V_g$
$\Rightarrow V_g < V_l < V_S$

16. (b)
Hint: 1 kHz = 1000 Hz.

17. (b)
As the simple pendulum cannot complete 20 oscillations in one second, its oscillations are not perceived by the human ear.

18. (a)
All vibrations produce sound but we can hear sound only when the frequency is between 20 Hz to 20,000 Hz.

19. (a)
The loudness of sound depends upon the amplitude of the vibrating body.

20. (b)
Harmonium is an example of wind or reed instrument.

21. (b)
1 decibel = $\frac{1}{10}$ of bell.

22. (d)
Sound above 150 dB, or 15 B are painful to human ear.

23. (c)

(i) Suspend a simple pendulum from a cork fixed to a stand (b).

(ii) Pull the bob of the simple pendulum from its initial position of rest and release (d).

(iii) Start the stop watch when the bob reaches the extreme position and count the number of oscillations (a).

(iv) Stop the stop watch at the end of 20 oscillations and determine the time taken to complete 20 oscillations (t_1) (e).

(v) Repeat the experiment and determine the time taken for 20 oscillations. (t_2) (c).

(vi) Determine the average of t_1 and t_2 as t. (f)

(vii) The time period of the oscillation is found using $T = \frac{t}{20}$ and frequency using $f = \frac{1}{T}$.(g)

24. (b)

(i) Let two persons P_1 and P_2 are separated by a distance of 1 km in an open place (a)

(ii) The person P_1 will fire the cracker and person P_2 will start the stopwatch as soon as he sees the light (b).

(iii) The person P_2 will stop the stopwatch as soon as he hears the sound of the cracker (d).

(iv) Note the time taken by the sound to travel from P_1 to P_2.(c)

(v) Measure the distance between the two places by using the survey chain (f).

(vi) The speed of the sound in air is the ratio of the distance between the two places to the time interval (e).

25. All vibrations produce sound but we can hear sound only when the frequency is between 20 Hz and 20,000 Hz

26. The maximum displacement of a vibrating body from its mean position is called amplitude.

27. Oboes is an example of wind instrument and musical sound is produced from it by vibrating air column in the tube by blowing air into it.

28. Human ear can hear two sounds separately only if they reach the ear after an interval of (1/10) of a second. So, the time taken by the sound from P_1 to P_2 should be greater than (1/10) s = 0.1 s.

The minimum distance between P_1 and P_2

$= v \times t = 330 \times 0.1 = 33$ m.

29. The pitch of sound increases with decrease in the thickness of a vibrating string.

30. The correct reason for A is that it is difficult to classify a given sound as music or noise as they may produce a pleasant effect on one person and an unpleasant effect on another person.

Hence, A and R are correct but R is not the correct reason for A.

31. The pitch of the sound produced by a vibrating string can be changed by changing the length, tension and thickness of the vibrating string. So, R is the correct explanation or reason for A.

32. Mega phone, Sonar, toy telephone, different kinds of sound are a few practical applications of reflection of sound.

33. The sound that produces a pleasant effect on our ears is called **music**.

34. From the given data, time gap = 3 s.

We know, $v = 330$ m s^{-1}.

$$\text{Speed} = \frac{\text{distance}}{\text{time}} \rightarrow \text{(c)}$$

Neglecting the time taken by the light to reach the ground because velocity of light is very large, that is, $C = 3 \times 10^8$ m s^{-1}. On substituting the values, the height of the lightning from the ground is equal to $330 \times 3 = 990$ m.

35. The frequency of vibration determines the pitch of any sound.

36. Take a metallic container and fill it with water. Place the two coins inside the water and hit one on the other and observe the sound produced.

Repeat the activity by placing the ear against the side of the container.

Now, a clear and louder sound is heard and this proves that sound also travels through liquids.

37. Loudness of sound decreases with increase in distance.

38. Veena, Sitar, Guitar, Violin, etc., are examples of stringed instruments.

39. The more is the energy spent to set the body into vibration, the more is the amplitude of the vibration.

40. Some instruments are just struck or beaten in a rhythm to produce music. They are called Percussion instruments.

Examples: manjira, the ghatam, jal tarang, etc.

41. Wind or reed instruments are made of long and hollow pipes with a certain number of holes on the sides.

42. Noise pollution results in loss of hearing, loss of work efficiency, and tension in humans.

43. A → d Speed of the sound = $\frac{\text{Height of the cloud}}{\text{time taken}}$

B → c $n = \frac{1}{T}$, If $n = 10$ Hz,

$\Rightarrow T = \frac{1}{n} = \frac{1}{10} = 0.1$ s

C → a Sound energy is absorbed by soft material, like gunny bags, carpets, etc.

D → b The sound of loudness more than 90 dB is painful to humans.

E → e Birds produce sound with the help of cartilage called syrinx.

44. A → e Sound is produced by vibrating bodies.

B → c Depth of ocean bed can be determined by SONAR.

C → d Maximum displacement is called as amplitude.

D → a Tabla is an example of a percussion instrument.

E → b Bell jar experiment is used to understand that sound requires a medium for propagation.

45. A → a 1MHz = 10^6 Hz

B → c The velocity of sound in air at 20 °C is 340 m s^{-1}.

C → e Music produces pleasant sensation of hearing.

D → b The loudness of sound is measured in decibel.

E → d Bats can produce ultrasonic sounds in the frequency range of 50 Hz to 80,000 Hz.

46. A → r

B → s

C → p

D → q

47. Time period of seconds pendulum = 2 s

$\text{Ratio} = \frac{f}{T} = \frac{1}{T^2} = \frac{1}{2^2} = \frac{1}{4}$

48. Frequency = $\frac{\text{Number of vibrations}}{\text{Time taken}}$

$= \frac{40}{4} = 10$ Hz

49. The distance from the point of suspension to the centre of the bob is called the length of the simple pendulum.

50. Number of oscillations made in a unit time is known as the frequency.

51. One to and fro motion of an oscillating pendulum is called one oscillation.

52. $t = 6$ s

$v = 330$ m s^{-1}

$d = ?$

$d = v\,t$

$= 330 \times 6$

$d = 1980$ m

53. The sound which is incident and reflected from a hard surface makes equal angle with the normal. This phenomenon is called reflection of sound.

54. When sound strikes a smooth and hard surface it is reflected back to the listener and the repetition of the sound is heard after a short time which is called an echo.

55. Infrasonic sounds have frequencies less than 20 Hz.

56. Sound does not travel through vacuum.

57. Frequency × Time period = $\frac{1}{2} \times 2 = 1$

58. Quality of a sound is a characteristic property which distinguishes two sounds of equal pitch and loudness.

59. The undesirable, loud and harsh sounds produced in the environment by different sources is called noise pollution.

60. A simple pendulum cannot complete 20 oscillations in one second. Hence its oscillations are not perceived by the human ear.

61. To hear two sounds distinctly the time gap between them should be 0.1s. This is called persistence of hearing.

62. The minimum distance between the reflector and the listener should be 16.5 m to hear an echo.

63. Megaphone works on the principle of reflection of sound.

64. The pitch of the sound decreases with increase in the length a vibrating air column.

65. Frequency = $\frac{50}{20} = 2.5$ Hz.

66. Time period (T) = 0.1 s.

Frequency, $f = \frac{1}{T} = \frac{1}{0.1} = 10$ Hz.

Short Answer Type Questions

67. Take a metallic container and fill it with water. Take two coins and hit one on the other inside water. You will be able to hear a sound. Now place your ear against the side of the container and again hit one coin on the other inside the water. You will hear a louder and clearer sound than the sound heard in the first case. Thus, sound also travels through liquids.

68. When two drums A and B having frequencies of 500 Hz and 216 Hz, respectively are vibrated simultaneously, then the shrillness of sound produced by drum 'A' is more than drum 'B'.

69. **Formation of thunder:** During lightning, nearly 75% of its electrical energy is used in heating the gases present in and around the flash. Due to this, the temperature of the surrounding region increases to about 10,000 K in a few seconds. As a result, a pressure wave is created giving rise to compressions and rarefactions and producing a violent sound called 'thunder'.

70. Given, $v = 330$ m s^{-1}, $t = 2$ s.

Distance from the earth where lightning has occurred, $d = v \times t = 330 \times 2 \Rightarrow d = 660$ m.

71.

Music	Noise
1. Music is pleasant to hear.	1. Noise is unpleasant to hear.
2. The vibrations are regular and periodic.	2. The vibrations are irregular.
3. Flute, veena, etc., are sources of music.	3. Sound of thunder, firing of crackers etc., are sources of noise.

72. When a sound is produced at one end of a metallic pipe, it travels through both the pipe and air. As the velocity of sound is different in air and solid, they reach the other end at different times. Hence the sound is heard twice.

73.

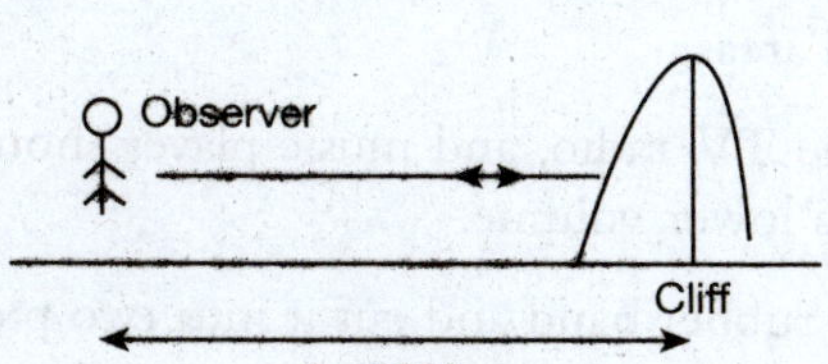

$v = 330$ m s^{-1}

$t = ?$

$$v = \frac{2d}{t}$$

$$t = \frac{2d}{v}$$

$$= \frac{2 \times 6600}{330}$$

$$T = 40 \text{ s}$$

74. The sources of noise pollution are
(i) exploding crackers,
(ii) thunder,
(iii) publicity announcements made by trading companies,
(iv) noise produced by factories,
(v) noise produced by vehicles, etc.

75. **Factors affecting the loudness of sound:** Loudness of sound depends upon the surface area of the vibrating body. For example the loudness of sound produced from a table of larger surface area is greater than the loudness of sound produced by a table of smaller surface area. Thus, loudness of sound increases as the surface area of the vibrating body increases. Loudness of sound decreases with increase in distance. As you move away from a source of sound the intensity of sound decreases. For example, if you sit on the first bench in your class the loudness of the sound heard will be more. But if you sit on the last bench in your classroom, the loudness of the sound heard by you will be less.

76. The pitch of a sound depends on the frequency. Higher the frequency of sound, greater is the pitch. For example a flute can produce the sound of different pitch. The pitch of the sound produced can be varied by changing the length of the vibrating body. In the case of the musical instruments like violin, the pitch of the sound is varied by changing the length of the vibrating part of the string. The frequency of vibration depends on the length of the vibrating part of the string. Thus, the pitch of a sound does not depend on the amount of energy spent in making the body to vibrate or the amplitude of vibration, but it is the effect produced in the brain by the sound of some particular frequency.

77. $T = 2\pi\sqrt{\frac{\ell}{g}}$.

The length of pendulum is increased by four times.

$\ell^1 = 4\,\ell$

$$T^1 = 2\pi\sqrt{\frac{\ell^1}{g}}$$

$$= 2\pi\sqrt{\frac{4\ell}{g}}$$

$T^1 = 2\,T$

78. **Mega phone:** It consists of a horn-shaped tube. Sound produced at the narrow end undergoes multiple reflections and comes out of the tube. It can travel longer distances.

SONAR (Sound Navigation and Ranging): It is a technique used in ships to calculate the depth of ocean beds. Ultrasonic sound is sent to the ocean beds from the ship. This ultrasonic sound gets reflected from the ocean beds. The reflected sound is received by a suitable detector in the ship. The time taken to receive the sound is measured. Let 't' be the time taken, 'v' be the velocity of sound in water and 'd' be the depth of the ocean bed.

Then, $v = 2d/t$ or $d = vt/2$.

79. Given speed of sound in air, $v = 340\ \text{m s}^{-1}$.
Minimum time required to hear echo, $t = 0.1$ s.

Using, $v = \dfrac{2d}{t}$.

$$340 = \frac{2d}{0.1} \Rightarrow d = \frac{340\times 0\cdot 1}{2} = 17\ \text{m}$$

$\therefore$ The minimum distance required to hear the echo = 17 m.

80. Experiment–To prove that the pitch of the sound decreases with increase in length of a vibrating air column. Fill a burette with water about $\frac{3}{4}$ th of its length. Blow air into the burette. A high pitched sound is produced. Now reduce the quantity of water in the burette by releasing the tap at the bottom of the burette. Blow air into the burette once again. A sound of low pitch is produced in this case. Repeat the experiment by reducing the quantity of water in the burette. You will observe that as the length of the air column in the burette increases the pitch of the sound decreases. This is due to the decrease in frequency of vibrating air column as the length of the air column increases.

81. Initial time period = $T_E = T$
Initial length of simple pendulum = ℓ
$g_e = 6\ g_m$

$$T_e = 2\pi\sqrt{\frac{\ell}{g}};\qquad T_m = 2\pi\sqrt{\frac{\ell}{g_m}}$$

$$\frac{T_m}{T_e} = \sqrt{\frac{\ell}{g_m}} \times \sqrt{\frac{g_e}{\ell}} = T_m = T\sqrt{\frac{g_e}{g_m}} = T_m = T$$

Essay Type Questions

82. The vibrations of air in the form of compressions and rarefactions produced by the source of sound reach the ear and they cause vibrations on the ear drum. These vibrations make the ear drum to vibrate and they are picked up by the auditory nerves which are sent as impulses to the centre of hearing in the brain.

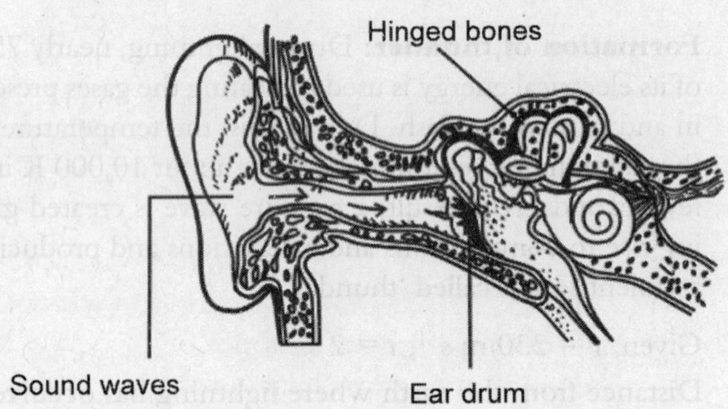

83. **Sound produced by human beings:** In humans the sound is produced by the vibration of vocal cords. The vocal cords are stretched across the larynx and it leaves a gap between them for the passage of air. The air from the lungs is forced through the slit and the vocal cords vibrate to produce sound. The frequency of sound produced depends on the thickness and the tension of vocal cords. When the vocal cords are tight and thin a high frequency sound (shrill sound) is produced and when the vocal cords are loose and thick, they produce sound of low frequency. The pitch of the sound produced depends on the muscles attached to the vocal cords.

84. The following measures must be taken to prevent and control noise pollution.

1. Silencers should be provided in automobiles.
2. Usage of loudspeakers should be reduced.
3. Factories should be located away from the residential areas.
4. The TV, radio, and music player should be played at a lower volume.

85. Take a rubber band and cut it into two pieces of equal lengths. Place the two pieces one above the other. Stretch them and blow air between them. Observe the pitch of the sound produced. Now stretch the rubber bands further and blow air between them and once again observe the pitch of the sound produced. It is observed that when the rubber bands are stretched further there is also an increase in the pitch of the sound. Now take a thin rubber band and cut it into two pieces. Blow air between them after stretching them. It is observed that the pitch of the sound produced is very high when a thin rubber band is used.

86. We know, sound is produced by vibrating objects. When an object vibrates, it moves back and forth about its mean position. When it moves forward, it pushes the air in front of it and compresses the air, creating a region of high pressure. This region is called compression (C), as shown in figure. This compression moves away from the vibrating object. When the vibrating object moves backwards, it creates a region of low pressure called rarefaction (R), as shown in figure. Hence, when the object moves back and forth rapidly, a series of compressions and rarefactions are created in the medium. These make the sound wave propagate through the medium. As sound waves propagate through air, the air molecules vibrate back and forth parallel to the direction of motion of the wave. Hence, sound waves are longitudinal in nature.

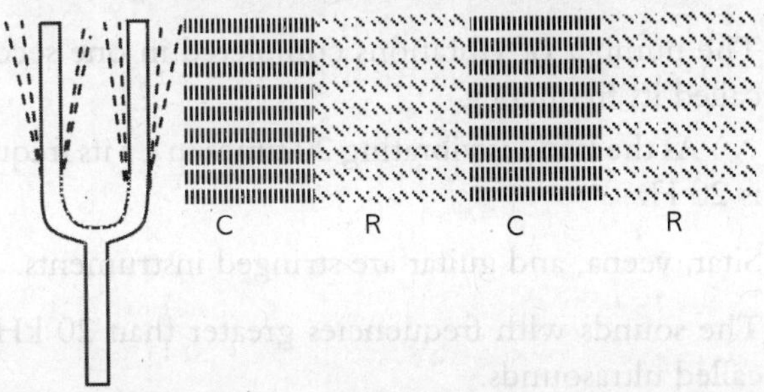

Compression is the region of high pressure and rarefaction is the region of low pressure. Pressure is related to the density of the medium. More density of the medium gives more pressure and vice versa.

Thus, propagation of sound can be visualized as propagation of pressure variations i.e., compressions and rarefactions or density variations in the medium.

87. (i) **Wind or reed instruments:** These instruments are made of long and hollow pipes with a certain number of holes on the sides. The air column in the tube is made to vibrate by blowing air into it. This vibrating air column produces musical sound. Flute, bassoon, oboes are examples of wind instruments.

(ii) **Percussion instruments (Drum instruments)** These instruments have stretched membranes made up of leather. Vibration of these membranes produce musical sound. Different musical sounds can be produced by exciting these membranes at different tensions. Drums, mridangam, tabla, etc., are examples of percussion instruments.

Some instruments are just struck or beaten in a rythym to produce music. They are called Ghana vadya. Example: manjira, the ghatam, jal tarang.

88. **(a)** Sonography is a system of ultrasound scanning, where the condition of foetus inside the womb can be found out.

(b) Bats produce ultrasonic sounds in the frequency range of 50 Hz to 80,000 Hz when they fly. When these sounds strike the insects the waves get reflected. They can locate their prey by receiving the reflected sound. Dolphins also locate their prey in a similar manner.

(c) Noise pollution results in loss of hearing, loss of work efficiency and tension in humans.

89. **(a)** The higher units of frequency are kilohertz (kHz) and megahertz (MHz). 1 kHz = 1000 Hz, 1 MHz = 10^6 Hz.

(b) The noise pollution can be determined by loudness and duration of sound at a particular place.

(c) Soft surfaces like cloth, gunny bags, carpets, porous material, etc., are sound absorbing materials.

90. Consider a glass jar with an outlet at the bottom as shown in the figure. Switch on the electric bell. We will be able to hear the sound produced by the bell. Connect a vacuum pump to the outlet of the jar and remove the air inside the jar. As the air is gradually removed, from the jar, the intensity of sound decreases and finally we do not hear the sound. When the air is removed a vacuum is created hence we are unable to hear the sound. This shows that a medium is required for the propagation of sound.

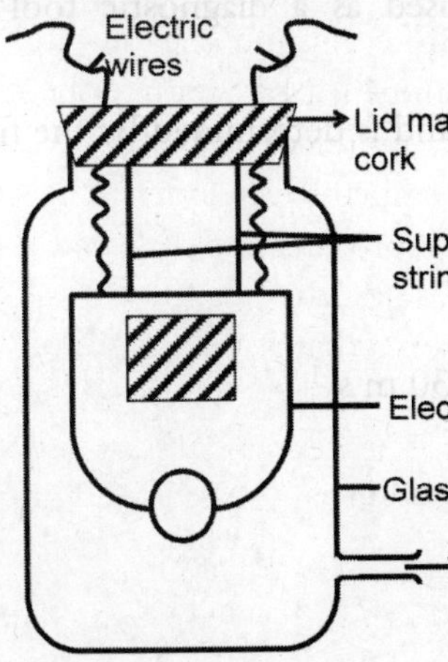

Bell jar experiment

Competition Wing

Level 1: Apply your Concepts

1. Frequency $= \frac{\text{Number of vibrations}}{\text{Time taken}}$

$= \frac{20}{2} = 10$ Hz

Time period $= \frac{1}{f} = \frac{1}{10} = 0.1$ s

2. Velocity of sound is the least in gases.

3. (45)

Let the time taken for one vibration be T.

∴ Time taken for 30 vibrations = 45T

= 45 × (Time taken for single vibration).

4. (500 Hz)

The number of vibrations completed in one second is called its frequency.

∴ As the body is vibrating 500 times in 1 s its frequency is 500 Hz.

5. Reflection of sound principle is used to locate shoals of fish under the seabed.

6. 1 kHz = 1000 Hz

7. Quality is a property of sound that distinguishes two sounds of the same frequency and loudness.

8. The time period of a simple pendulum is independent of amplitude of oscillation.

9. The larger the amplitude of vibration, the more the loudness, and hence, loudness of sound is determined by its amplitude.

10. Ultrasound is used as a diagnostic tool in medical science.

11. The pitch of sound is determined by the frequency.

12. $t = 4$ s

$d = 1320$ m

$v = ?$

$v = \frac{d}{t} = \frac{1320}{4} = 330 \text{ m s}^{-1}$

13. $d = 990$ m

$v = 330 \text{ m s}^{-1}$

$t = ?$

$v = \frac{d}{t}$

$t = \frac{d}{v}$

$t = \frac{990}{330}$

$t = 3$ s

14. Propagation of sound can be visualized as propagation of pressure variations in the medium.

15. The number of oscillations completed in one second is called frequency. Therefore, 1 Hz frequency means one oscillation per second.

16. To and fro motion of an object is called vibration.

17. The maximum displacement of a bob from its mean position is called amplitude.

18. The unit of frequency is cycles per second (or) Hertz.

19. Let the time taken for one vibration be T.

∴ Time taken for 30 vibrations = $30T$

= 30 (T)

= 30 × (Time taken for single vibration)

20. The number of vibrations completed in one second is called its frequency.

∴ As the body is vibrating 20 times in 1 s its frequency is 20 Hz.

21. Sitar, veena, and guitar are stringed instruments.

22. The sounds with frequencies greater than 20 kHz are called ultrasounds.

23. Velocity of light is more than the velocity of sound in a given medium, i.e., light travels faster than sound in a given medium.

24. Sound requires a medium to propagate from one location to another. Sound does not travel through vacuum.

25. The frequency of vibration determines the shrillness or pitch of any sound. If the frequency of vibration is low, we say that the sound has low pitch. If the frequency of vibration is high, we say that the sound has a high pitch.

In the case of women, the sound produced is high pitched. So, voice of women has a higher frequency than that of men.

26. Ultrasonic sound waves are used in

(a) dishwashers (ultrasonic bath),

(b) medical diagnostics,

(c) detection of flaws in materials, etc.

27. Distance of the person, $(d) = 110$ m.

Velocity of sound, $(V) = 330 \text{ m s}^{-1}$.

Time taken, $(t) = ?$

$$\text{Velocity} = \frac{\text{distance}}{\text{time taken}} \Rightarrow t = \frac{110}{330} = \frac{1}{3} \text{ s.}$$

28. $$\text{Velocity} = \frac{\text{distance}}{\text{time}} \Rightarrow \text{distance} = \text{velocity} \times \text{time}$$

$$= 220 \times 2 = 440 \text{ m}$$

29. The time after which echo is heard, $(t) = 1.5$ s.

Speed of sound in air, $(v) = 330 \text{ m s}^{-1}$.

Distance of tower, $(d) = ?$

As the sound wave travels twice, i.e., from person to tower and from tower to again the person.

$$\therefore \quad V = \frac{\text{distance}}{\text{time}} = \frac{2d}{t} \Rightarrow d = \frac{V \times t}{2} = \frac{330 \times 1.5}{2}$$

$$= 247.5 \text{ m}$$

30. The lightning is seen much before we hear the thunder because the speed of light is more than the speed of the sound in a given medium.

31. Among the given substances cork is the good absorber of sound.

32. The pitch of sound is determined by the frequency of vibration.

33. The frequency of vibration determines the shrillness or pitch of any sound. If the frequency of vibration is low, we say that the sound has low pitch. If the frequency of vibration is high, we say that the sound has a high pitch. In the given question turning fork A has more frequency, and hence, the pitch of sound produced by A will be more.

34. A pendulum whose time period is 2 s is called seconds pendulum.

35. Given, $f = 100$ Hz.

$$T = \frac{1}{f} = \frac{1}{100} = 0.01 \text{ s.}$$

36. The velocity of sound is zero in vacuum.

Sound cannot be propagated through vacuum.

37. The time in which a vibrating body completes one vibration is called time period. So, the time taken by a vibrating body to displace from its mean position to maximum displacement is $= \dfrac{\text{time period}}{4}$

38. Ultrasonic vibrations are used for homogenizing milk.

39. The loudness of sound depends upon the amplitude of the vibrating body, i.e., the more the amplitude, the more is the loudness.

40. Tabla is an example of percussion instrument.

41. The loudness of sound is measured in decibels (dB).

42. The sounds of loudness below 10 dB are not audiable.

43. The period of oscillation depends upon the length of the pendulum. If the length of the pendulum is increased, the time period also increases.

44. (a) The correct order is DACEFBG

45. (c) The correct order is CADBE

46. $$\text{Speed of sound in water} = \frac{\text{distance covered by sound}}{\text{Time}}$$

distance covered by sound $= v \times t$

$$= 1500 \times 1 = 1500 \text{ m.}$$

47. The frequency of vibration determines the pitch of any sound.

48.

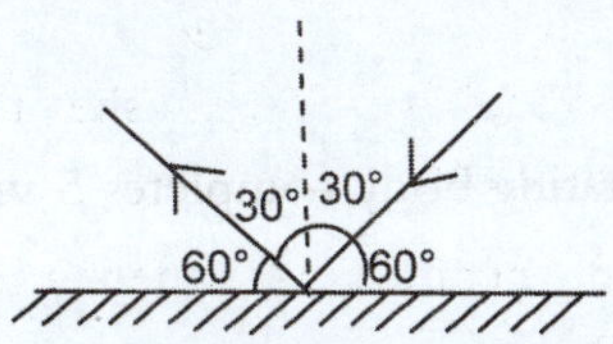

49.

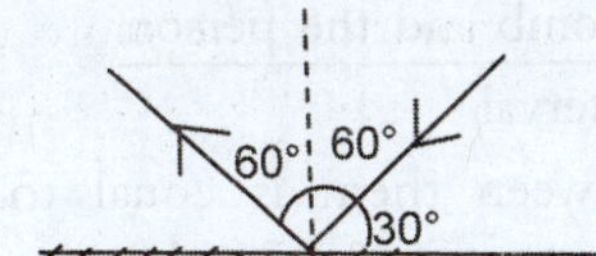

50. The pitch of sound increases with decrease in the thickness of a vibrating string.

51. Speed of sound in water

$$= \frac{\text{Distance covered by sound}}{\text{Time}}$$

$$\text{Time} = \frac{\text{distance covered by sound}}{\text{speed of sound in water}} = \frac{2 \times 1125}{1500} = 1.5 \text{ s}$$

52.

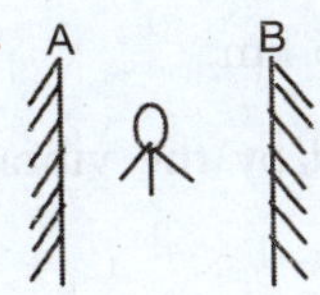

The distance between the man and the wall A

$= v \times t = 330 \times \frac{1}{2} = 165$ m

The distance between the man and the wall B

$= 330 \times \frac{2}{2} = 330$ m

Distance between the wall's = 330 + 165 = 495 m

53. Velocity of sound 'v' = 330 m s^{-1}

distance between P_1 and P_2 = 330 m

So, time taken to hear the sound

$t = \frac{330}{330} = 1$ s

Human ear can hear two sounds separately only if they reach at interval of 1/10 of a second. So, the time taken by the sound from P_3 to reach P_2 is minimum of $1 + \frac{1}{10} = 1.1$ s.

So, the distance between P_2 and $P_3 = t \times v$

$= 1.1 \times 330 = 363$ m.

54. The time period $= \frac{1}{\text{frequency}}$

$T = \frac{1}{10} = 0.1$ s

Time in which the vibrating body completes 5 vibrations is $= 5 \times 0.1 = 0.5$ s

55. Speed of sound =

$\frac{\text{distance between the bomb and the person}}{\text{Time interval}}$

Minimum distance between them is equal to the distance travelled by the sound in 6 – 5 = 1 s

$d_1 = s \times t = 330 \times 1 = 330$ m

The maximum distance between them is equal to the distance travelled by the sound in 6 + 5 = 11 s

$d_2 = v \times t = 330 \times 11$

$d_1 : d_2 = \frac{d_1}{d_2} = \frac{330 \times 1}{330 \times 11} = \frac{1}{11} = 1:11$

56. Speed of sound $= \frac{\text{distance}}{\text{time}}$

$d = s \times t = 330 \times 5 = 1650$ m = 1.65 km

57. The number of vibrations produced by the vibrating body in one second is $= \frac{20}{10} = 2$.

So, frequency = 2 Hz

58. Higher the frequency of sound, greater is the pitch.

59. When two boys of same age screamed with same loudness at once, even then we can distinguish both the sounds because of timbre or quality of sound.

60. A → c When a sound wave is reflected, the angle of incident sound (i) is equal to the angle of reflected sound.

B → a The persistence of hearing for humans is 0.1 s.

C → d Dolphins use echo method to catch their prey.

D → e Carpets are sound absorbing materials and reduce noise pollution.

E → b Sound with frequency less than 20 Hz is known as infrasonic.

61. A → q
B → s
C → p
D → r

62. A → b Sound wave propagates in the form of compressions and rarefactions.

B → a Birds produce sound with the help of a ring of cartilage called syrinx.

C → e Ultrasonic sound is used for imaging the internal organs of a human body.

D → c The sound of thunder produces noise.

E → d Intensity of sound depends on the surface area of the vibrating body.

Level 2: Review your Concepts

63.

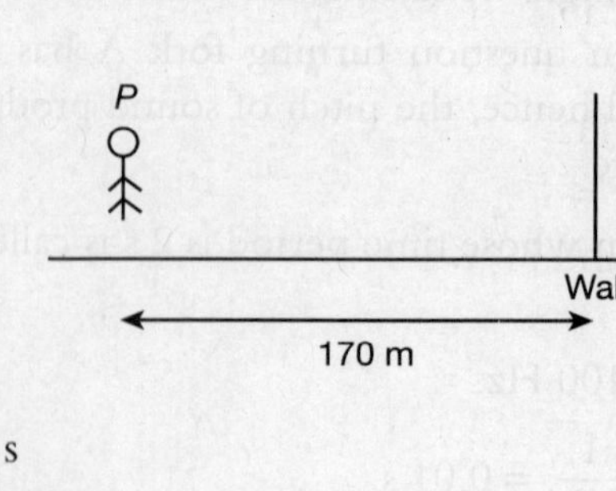

$t = 1$ s

$d = 170$ m

$v = ?$

$v = \frac{2d}{t}$

$= \frac{2 \times 170}{1}$

$V = 340$ m s^{-1}

64.

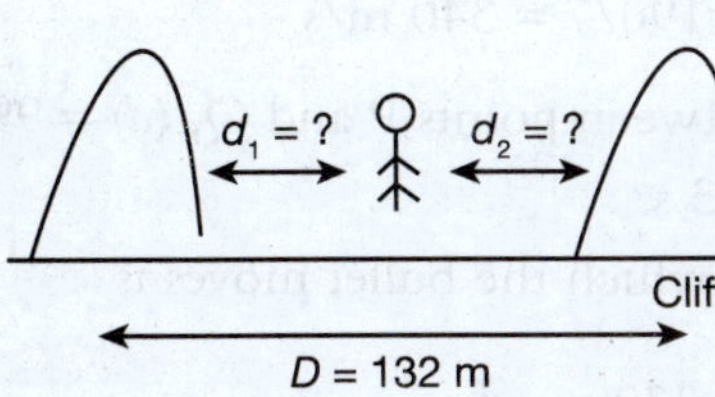

$t_1 = 0.4$ s

$t_2 = 0.8$ s

$v_1 = v_2 = 330$ m s^{-1}

$d_1 = ?$

$v_1 = \frac{2d_1}{t_1}$ $\qquad v = \frac{2d_2}{t_2}$

$\frac{2d_1}{t_1} = \frac{2d_2}{t_2}$ ($\because V_1 = V_2$)

$\frac{2d_1}{t_1} = \frac{2(132 - d_1)}{t_2}$

$\frac{2d_1}{0.4} = \frac{2(132 - d_1)}{0.8}$

$2d_1 = 132 - d_1$

$3d_1 = 132$

$d_1 = \frac{132}{3} = 44$ m.

65. (i) Frequency of body, (n) = 250 Hz.

Distance, (d) = 175 m.

Speed (velocity) of sound (V) = 350 m s^{-1}.

$\therefore$ Time taken by the sound to travel 175 m in air

$= \frac{\text{distance}}{\text{speed}} = \frac{175 \text{ m}}{350 \text{ m s}^{-1}} = \frac{1}{2}$ s.

(ii) When it is vibrated in water, the number of vibrations completed in 1 second (i.e., frequency) is the same

$\therefore$ $n = 250$ Hz.

Distance, (d) = 175 m.

Speed of sound in water (v) = 1400 m s^{-1}.

$\therefore$ Time taken by sound to travel 175 m in water (t).

$= \frac{175 \text{ m}}{1400 \text{ m s}^{-1}} = 1/8$ s

$\therefore$ Time difference $= \left(\frac{1}{2} - \frac{1}{8}\right)$s

$= \left(\frac{1}{2} - \frac{1}{8}\right)\text{s} = \left(\frac{4}{8} - \frac{1}{8}\right)\text{s} = \frac{3}{8}$ s.

66. (i) If the frequency of vibration of a body is less than 20 Hz, the vibrations are known as subsonic or infrasonic vibrations. Human ear cannot hear infrasonic vibrations. As the simple pendulum executes 10 oscillations in one second, its frequency is 10 Hz. Hence, the sound of its oscillations are not heard.

(ii) If the frequency of vibration of a body is more than 20,000 Hz, the vibrations are known as ultrasonic vibrations. Human ear cannot hear ultrasonic vibrations. The Galton whistle produces ultrasonic vibrations. Hence, its sound is not heard.

(iii) In a fully evacuated room, the air is removed, and vacuum is created. A medium is required for the propagation of sound and sound cannot propagate in vacuum. Hence, the music played cannot be heard.

(iv) Humans are sensitive to sound of loudness from 10 dB to 180 dB

Hence, a 5 dB whisper cannot be heard.

67. Speed of sound in air = 330 m s^{-1}.

Speed of sound in water = 1350 m s^{-1}.

Speed of sound in solid = 1500 m s^{-1}.

Frequency of tuning fork, (n) = 150 Hz.

i.e., it performs 150 vibrations in 1 second.

$\therefore$ The time taken by the tuning fork to complete 50 vibrations $= \frac{1}{3}$ s.

The distance travelled by sound in three media in 1 second is 330 m, 1350 m, 1500 m.

$\therefore$ The distance covered by sound in the three given media in 1/3 s is

$330 \times \frac{1}{3} = 110$ m in air.

$1350 \times \frac{1}{3} = 450$ m in water.

$1500 \times \frac{1}{3} = 500$ m in solid.

68. Because of the presence of water inside the glass, the amplitude of vibration decreases, and hence, the loudness of sound also decreases.

69.

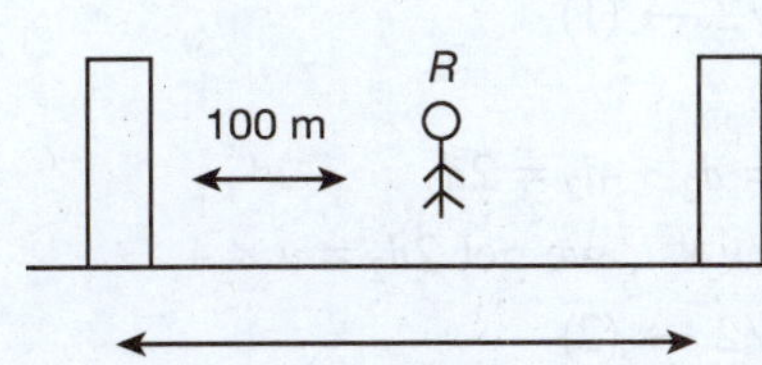

$d_1 = 100$ m $\quad d_2 = ?$

$D = d_1 + d_2 \quad d_2 = D - 100$

$t_1 = 0.2$ s $\quad t_2 = 0.4$ s

$v_1 = v_2 = 330$ m

$v_1 = \frac{2d_1}{t_1} \quad v_2 = \frac{2d_2}{t_2}$

$\frac{2d_1}{t_1} = \frac{2d_2}{t_2}$

$\frac{2 \times 100}{0.2} = \frac{2 \times (D - 100)}{0.4}$

$200 = D - 100$

$D = 300$ m

70. Sound requires a medium to propagate. As there is no atmosphere (or) medium on the moon for propagation of sound, the words of one astronaut cannot be heard by another. If they have an medium for propagation of sound between them (like a toy phone), they can communicate with each other with the help of radio waves.

71. The time period of a simple pendulum is

$T = 2\pi\sqrt{\frac{\ell}{g}}$

When length is decreased to $1/4^{th}$ of its initial value then $\ell^1 = \frac{\ell}{4}$.

∴ New time period, (T^1)

$= 2\pi\sqrt{\frac{\frac{\ell}{4}}{g}} = \frac{2\pi}{2}\sqrt{\frac{\ell}{g}} = \frac{1}{2}(T)$

∴ Time taken to perform one oscillation is reduced to half of its initial value.

∴ Frequency of oscillation becomes double that of the initial value.

72. Let 'v' be the speed of sound.

For Hill 1:

Distance $= d_1 + d_1 = 2d_1$

Using $d = v \times t$, we get $2d_1 = v \times 3$

$\therefore d_1 = 3v/2 \rightarrow (1)$

For Hill 2:

Distance $= d_2 + d_2 = 2d_2$

Using $d = v \times t$, we get $2d_2 = v \times 4$

$\therefore d_2 = 4v/2 \rightarrow (2)$

Given $d_1 + d_2 = 1190$ m

$\therefore 3v/2 + 4v/2 = 7v/2 = 1190$

$\Rightarrow v = 2 \times 1190/7 = 340$ m/s

73. Distance between points P and Q, $(d) = 990$ m.

Time, $(t) = 3$ s.

Speed with which the bullet moves is

$= \frac{990 \text{ m}}{3 \text{ s}} = 330 \text{ m s}^{-1}$.

As the speed of body matches the speed of sound, the time interval is zero. The thief cannot escape the bullet.

74. Mega phone, loudspeaker, hearing aid, etc., are the devices which work on the reflection of sound.

The main part of the mega phone or the loudspeaker is a horn shaped tube.

This tube prevents the spreading of sound waves in all directions. The sound entering the tube undergoes multiple reflections and comes out of the tube with a high directionality and it can propagate through longer distances.

75. Distance of clouds above the ground, $(d) = 10$ km $= 10 \times 10^3$ m $= 10,000$ m.

Velocity of sound, $(V) = 330 \text{ m s}^{-1}$.

Time taken to hear thunder, $(t_2) = \frac{10^4 \text{ m}}{330 \text{ m s}^{-1}}$

$= \frac{10^3}{33} = \frac{1000}{33}$ s $= 30.30$ s $- (2)$

∴ time gap $(\Delta t) = t_2 - t_1 = 30.30 - 0 = 30.30$ s

76. The vocal cord of a man is about 20 mm long and it is about 5 mm shorter in women than in men. Children have very short vocal cords, and hence, the frequency of their voice is higher. Hence, the voices of children are shriller than that of adults.

77. Shrillness of a sound is determined by its pitch. Pitch increases with frequency of sound.

Women have shorter vocal cords which vibrate more quickly and produce a higher frequency, compared to men.

Shorter the vocal cord, more is the pitch and hence shriller is the voice.

The length of vocal cord of: Infant baby < 5th class girl < women of age 40 < man of age 40.

Hence, the ascending order of shrillness in voice is:

Man of age 40 < woman of age 40 < 5th class girl < infant baby

78. Time gap between 'incident' and received sound signal is $(t) = 0.5$ s.

Speed of sound in water, $(v) = 1400 \text{ m s}^{-1}$.

$$\text{speed} = \frac{\text{distance}}{\text{time}}$$

$$v = \frac{2d}{t}$$

$$d = \frac{v \times t}{2} = \frac{1400 \times 0.5}{2} = 350 \text{ m}$$

$\therefore$ The distance of shoal of fish from the ship d = 350 m.

79. In theatres, auditoria, big halls, etc., due to the reflection of sound from the walls, the floor and the ceiling, the music or the speech rendered becomes uninteresting or unintelligible. To avoid this problem the windows, doors, etc., are covered with thick curtains and the seats and steps are covered with sound absorbing material like carpets.

80. Concave reflectors are used in big auditoria to distribute the sound evenly in all directions. When the speaker is placed at the focus of the concave reflector, then the reflected sound waves travel parallel, in all directions and can be distributed evenly.

Level 3: Assess Your Concepts

81. $f_1 = 20$ Hz

$$T_1 = \frac{1}{20} \text{ s} = 5 \times 10^{-2} \text{ s.}$$

$f_2 = 20{,}000$ Hz

$$\text{From } T_2 = \frac{1}{20{,}000} \text{ s} = 5 \times 10^{-5} \text{ s.}$$

Range is 5×10^{-2} s to 5×10^{-5} s.

82. When the bat is inside the well, it produces the ultrasonic sound to come out of it. The sound produced by it gets reflected from all the sides, and hence, it becomes difficult for the bat to find a path to come out of the well.

83. Speed of sound, $v = 310 \text{ m s}^{-1}$

Time taken to get the sound from the instant the cracker is fired, t = 08:00:02 – 08:00:00 = 2 s

$\therefore$ Distance between Ramu and Numu = $v\,t = 310 \text{ m s}^{-1} \times 2 \text{ s} = 620$ m

84. Initially, inside the bulb, low pressure inert gases are present. When the student breaks the bulb, air gushes inside the bulb, and hence, sounds like an explosion is heard.

85. Dogs can hear sounds of frequencies greater than 20 kHz, which can not be heard by human beings. So, the crime department use galton whistle to alert the dog by producing ultrasound waves which are heard by dogs.

86. Let the distance from Ravi to John be d_1, and the distance from Asif to John be d_2.

$$V = \frac{d_1}{t_1}$$

Let $t_1 = 2$ s

$\therefore\ d_1 = 2 \times 330 = 660$ m

Let $t_2 = 2.5$ s

$\therefore\ d_2 = 2.5 \times 330 = 825$ m.

Total distance = 660 + 825 = 1485 m.

Thus, the distance between Ravi and Asif = 1485 m

87. Number of numbers counted = number of oscillations.

Total time, $t = 60$ s

Time period, $T = 2.5$ s

Number of oscillations = $t/T = 60/2.5 = 24$

$\therefore$ Number of numbers counted = 24

Frequency = $(\text{Time period})^{-1} = 2.5^{-1} = 10/25 = 0.4$ Hz

CHAPTER 6

Electricity

Remember

Before beginning this chapter, you should be able to:

- Know applications of electricity in daily life, such as electric bulbs, radio, TV, etc.
- Define conductors of electricity

Key Ideas

After completing this chapter, you should be able to:

- Discuss the nature of electric charges and electroscopes
- Understand electric circuits and symbols used in them
- Define cell and its types—Voltaic cell, Leclanché cell, Dry cell, Bichromate cell
- Study household distribution of electrical energy
- Learn about heating effect of electricity
- Understand magnetic effects of electric current

Scientific Crypt

A Tribute to Thomas Alva Edison (1847–1931)

Thomas Alva Edison, a legend in field of technology, was an American inventor. He was born on 11th February, 1847 in Milano, Ohio. He was the seventh and last child of Samuel Edison, Jr. and Nanly Eeliot Edison. He moved from Milano to Port Huron at the age of seven as his father became a carpenter at the Fort Gratiot military post at Port Huron. He did his schooling in Port Huron. His teachers considered him a dull student but he was having difficulty following the lessons because of his hearing problems.

He set up his first laboratory in the basement of his house but he shifted it to an empty freight car because his mother could not bear the smell of the chemicals. By the age of 12, he started printing his weekly newspaper "Grand Trunk Herald". By 1869, Edison became a full time inventor and entrepreneur and invented duplex telegraph, message printer, etc., He then opened a workshop in New York, New Jersey. From there, he produced universal stock printer, the automatic telegraph, the quadruplex, as well as other printing telegraphs. In 1877, Edison invented carbon – button transistor, tinfoil phonograph and with the help of leading financiers opened the Edison Electric light company and in 1879, he invented incandescent electric light bulb. He started a new laboratory and research facility in West Orange, New Jersey and employed nearly 60 workers. From here, he produced the commercial phonograph, the kinetoscope, the Edison storage battery, the electric pen, the mimeograph and micro taximeters. Thus, he patented more than 1000 discoveries. He was appointed president of the U.S Navy Consulting Board.

This great inventor, who has contributed immensely to the shaping of modern society, left the world on 18th October, 1931 in West Orange, New Jersey.

FUN TIME

CROSSWORD

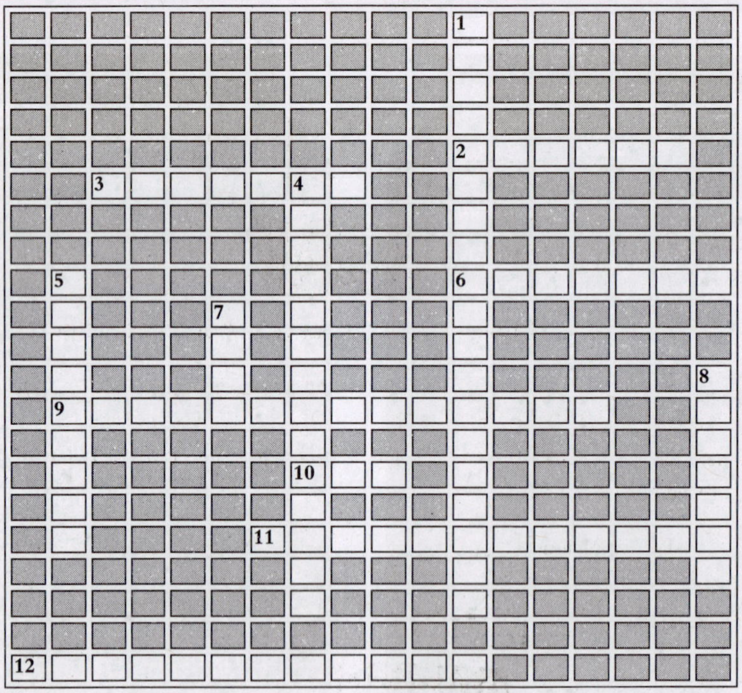

Across

2. Electrical appliances do not work to their capacity when they are connected in _____.
3. The scientist who discovered the magnetic effect of electric current.
6. The metal coated on a zinc plate to prevent local action in voltaic cell.
9. The chemical used as a depolariser in a voltaic cell.
10. It is an example of an insulator.
11. Commercial unit of electric energy.
12. The device used to detect the presence of a charge on a body.

Down

1. The chemical which oxides the hydrogen produced in a bichromate cell.
4. Study of electric charges at rest.
5. The process responsible for the attraction of an uncharged body by a charged body.
7. The device which prevents the flow of excess current.
8. A group of cells.

INTRODUCTION

Electricity is the most widely used form of energy. We cannot imagine the world without 'electricity'.

What is electricity? Why is it the most convenient and useful form of energy? What do we do to make the electric bulb glow? What happens when we switch it ON? Let us try to understand some of these aspects in this chapter.

Certain materials, like glass, plastic, etc., attract small objects like bits of paper after they have been rubbed with certain other materials. For example, a plastic pen does not attract small bits of paper. Rub one end of the plastic pen with a silk cloth for one minute and bring the rubbed end near the bits of small paper. We can observe that the pen attracts bits of paper after it has been rubbed with silk cloth. Not only a plastic pen, but also many other materials and objects exhibit this property of attracting small objects after they are rubbed. Any substance showing such attraction is said to be charged. In the above example, the plastic pen is said to be charged.

Nature of Charges

The nature of charges can be discussed on the basis of charging and behaviour of charges with each other.

Charged Object Attracts Uncharged Object

A glass rod when rubbed with a piece of woollen cloth acquires charge and becomes a charged body. This charged glass rod can attract small pieces of uncharged straw.

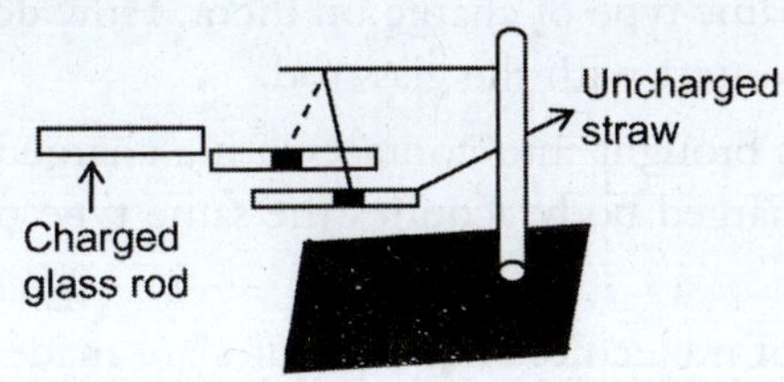

Figure 6.1 Charged objects attract uncharged objects

Like Charges Repel Each Other

Take two glass rods and charge them by rubbing each with a silk cloth. When both these charged glass rods are brought nearer, we observe them repelling each other.

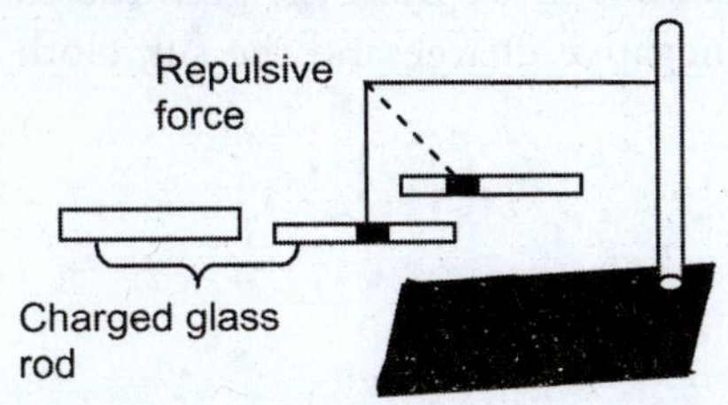

Figure 6.2 Experiment to show that like charges repel each other

Info Bytes!

Charge acquired by different bodies is either positive or negative.

Unlike Charges Attract Each Other

When an ebonite rod rubbed with woollen cloth and a glass rod rubbed with silk cloth are brought close to each other, then we observe that they attract each other.

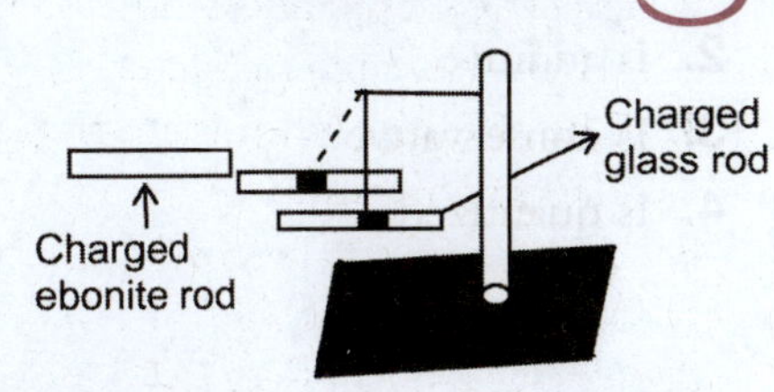

Figure 6.3 Experiment to show that unlike charges attract each other

With these experiments, we can conclude that two charged objects may attract or repel each other. After some more similar experiments, scientists came to the conclusion that two types of charges exist in nature. They are named as 'positive charge' and 'negative charge'.

In the light of this knowledge, if we analyze the above experiments, we can conclude that 'like charges repel each other and unlike charges attract each other'.

Types of Charging

Some materials allow electric charge to flow through them while some others do not. Materials that do not allow electricity or an electric charge to pass through them are called insulators. Wood, plastic, air, etc., are some examples of insulators. Those substances which allow charges to pass through them are called conductors. All metals are good conductors.

Charging a Body by Friction

When a glass rod is rubbed with a silk cloth, glass rod acquires charge and becomes a charged body. What happened to the silk cloth? It is experimentally found that after rubbing the glass rod, even the silk cloth also attracts small pieces of paper. Hence, even the silk cloth also acquired charge when rubbed with glass rod.

When two bodies are rubbed together, both of them get charged and this process of charging a body by rubbing is called charging by friction. The two bodies acquire equal but opposite charges. When a glass rod is rubbed with a silk cloth, the charge acquired by the glass rod is positive and the charge acquired by the silk cloth is negative. S.I. unit of charge is Coulomb, denoted by C. Charge on the electron is smallest i.e., -1.6×10^{-19} C.

Charging a Body by Conduction

We observe a charged glass rod attracting small pieces of uncharged bits of paper. Will the small piece of paper stick to the glass rod? Normally, we observe the piece of paper being pushed away by the glass rod once it is in contact. How does the attraction turn to repulsion when the uncharged paper is in contact with the glass rod? Repulsion indicates that both the glass rod and the piece of paper have same type of charge on them. How does the piece of paper acquire charge? This must have happened when it came into contact with the glass rod.

A neutral body gets charged when it is brought into contact with a charged body. This method of charging a body is called charging by conduction. The uncharged body acquires the same type of charge as that of the charged body with which it is brought into contact.

We know that the matter is made up of molecules and molecules are made up of atoms. Atoms of different elements are different from each other. Every atom contains smaller particles with positive and negative charges. Atom as a whole is neutral because it contains an equal number of particles with negative and positive charges on them. Normally these charged particles remain with the atom. But it is possible for negatively charged particles to move within the matter. Sometimes, these negatively charged particles move out of the atom if enough energy is provided to it. The negatively charged particle in an atom is called electron.

When a glass rod is rubbed with a silk cloth, some electrons move from the glass rod to the silk cloth. As a result, the glass rod has excessive positive charge compared to the negative charge and the silk cloth has excessive negative charge compared to the positive charge.

Properties of Charges

A charge

1. Has magnitude only
2. Is additive
3. Is conservative
4. Is quantized

Electrical Induction

Figure 6.4 Electrical induction

A neutral body has equal number of positive charges and negative charges in it. Let us place a positively charged body near a neutral body. The negatively charged particles get attracted and the positively charged particles get repelled by the positively charged body. As a result, at one end of the neutral body there is an excess of negatively charged particles, and at the other end there is an excess of positively charged particles.

The phenomenon of redistribution of charges in an uncharged body in the presence of a charged body is called electrical induction. In fact, induction is responsible for the attraction of an uncharged body by a charged body.

The Electroscope

How do we identify whether a body is charged or not? If a body is charged, how do we know the nature of the charge?

Electroscope is a device used to detect the presence of a charge on a body and its nature. An electroscope consists of a metal rod fitted in one holed cork stopper which in turn is fixed to a glass jar as shown in the Fig. 6.5. A metal disc or metallic sphere is attached at one end of the rod and two metal strips are attached at the other end of the rod which is kept in a glass jar. By observing the deflection in the metallic strips, we can identify the presence and nature of the charge on the body.

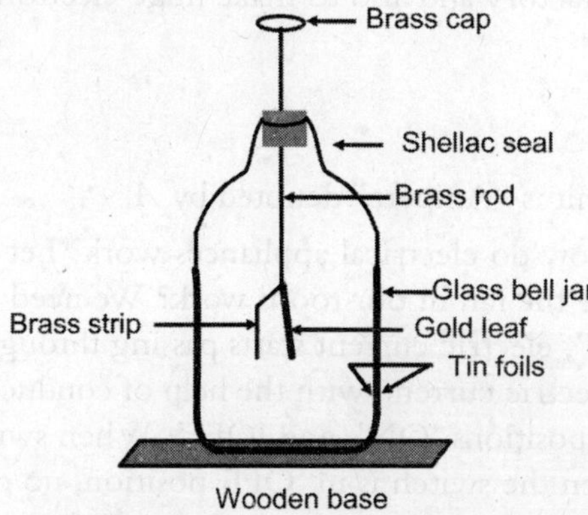

Figure 6.5 Gold leaf electroscope

Lightning

Lightning and thunder are a familiar phenomenon to all of us. Benjamin Franklin proved that lightning is a natural phenomenon involving charged particles. It is observed that in a cloud, smaller droplets acquire positive charge and heavier droplets acquire negative charge. Lighter positively charged droplets go to upper region and heavier negatively charged droplets reach the lower region of the cloud. In this process, a small region of positive charge is also created near the lower parts of the cloud.

Opposite charges in the clouds are separated by air which is a very good insulator. When large amounts of charge is separated by a small gap of air, the insulation may break down and air allows charges to pass through it. This phemenon is called discharge and is accompanied with a spark and crackling sound.

Lightning is a phenomenon caused due to discharge of huge charge accumulated on clouds through air. Sometimes the discharge may pass to earth through tall trees or buildings. Radio towers, trees, multistoried buildings get damaged when lightning strikes them.

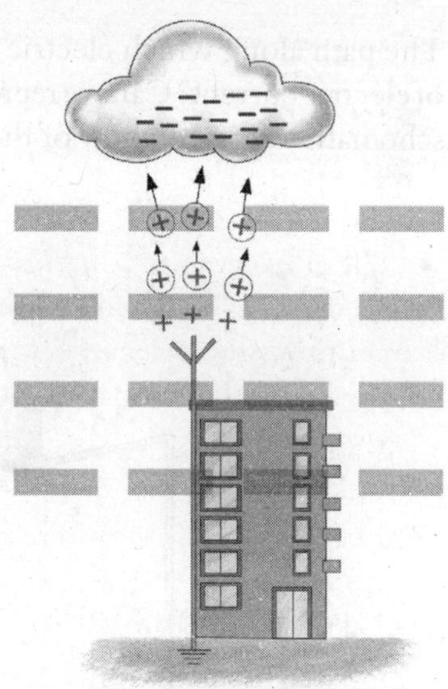

Figure 6.6 Lightning

Lightning Conductor

Lightning conductors are used to protect buildings and other important structures from potential damages caused by lightning. Lightning conductor is a thick metallic strip with a spike like top that is projected up from the top of the building. From the top of the building to be protected, the lightning conductor runs to the ground along the outer wall of the structure. The lower end of the lightning conductor is joined to a metal plate that is buried deep inside the earth.

Electric Current

So far we studied some properties of charges when they are at rest. This study of electric charges at rest is known as 'electrostatics'. But many of the applications of electrical energy make use of the properties of charges when they are in motion.

Charges can move through conductors and we say there is 'electric current' in the conductor when charges are moving from one end to other end. We use electric current in different ways and we have different appliances which work due to the passage of electric current through them. Current passed through the filament of a bulb gives heat and light. The electric current passing through 'electric motor' rotates the fan connected to it. Electric current is used to run machines in a factory and also to make huge electromagnets in an industry.

$$\text{Current} = \text{Charge/time}$$

$$I = q/t$$

SI unit is "Ampere" denoted by A

How do electrical appliances work? Let us understand this by studying an example of electric fan. What do we do to make the fan in our room work? We need to switch it 'ON'. What happens when we switch it ON? When we switch it 'ON', electric current starts passing through the appliance. In general, all electrical appliances are connected to a 'source of electric current' with the help of conducting wires. This connection is made through a device called switch. Switch has two positions 'ON', and 'OFF'. When switch is in 'ON' position, current from the source passes through the appliance. When the switch is in 'OFF' position, no current passes through the appliance.

Electric Circuit

The path along which electric current passes is called electric circuit. How different appliances are connected to the source of electric current? Can we represent all these connections schematically with the help of a circuit diagram? A diagrammatically schematic representation of the path along which electric current flows is called circuit diagram.

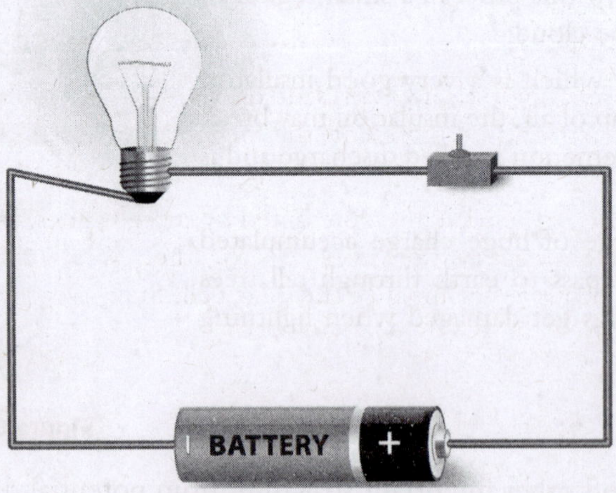

Figure 6.7 Electric circuit

Konnect

In a series circuit, current has only one path to follow, while in parallel circuits, it has multiple!

To represent the electrical connections with the help of a circuit diagram, some common electrical components are represented by symbols. Symbols of some commonly used components are given below.

Table 6.1 Symbols of Commonly used Components

Component	Symbol
Cell (source of electricity)	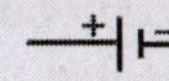
A battery (source of electricity)	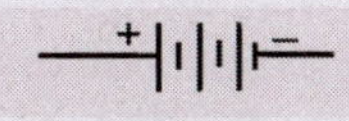
Plug key (switch) in closed condition	
Plug key in open condition	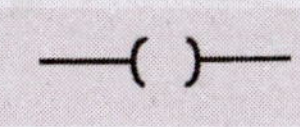
Tap key (switch) in open condition	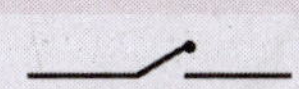
Tap key in closed condition	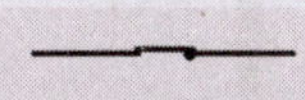
Bulb	
Ammeter (electric current measuring device)	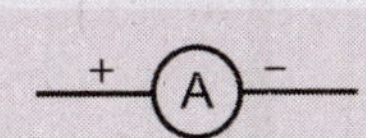
Voltmeter	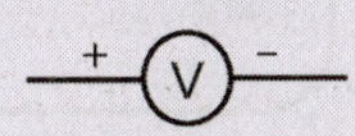
Fixed Resistance	
Fuse	
Rheostat or variable resistance	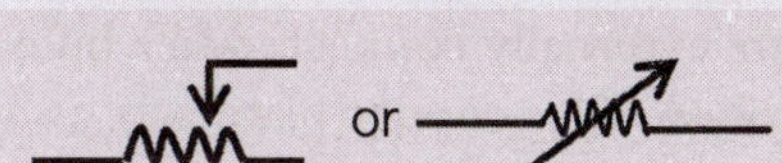
Galvanometer	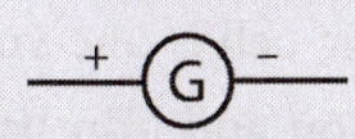

1. An **electric cell** is a source of electric current and is graphically represented by ' —||— '. The longer vertical line represents the 'positive terminal' and the shorter vertical line represents the 'negative terminal'. Usually '+' and '–' symbols are printed on the cell.
2. The **wires** used to connect the various components in a circuit are represented by straight lines. In order to increase the strength of current, for some applications, we connect two or more cells together. While connecting cells, the positive terminal of one cell is connected to the negative terminal of the next cell. Such a combination of two or more cells is called battery and it is represented by the symbol —||||||—
3. **Switch** is a device used to close or open an electric circuit. Switch in a circuit can be placed any where.

When the switch is in the 'ON' position, the circuit from the positive terminal of the battery to the negative terminal is complete. The circuit is then said to be closed and the current passes through out the circuit instantly.

When the switch is in the 'OFF' position, the circuit is incomplete. It is said to be open and no current flows through any part of the circuit.

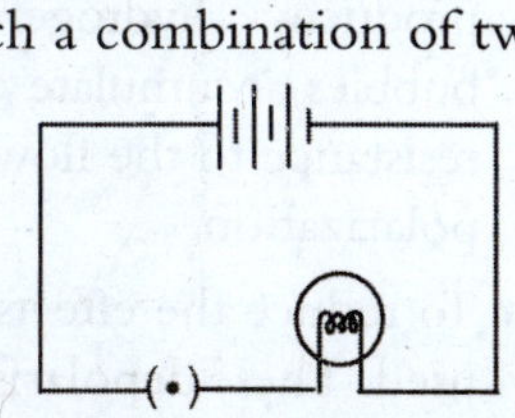

Figure 6.8 A closed circuit

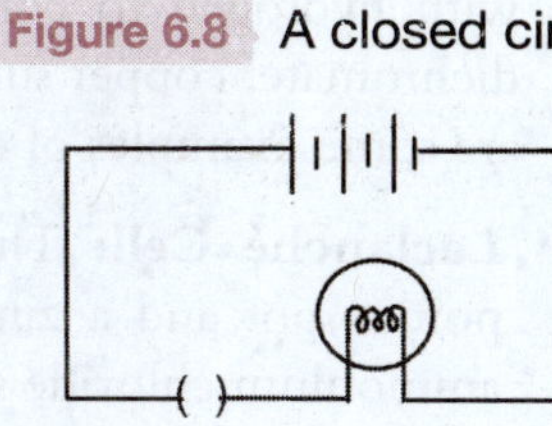

Figure 6.9 An open circuit

Cells

A cell is a source of electrical energy. A cell converts chemical energy into electrical energy. A cell or a battery can be used to operate small electrical appliances. The electric current used in houses or industries is of a very large magnitude and a cell or battery cannot produce this energy. Let us discuss some cells in detail.

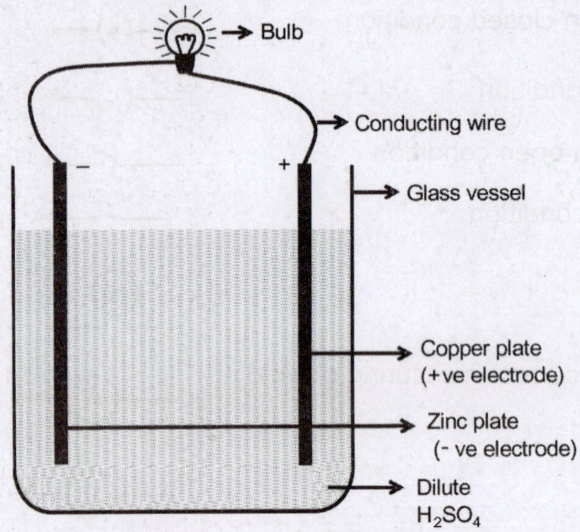

Figure 6.10 Voltaic cell

- **Voltaic Cell:** This consists of a glass vessel, with dilute sulphuric acid. Two plates, one made up of copper and the other made of zinc, are placed in the jar such that each one of them is immersed in the acid.

When these plates are externally connected to a bulb, electricity flows through the bulb and it glows. The dilute sulphuric acid is called electrolyte. The copper plate acts as a positive pole and the zinc plate acts as a negative pole and in the external circuit electricity passes from the copper plate to the zinc plate.

The electromotive force of a Voltaic cell is one volt. There are two defects in the Voltaic cell:

1. **Local action:** Normally, carbon and iron particles are present in a zinc plate as impurities. These particles react with the acid and with the zinc particles to form a large number of tiny cells creating local electric circuits. This is the local action in a Voltaic cell.
   To prevent local action, usually the zinc plate is coated with mercury. Mercury prevents the impurities from coming into contact with acid and prevents local action.
2. **Polarization:** When current passes through the cell, zinc plate starts dissolving in the acid and produces hydrogen bubbles. These hydrogen bubbles accumulate on the copper plate and develop resistance to the flow of current. This defect is called polarization.
   To reduce the effects of polarization, depolarisers are used. These depolarisers are oxidizing agents and react with hydrogen to convert it into water. Potassium dichromate, copper sulphate, and manganese dioxide are some examples of depolarizers.

- **Leclanché Cell:** The Leclanché cell consists of a porous pot and a zinc rod placed in a solution of ammonium chloride solution in a glass jar.

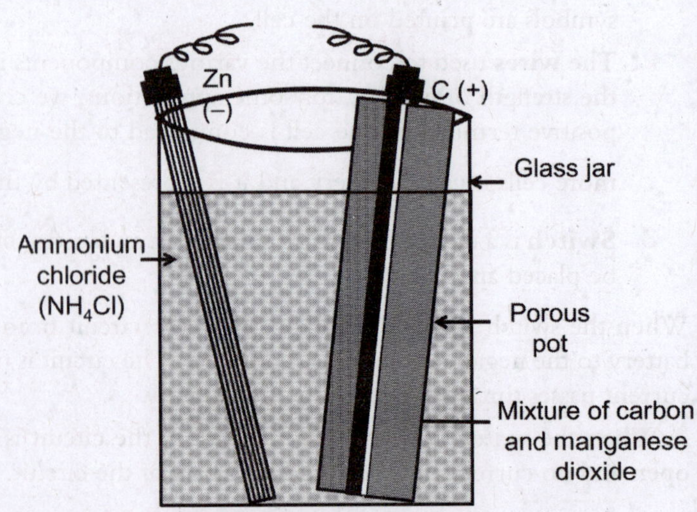

Figure 6.11 Leclanché cell

The porous pot contains powdered carbon and manganese dioxide with a carbon rod dipped into it. Zinc rod acts as the negative plate and carbon rod acts as the positive plate. Electromotive force of this cell is 1.46 volt.

- **Dry Cell:** This is a modified form of Leclanché cell. This consists of a cylindrical zinc container with a chemical mixture of ammonium chloride, zinc chloride with manganese dioxide, and powdered carbon present in the form of a paste. In the middle of this can, there is a carbon rod with a brass cap. The brass cap of the carbon rod and the zinc can act as the positive and negative poles of the cell, respectively. The e.m.f of a dry cell is 1.46 volt.
- **Bichromate Cell:** This cell consists of a flat bottomed glass flask with a special stopper as shown in the Fig. 6.12.

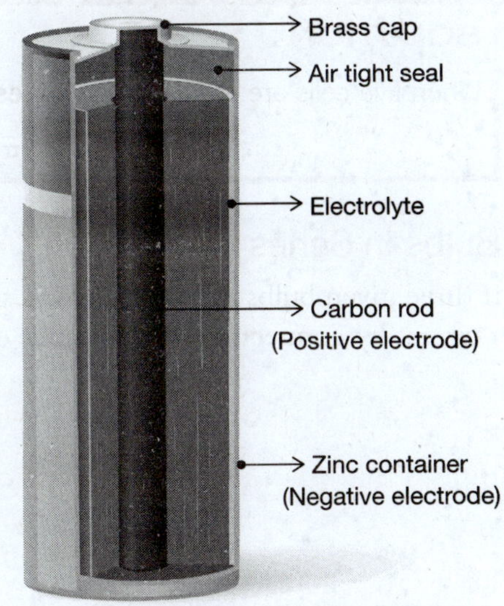

Figure 6.12 Dry cell

A solution of potassium dichromate and dilute sulphuric acid is used as an electrolyte. Two carbon plates act as the positive poles and the zinc plate act as the negative pole. The zinc plate fixed to the stopper can be moved up and down. When the cell is not in use, the zinc plate is placed above the electrolyte. The hydrogen produced in the reaction gets oxidized by potassium bichromate. The e.m.f of this cell is 2 volt.

Some fishes like the eel fish in the Amazon area have the ability to generate electric power. If someone touches it, he receives an electric shock.

There are certain other types of cells in usage. Button cells are used for operating calculators and wrist watches. Storage cells are used in cars and motor cycles to provide electric current for head lights and in the operation of engine.

A cell or a battery can be used to operate small electrical appliances. The electric current used in houses or industries is of a very large magnitude and a cell or battery cannot produce this energy.

Usually, large quantities of electrical energy is generated in power plants. In power plants, a device called electrical generator is used to convert mechanical energy to electrical energy. An electric generator consists of two parts, namely, turbine and dynamo. The energy of flowing water or steam is used to rotate the turbine. Dynamo that is connected to the turbine also gets rotated and it converts the mechanical energy into electrical energy. Electricity generated in power plants is carried to cities and villages by electric cables.

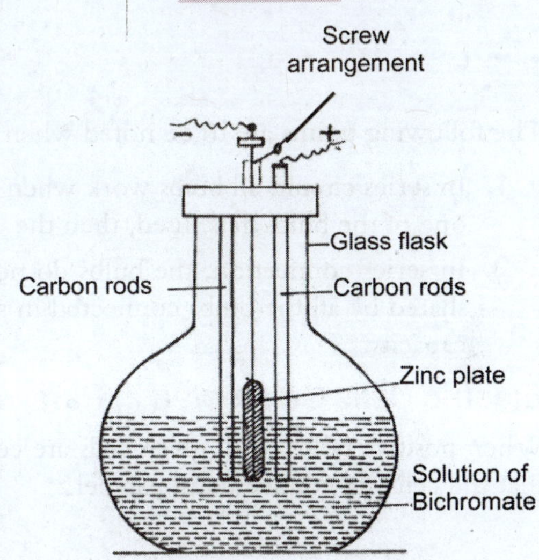

Figure 6.13 Bichromate cell

Parallel and Series Connections

In an electric circuit, components can be connected in two different ways. One is called parallel connection and the other is called series connection.

Electric Cells Connected in Series

In this method, the positive terminal of one cell is connected to the negative terminal of the next cell. After connecting all available cells as described, the negative terminal of the first and the positive terminal of the last are connected to a bulb.

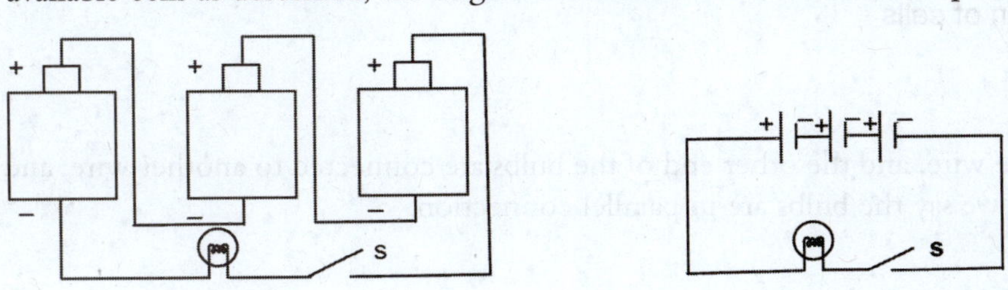

(a) (b)

Figure 6.14 Series connection of cells

Konnect

When cells are connected in series, their total electromotive force (e.m.f) is equal to the sum of the e.m.f of all the cells used.

EXAMPLE 6.1 Five cells, each of e.m.f 2 V, are connected in series to form a battery. Find the e.m.f of the battery.

SOLUTION

When five cells are connected in series, the e.m.f of the battery.

$$E = E_1 + E_2 + E_3 + E_4 + E_5 = 2 + 2 + 2 + 2 + 2 = 10 \text{ V.}$$

Bulbs in Series Connection

If three given bulbs are connected as shown in the circuit diagram, we say that they are connected in series. We can form a circuit by connecting the free ends of connecting wires to a battery through a switch.

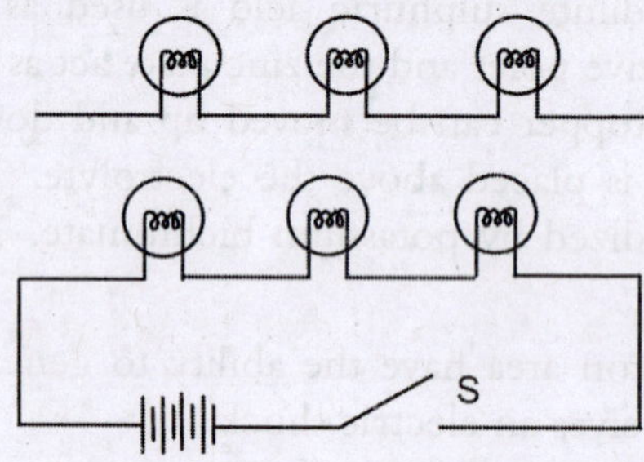

Figure 6.15 Bulbs in series

The following points are to be noted when bulbs (or appliances) are connected in series.

1. In series circuit, all bulbs work when the circuit is closed or all bulbs stop working when the circuit is open. If any one of the bulbs gets fused, then the other bulbs also stop working.
2. In series connection, the bulbs do not glow brightly. In this case, the electrical energy drawn from the battery is shared by all the bulbs connected in series. In fact, when connected in series, the appliances do not work to their capacity.

Electric Cells Connected in Parallel

When positive poles of all given cells are connected together and all negative poles are connected together, then we say that the cells are connected in parallel.

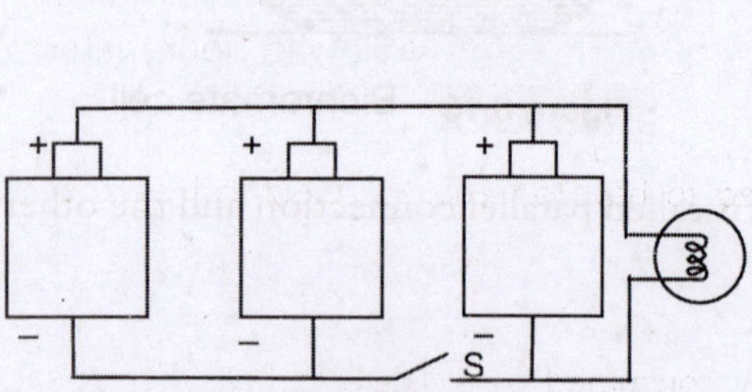

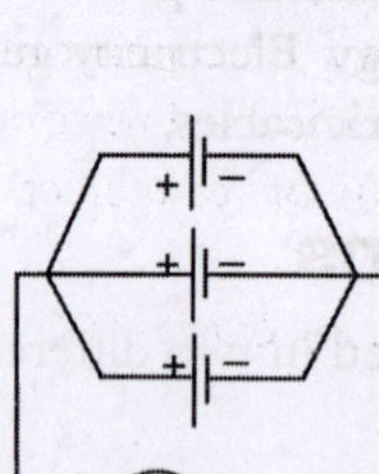

Figure 6.16 Parallel connection of cells

Konnect

When identical cells are connected in parallel, their total electromotive force is same as that of any one of them.

Bulbs in Parallel Connection

When one end of the bulbs are connected to one wire, and the other end of the bulbs are connected to another wire, and these two wires are connected to a battery, then we say the bulbs are in parallel connection.

In parallel connection, all the appliances are directly connected to the battery.

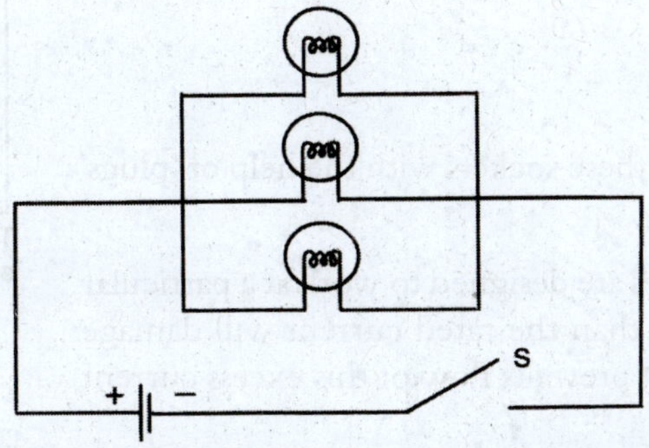

Figure 6.17 Bulbs in parallel connection

The following points are to be noted about the bulbs connected in parallel.

1. All the bulbs are connected directly to a battery, and hence, work independently. Even if one bulb is fused out, the remaining bulbs work normally.
2. All the bulbs derive the required electrical energy and glow brightly.

Household Distribution of Electrical Energy

As discussed earlier, the electrical energy required for houses is generated at power plants and distributed to our homes through cables.

When our household draws electricity from the transformer the power cables first are connected to a meter, known as kilowatt hour meter, (kW h meter) which measures the amount of electrical energy used by us. In general, the manufacturer of any electrical appliance provides the information about how much electrical energy the appliance consumes. The electrical energy consumed in one second is called electric power and it is expressed in watt. For example, you might have seen filament bulbs of different rated powers, like 60 watt, 100 watt, etc. The kilowatt hour meter measures the electrical energy consumed by a household in kilowatt hour or commonly known as electrical 'units'. If an appliance of 1000 watt power is used for one hour, then the electrical energy consumed is one kilowatt hour or 'one electrical unit'.

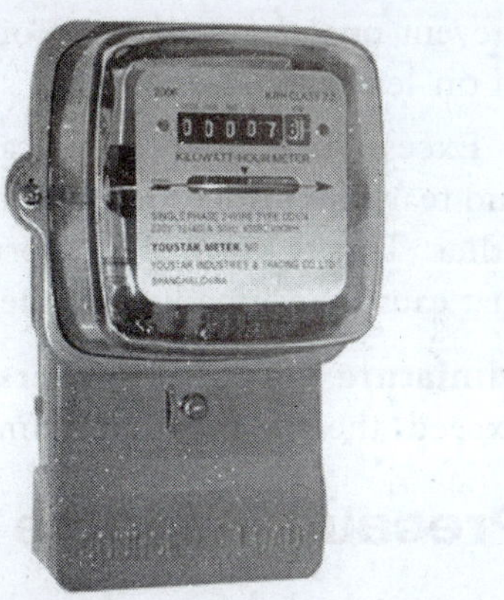

Figure 6.18 Kilowatt hour meter

EXAMPLE 6.2 For how many hours can a 100 W bulb be used to have one unit of electrical energy consumption?

SOLUTION

When used for identical time, a 100 W bulb consumers only $\frac{1}{10^{th}}$ of the energy consumed by a 1000 W bulb. For equal consumption of electrical energy, a 100 W bulb is used for a time that is 10 times the time a 1000 W bulb is used. If a 1000 W bulb consumes one unit of electrical energy when used for one hour, then a 100 W bulb consumes the same one unit of electrical energy if it is used for 10 hours.

From the power supply company, through a transformer, two wires are connected to the kW h meter and they are called live wire and neutral wire. From kW h metre, these wires enter the main fuse and then the main switch. These wires are then connected either to the appliances through switches or to sockets provided in various rooms of the house. We have two types of the sockets: two-pin socket and three-pin socket. In the case of a three-pin socket, there is a provision for 'earth connection'.

Live wire: Red

Earth wire: Green

Neutral wire: Black

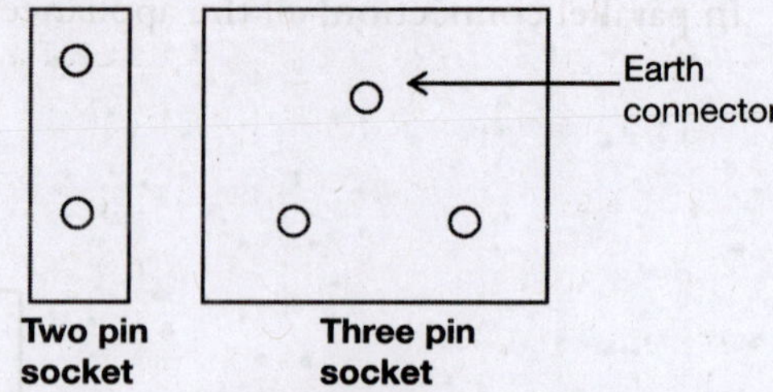

Figure 6.19 Sockets

Different appliances can be connected to these sockets with the help of 'plugs' through switches.

Electric Fuse: Many electrical appliances are designed to work at a particular rated current. Passage of current greater than the rated current will damage the appliance. 'Fuse' is a safety device that prevents flow of this excess current through an appliance.

A wire becomes heated when electric current passes through it. Wires made up of some special material melt quickly and break when large electric currents are passed through them. Such wires are used for making electric fuses.

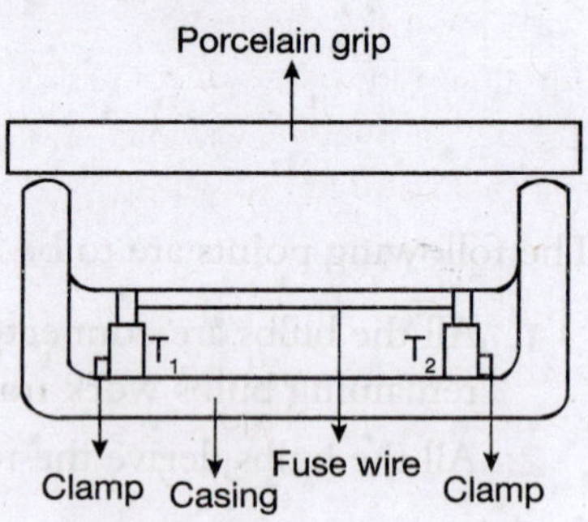

Figure 6.20 Main fuse

Electric fuse consists of a solid porcelain grip with two copper clamps. A fuse wire is fixed between the two copper clamps. Fuses of different kinds are used for different purposes. Different fuse wires can have different thickness. Thicker wires can withstand more electric current.

There is a maximum limit on the current which can pass through an appliance or circuit. If by accident the current exceeds the limits, excess current first passes through the fuse wire and melts it. This breaks the circuit and protects the appliance. The main fuse at the kW h metre is used to prevent unauthorized usage of current. Fuse wire is always connected in series with the appliance. Electric fuse is made of tin-lead alloy.

Excess currents in electrical circuits may be due to either (a) short circuiting or (b) over loading. Because of wear and tear, the insulation on conducting wires used may come off and the wires may come into direct contact with each other. This is known as 'short circuit'. If many devices are connected to a single socket, they may draw excess current that causes 'overloading' in the circuit.

Miniature Circuit Breakers (MCBs): These are switches which automatically turn off when current in the circuit exceeds the safe maximum limit. These are connected in series with live wires and act as a good substitute for 'fuse'.

Precautions to be Taken while Using Household Electrical Appliances

A human body is a good conductor of electricity and we receive shock when the electric current flows through our body. Whenever we use electrical appliances, we must be careful to see that no part of our body comes into direct contact with a wire carrying current.

1. Always use appliances carrying ISI mark.
2. For performing any experiments in electricity use only cells and not the mains supply to your household.
3. Do not put a finger or a metallic wire in the sockets.
4. Avoid touching switches with wet hands.
5. Always use a tester to know the presence of current.
6. One should not touch the metal parts of an electrical appliances or electrical pole with bare hands.

Heating Effect of Electricity (Joule's Law of Heating)

A conducting wire connected to a cell for a few minutes will become heated. This is the heating effect of electric current and in this case the electrical energy is converted to heat energy. An electric iron, electric heater, electric oven, filament bulbs, etc., all work on heating effect of the electric current.

Heat is:

1. directly proportional to square of amount of current
2. directly proportional to resistance
3. directly proportional to the time

All these appliances, which work on heating effect of electricity, contain a coil of wire, known as an 'element', or a 'heating element' which becomes red hot and gives heat when current passes through it. The amount of heat produced in a wire depends on its length, thickness, nature of the material, amount of current flowing and time for which the current flows.

As such for different requirements, wires of different materials are used. The filament of an electric bulb gets heated to such a high temperature that it starts glowing. Whereas the wire used for making electric circuits does not normally became hot.

Filament bulbs give out undesired heat resulting in wastage of electricity. Fluorescent tube lights and compact fluorescent lamps (CFLs) do not give much heat and by using them for lighting purposes, we can reduce wastage of electricity.

1. Wires used for electric circuits are copper
2. Wires if heating element in toasters is nichrome
3. Heating element of electric bulbs is 'Tungsten'

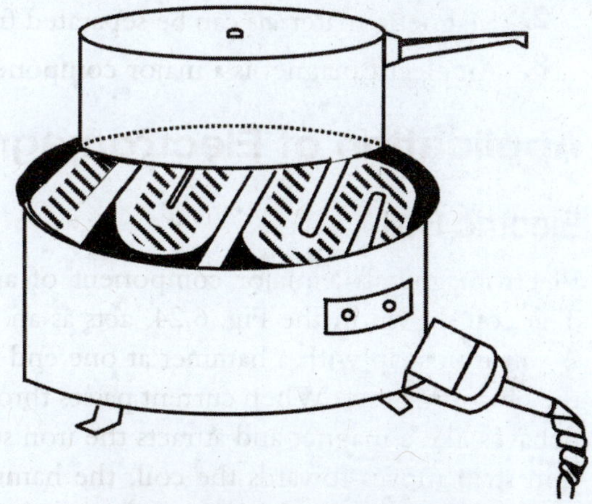

Figure 6.21 An electric heater

Electric Heater

Nichrome wire, usually in the form of a spring, is used to make a heating element. This is fixed in a kaolin or asbestos frame. This frame is fixed firmly into a metallic or asbestos body. A plug and the connecting wires are provided to pass current to nichrome wire.

Because of the resistance offered to the flow of electric current, nichrome wire gets heated and becomes red hot and transfers heat energy to the vessel kept on the heater. If a thick iron plate is fixed over the heating element, this becomes an electric hot plate which is used in iron boxes and some kitchen appliances. Even an electric fuse works on the basis of heating effect of the electric current.

Magnetic Effects of Electric Current

Hans Christian Oersted, in 1800 CE, first observed that a conducting wire behaves like a magnet when electric current passes through it. This is the magnetic effect of the electric current. Can we demonstrate this effect?

Take a magnetic compass and wind an insulated conducting wire around it. Free ends of the wire are to be connected to a cell E through a switch. Normally the magnetic needle in the compass is in north-south direction. What happens when the switch is closed? We observe the compass needle deflecting from its initial position. Now if the switch 'S' is open again, the needle comes back to its initial position. We know that the compass needle is a small magnet. When current is passing through the conducting wires, it behaves, like a magnet and deflects the compass needle. In fact, we can make use of this observation, to prepare magnets called electromagnets.

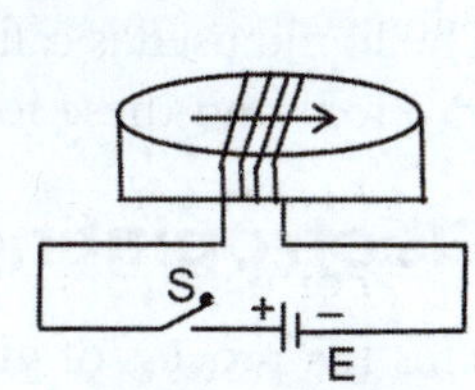

Figure 6.22 Magnetic effects of electric current

Electromagnets

Take a cylindrical iron rod and insulated conducting wire. Wind this wire around the iron rod and connect its free ends to a cell 'E' through a switch 'S' as shown in the Fig. 6.23.

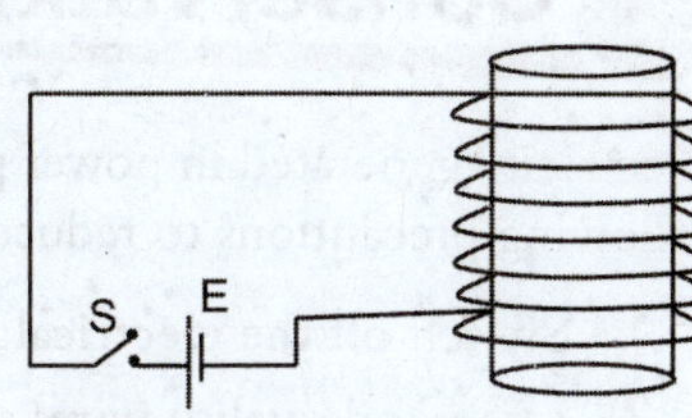

Figure 6.23 Electromagnet

Place a few iron nails below the cylinder. When the switch 'S' is in the 'ON' position, current passes through the wire and iron nails get attracted by the cylinder. When the switch 'S' is in the 'OFF' position, we observe that the nails get detached from the cylinder.

The coil around the cylinder behaves like a magnet when a current passes through it. This is known as an electromagnet.

Info Bytes!

The strength of the electromagnet can be increased by increasing the amount of current passing through the coil.

Uses of Electromagnets

1. Electromagnetic cranes are used to lift heavy loads.
2. Magnetic materials can be separated from junk with the help of an electromagnet.
3. An electromagnet is a major component of an electric bell.

Application of Electromagnets

Electric Bell

Electromagnet is a major component of an electric bell. The coil shown in the Fig. 6.24, acts as an electromagnet. A soft iron strip with a hammer at one end is kept close to the electromagnet. When current passes through the coil, it behaves like a magnet and attracts the iron strip. When the iron strip moves towards the coil, the hammer connected to it strikes the gong and a sound is produced. When the iron strip is pulled towards the coil, it loses contact with the screw and the circuit is now open. When the circuit is broken, the coil no longer acts as an electromagnet and there is no attraction between the coil and the iron strip. This leaves the iron strip back to its original position and touches the contact screw. This once again completes the circuit, and the above process is repeated once again.

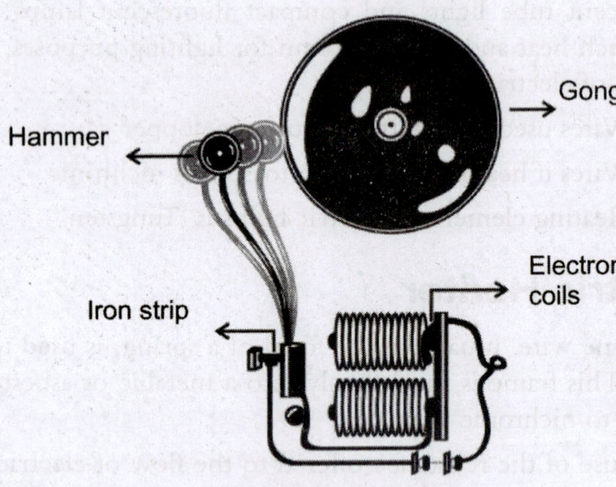

Figure 6.24 Electric cell

Chemical Effects of Electrical Current

When electric current passes through certain liquids, like copper sulphate, it causes chemical reactions in those liquids. The liquid used is called electrolyte. When current passes through an electrolyte, the molecules in the electrolyte dissociate into ions and these ions move towards opposite poles. This is called electrolysis.

Electroplating

This is a process of giving an expensive gold or silver coating on articles made of cheap metals.

Electrolysis is very useful in purifying metals. An impure metal is taken at the positive pole and a pure metal is obtained at the negative pole. Solution of a metallic salt is used as an electrolyte.

Conservation of Electricity

Electricity generated in power plants costs a lot, hence, it is to be used only when it is absolutely necessary. We can take the following precautions to reduce the consumption of electricity.

1. Switch off the electrical appliances when they are not in use.
2. Use good quality wires and appliances to minimize the loss of electrical energy.
3. Every individual must remember the wise saying 'energy saved is energy generated'.

POINTS TO REMEMBER

- There are two kinds of charges, positive and negative. Like charges repel and unlike charges attract each other.
- A body can be charged by friction, conduction and induction. Electroscope is a device used to detect the presence of charge on a body.
- (i) Materials that do not allow electric charges to pass through them are called insulators.

  Examples: wood, plastic, air, etc.

  (ii) The substances which allow charges to pass through them are called conductors.

  Examples: All metals.
- Lightning is the phenomena caused due to discharge of huge charge accumulated on clouds, through air to the ground. Lightning conductors are used to protect buildings and other important structures from damages caused by lightning.
- An electric cell is a 'source of electric current' and is represented by —|⊢— . The combination of two or more cells is called battery and is represented by a symbol —|⊢|⊢—. It produces electric current at the cost of chemical energy stored in it.
- When current flows through a circuit, it is called closed circuit. Open circuit does not conduct any electric charge (current) through it.
- (i) When cells are connected in series, their total e.m.f (E) is equal to the sum of the e.m.f of all the cells used, i.e., $E = E_1 + E_2 + E_3 + E_4 + \ldots$

  (ii) When identical cells are connected in parallel, their total electromotive force is the same as that of any one of them.

  (iii) Household appliances are connected in parallel combination.
- (i) Fuse is a safety device that prevents flow of excess current through an appliance.

  (ii) Miniature circuit breakers (MCBs) are the switches which automatically turn off when current in the circuit exceeds the safe limit. These are good substitutors for a fuse.
- An incandescent bulb and a heater, work on heating effect of electric current.
- A galvanoscope, an electromagnet and an electric bell work on the principle of magnetic effect of electric current.
- Electric generator is used to convert mechanical energy to electrical energy.
- The electrical energy consumed in one second is called electric power and is measured in watts.
- One unit or one kilowatthour is the amount of electrical energy consumed by an appliance of power 1000 W in one hour.

  $$\therefore 1 \text{ unit} = 1 \text{ kW h} = 1000 \times 60 \times 60 \text{ J} = 36 \times 10^5 J = 3.6 \times 10^6 \text{ J} = 3.6 \text{ MJ.}$$
- The process of dissociation of an electrolyte into its constituent ions when current passes through it is called electrolysis.
- (i) Electroplating is the process of depositing a thin layer of metal over another metal by passing current through the electrolytes, such as $CuSO_4$, $ZnSO_4$, etc.

  (ii) An electrotype setting works on chemical effect of electric current.

PRACTICE QUESTIONS CLASSROOM WING

Very Short Answer Type Questions

***Directions for questions from 1 to 5:* Fill in the blanks**

1. ______ acts as a positive pole and ______ as a negative pole in a dry cell.

2. ______ and ______ are two defects of voltaic cell.

3. Four cells of e.m.f 2.5 V each are connected in series to form a battery, the total e.m.f of the battery is ______.

4. ______ or ______ is used to protect electrical appliances from damages due to excess current.

5. Electrotype setting works on the basis of ______ effect of electric current.

***Directions for questions from 6 to 45:* For each of the questions, four choices have been provided. Select the correct alternative.**

6. A glass rod P is observed to be attracting an ebonite rod Q, then
   (a) P and Q are uncharged bodies.
   (b) Both P and Q are charged with identical charge.
   (c) Both P and Q are charged oppositely.
   (d) Either P is charged, or Q is charged. If both are charged, they are opposite in nature.

7. An uncharged body X is brought into contact with a negatively charged body Y, then
   (a) X gains negative charge.
   (b) Y loses negative charge.
   (c) Negative charge gained by X is equal to the negative charge lost by Y.
   (d) All of the above

8. Which of the following is not a source of electrical energy?
   (a) A cell (b) A battery
   (c) An electric motor (d) A generator

9. Which of the following is a false statement about Leclanché cell?
   (a) Electrolyte is a liquid.
   (b) Zinc rod and carbon rod acts as negative and positive electrodes.
   (c) It can be easily portable from place to place.
   (d) Dry cell is a modified form of Leclanché cell.

10. Which of the following is not a depolarizer?
   (a) Potassium dichromate
   (b) Copper sulphate
   (c) Mercury oxide
   (d) Manganese dioxide

11. Which of the following is not an electrical appliance?
   (a) Washing machine (b) TV
   (c) Fire extinguisher (d) Water cooler

12. Six identical cells are connected as shown in the circuit. The total e.m.f is across the end points ______

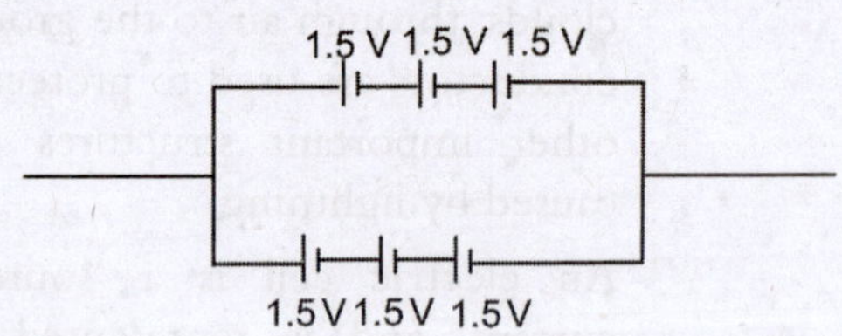

   (a) 1.5 V (b) 4.5 V
   (c) 9 V (d) 0 V

13. Which of the following statements is false about using household electrical appliances?
   (a) Appliances with ISI mark is to be used.
   (b) Switches may be used with wet hands.
   (c) Fingers or metallic wires should not be kept in sockets.
   (d) To know the presence of current, tester is to be used.

14. Which of the following devices does not work on the principle of magnetic effects of electric current?
   (a) Electromagnet (b) Electric motor
   (c) Electric generator (d) Telegraph

15. In which of the following the principle of 'chemical effects of electricity' is not used?
   (a) Telephone (b) Purification of metals
   (c) Electroplating (d) Electro typing

16. A charge
   (a) Has magnitude only (b) Is additive
   (c) Is conservative (d) All of these

17. Which of the following is/are example of insulator?

(a) Wood (b) Plastic

(c) Air (d) All of these

18. A negatively charged body is connected to the ground, then choose the correct statement.

(A) Electrons flow from body to ground.

(B) It becomes positively charged.

(a) Only A is true

(b) Only B is true

(c) Both A and B are true

(d) Both A and B are false

19. A current carrying conductor produces ______.

(a) Only heat

(b) Only magnetic field

(c) Both heat and magnetic field

(d) None of the above

20. Heat is:

(a) directly proportional to square of amount of current

(b) directly proportional to resistance

(c) directly proportional to the time

(d) All of these

21. Heating element of electric bulbs is made up of ______.

(a) copper (b) Nichrome

(c) Tungsten (d) None of these

22. Which of the following is the symbol of a battery?

(a) 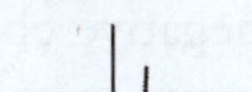 (b) 

(c) 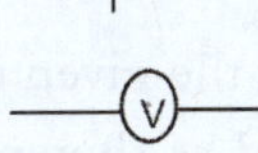

(d) 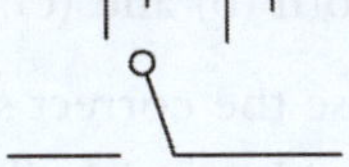

23. Unit of electromotive force is ______.

(a) Volt (b) Second

(c) Metre (d) m s^{-1}

24. The device that can be used to detect the presence of current in a circuit is ______.

(a) Magnetic compass (b) Cell

(c) An inverter (d) Voltmeter

25. Write the following steps in sequential order to explain the working of an electric bell.

(A) When current passes through the coil, it behaves like a magnet and attracts (pulls) the iron strip.

(B) No more does the coil behave as an electromagnet and the attraction between the coil and the iron strip is lost. Because of this the iron strip gets back to its original position and touches the screw.

(C) The hammer connected to iron strip also moves and strikes the gong because of which, sound is produced.

(D) When the iron strip is pulled towards the coil, it loses contact with the screw and the circuit becomes open circuit.

(E) Once again the circuit is closed, and the above process is repeated.

(a) ABCDE (b) EDCBA

(c) BADEC (d) ACDBE

26. Write the following steps in sequential order to prove that like charges repel each other.

(A) Take two glass rods.

(B) Now bring these two charged rods nearer.

(C) Charge them by rubbing each glass rod with a silk cloth.

(D) The glass rods repel each other showing that like charges repel each other ungsten.

(a) ABCD (b) ACBD

(c) DCBA (d) BDAC

27. Which of the following is a bad conductor of electricity?

(a) Gold (b) Copper

(c) Pure alcohol (d) Living plant

28. An electric motor converts

(a) Electrical energy into mechanical energy.

(b) Mechanical energy into electrical energy.

(c) Heat energy into electrical energy.

(d) None of the above.

29. Which of the following is incorrect about electromagnets?

(a) Electromagnetic cranes are used to lift heavy loads.

(b) Magnetic materials can be separated from junk with the help of an electromagnet.

(c) An electromagnet is a major component of an electric bell.

(d) All of these

30. Assertion (A): A 200 W bulb consumes 2 units of electrical energy when it is used for 10 hours.

Reason (R): 1 unit of electrical energy = 1000 kWh.

(a) Both A and R are true and R is the correct explanation of A.

(b) Both A and R are true, but R is not the correct explanation of A.

(c) A is true but R is false.

(d) Both A and R are false.

31. Wires used for electric circuits are made up of

(a) Copper (b) Nichrome

(c) Tungsten (d) None

32. Write the following steps in sequence that explain the phenomenon of redistribution of charges in an uncharged body in presence of a charged body.

(A) As a result, at one end of the neutral body there is an excess of negatively charged particles and the other end there is an excess of positively charged particles.

(B) Place a positively charged body near a neutral body.

(C) The negatively and positively charged particles in the neutral body get attracted and repelled by the positively charged body.

(a) BCA (b) CAB

(c) ACB (d) BAC

33. Write the following steps in sequence to show that the unlike charges attract each other.

(A) Take an ebonite rod and a glass rod and tie two silk threads so that they can be suspended.

(B) The glass rod and ebonite rod when brought near attract each other showing that unlike charges attract each other.

(C) Rub ebonite rod with woollen cloth and glass rod with silk cloth and suspend them in air by holding silk threads.

(a) ACB (b) CBA

(c) BCA (d) ABC

34. Identify the correct statement/s related to polarization in voltaic cell.

(A) When current passes through the voltaic cell, zinc plate starts dissolving in the acid and produces hydrogen bubbles.

(B) These hydrogen bubbles accumulate on the copper plate and develop resistance to the flow of current.

(a) Only (A) is true.

(b) Only (B) is true.

(c) Both (A) and (B) are true.

(d) Both (A) and (B) are false.

35. Which of the following precautions should be taken while using household electrical appliances?

(a) Always use appliances carrying ISI mark.

(b) For performing any experiments in electricity use only cells and not the mains supply to your household.

(c) Do not put a finger or a metallic wire in the sockets.

(d) All of these

36. **Assertion (A):** The electrical appliances connected in series do not work to their full capacity.

Reason (R): The electrical energy drawn from the battery is shared by all the appliances connected in series.

(a) Both A and R are true and R is the correct explanation of A.

(b) Both A and R are true, but R is not the correct explanation of A.

(c) A is true but R is false.

(d) Both A and R are false.

37. **Assertion (A):** A 1000 W bulb when used for 1 hour consumes the same number of electrical units as that of 100 W bulb that is used for 10 hours.

Reason (R): One electrical unit is charged when one kilowatt hour electrical energy is consumed.

(a) Both A and R are true and R is the correct explanation of A.

(b) Both A and R are true, but R is not the correct explanation of A.

(c) A is true but R is false.

(d) Both A and R are false.

38. When a neutral body is brought closer to a negatively charged body, then

(a) It becomes positively charged.

(b) The net charge on it is zero.

(c) It consists of equal positive and negative charge.

(d) Both (b) and (c).

39. Choose the correct statement about the given circuit: Three identical bulbs are connected as shown in the figure.

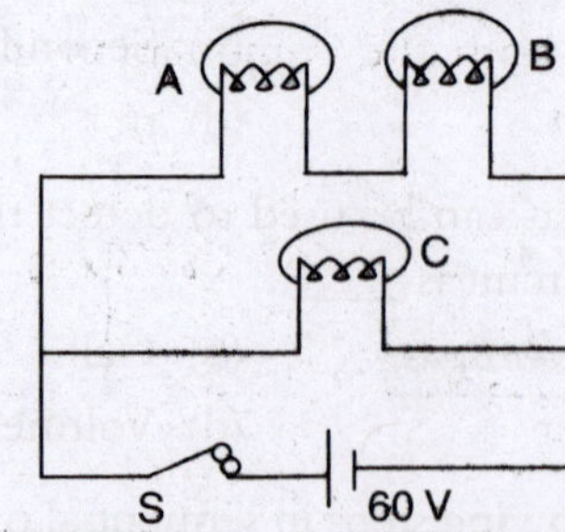

(a) Bulbs A and B are in parallel with bulb C.

(b) The potential (e.m.f) in the circuit is 60 V.

(c) When switch 'S' is turned on all bulbs glow with the same brightness.

(d) Both (a) and (b).

40. Choose the correct statement:

(A) In case of an electric cell, chemical energy is converted into electrical energy.

(B) Combination of electric cells is called battery.

(a) Only (A) is true.
(b) Only (B) is true.
(c) Both (A) and B are true.
(d) Both (A) and (B) are false.

41. The brass cap of the carbon and the zinc can of the dry cell act as ______ and ______ poles, respectively.

(a) Positive, negative (b) Positive, positive
(c) Negative, positive (d) Negative, negative

42. ______________ is a good conductor of electricity?

(a) Impure water (b) Glass
(c) Ebonite (d) Wood

43. An electric generator (dynamo) converts ___________ into ___________

(a) Mechanical energy into electrical energy.
(b) Electrical energy into mechanical energy.
(c) Chemical energy into electrical energy.
(d) Chemical energy into mechanical energy.

44. The e.m.f of a dry cell is _____ volt.

(a) 1.26 (b) 1.36
(c) 1.46 (d) 1.56

45. Choose the correct statement:

When the same current(i) flows through two circuits as shown in the figures, then (assume that all bulbs are identical)

(A) Bulbs in first combination glow with more brightness.

(B) Bulbs in second combination glow with more brightness.

(C) Bulbs in both the combination glow with equal brightness.

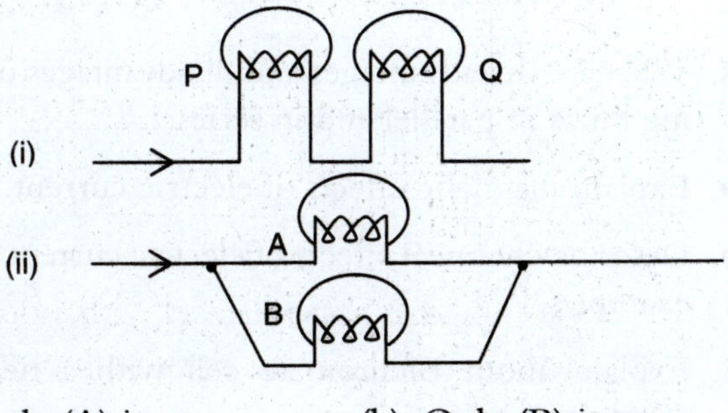

(a) Only (A) is true (b) Only (B) is true
(c) Only (C) is true (d) Cannot be determined

***Directions for questions from 46 and 48:* Match the entries given in Column A with the appropriate ones in Column B.**

46.

	Column A		Column B
A.	Nature of the charge	a.	Acts as negative and positive plates
B.	Lightening	b.	Live wire and neutral wire are connected
C.	Cells connected in series	c.	Involves charged particles
D.	Zinc and carbon rods in Leclanché cell	d.	Their total emf is sum of e.m.f of all the cells used
E.	kW h meter	e.	Deflections in the metallic strips

47.

	Column A		Column B
A.	A cell	a.	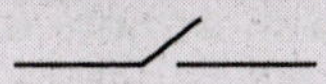
B.	An open tap key	b.	Lightning rod
C.	Electric power	c.	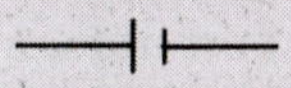
D.	Benjamin Franklin	d.	Magnetic effect of electric current
E.	Electric bell	e.	Eel fish

48.

	Column A		Column B
A.	Porous pot	a.	Carbon rod with brass cap
B.	Dry cell	b.	Convert hydrogen into water
C.	Depolarizer	c.	Heating effect of electric current
D.	Electric fuse	d.	Carbon and manganese dioxide

***Directions for questions from 49 to 68:* Answer the following questions.**

49. How many types of charges are there and what are they?

50. What is an 'electron'?

51. What is an electroscope?

52. When do we say that there is an electric current in a conductor?

53. What is an electric circuit?

54. What is the practical unit of electrical energy?

55. Name two different ways of connecting components in an electric circuit.

56. How many types of sockets are in use and what are they?

57. What is a miniature circuit breaker? Where is it used?

58. How many hours should a 200 W bulb glow to consume 2 units of electrical energy?

59. How can we describe the force between two charged bodies?

60. Which charged particle is free to move within the body as well as from one body to another body?

61. Distinguish between conductors and insulators.

62. Write any two sources of electrical energy.

63. What is a battery?

64. What is an electric generator?

65. What is 'one unit' or 'one kilowatthour' of electrical energy?

66. The amount of heat produced in a wire depends upon what parameters?

67. What happens when current passes through an electrolyte?

68. Three identical cells each of emf 2.5 V are connected in parallel. What is the total emf of the combination?

Short Answer Type Questions

69. Describe how we can charge a body by friction.

70. Write a short note on lightning conductor.

71. Describe Leclanché cell.

72. Write a short note on parallel and series connections of cells.

73. What are the precautions to be taken in using household electrical appliances?

74. How can we charge a body by conduction?

75. Distinguish between open and closed circuits.

76. State whether the following statement about the given circuit is true or false:
When Bulb B is fused, Bulb C will not glow.

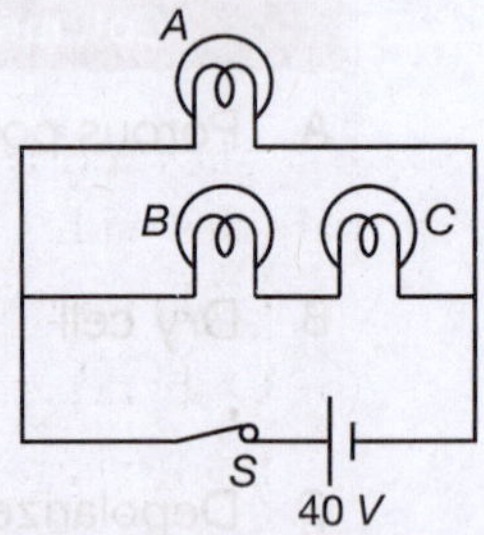

77. Write a short note on (a) short circuit and (b) overload.

78. Write the uses of electromagnets.

79. Describe 'electroscope' and explain briefly how it works.

80. Three cells of 1.5 V, 2.5 V and 3.5 V, respectively, are connected in series to form a battery. Find the e.m.f of the battery.

81. Describe a dynamo.

82. What is an electromagnet? How the strength of the electromagnet can be increased?

83. Write the major defects in Voltaic cell.

Essay Type Questions

84. Write a note on 'electrical induction'.

85. Describe Voltaic cell and write two major defects of it.

86. Describe with an example 'heating effects of electric current'.

87. Write a short note on electric bell.

88. What are the advantages and disadvantages of connecting bulbs in parallel and in series?

89. Explain magnetic effects of electric current.

90. Describe chemical effects of electric current with a few examples.

91. Explain about Bichromate cell with a neat labelled diagram.

PRACTICE QUESTIONS COMPETITION WING

Level 1: Apply your Concepts

***Directions for questions from 1 to 15:* Fill in the blanks**

1. To prevent local action in a voltaic cell, usually zinc plate is coated with _______.
2. When two bodies A and B are rubbed, they acquire charge by friction. If the charge on A is positive, then the charge on B is ______.
3. An electric generator (dynamo) converts ______ energy to _______ energy.
4. _______ is used to protect buildings from lightning.
5. When charges are moving from one end to the other end of a conductor, we say there is _______ in the conductor.
6. Atom is considered neutral because it contains an equal number of ______ and _____ charges.
7. ________ is a major component of an electric bell.
8. Nichrome is the material used to make _______ elements.
9. Materials that do not allow electric charges to flow through them are called_______.
10. Lightning is a natural phenomenon involving ______ particles.
11. In symbolic representation of an electric cell, the longer and shorter vertical lines represent _____ and _______ terminals, respectively.
12. Mercury coated on zinc plate prevents the impurities from coming into contact with acid and prevents _____.
13. ______ is a safety device that prevents excess flow of current through an appliance.
14. When bulbs are connected to the same source, the brightness of bulbs connected in parallel is _____ than the brightness of identical bulbs connected in series.
15. Electric heater works on the basis of ______ the electric current.

***Directions for questions from 16 to 25:* State whether the following statements are true or false.**

16. Copper is a good conductor of electricity.
17. The charged particle in an atom that contributes positive charge is 'electron'.
18. Substances which allow charges to pass through them are called conductors.
19. A switch is used to make or break an electric circuit.
20. The zinc plate in a voltaic cell is usually coated with mercury to prevent polarization.
21. When bulbs are connected to the same source, the brightness of bulbs connected in series is more than the brightness of identical bulbs connected in parallel.
22. In household connections, no current passes through neutral wire when the switch is off.
23. Connecting many devices to a single socket leads to 'short circuit'.
24. 'Nichrome' is the material used to make heating elements.
25. Electric bell works on 'heating effects of electric current'.

***Directions for questions from 26 to 47:* For each of the questions, four choices have been provided. Select the correct alternative.**

26. If a glass rod is positively charged, then it consists of particles with
    (a) Only positive charge.
    (b) Only negative charge.
    (c) Both negative and positive charges, but the number of positively charged particles are more than the number of negatively charged particles.
    (d) Both negative and positive charges but the number of negatively charged particles are more than the number of positively charged particles.
27. A body can be charged by
    (a) Friction (b) Induction
    (c) Conduction (d) All of the above
28. Which of the following is not a consumer of electrical energy?
    (a) A generator (b) An electric motor
    (c) An electromagnet (d) A bulb

29. Find the false statement about a cell.

(a) Symbol of a cell is 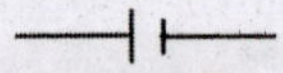

(b) Longer line represents positive terminal.

(c) Shorter line represents negative terminal.

(d) Cell is a major source of electrical energy.

30. Three identical cells of e.m.f 1.5 V are connected in parallel. The total e.m.f of the combination is ______ V.

(a) 1.5 (b) 4.5 (c) 0.5 (d) 3

31. Three bulbs are connected in a circuit in an identical way. When a fourth bulb is also connected to the same circuit in the same way, brightness is reduced then the bulbs are connected in ______.

(a) Series

(b) Parallel

(c) It can happen in both cases

(d) It is not possible

32. How many hours must a 200 W bulb glow to consume 1 unit of electrical energy?

(a) 1 (b) 2 (c) 5 (d) 10

33. The amount of heat produced in a heating element depends on ______.

(a) Its length

(b) Its cross-sectional area

(c) Nature of the material

(d) All of the above

34. Which of the following statements is/are true about electromagnet?

(a) It works on the principle of 'magnetic effects of electric current'.

(b) Electromagnets are used in electric bell.

(c) Electromagnets are used to lift heavy loads.

(d) All of the above

35. A neutral body gets charged when it is brought into contact with a charged body. This method of charging a body is called

(a) Charging by conduction

(b) Charging by friction

(c) Charging by Induction

(d) None of the above

36. Which of the following electrical appliances work on the principle of the heating effect of electric current?

(a) Electric iron (b) Electric heater

(c) Electric bulb (d) All of the above

37. Choose the correct statement(s) in case of a voltaic cell.

(A) Cathode used is Zn and anode used is copper.

(B) The electrolyte used is dilute sulphuric acid.

(a) Only A is true

(b) Only B is true

(c) Both A and B are true

(d) Both A and B are false

38. Choose the correct statement:

When a positively charged body is placed on the ground,

(A) The electrons flow from the ground and neutralize the charge.

(B) The electrons flow from the ground and charge it negatively.

(a) Only A is true

(b) Only B is true

(c) Both A and B are true

(d) Both A and B are false

39. A magnetic needle placed near a current carrying conductor, deflects due to the

(a) Heating effect of electric current.

(b) Magnetic effect of electric current.

(c) Chemical effect of electrical current.

(d) Both (b) and (c)

40. In an electric circuit, components can be connected in ______ different ways.

(a) two (b) three (c) four (d) five

41. Which of the following statements is incorrect?

(a) All metals are good conductors.

(b) Those substances which allow charges to pass through them are called conductors.

(c) Wood, plastic, air, etc., are some examples of insulators.

(d) Materials that do not allow electricity or an electric charge to pass through them are called conductors.

42. Which of the following is the symbol of fuse?

(a) 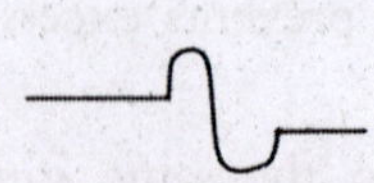 (b) 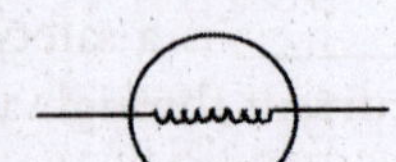

(c) 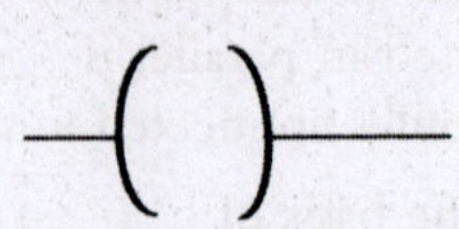 (d) 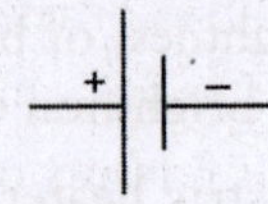

43. The commercial unit of electrical energy is ______.

(a) W h (b) kW h

(c) Joule (d) None of these

44. The bulbs in houses are connected in

(a) Parallel combination.

(b) Series combination.
(c) Series and parallel.
(d) Neither in series nor in parallel.

45. The device used to measure electric current in a circuit is called ______.

(a) Speedometer (b) Ammeter
(c) Voltmeter (d) Kilowatt hour meter

46. Write the following steps in sequential order to prove that unlike charges attract each other.

(A) Take a glass rod and an ebonite rod.
(B) Now bring these two charged rods nearer.
(C) Charge them by rubbing the glass rod with silk cloth and an ebonite rod with fur cloth.
(D) Two rods attract each other showing that unlike charges attract each other.

(a) ACDB (b) CABD
(c) ABCD (d) ACBD

47. Two electric bulbs of 100 W each is used for 10 hours in the month of June. Write the following steps in sequential order to find the number of units of electricity consumed in the month of June.

(A) The number of units of electricity consumed by both bulbs in the month of June is the total electrical energy consumed by bulbs expressed in W h divided by 1000 W h.
(B) Note the rated power of each electric bulb, time of electrical consumption of each bulb per day from the given data.
(C) We know, one electrical unit = 1 kW h or 1000 W h.
(D) Calculate the amount of electrical energy consumed by both the bulbs in the month of June using, (sum of the electrical power of both the bulbs) × (time of consumption in one day) × 30 days.

(a) BACD (b) ABCD
(c) BDCA (d) DCBA

48. When a neutral body is brought closer to a negatively charged body, then

(a) It becomes positively charged.
(b) The net charge on it is zero.
(c) It consists of equal positive and negative charge.
(d) Both (b) and (c)

49. A current carrying metallic comb is placed close to small iron filings, then the

(a) Iron filings will fly away from the comb, when switch is turned off.
(b) Iron filings align in the direction of the magnetic field produced around the metallic comb.
(c) Iron filings will be attracted by the comb.
(d) Both (b) and (c)

50. Three batteries are connected as shown in the figure. Then the total emf in the circuit is _____V.

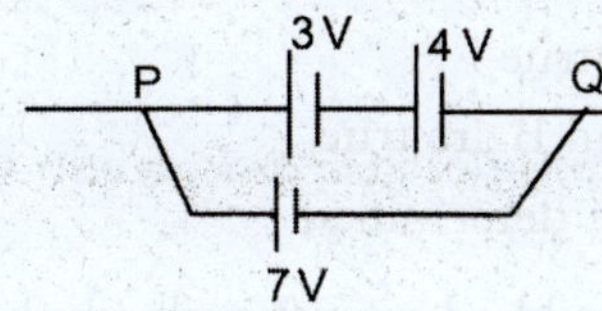

(a) 3
(b) 4
(c) 7
(d) 14

51. Three identical bulbs are connected as shown in figure. Choose the correct statement.

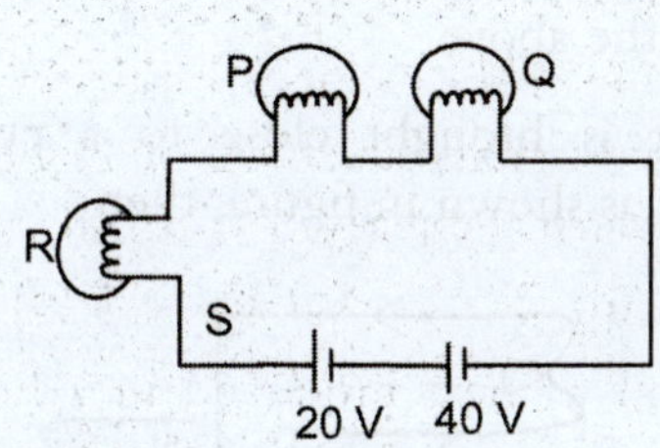

(a) All bulbs are in a series combination.
(b) If bulb R is removed, bulbs P and Q will still glow.
(c) The total e.m.f in the circuit is 40 V.
(d) The given circuit is an open circuit.

52. A positively charged body is brought in contact with the cap of the gold leaf electroscope, whose strips are neutral, then

(a) Positive charge flows from the body to the strips and both the strips acquire positive charge.
(b) Due to like charges on strips, they attract each other.
(c) If a positively charged body is removed the gap between the strips decreases.
(d) Both (a) and (c).

53. Choose the correct statement:

When the same current(i) flows through two circuits as shown in the figures, then (assume that all bulbs are identical)

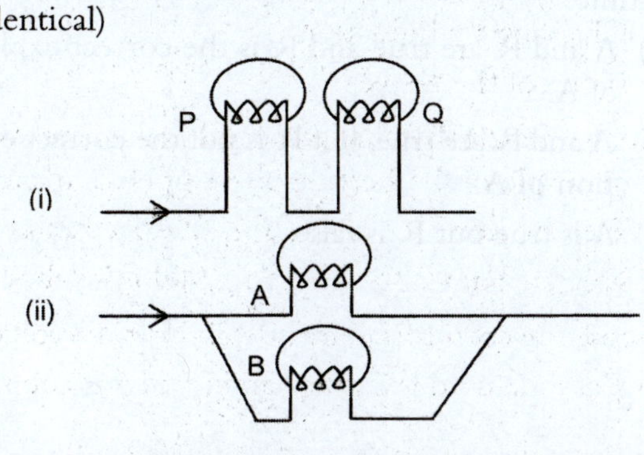

(A) Bulbs in first combination glow with more brightness.

(B) Bulbs in second combination glow with more brightness.

(a) Only A is true

(b) Only B is true

(c) Both A and B are true

(d) Cannot be determined

54. A glass rod is rubbed against a silk cloth, then

(a) The glass rod acquires a positive charge due to loss of electrons.

(b) The silk cloth acquires negative charge due to gain of electrons.

(c) If these two bodies are again brought in contact the net charge on them is zero.

(d) All of the above

55. A magnet is brought close to a current carrying conductor as shown in figure, then

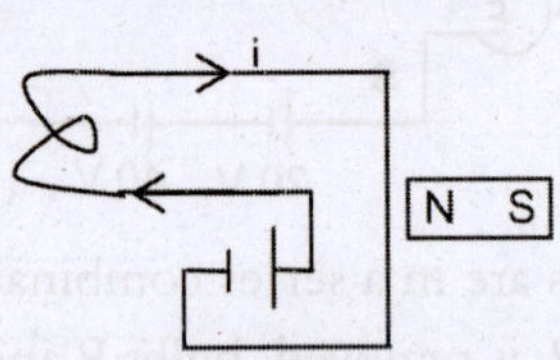

(a) It will be repelled by the conductor.

(b) It will be attracted by the conductor.

(c) It will not show any effect.

(d) It will be just deflected.

56. Three dry cells are connected as shown in the 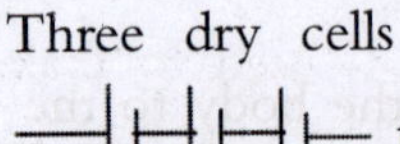 figure. If e.m.f of each cell is 2 V, then the total e.m.f. of the combination is ______ V.

(a) 2 (b) 6

(c) 3 (d) 4

57. Assertion (A): A 500 W electric heater when used for 2 hours consumes the same number of electrical units as that of 100 W bulb that is used for 10 hours.

Reason (R): The number of units is given by power × time.

(a) A and R are true and R is the correct explanation of A.

(b) A and R are true, but R is not the correct explanation of A.

(c) A is true but R is false.

(d) Both A and R are false.

58. Assertion (A): The electrical appliances connected in parallel work to their full capacity.

Reason (R): All the electrical appliances are connected directly to a battery and derive the required electrical energy.

(a) A and R are true and R is the correct explanation of A.

(b) A and R are true, but R is not the correct explanation of A.

(c) A is true but R is false.

(d) Both A and R are false.

***Directions for questions from 59 and 60:* Match the entries given in Column A with the appropriate ones in Column B.**

59.

Column A	Column B
A. A battery	a. Good conductor
B. Metal	b. Mechanical energy is converted into electric energy
C. A generator	c. 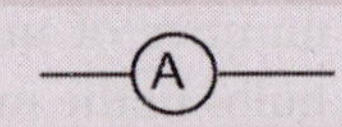
D. Filament bulb	d. Heating effect of electricity
E. Ammeter	e. 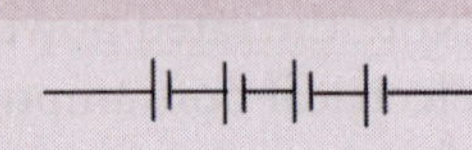

60.

Column A	Column B
A. A cell	a. Study of electric charges at rest
B. Bulb	b. Close or open an electric circuit
C. Static electricity	c. Substitute for fuse
D. Switch	d. 
E. MCBs	e. Prevent unauthorized usage of current
F. Main fuse at kW h metre	f. Converts chemical energy into electrical energy

Level 2: Review your Concepts

61. (a) Two charged bodies, A and B, are suspended from a fixed point with the help of silk threads as shown in the figure. If A is positively charged, can we identify the nature of charge on 'B'?

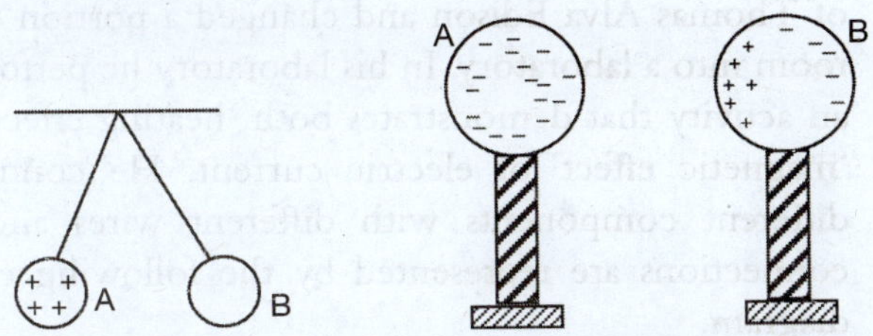

(a) **(b)**

(b) A negatively charged conducting sphere A and a neutral sphere B are kept on insulating stands and brought close to each other. The charge distribution is as shown in the figure.

Is B charged? What type of force exists between A and B?

62. Raghavan found a metallic rod AB and a glass rod CD both positively charged and placed on an insulating table. He wanted to know what would happen to the charges on AB and CD if he touched both the rods at A and C? Discuss.

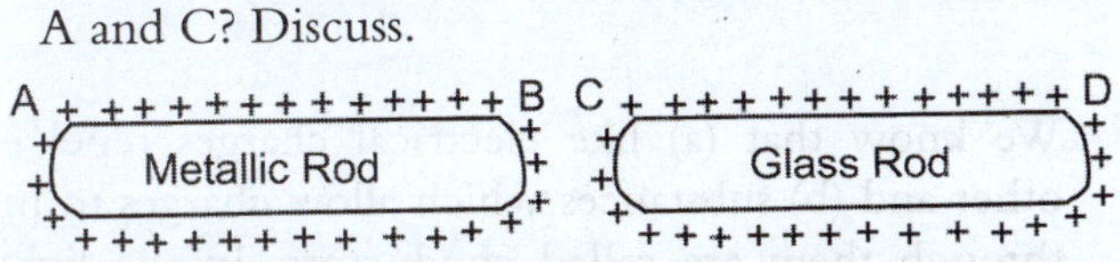

63. Two identical, small metallic spheres A and B are placed side by side on an insulating smooth table as shown in the figure. If A is positively charged and held fixed with the table, discuss the motion of B.

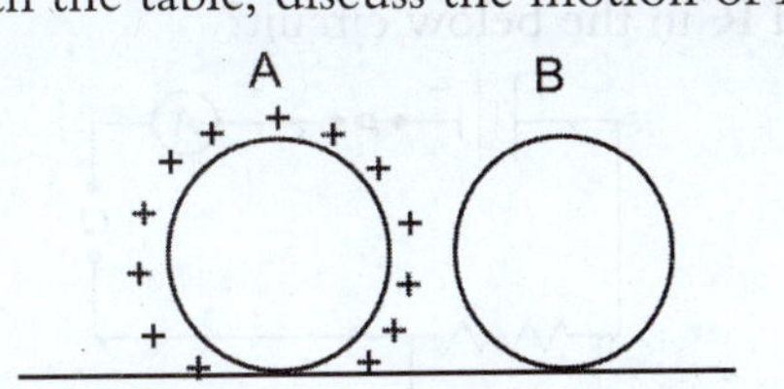

64. Observe the circuit and state whether the cells are connected in series or parallel. If each cell is of e.m.f 1.5 V, then find the total e.m.f applied across the bulb connected.

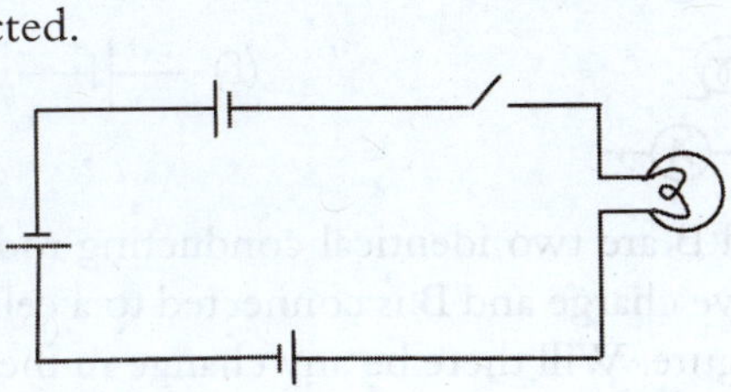

65. Three identical cells of e.m.f 1.5 V are given. Find how we can arrange them to get a total e.m.f of

(a) 1.5 V (b) 3 V (c) 4.5 V

66. Prahar took two identical heating elements and connected them to a battery in two different ways as shown in the figure. When he switched ON the switch, is the heat developed in each element the same or different in both the cases?

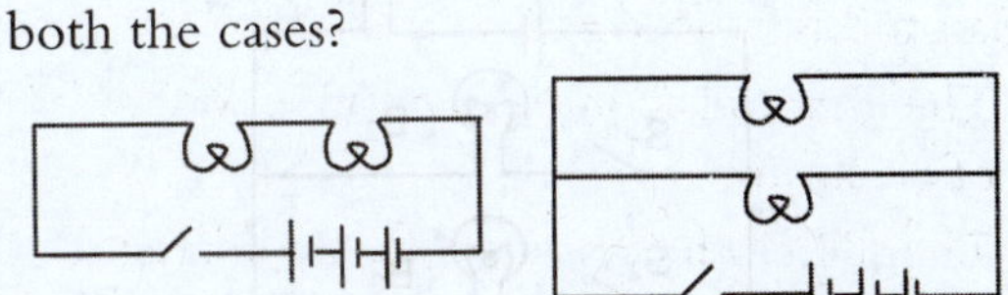

(a) (b)

67. Identify whether the following circuits are open or closed.

(a)

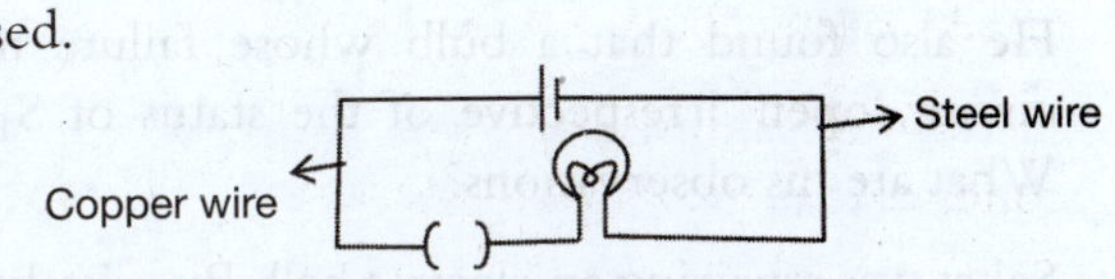

(b)

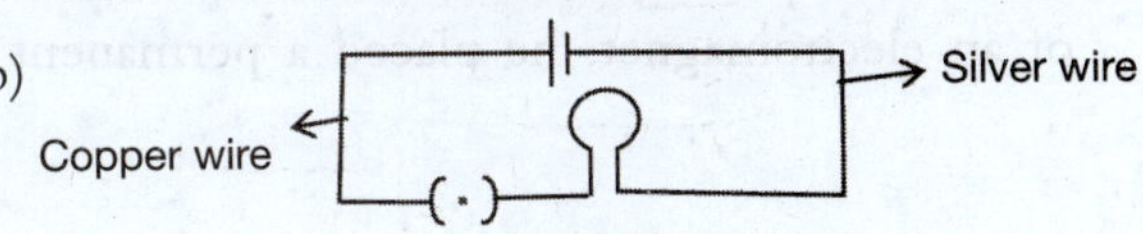

(c)

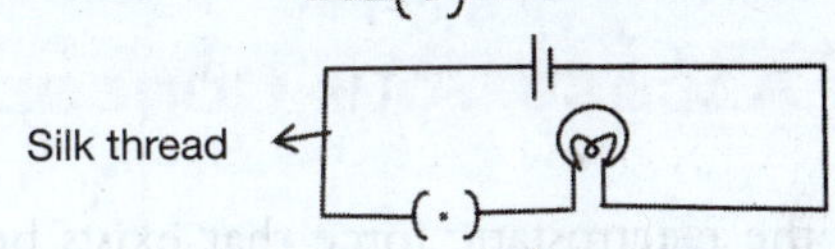

(d)

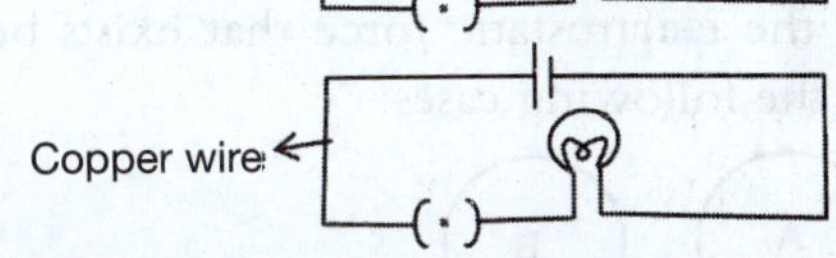

68. Compare the nature of materials used to make the 'filament' of an electric bulb and the 'fuse wire' used in electric fuse?

69. During lightning, if we touch a metallic object, we experience electric shock. Explain the reason for this?

70. What are live and neutral wires?

71. Represent the connections shown below by a circuit diagram.

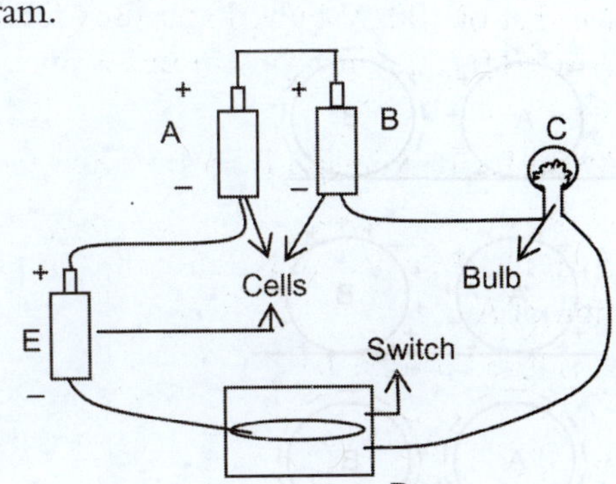

72. We observe the bulb glowing when the switch is 'ON'. Can we conclude that charges instantly move from the 'switch' to the 'bulb'? Discuss.

73. What is a depolarizer and how does it work?

74. Gourang made an electric circuit with three bulbs B_1, B_2 and B_3, a cell and two switches S_1 and S_2 as shown in the figure. He noted his observation when

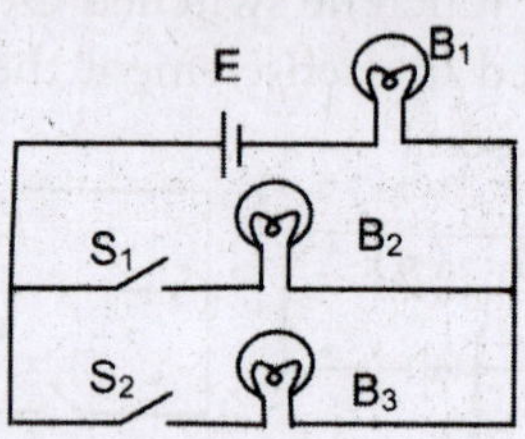

(a) S_1 is closed and S_2 is open,

(b) S_2 is closed and S_1 is open.

He also found that a bulb whose failure made the circuit 'open' irrespective of the status of S_1 and S_2. What are his observations?

75. Saket was repairing an electric bell. By mistake, instead of an electromagnet, he placed a permanent magnet in the electric bell. Explain, what changes do you observe.

76. Why Nichrome wire is preferable in the heating elements?

77. Ravinder was inspired by reading the autobiography of Thomas Alva Edison and changed a portion of his room into a laboratory. In his laboratory he performed an activity that demonstrates both 'heating effect' and 'magnetic effect' of electric current. He connected different components with different wires and the connections are represented by the following circuit diagram.

To his disappointment, he was not successful in his effort. Observe the circuit and suggest modifications to make his effort successful.

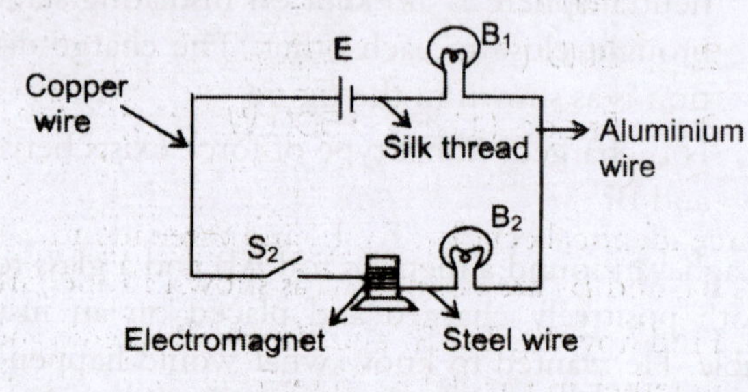

Level 3: Assess Your Concepts

78. Describe the electrostatic force that exists between A and B in the following cases.

(a)

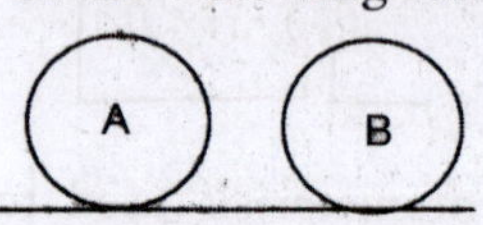

(b)

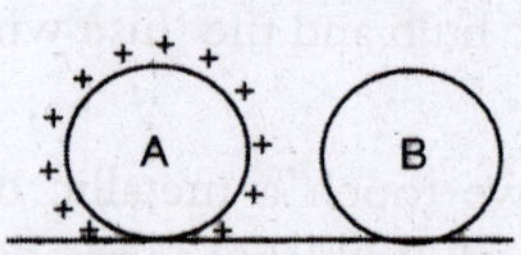

(c)

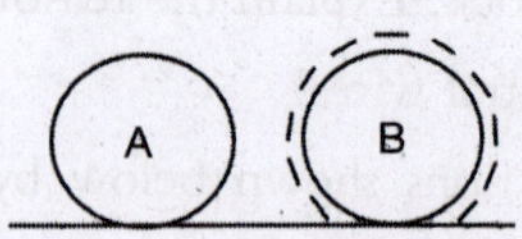

(d)

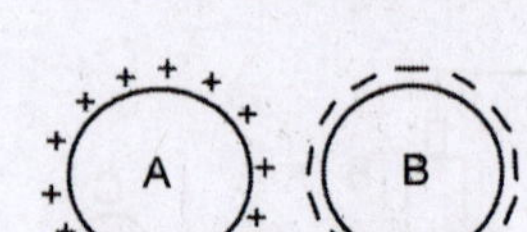

(e)

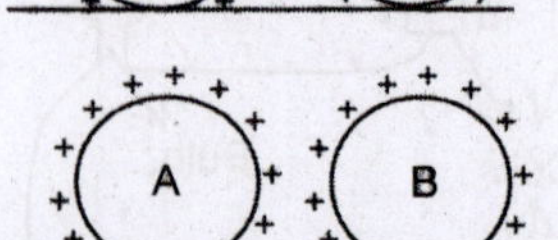

(f)

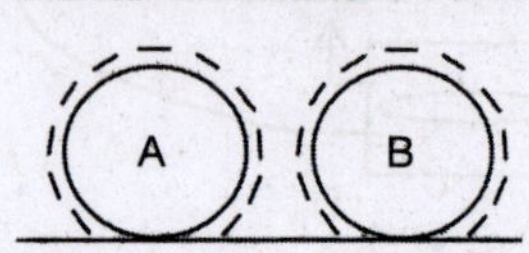

79. We know that (a) like electrical charges repel each other and (b) substances which allow charges to move through them are called conductors. In the light of these facts, find where the charge placed on a conductor resides?

80. Which of the following symbols is suitable at places P, Q and R in the below circuit?

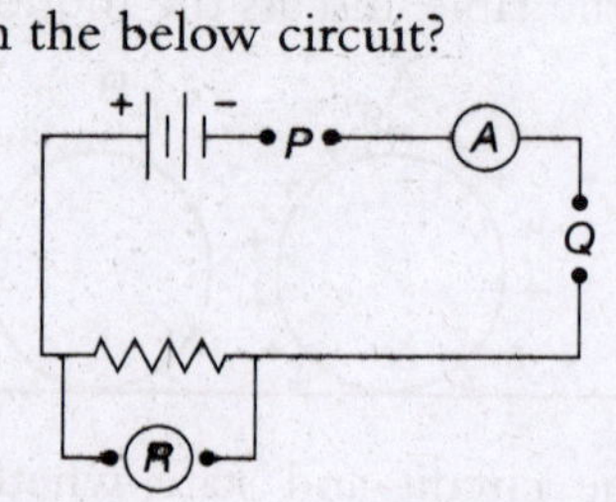

(a) 

(b) 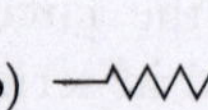

(c)

(d)

(e) 

(f) 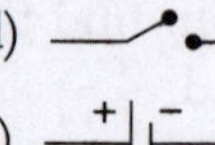

(g) 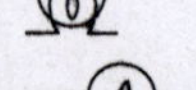

81. A and B are two identical conducting rods. A is given positive charge and B is connected to a cell as shown in the figure. Will there be any change in the electrostatic force between A and B if the switch is closed?

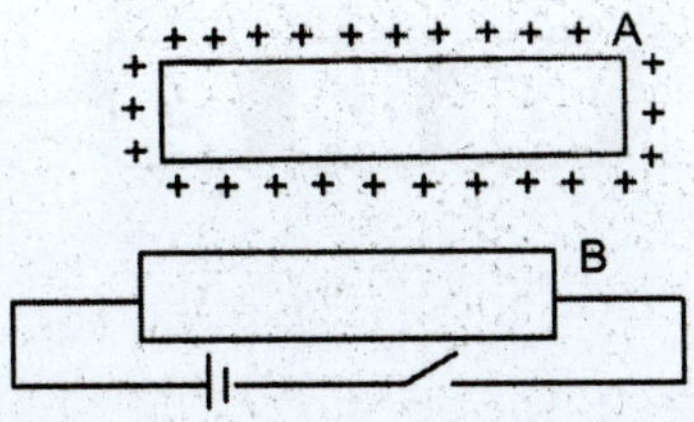

82. With the help of an electroscope, how can we identify the presence and nature of charge on a body?

83. Geetha wanted to know the power consumption of all the electrical appliances in her house. Help her out in finding the list of appliances in her house and their usage based on the data given below.

S. NO	Electrical Appliance	Power (Wattage)	Usage in hours per day
1.	Fan (2)	200 W	12
2.	Bulb (3)	100 W	7
3.	Fridge (1)	1500 W	3

84. Three identical cells E_1, E_2, E_3 and three identical bulbs B_1, B_2, and B_3 are connected as shown in the circuit.

(a) Find how E_1, E_2, E_3 and B_1, B_2, B_3 are connected, whether in parallel or in series?

(b) Compare the brightness of the bulbs.

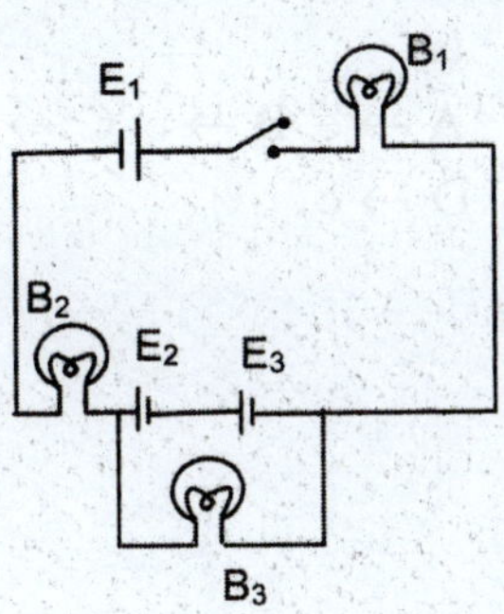

85. Usually we use two different types of sockets (a) two-pin socket and (b) three-pin socket. What purpose does the third pin in a three-pin socket serve?

86. Pranith received an electric bill for the month of April. He started verifying it by calculating the electrical energy consumed by a 2000 W electrical appliance that is used for two hours every day in his workshop. In his house he used bulbs of 100 W for 4 hours every day in the month of April, which consumes the same electrical energy as that of the electrical appliance in the work shop. Find the number of bulbs Pranith uses in his house.

87. Find the resultant emf's of the following combination of cells.

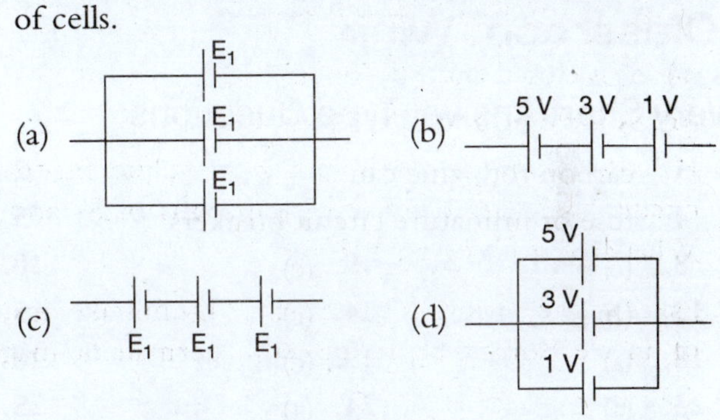

88. Which effect of electricity is used in electrotype setting? Discuss.

89. Do all bulbs we use work on the principle of heating effects of electric current? Discuss.

90. What makes electrical energy so useful for mankind?

AT

ANSWER KEYS

Crossword

Across

2. Series 3. Oersted 6. Mercury 9. Copper sulphate 10. Air
11. Kilowatt hour 12. Electroscope

Down

1. Potassium bichromate 4. Electrostatics 5. Induction 7. Fuse
8. Battery

Classroom Wing

Very Short Answer Type Questions

1. carbon rod, zinc can 2. polarization, local action 3. 10 V
4. fuse or miniature circuit breakers 5. chemical 6. (d) 7. (d)
8. (c) 9. (c) 10. (c) 11. (c) 12. (b)
13. (b) 14. (c) 15. (a) 16. (d) 17. (d)
18. (a) 19. (c) 20. (d) 21. (c) 22. (b)
23. (a) 24. (a) 25. (d) 26. (b) 27. (c)
28. (a) 29. (d) 30. (c) 31. (a) 32. (a)
33. (a) 34. (c) 35. (d) 36. (a) 37. (a)
38. (d) 39. (d) 40. (c) 41. (a) 42. (a)
43. (a) 44. (c) 45. (a) 46. A → e, B → c, C → d, D → a, E → b
47. A → c, B → a, C → e, D → b, E → d 48. A → d, B → a, C → b, D → c
54. kWh 58. 10

Short Answer Type Questions

80. 7.5 V

Competition Wing

Level 1: Apply your Concepts

1. mercury 2. negative 3. mechanical, electrical 4. lightning conductor
5. electric current 6. positive and negative 7. an electromagnet 8. heating
9. insulators 10. charged 11. positive; negative 12. local action 13. fuse
14. more 15. heating effect 16. True 17. False 18. True
19. True 20. False 21. False 22. True 23. False
24. True 25. False 26. (c) 27. (d) 28. (a)
29. (d) 30. (a) 31. (a) 32. (c) 33. (d)
34. (d) 35. (a) 36. (d) 37. (c) 38. (a)
39. (b) 40. (a) 41. (d) 42. (a) 43. (b)

44. (a)	**45.** (b)	**46.** (d)	**47.** (c)	**48.** (d)
49. (b)	**50.** (c)	**51.** (a)	**52.** (a)	**53.** (a)
54. (d)	**55.** (d)	**56.** (b)	**57.** (a)	**58.** (a)

59. A → e, B → a, C → b, D → d, E → c

60. A → f, B → d, C → a, D → b, E → c, F → e

Level 2: Review your Concepts

64. 4.5 V

Hints and Explanations

Classroom Wing

Very Short Answer Type Questions

1. (carbon rod, zinc can)

   A carbon rod acts as a positive pole and a zinc can acts as a negative pole in a dry cell.

2. (polarization, local action)

   Two defects in a voltaic cell are polarization and local action.

3. (10 V)

   $E = E_1 + E_2 + E_3 + E_4 = 2.5 + 2.5 + 2.5 + 2.5 = 10$ V

4. (fuse or miniature circuit breakers)

   Fuse or MCB is used to protect electrical appliances from damages due to excess current.

5. Electrotype setting works on the basis of chemical effect of electric current.

6. (d)

   A glass rod 'P' can attract another glass rod 'Q' only when one of them is charged or both are charged with opposite polarity.

7. (d)

   When an uncharged body 'X' is brought into contact with a negatively charged body 'Y', then a negative charge flows from 'Y' to X.

8. (c)

   An electric motor converts electrical energy to mechanical energy and hence it is a consumer of electric energy.

9. (c)

   Leclanche cell is not easily portable.

10. (c)

    Mercury oxide is not a depolarizer.

11. (c)

    A fire extinguisher is not an electrical appliance.

12. (b)

    In the given circuit, three cells in both rows are connected in series and these cells are connected in parallel. The total e.m.f of cells connected in series = 4.5 V. When identical cells are connected in parallel, then the total e.m.f is equal to the e.m.f of the three cells connected in parallel combination.

13. (b)

    It is not safe to use a switch with wet hands.

14. (c)

    'Electric generator' does not work on the principle of magnetic effects of electric current".

15. (a)

    Telephone does not work on the principle of 'chemical effects of electricity'.

16. (d)

    A charge

    1. Has magnitude only
    2. Is additive
    3. Is conservative
    4. Is quantized

17. (d)

    Materials that do not allow electricity or an electric charge to pass through them are called insulators. Wood, plastic, air, etc., are some examples of insulators.

18. (a)

    (i) As the body has a negative charge (i.e., it has excessive electrons), when it is connected to the ground the excess charge flows to the ground, until all the charge exhausts and then becomes neutral. So it becomes a neutral body.

19. (c)

    A current carrying conductor produces heat and also a magnetic field around it.

20. (d)

    Heat is:

    (i) directly proportional to square of amount of current

    (ii) directly proportional to resistance

    (iii) directly proportional to the time

21. (c)

    Heating element of electric bulbs is 'Tungsten'.

22. (b)

As we know that a combination of cells is called a battery, the symbol for a battery will be

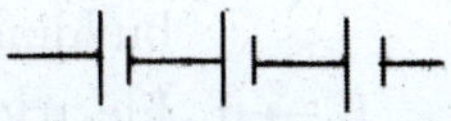

23. (a)

The amount of work done by a battery (or) cell to drive the charge carriers in a circuit is called e.m.f. (potential). It is measured in volts.

24. (a)

When magnetic needle (or compass) is brought closer to a circuit carrying current it will be deflected and hence we can use magnetic needle (or compass) to detect the presence of flow of charge (or current) in a circuit.

25. (d)

(i) When current passes through the coil, it behaves like a magnet and attracts (pulls) the iron strip (a).

(ii) The hammer connected to Iron strip also moves and strikes the gong and because of this, sound is produced (c).

(iii) When the iron strip is pulled towards the coil it loses contact with the screw and the circuit becomes open circuit (d).

(iv) The coil, does not behave as an electromagnet any more and the attraction between the coil and the iron strip is lost. Because of this the iron strip gets back to its original position and touches the screw (b).

(v) Once again the circuit is closed and the above process is repeated (e).

26. (b)

(i) Take two glass rods (a).

(ii) Charge them by rubbing each glass rod with a silk cloth (c).

(iii) Now bring these two charged rods nearer (b).

(iv) The glass rods repel each other showing that like charges repel each other (d).

27. Among the given options pure alcohol is a bad conductor of electricity.

28. An electric motor is a device which converts electrical energy into mechanical energy.

29. Uses of electromagnets:

(i) Electromagnetic cranes are used to lift heavy loads.

(ii) Magnetic materials can be separated from junk with the help of an electromagnet.

(iii) An electromagnet is a major component of an electric bell.

(iv) Doctors use electromagnets to remove small pieces of magnetic materials that may have accidentally fallen into the eyes.

30. 1 Unit = 1 kWh

$E = P \times t$

= 2 kWh = 2 unit

31. Wires used for electric circuits are copper.

32. Place a positively charged body near a neutral body. The negatively- and positively charged particles in the neutral body get attracted and repelled by the positively charged body, respectively.

As a result, at one end of the neutral body there is an exces of negatively charged particles, and the other end there is an excess of positively charged particles.

33. Take an ebonite rod and a glass rod and the two silk threads so that they can be suspended.

Now take ebonite rod and rub it with woolen cloth and rub glass rod with the silk cloth and suspend them in air by holding silk threads. The glass and ebonite rods when brought nearer attract each other showing that unlike charges attract each other.

34. When current passes through the voltaic cell, zinc plate starts dissolving in the acid and produces hydrogen bubbles and these hydrogen bubbles accumulate on the copper plate and develop resistance to the flow of current.

35. Precautions to be taken while using household electrical appliances:

(i) Always use appliances carrying ISI mark.

(ii) For performing any experiments in electricity use only cells and not the mains supply to your household.

(iii) Do not put a finger or a metallic wire in the sockets.

(iv) Avoid touching switches with wet hands.

(v) Always use a tester to know the presence of current.

(vi) One should not touch the metal parts of an electrical appliances or electrical pole with bare hands.

36. The electrical appliances connected in series do not work to their full capacity because the electrical energy drawn from the battery is shared by all the appliances connected in series.

37. We know, 1 unit = 1 kWh = 1000 W h = 1000 W × 1 h = 100 W × 10 h

So, 100 W bulb used for 10 h and 1000 W bulb used for 1 h consumes same amount of electrical energy, i.e., 1 kWh or one electrical unit.

38. When a neutral body (i.e., a body which possesses equal positive and negative charge) is brought closer to

a negatively charged body, the end of the body which is facing the negatively charged body acquires a positive charge and the opposite end (farther end) acquires the negative charge, but the net charge present in the body is zero, i.e., still the body will be neutral.

39. From the circuit diagram it is clear that bulbs A and B which are in series with each other are in parallel with bulb C, and the total e.m.f. (potential) in the circuit is 60 V.
When switch is turned on, the bulbs in series combination glow with less brightness than the bulb C which is in parallel with A and B.

40. Both the given statements are true. In the case of an electric cell, chemical energy is converted into electrical energy. And the combination of electric cells is called battery.

41. The brass cap of the carbon rod and the zinc can of the dry cell act as positive and negative poles, respectively.

42. Among the given options impure water is the best conductor of electricity.

43. An electric generator (dynamo) converts mechanical energy into electric energy.

44. The e.m.f of a dry cell is 1.46 volt.

45. When same current flows through the circuit, the bulbs in series combination glow with more brightness than the bulbs in parallel combination.

46. A → e By deflections in the metallic strips in gold leaf electroscope it is possible to detect the nature of the charge on the body.
B → c Lightening phenomenon involves charged particles.
C → d The total (effective) emf of the cells connected in series is equal to the sum of emf all the cells used.
D → a The zinc and carbon rods in Leclanché cell acts as negative and positive plates.
E → b Live wire and neutral wire from pole are connected to kWh meter.

47. A → c A cell is denoted as —|⊢—.
B → a An open tap key is symbolized as —/—.
C → e The eel fish has the ability to generate electric power.
D → b Benjamin Franklin proved that lightning is a natural phenomenon involving charged particles and lightning rods are used to protect building from lightning.
E → d Electric bell works on the magnetic effect of electric current.

48. (d) Carbon and manganese dioxide
(a) Carbon rod with brass cap
(b) Convert hydrogen into water
(c) Heating effect of electric current

49. Two types of charges exist in nature. They are named as "positive charge" and "negative charge".

50. The negatively charged particle in an atom is called 'electron'.

51. Electroscope is a device used to detect the presence of charge on a body and its nature.

52. We say there is "electric current" in the conductor when charges are moving from one end to other end.

53. The path along which electric current flows is called electric circuit.

54. Practical unit of electrical energy is kWh.

55. In an electric circuit, components can be connected in two different ways. One is called parallel connection and the other is called series connection.

56. We have two types of the sockets, two pin sockets and three pin sockets.

57. MCBs are switches which automatically turn off when current in the circuit exceeds the safe maximum limit. These are connected in series with live wires and act as a good substitute for 'fuse'.

58. Number of units $= p \times t = 0.2 \times t = 2/0.2 = 10$.

59. "Like charges repel each other and unlike charges attract each other".

60. Negatively charged electrons are free to move within the body as well as from one body to another body.

61.

Insulators	Conductors
Materials that do not allow electricity or electric charge to pass through them are called "insulators". Wood, plastic, air, etc., are some examples of insulators.	Those substances which allow charges to pass through them are called "conductors". All metals are good conductors.

62. **Component** | **Symbol**

Cell (source of electricity) —|¦—

A battery (source of electricity) —|¦|¦—

63. A combination of two or more cells is called a 'battery' and it is represented by the symbol

—|¦|¦|¦—

64. A device called "electrical generator" is used to convert mechanical energy to electrical energy.

65. If an appliance of 1000 watt power is used for one hour then the electrical energy consumed is one kilowatt hour or 'one electrical unit'.

66. The amount of heat produced in a wire depends on its length, its thickness and nature of material, the amount of current and also the time for which the current is passing.

67. When current passes through an electrolyte, the molecules in the electrolyte dissociate into ions and these ions move towards opposite poles. This is called 'electrolysis'.

68. When a number of identical cells are connected in parallel, the total emf of the combination is equal to the emf of a single cell.

Short Answer Type Questions

69. When two bodies are rubbed together, both of them get charged and this process of charging a body by rubbing is called "charging by friction". The two bodies acquire equal but opposite charges. When a glass rod is rubbed with a silk cloth, the charge acquired by the glass rod is positive and the charge acquired by the silk cloth is negative.

70. Lightning conductors are used to protect buildings and other important structures from potential damages caused by lightning.

Lightning conductor is a thick metallic strip with a spike like top that is projected up from the top of the building. From the top of the building to be protected, the lightning conductor runs to the ground along the outer wall of the structure. The lower end of the lightning conductor is joined to a metal plate that is buried deep inside the earth.

71. The leclanche cell consists of a porous pot and a zinc rod placed in a solution of ammonium chloride solution in a glass jar.

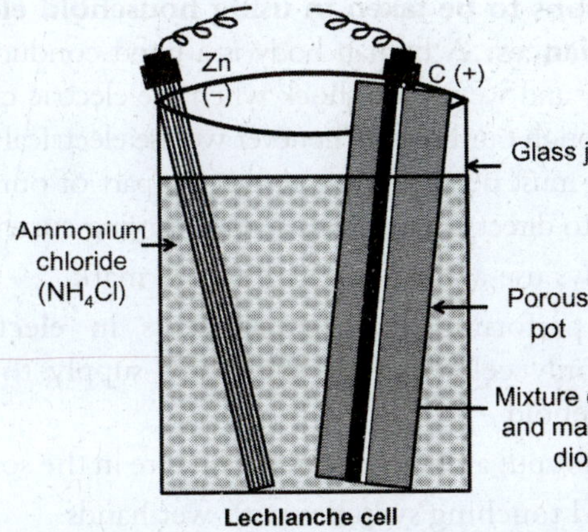

Lechlanche cell

The porous pot contains powdered carbon and manganese dioxide with a carbon rod dipped into it.

Zinc rod acts as the negative plate and carbon rod acts as the positive plate.

Electromotive force of this cell is 1.46 volt.

72. **Electric cells connected in series:** In this method, the positive terminal of one cell is connected to the negative terminal of the next cell. After connecting all available cells as described, the negative terminal of the first and the positive terminal of the last are connected to a bulb.

When cells are connected in series, their total electromotive force (e.m.f) is equal to the sum of the e.m.f of all the cells used.

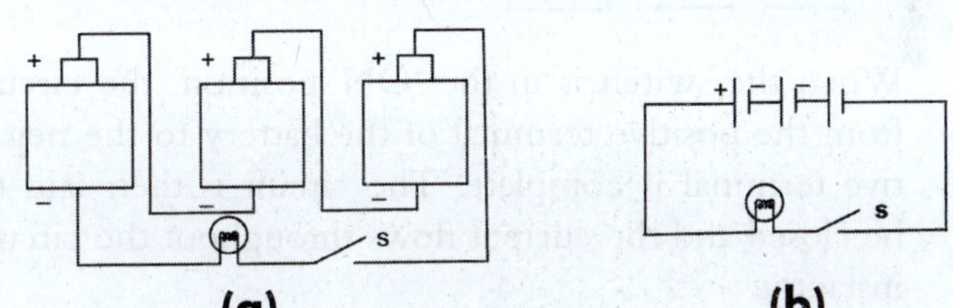

Series connection of cells

Electric cells connected in parallel: When positive poles of all given cells are connected together and all negative poles are connected together, then we say that the cells are connected in parallel.

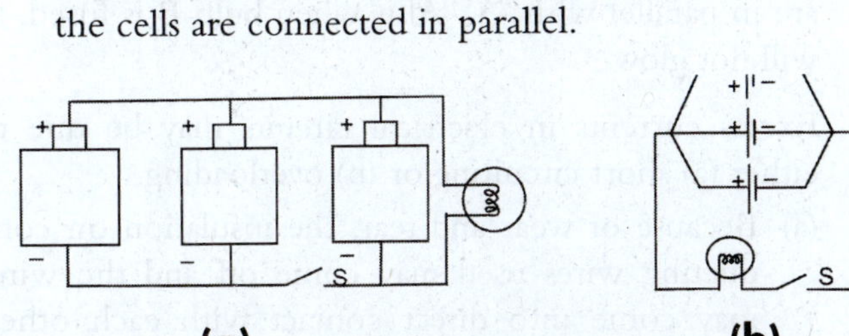

When identical cells are connected in parallel their total electromotive force is same as that of any one of them.

73. Precautions to be taken in using household electrical appliances: A human body is a good conductor of electricity and we receive shock when the electric current flows through our body. Whenever we use electrical appliances we must be careful to see that no part of our body comes into direct contact with a wire carrying current.

(i) Always use appliances carrying ISI mark.

(ii) For performing any experiments in electricity use only cells and not the mains supply to your household.

(iii) Do not put a finger or a metallic wire in the sockets.

(iv) Avoid touching switches with wet hands.

(v) Always use a tester to know the presence of current.

(vi) One should not touch the metal parts of an electrical appliance or electrical pole with bare hands.

74. A neutral body gets charged when it is brought into contact with a charged body. This method of charging a body is called "charging by conduction". The uncharged body acquires the same type of charge as that of the charged body with which it is brought into contact.

75. Switch is a device used to close or open an electric circuit. Switch in a circuit can be placed anywhere.

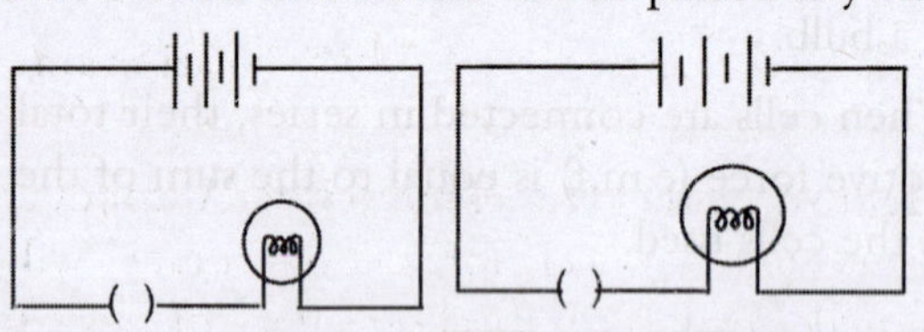

When the switch is in the 'ON' position, the circuit from the positive terminal of the battery to the negative terminal is complete. The circuit is then said to be closed and the current flows throughout the circuit instantly.

When the switch is in the 'OFF' position, the circuit is incomplete. It is said to be open and no current flows through any part of the circuit.

76. True. Bulbs B and C are connected in series B and C are in parallel with 'A'. Also when bulb B is fused, C will not glow.

77. Excess currents in electrical circuits may be due to either (a) short circuiting or (b) overloading.

(a) Because of wear and tear, the insulation on conducting wires used may come off and the wires may come into direct contact with each other. This is known as "short circuit".

(b) If many devices are connected to a single socket, they may draw excess current that causes 'overloading' in the circuit.

78. Uses of electromagnets:

(i) Electromagnetic cranes are used to lift heavy loads.

(ii) Magnetic materials can be separated from junk with the help of an electromagnet.

(iii) An electromagnet is a major component of an electric bell.

(iv) Doctors use electromagnets to remove small pieces of magnetic materials that may have accidentally fallen into the eyes.

79. Electroscope is a device used to detect the presence of a charge on a body and its nature.

An electroscope consists of a metal rod fitted in one holed cork stopper which in turn is fixed to a glass jar as shown in the figure below. A metal disc or metallic sphere is attached at one end of the rod and two metal strips are attached at the other end of the rod which is kept in a glass jar. By observing the deflection in the metallic strips, we can identify the presence and nature of the charge on the body.

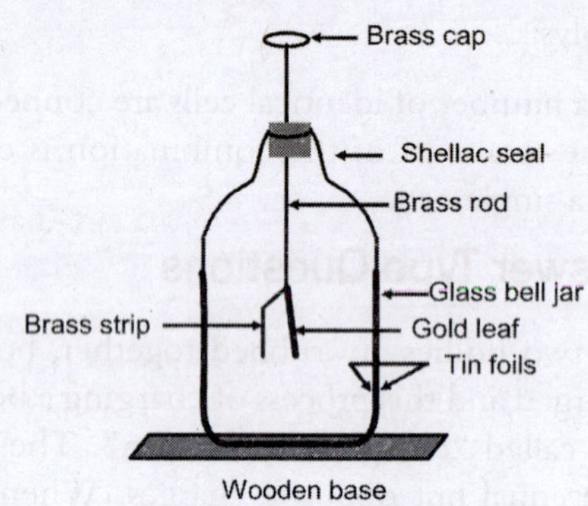

Gold leaf electroscope

80. The three cells are connected in series, the e.m.f of the battery

$$E = E_1 + E_2 + E_3 = 1.5 + 2.5 + 3.5 \text{ V} = 7.5 \text{ V}$$

81. In power plants, a device called "electrical generator" is used to convert mechanical energy to electrical energy. An electric generator consists of two parts, namely, turbine and dynamo. The energy of flowing water or steam is used to rotate the turbine. Dynamo that is connected to the turbine also gets rotated and it converts the mechanical energy into electrical energy.

82. The coil around the cylinder made up of soft iron behaves like a magnet when a current passes through it. This is known as an electromagnet. The strength of the electromagnet can be increased by increasing the amount of current passing through the coil.

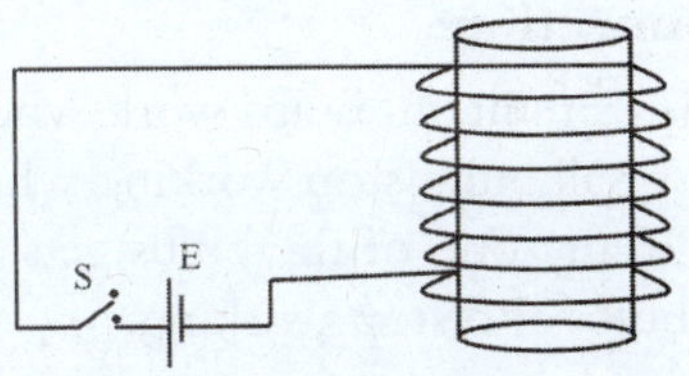

83. There are two defects in the Voltaic cell.

(1) Local action (2) Polarization

Local action: Normally, carbon and iron particles are present in a zinc plate as impurities. These particles react with the acid and with the zinc particles to form a large number of tiny cells creating local electric circuits. This is the local action in a Voltaic cell. To prevent local action, usually the zinc plate is coated with mercury. Mercury prevents the impurities from coming into contact with acid and prevents local action.

Polarization: When current passes through the cell, zinc plate starts dissolving in the acid and produces hydrogen bubbles. These hydrogen bubbles accumulate on the copper plate and develop resistance to the flow of current. This defect is called "polarization".

Essay Type Questions

84. Electrical Induction: A neutral body has equal number of positive charges and negative charges in it. Let us place a positively charged body near a neutral body. The negatively charged particles get attracted and the positively charged particles get repelled by the positively charged body.

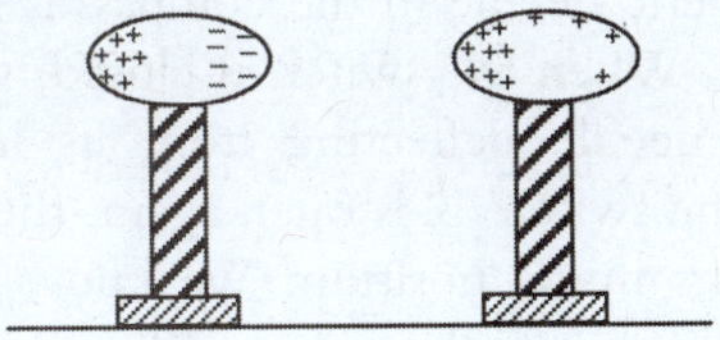

As a result, at one end of the neutral body there is an excess of negatively charged particles, and at the other end there is an excess of positively charged particles.

The phenomenon of redistribution of charges in an uncharged body in the presence of a charged body is called electrical induction.

Infact, induction is responsible for the attraction of an uncharged body by a charged body.

85. Voltaic cell: This consists of a glass vessel, with dilute sulphuric acid. Two plates, one made up of copper and the other made of zinc, are placed in the jar such that each one of them is immersed in the acid.

When these plates are externally connected to a bulb, electricity flows through the bulb and it glows. The dilute sulphuric acid is called electrolyte. The copper plate acts as a positive pole and the zinc plate acts as a negative pole and in the external circuit electricity flows from the copper plate to the zinc plate.

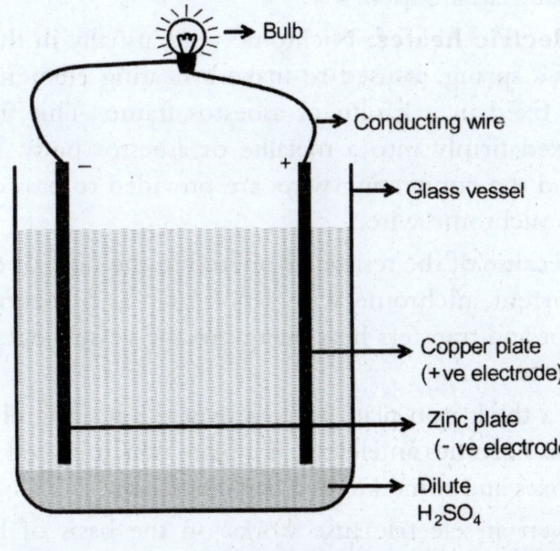

Voltaic Cell

The electromotive force of a Voltaic cell is one volt.

There are two defects in the Voltaic cell:

(1) Local action (2) Polarization

86. Heating effect of electricity: A conducting wire connected to a cell for a few minutes will become heated. This is the heating effect of electric current and in this case the electrical energy is converted to heat energy. An electric iron, electric heater, electric oven, filament bulbs etc all work on heating effect of the electric current.

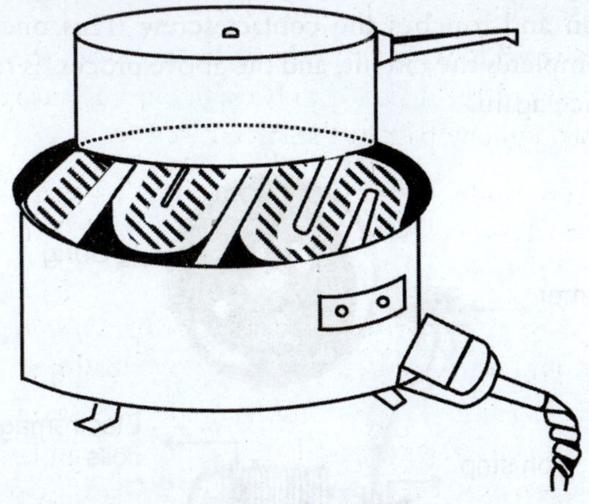

An electric stove

All these appliances, which work on heating effect of electricity, contain a coil of wire, known as an "element", or a "heating element" which becomes red hot and gives heat when current passes through it. The amount of heat produced in a wire depends on its length, thickness, nature of the material, amount of current flowing and time for which the current flows. As such for different requirements, wires of different materials are used.

Electric heater: Nichrome wire, usually in the form of a spring, is used to make a heating element. This is fixed in a kaolin or asbestos frame. This frame is fixed firmly into a metallic or asbestos body. A plug and the connecting wires are provided to pass current to nichrome wire.

Because of the resistance offered to the flow of electric current, nichrome wire gets heated and becomes red hot and transfers heat energy to the vessel kept on the heater.

If a thick iron plate is fixed over the heating element, this becomes an electric hot plate which is used in iron boxes and some kitchen appliances.

Even an electric fuse works on the basis of heating effect of the electric current.

87. **Electric bell:** Electromagnet is a major component of an electric bell. The coil shown in the figure acts as an electromagnet. A soft iron strip with a hammer at one end is kept close to the electromagnet. When current passes through the coil, it behaves like a magnet and attracts the iron strip. When the iron strip moves towards the coil, the hammer connected to it strikes the gong and a sound is produced. When the iron strip is pulled towards the coil, it loses contact with the screw and the circuit is now open. When the circuit is broken, the coil no longer acts as an electromagnet and there is no attraction between the coil and the iron strip. This leaves the iron strip back to its original position and touches the contact screw. This once again completes the circuit, and the above process is repeated once again.

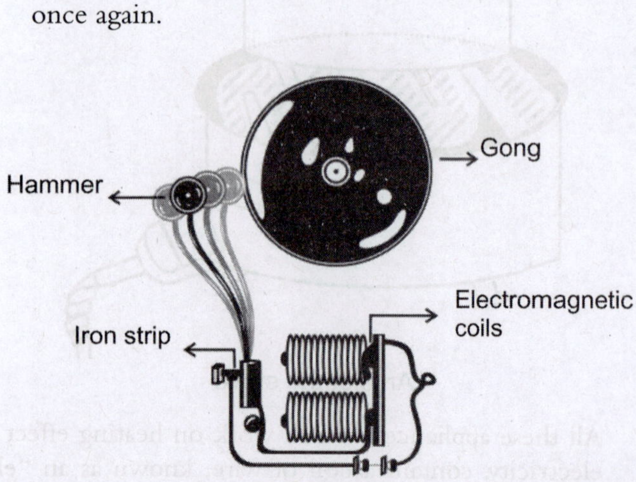

88. **Series connection:**

(i) In series circuit, all bulbs work when the circuit is closed or all bulbs stop working when the circuit is open. If any one of the bulbs gets fused, then the other bulbs also stop working.

(ii) In series connection, the bulbs do not glow brightly. In this case the electrical energy drawn from the battery is shared by all the bulbs connected in series. In fact, when connected in series, the appliances do not work to their capacity.

Parallel connection:

(i) All the bulbs are connected directly to a battery and hence work independently. Even if one bulb is fused out, the remaining bulbs work normally.

(ii) All the bulbs derive the required electrical energy and glow brightly.

89. **Magnetic effects of electric current:** Hans Christian Oersted, in 1800 AD, first observed that a conducting wire behaves like a magnet when electric current passes through it. This is the magnetic effect of the electric current. It can be demonstrated as follows.

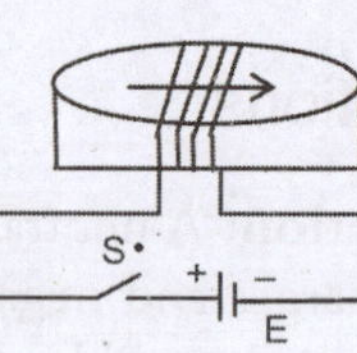

Take a magnetic compass and wind an insulated conducting wire around it. Free ends of the wire are to be connected to a cell E through a switch. Normally the magnetic needle in the compass is in north-south direction. When the switch is closed, we observe the compass needle deflecting from its initial position. Now if the switch 'S' is open again, the needle comes back to its initial position. We know that the compass needle is a small magnet. When current is passing through the conducting wires, it behaves like a magnet and deflects the compass needle.

90. **Chemical effects of electrical current:** When current passes through certain liquids, like copper sulphate, it causes chemical reactions in those liquids. The liquid used is called 'electrolyte'. When current passes through an electrolyte, the molecules in the electrolyte dissociate into ions and these ions move towards opposite poles. This is called 'electrolysis'.

Electrolysis is very useful in purifying metals. An impure metal is taken at the positive pole and a pure metal is obtained at the negative pole. Solution of a metallic salt is used as an electrolyte.

Even electro-type setting works on the basis of chemical effects of electric current.

Electroplating: This is a process of giving an expensive gold or silver coating on articles made of cheap metals.

91. The Bichromate cell: This cell consists of a flat bottomed glass flask with a special stopper as shown in the figure.

A solution of potassium dichromate and dilute sulphuric acid is used as an electrolyte. Two carbon plates act as the positive poles and the zinc plate act as the negative pole. The zinc plate fixed to the stopper can be moved up and down. When the cell is not in use the zinc plate is placed above the electrolyte. The hydrogen produced in the reaction gets oxidized by potassium bichromate. The e.m.f of this cell is 2 volt.

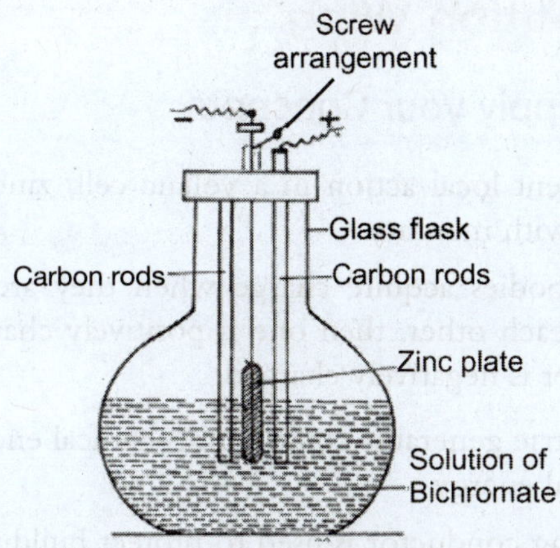

Bichromate Cell

Competition Wing

Level 1: Apply your Concepts

1. To prevent local action in a voltaic cell, zinc plate is coated with mercury.
2. If two bodies acquire charge when they are rubbed against each other, then one is positively charged and the other is negatively charged.
3. An electric generator converts mechanical energy into electrical energy.
4. Lightning conductor is used to protect buildings from lightning.
5. When charges move through a conductor, we say there is electric current in the conductor.
6. Atom is considered neutral because it contains an equal number of positive and negative charges.
7. An electromagnet is a major component of an electric bell.
8. Nichrome is the material used to make heating elements.
9. Materials that do not allow electric charges to flow through them are called insulators.
10. Lightning is a natural phenomenon involving charged particles.
11. In symbolic representation of an electric cell, the longer and shorter vertical lines represent positive and negative terminals, respectively.
12. Mercury coated on zinc plate prevents the impurities from coming into contact with acid and prevents local action.
13. Fuse is a safety device that prevents excess flow of current through an appliance.
14. When the bulbs are connected to the same source the brightness of bulbs connected in parallel is more than the brightness of identical bulbs connected in series.
15. Electric heater works on the basis of heating effect of the electric current.
16. True. Copper is a good conductor.
17. Electron in an atom contributes to the negative charge.
18. Substances which allow charges to pass through them are called conductors.
19. Switch is a device used as maker or breaker of an electric circuit.
20. A mercury coating is given to the zinc plate in a voltaic cell to reduce 'local action'.
21. Bulbs glow with more brightness when they are connected in parallel.
22. A switch is always connected to a live wire. When it is 'off' no current passes through a neutral wire.
23. Connecting many devices to a single socket leads to overload in the circuit.
24. Nichrome is usually preferred to make heating elements.
25. Electric bell works on 'magnetic effects of electric current'.
26. All bodies are made up of negatively charged and positively charged particles. If a body is positively charged, then the number of positively charged particles are more than the number of negatively charged particles.
27. A body can be charged by friction, conduction, and induction.
28. A generator is not a consumer of electrical energy.
29. A cell is a source of electrical energy, but not a major source of electrical energy.
30. When identical cells are connected in parallel, the total e.m.f of the combination is equal to the e.m.f of one of the cells.
31. When bulbs are connected in series, their brightness decreases.
32. 1 unit = 1 kilowatt hour = 1000 watt hour.

    200 W bulb working for 5 hours consumes, 1 kilowatt hour.
33. The amount of heat produced in a heating element depends on length, cross-sectional area, and nature of the material.
34. Electromagnets are used in electric bells and to lift heavy loads and work on the principle of magnetic effects of electric current.
35. In charging by conduction method, a neutral body gets charged when it is brought into contact with a charged body.
36. Electric iron, electric heater, and electric bulb all work on the principle of the heating effect of electric current.

37. In voltaic cell zinc is the negative electrode, i.e., cathode and copper is the positive electrode, i.e., anode. The electrolyte used is dilute sulphuric acid.

38. When a positively charged body is kept on the ground, electrons from the ground flow to the body and neutralizes the excess charge (positive) present in the body, and hence, the body acquires no charge, i.e., it becomes neutral body.

39. A magnetic needle placed close to a current carrying conductor deflects due to the magnetic effect of the electric current. Because the magnetic needle (or its field) interacts with the magnetic field produced by the current carrying conductor it deflects.

40. In an electric circuit, components can be connected in two different ways. One is called parallel connection and the other is called series connection.

41. Materials that do not allow electricity or an electric charge to pass through them are called insulators.

42. Symbol of fuse is as follows:

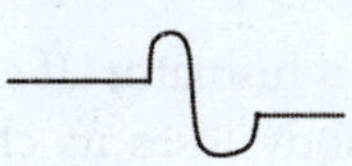

43. Kilowatt hour is the commercial unit of electrical energy. It is denoted by kW h.

44. Generally the bulbs or electrical appliances of house hold are connected in parallel combination. It is to avoid the interruption of power for the glow (working) of bulb (appliance) when any of the electrical appliance (bulb) gets damaged.

45. The device used to measure electric current in a circuit is 'Ammeter'.

46. (d)

(A) Take a glass rod and ebonite rod.

(C) Charge them by rubbing the glass rod with silk cloth and an ebonite rod with fur cloth.

(B) Now bring these two charged rods nearer.

(D) Two rods attract each other showing that unlike charges attract each other.

Hence, the correct order is ACBD.

47. The power of electric bulb, $P = 100$ W.

The time for which bulb utilizes electric power per day = 10 h.

In the month of June, $t = 10\ h \times 30$ days = 300 h.

The electric energy consumed by a bulb is = $P \times t$

= $100 \times 300 = 3 \times 10^4$ W h

= 30 kW h

The total energy consumed by both the bulbs,

$E = 2 \times 30$ kW h = 60 kW h.

$\therefore$ The number of electric units = 60 units.

($\neq$ 1 unit = 1 kW h)

48. When a neutral body (i.e., a body which possesses equal positive and negative charge) is brought closer to a negatively charged body, the end of the body which is facing the negatively charged body acquires a positive charge and the opposite end (farther end) acquires the negative charge, but the net charge present in the body is zero, i.e., still the body will be neutral.

49. As the switch is turned ON, the current flows through the circuit and magnetic field will be produced around it. All iron filings will align in the direction of a magnetic field. But the metallic comb will not behave, like an electro magnet, and hence, the iron filings will neither be attracted nor repelled.

50. From the circuit diagram, it is clear that 3 V battery and 4 V battery are in series, and hence, the net e.m.f of these two is (3 + 4)V = 7 V and these two are in parallel with 7 V battery. We know that when identical electric cells are connected in parallel combination the total e.m.f. will be equal to the e.m.f. of any one of the cell, and hence, the e.m.f. in the circuit is 7 V.

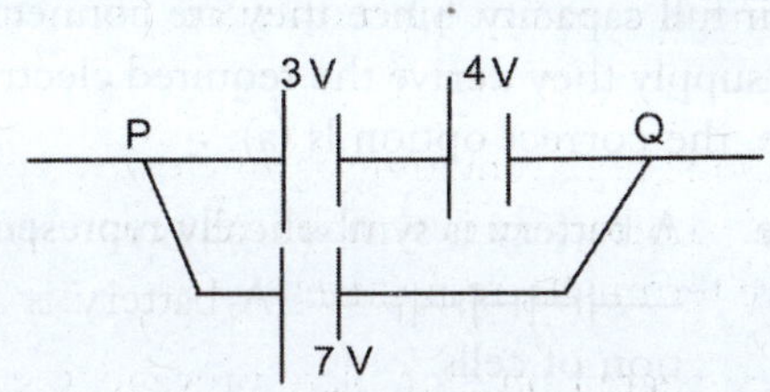

51. (a) From the circuit diagram it is clear that all the single bulbs are in a series combination:

(b) If bulb R is removed from the given series combination, the remaining bulbs will not glow, because it creates an open circuit.

(c) The cells in the given circuit are in series with each other, and hence, the total e.m.f of this combination = (20 + 40) V = 60 V

(d) The switch 'S' in the circuit is switched ON, and hence, it is a closed circuit.

52. When a positively charged body is brought in contact with the cap of gold leaf electroscope, the charge flows from the body to the strips through the conducting rod (brass rod), and hence, both the strips acquire same positive charge. Due to the presence of the like charges on strips, they will repel each other. When we remove the body from contact, the strips will remain apart.

53. When same current flows through the circuit, the bulbs in series combination glow with more brightness than the bulbs in parallel combination.

54. We know that, a body which looses electrons acquires a positive charge and a body which gains electrons acquires a negative charge. And when these two charged bodies are brought in contact again, the net charge will be zero, due to neutralization of charge.

55. When a current is allowed to pass through a conductor, it produces a magnetic field around it, and hence, when a magnet is brought closer to it, it will be deflected by the field produced by the current carrying conductor.

56. As all the cells are in series, the total e.m.f. will be the sum of the all e.m.f.

$\therefore$ e.m.f. = 2 + 2 + 2 = 6 V.

57. 500 W electric heater when used for 2 hours consumes 1 unit of electrical energy. (500 × 2 = 1000 Wh = 1kWh)

Also 100 W bulb when used for 10 hours consumes 1 unit of electrical energy (100 × 10 = 1000 Wh = 1 kWh)

Since 1 kWh = 1unit of electrical energy

Hence, the correct option is (a).

58. Electrical appliances when connected in parallel work to their full capacity. Since they are connected directly to the supply they derive the required electrical energy. Hence, the correct option is (a).

59. A → e A battery is symbolically represented as 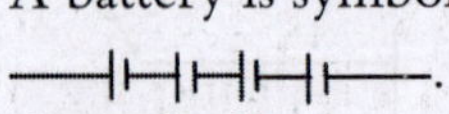. A battery is a combination of cells.

B → a Metals are good conductors of heat and electricity.

C → b A generator converts mechanical energy into electrical energy.

D → d Filament bulb works on the basis of heating effect of electricity.

E → c Ammeter is an electrical device denoted as.

60. A → f A cell converts chemical energy into electrical energy.

B → d A bulb is represented as  in an electric circuit.

C → a Electrostatics is a branch of electricity that deals with the properties exhibited by charges at rest.

D → b A switch is used to close or open an electric circuit.

E → c MCBs are miniature circuit breakers, which act as a good substitute for fuse.

F → e Main fuse at kW h meter can prevent unauthorized usage of current.

Level 2: Review your Concepts

61. (a) From the figure, we know that there is a repulsive force between A and B. A repulsive force exists between like charges. Since A is positively charged, B must be positively charged.

(b) If we observe the figure, we see that on B, positive charge is distributed on left side whereas, negative charge is distributed on the right side. As they are equal in magnitudes, the net charge on B is zero. Redistribution of charges has taken place in B when it is placed near a negatively charged body A because of electric induction.

There will be attractive force between A and B.

62. Metals are conductors and glass is an insulator. If a person touches a charged body, the body loses its charge to ground and this is known as 'earthing'. In case of a metallic rod, charges are free to move through the body, and even if the person touches the body at 'A', the body loses its whole charge to the earth. Where as in case of glass rod, only the charge that is in contact with the person gets earthed and the remaining charge on 'CD' will remain as it is.

63. 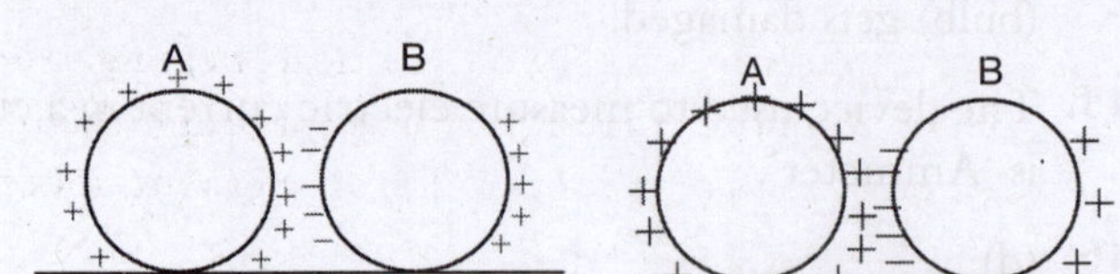

(a) (b)

When A is charged positively, then negative and positive charges are induced on B as shown in Fig. (a). Then B will be attracted by A and comes into contact with A. When B is in contact with A, due to conduction, positive charge flows from A to B and B also becomes positively charged. [Fig. (c)]

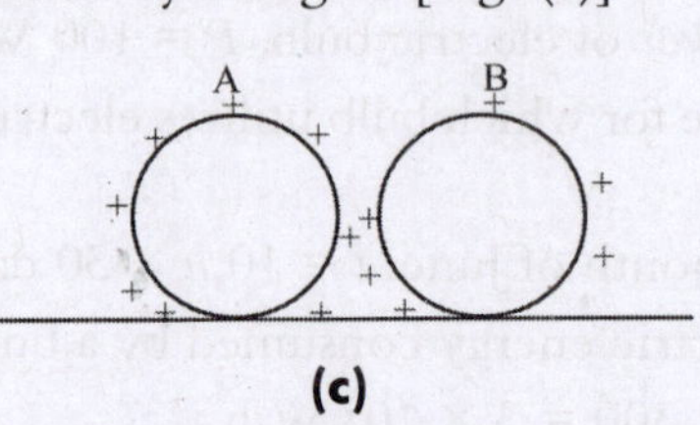

(c)

Then A and B repel each other and B moves away from A (Fig. d).

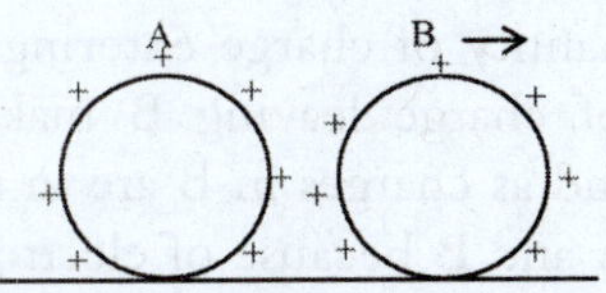

(d)

64. The positive terminal of each cell is connected to the negative terminal of the other cell. This shows that the cells are connected in series. When cells are connected in series,

total e.m.f $= E_1 + E_2 + E_3$

$= 1.5 + 1.5 + 1.5 = 4.5$ V

65. (a) When all cells are connected in parallel.

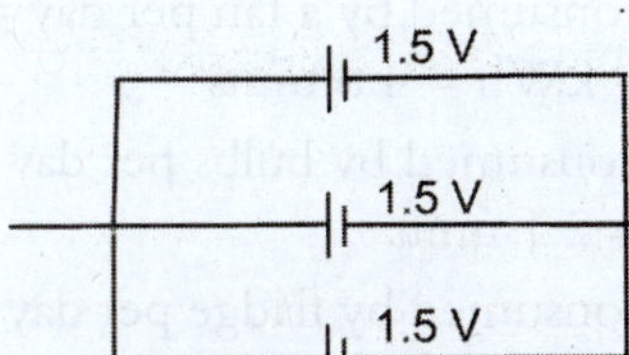

The total e.m.f of the combination is 1.5 V.

(b) When cells are connected as shown in figure, two of them in series and one in parallel, then the total e.m.f of the combination is 3 V.

(c) When all the three cells are connected in series, then the total e.m.f is 4.5 V.

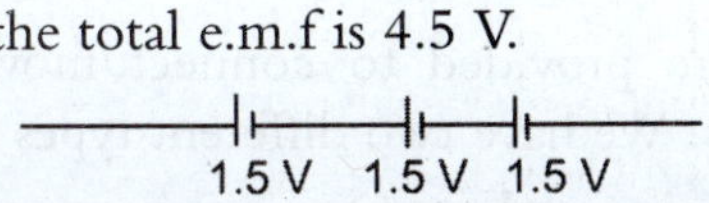

66. Heat generated in two identical heating elements depends on the current that flows through them. More the current that passes through an element, more is the heat generated.

In Fig. (A) heating elements are connected in series and in Fig. (B) heating elements are connected in parallel. The current that flows through the heating elements when they are connected in series is less than the current that flows through them when they are connected in parallel. As such more heat is generated when they are connected as shown in the Fig. (B).

67. (a) Open circuit as key is not closed.

(b) Open circuit as the bulb used is fused out.

(c) Open circuit as silk an insulator, is used to connect different appliances.

(d) Closed circuit.

68. A filament used in a bulb must withstand the high temperatures to emit light. The material used to make filament must have high resistance and high melting point. Usually tungsten is used to make a filament. The fuse wire must get heated and melt whenever excess current passes through it. Hence, it must be made of an alloy with high resistance and low melting point. Usually an alloy of lead and tin is used for this purpose.

69. During lightning, metal objects nearby gain electric charge, so if we touch then we will experience electric shock due to the process of electrification.

70. Electrical energy is supplied to houses through two wires, live and neutral wires. If any appliance is to use electrical energy, one end of the appliance is to be connected to a live wire and other end of the appliance is to be connected to a neutral wire. Electric current passes from the live wire to the neutral wire through the appliance. In this process, electrical energy is converted into other forms of energy.

71.

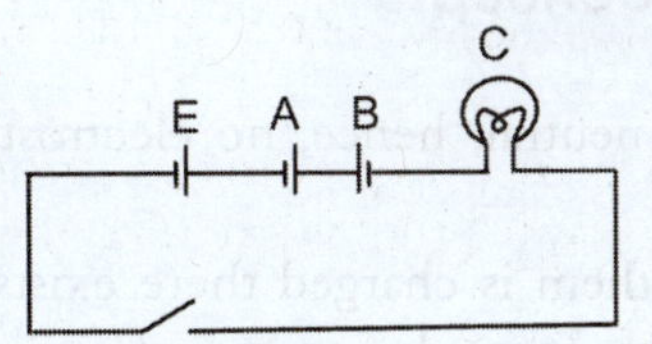

72. In any electric circuit, wires made up of good conductors are used to connect different appliances. All conductors have free charges moving in all directions. When the switch is 'ON', free charges throughout the circuit start moving in a specific direction instantly. Even though no charge moves from switch to bulb instantly, charges at the end of the conductor that are connected to the bulb start moving through the bulb when switch is 'ON'.

73. When a voltaic cell is made to work for some time, a thin layer of hydrogen is formed around the copper electrode. This restricts the further flow of charges through the electrolyte. This defect is called polarization. Depolarizer is a substance used to get rid of this problem in a voltaic cell. Depolarizers work as an oxidizing agent and they react with hydrogen and change it to water.

74. (a) If S_1 is closed and S_2 is open, only B_1 and B_2 glow.

(b) If S_2 is closed and S_1 is open, only B_1 and B_3 glow.

If B_1 fails, the circuit becomes open, even if both S_1 and S_2 are closed.

75. Electromagnets are used in electric bells. When current passes through the coil, the electromagnet attracts a metallic plate. The hammer attached to this metallic plate hits the gong and produces sound. When the plate is attracted by the electromagnet, it breaks the circuit and the electromagnet stops working as a magnet and after hitting the gong, the plate retains its contact with contact screw. Instead of an electromagnet, if we use a normal magnet, the metallic plate cannot regain its original contact.

76. Because of high resistance of nichrome wire to the flow of electric current, it gets heated and becomes red hot and transfers heat energy to the substances.

77. (1) He has to change the silk thread used to connect one of the bulbs with a battery because silk thread is not a conducting wire.

(2) He has to replace 'fused' bulb with a good normal bulb to make the circuit closed.

(3) Switch to be made 'ON'.

Level 3: Assess Your Concepts

78. (a) Both A and B are neutral, hence, no electrostatic force.

(b) and (c) As one of them is charged there exists an electrostatic attractive force due to induction.

(d) As A and B are oppositely charged, there exists an attractive force between them.

(e) and (f) As A and B are identically charged, there exists a repulsive force between them.

79. Let us consider a spherical conductor, and negative charge is placed at the centre. Different negatively charged particles repel each other. Because the body is a conductor, the charges can move freely through the body. They are repelled to the boundaries. As such charge placed on a conductor, always resides on outer surface of it.

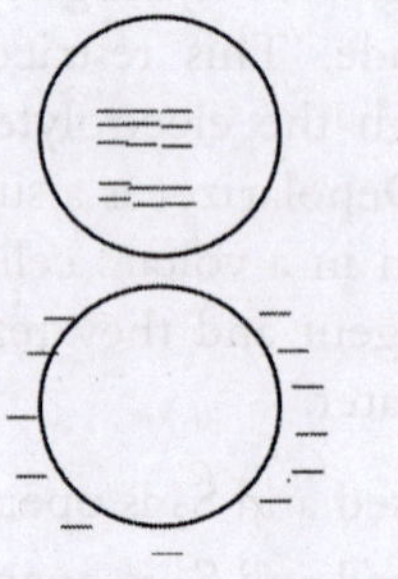

80. Instead of P we can connect a bulb, (or) a key (or) a cell (or) a resistor.

Instead of Q a tap key (or) a resistor (or) a cell (or) a bulb.

R is a voltmeter

81. There will be no electrostatic force between A and B. When switch is closed, electric current passes through B. The quantity of charge entering B is equal to the quantity of charge leaving B making it electrically neutral. And as charges in B are in motion, attraction between A and B because of electrostatic induction is negligible.

82. If metal strips in the jar deviate when a body is brought in contact with the metallic disc, then the body is charged. To know the nature of charge on the body, first we must charge the electroscope with known polarity. Then if a body of identical polarity is brought near the metallic disc, we observe increased deviation in metal strips. If it is of opposite polarity, the metal strips collapse or come closer.

83. No. of units consumed by a fan per day $= 2 \times 200 \times 12 = 4800 \times 10^{-3}$ kWh $= 4.8$ units

No. of units consumed by bulbs per day $= 3 \times 100 \times 7 \times 10^{-3}$ kWh $= 2.1$ units

No. of units consumed by fridge per day $= 2500 \times 10^{-3} \times 3$ kWh $= 7.5$ units

84. All the three cells are connected in series. B_1 and B_2 are in series whereas B_3 is in parallel connection.

As B_1 and B_2 are connected in series, the brightness of them is same and is less than the brightness of B_3, which is connected across two cells.

85. Sockets are provided to connect movable electrical appliances. We have two different types of sockets.

(a) **Two-pin socket:** One pin is connected to a live wire and other pin is connected to a neutral wire.

(b) **Three-pin socket:** One pin is connected to a live wire, second pin is connected to a neutral wire and the third pin, called earth pin, is connected to earth. Earth connection is essential to ground leakage current or the unwanted current that flows accidentally through the outer cover of the appliance.

86. Electrical energy consumed by 1000 W appliance used for one hour is one unit.

2000 W appliance used for two hours consumes 4 units of electrical energy.

In thirty days, the consumption is 120 units. Ten 100 W bulbs used for one hour consume for 1 unit of energy.

If they are used for 4 hours, energy consumed = 4 units.

In thirty days, they consume 120 units.

87. (a) $E = E_1$

(b) $E = 5\ V + 3 + 1 = 9\ V$

(c) $E = 3E_1$

(d) $E = 5\ V$

88. In the newspaper press, a page is composed using ordinary types. Moulds of letters first prepared by using wax and graphite powder is spread over it to make it to conduct electricity. This is used as a cathode in the electrolysis of copper sulphate. A piece of copper is used as the anode. A thick plating of copper is obtained and the wax inside it is melted and removed. These copper letters are used to print thousands of copies of the newspaper page. This is called electrotype setting. Thus, chemical effect of electric current is used in electrotype setting

89. No, filament bulbs we use work on heating effect of electric current. In these bulbs, in addition to light, lot of unwanted heat is also generated and this results in the wastage of electricity. We have different types of bulbs, known as fluorescent tube lights which work on a different principle. By using them we can reduce wastage of current. Compact fluorescent lamps (CFL) also reduce wastage and can be fixed in the ordinary bulb holders.

90. If there is a form of energy without which present days human life is very difficult to imagine, then it is electrical energy. We depend on electrical energy for everything. The usefulness of electrical energy comes because we have devices that convert electrical energy into any other form. Here is a list of devices that convert electrical energy into different other forms.

Device	Input energy	Output energy
Electric heater	Electrical	Heat
Electric bulb	Electrical	Heat and light
Electric motor	Electrical	Mechanical energy
Induction coil	Electrical	Magnetic energy

(vi) (a) E = E₁ [illegible]

(b) E = 5 V + 3 + 1 = 9 V

(c) E = 3E₁

(d) E = 5 V

CHAPTER 7

Machines and Tools

Remember

Before beginning this chapter, you should be able to:

- Recognize simple tools in daily life, such as hammer, scissors, etc.

Key Ideas

After completing this chapter, you should be able to:

- Study the working principles of hammer, divider, hacksaw and hacksaw blade, vice, tin-cutter, multipurpose tool, wooden plough, improvised plough, wooden plank, leveller, seed drill, harrow, etc.
- Discuss the construction of commonly used tools
- Know the working and maintenance of different types of tools and machines

Scientific Crypt

A Tribute to Archimedes (287–212 BC)

Archimedes was a great ancient Greek mathematician and scientist who lived during the time of turmoil and wars. He was born in Syracause, Silicy and educated at Egypt. War or threat of war was present in his city and his studies were effected by that. He determined the value of pie (π) to the most accurate approximation at that time. He has formulated integral calculus which is an important branch of mathematics and is also applied widely in physics. A device known as Archimedes screw used to pump water out of a ship which is used even now in many parts of the world was invented by him. When Archimedes was 27 years old, he explained how pulleys and levers can be used to move heavier objects. He discovered the theorems concerning the centre of gravity of plane figures and solids by applying geometry.

FUN TIME

CROSSWORD

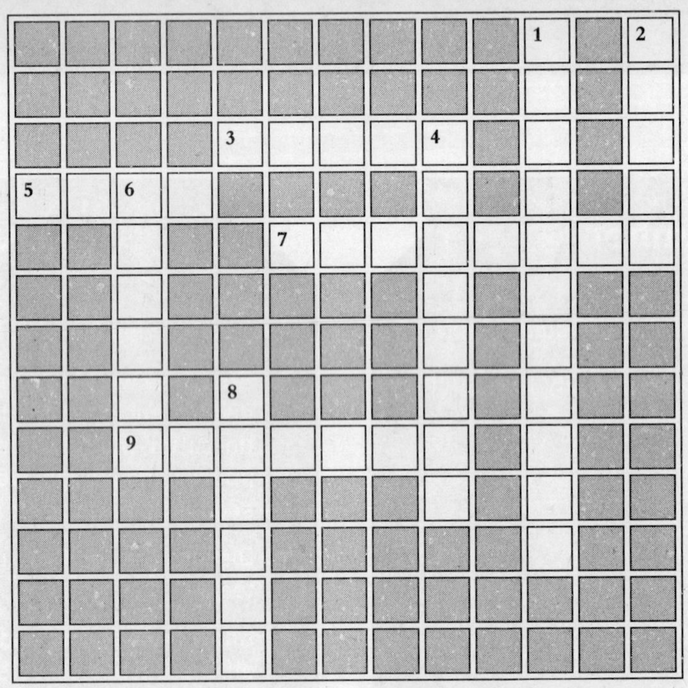

Across

3. Hammer with a fork is used to remove ______.
5. A device which is used to hold the metal plate or rod.
7. A device used to draw circles on wood.
9. All the agricultural tools are operated with the help of______.

Down

1. Device used to break the mud rocks.
2. Function of harrow in a field is to remove ______.
4. The tin cutter device is similar to pair of ______.
6. The part to which different tools can be fixed to a multipurpose tool.
8. Seed drill can also be used to drop ______.

INTRODUCTION

For fixing a screw, a carpenter uses a screw driver. Similarly, for removing the screw also a screw driver is used. Imagine how difficult it would be to do this work without using the screw driver. For doing different types of work different tools, like knives, scissors, hammers, tin-cutters, etc., are used. These tools help the carpenter to do his work with less effort. It is important to understand that these tools are help to do the work with less effort but do not reduce the work done.

Machine and Tools

The various types of machines and tools used are discussed as follows:

The Hammer

A hammer is mainly used to fix or remove nails. It is made of a heavy metal head provided with a wooden handle. Hammers are also used to break stones and to flatten metals. There are two kinds of hammers.

1. An ordinary hammer
2. A hammer with a fork.

Ordinary hammers are used only to fix the nails whereas hammers with a fork are used to fix nails as well as to remove them. The forked side of these hammers is used to remove the nails.

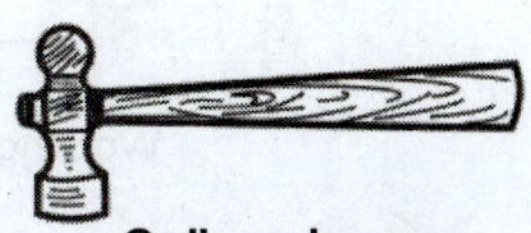

Figure 7.1 Ordinary hammer

Figure 7.2 Hammer with a forked part

The Dividers

A pair of dividers is used to measure distance and to take equal measures. They can also be used to draw circles on plastics and wood. It consists of a pair of iron strips of equal length which are fixed to a fulcrum. They can be moved about the fulcrum. The other ends of the iron strips are pointed.

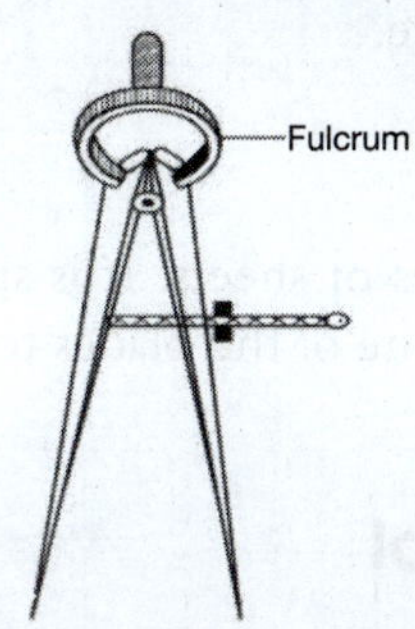

Figure 7.3 Dividers

Info Bytes!

Dividers have been used in navigation and map-making for centuries.
The oldest known divider was found in the wreckage of a ship from the 16th century.

The Hacksaw and Hacksaw blade

This is used for cutting metal rods. It consists of a blade made of steel with sharp teeth on it. This blade is fixed to a metal frame with a handle. It can also be used to cut soft materials, like wood and plastics.

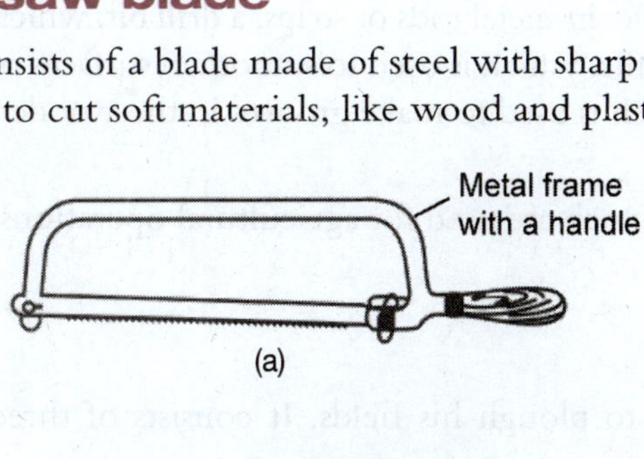

Figure 7.4 (a) Hacksaw; (b) Hacksaw blade

Konnect

Different hacksaw blades have varying numbers of teeth per inch, designed for specific materials and cuts.

The Vice

While cutting a metal plate or metal rod, it is very difficult to hold it in one hand and to cut with the other. Hence, a device called vice is used to hold the metal plate or rod. A vice is fixed at the edge of a table by using a screw arrangement. There are two jaws on it, out of which one is fixed to the table and the other is movable. This movable jaw can be moved with the help of a screw. The vice is tightened by rotating the screw in a clockwise direction and it is loosened by rotating the screw in an anti-clockwise direction. The material to be fixed is placed between the jaws and the screw is rotated in a clockwise direction to tighten it.

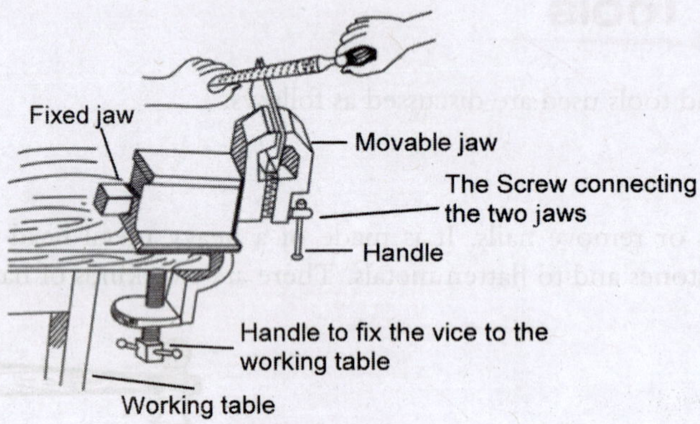

Figure 7.5 Vice

Metal plates and pipes can be cut by fixing them between the jaws of a vice. Threads can be easily made on pipes by fixing them between the jaws. Similarly, the surfaces can be made smoother by using the vice.

The Tin-Cutter

This is used to cut thin metal plates or sheets. It is similar to pair of scissors. A spring is connected between the handle of one of the blades to the other blade. The energy stored in the spring reduces the effort.

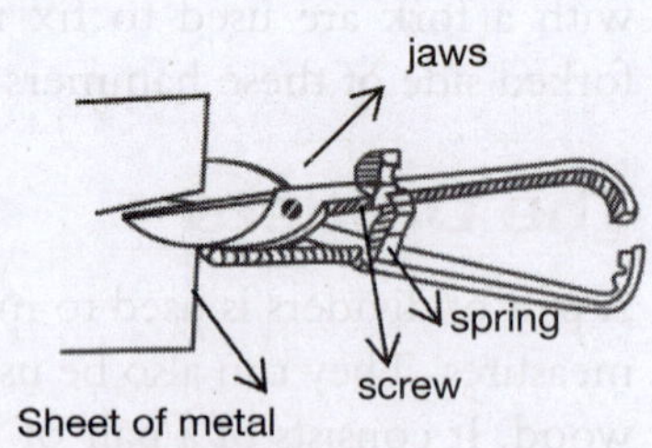

Figure 7.6 Tin-cutter

The Multipurpose Tool

A multipurpose tool can be used to perform different kinds of work. It has a collet and different kinds of tools can be fixed in the collet depending upon the work to be performed.

The tools which can be fixed in the collet are a carpenter's hand saw, which is used by carpenters to cut wood, a screw driver, which is used to tighten or loosen screws, a poker, which is used to make holes in metal rods or strips, a drill bit, which is used to drill holes in wooden planks, a file, which is used to smoothen surfaces of metals and wooden articles, a chisel, which is used to make grooves in the wooden planks.

Let us now discuss about some tools which are used for agricultural operations.

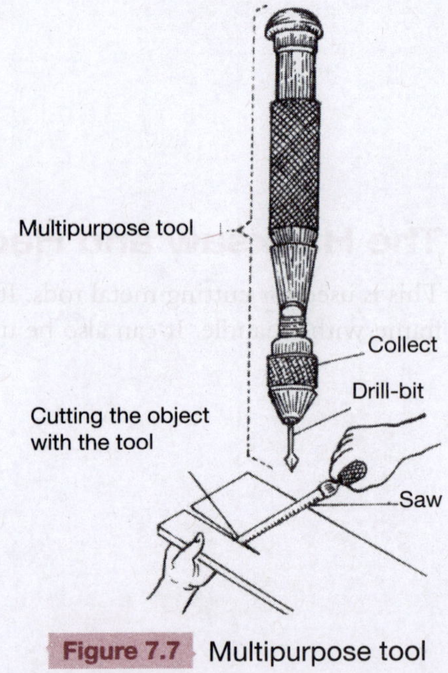

Figure 7.7 Multipurpose tool

The Wooden Plough

A wooden plough is used by a farmer to plough his fields. It consists of three main parts:

1. **The main plough:** This is made of wood and is slightly bent like an 'L'. At the top, there is a provision to fix the handle, and a hole is also provided to fix a long pole into it. One end of this is sharply pointed and on this pointed end there is a metallic blade fixed with nails. The blade helps the plough to go deep into the soil more easily.
2. **The long pole:** The long pole is a long wooden pole of length $2\frac{1}{2}$ m. One end of it is fixed to the plough and the other end to the yoke of the bullocks.
3. **The handle:** This is fixed on the other side of the pointed end of the plough. The farmer uses it to change the direction of ploughing. It can also be used to control the depth of the soil to be ploughed.

The Improvized Plough

All the parts of the improvised plough are made of iron or steel plates and strips. This lasts for a longer period of time as compared to a wooden plough and it can plough the soil deeper. This is also helpful in making shallow grooves in the soil and sow seeds into them. By changing the angle of blades these shallow grooves can also be covered after sowing of the seeds is done.

Konnect

- In some developing countries, improvised ploughs are made from recycled materials like old car parts.
- Improvised ploughs often incorporate local materials and knowledge, making them well-suited to specific environmental conditions.

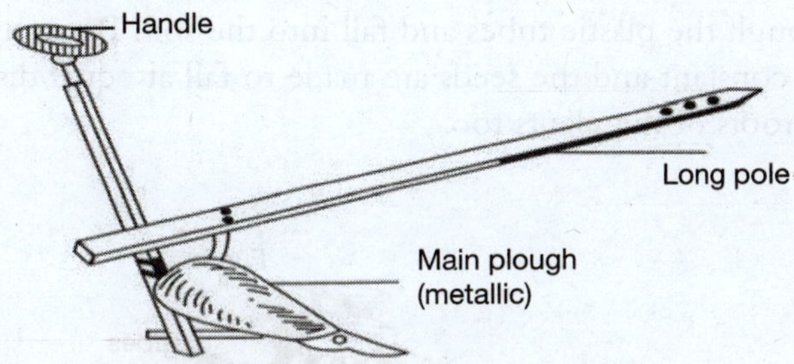

Figure 7.8 Improvized plough

The Wooden Plank

A wooden plank consists of three straight wooden planks fixed by using two metal strips as shown in the Fig. 7.9. The mud rocks present on the soil surface do not allow the seeds to sprout, and hence, the plants cannot grow properly. To break these mud, rocks wooden plank is used. This is fixed to the yoke of the two bullocks and mud rocks are broken.

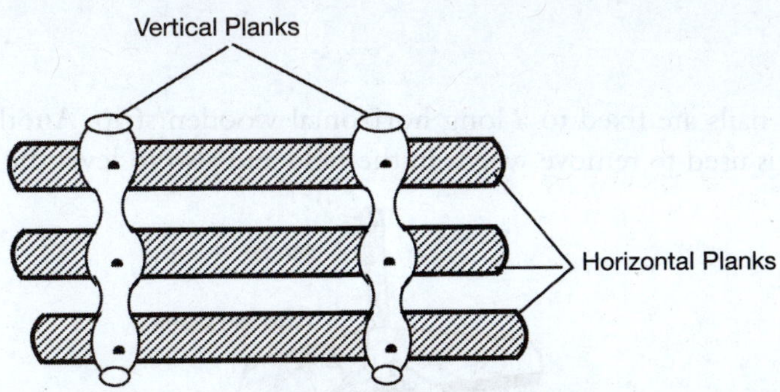

Figure 7.9 Wooden plank

The Leveller

It is used to level the surface of the soil. It consists of a heavy wooden frame, and to its lower end a metallic strip is fixed horizontally. On the other end of the wooden frame a handle is provided. Two rings are fixed to the wooden frame as shown in the Fig. 7.10. This is pulled by bullocks or tractors. The farmer holds the handle while using the leveller.

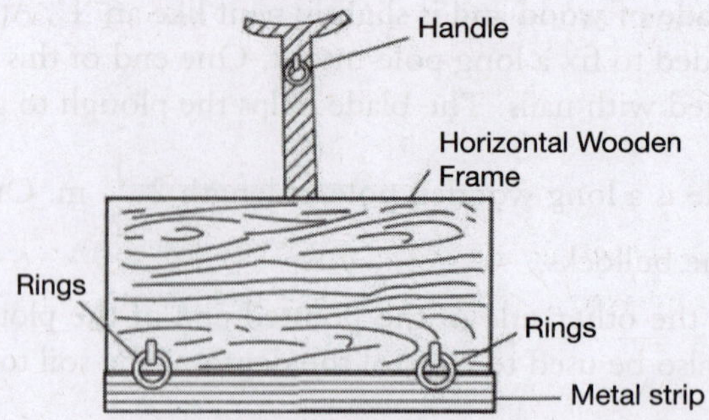

Figure 7.10 Leveller

> **Info Bytes!**
> - Levellers are essential in construction for ensuring a flat and even surface.
> - The largest area ever levelled in a single day covered more than 300,000 square feet.

The Seed Drill

It is a tool used to sow seeds. Shallow grooves are made on the soil by using this. Four or five wooden ploughs with holes are fixed to a horizontal wooden plank or a metal tube. The holes on the wooden plank are connected by using plastic tubes. The other ends of these plastic tubes are connected to a funnel. The seeds are put into the funnel and they pass through the plastic tubes and fall into the soil. By using this the distance between two rows of seeds sown can be maintained constant and the seeds are made to fall at equal distances. Through this the fertilizer or manure can be dropped near the roots of the plants too.

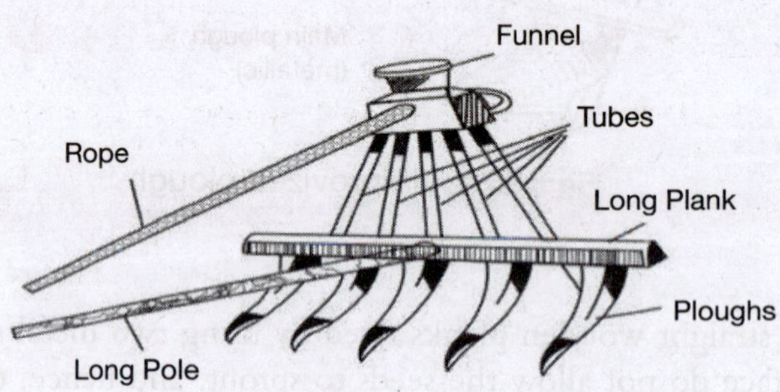

Figure 7.11 Seed-Drill

The Harrow

A large number of sharp metal nails are fixed to a long horizontal wooden strip. Another wooden plank with a handle is fixed to this wooden strip. It is used to remove weeds in the field and also to level the wet field before transplantation.

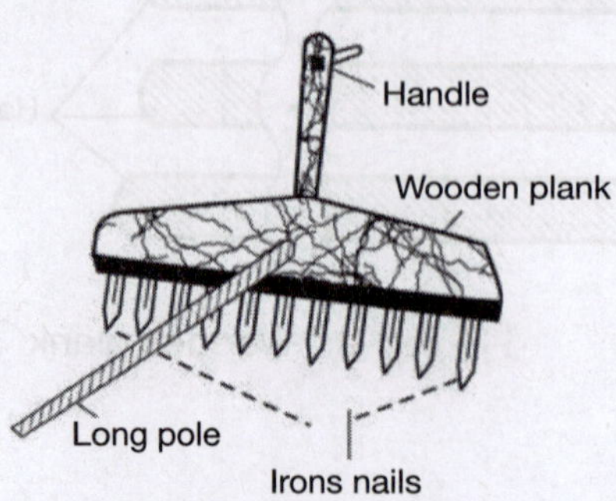

Figure 7.12 Harrow

All the agricultural tools discussed above can be operated with the help of a pair of bullocks or a tractor.

The Maintenance of Tools

All tools, including the agricultural tools should be maintained properly. After every use, the wooden tools are to be cleaned. Metal tools are to be oiled or greased at regular intervals to prevent them from rusting.

POINTS TO REMEMBER

- ✔ Tools help us in doing work with less effort.
- ✔ A divider is used to take measurements and to draw circles on soft material.
- ✔ A hacksaw is used for cutting metal rods.
- ✔ Different tools can be fixed to the collet of a multipurpose tool.
- ✔ The three parts of a wooden plough are main plough, long pole, and a handle.
- ✔ A wooden plank is used to break the mud rocks.
- ✔ A leveller is used to level the surface of the soil.
- ✔ A seed-drill is used to sow seeds.
- ✔ A harrow is used to remove weeds in a field.

DW

PRACTICE QUESTIONS CLASSROOM WING

Very Short Answer Type Questions

Directions for questions from 1 to 3: **Fill in the blanks.**

1. When the screw used to fix the object between the jaws is rotated in the clockwise direction, then the ________ jaw moves towards ________.

2. To draw circles on the wood, ________ is used.

3. The tool used to sow seeds is ________.

Directions for questions from 4 to 13: **For each of the questions, four choices have been provided. Select the correct alternative.**

4. Which of the following geometrical plane figure cannot be drawn on a wooden board only by using a divider?

(a) 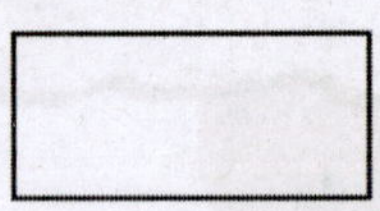

(b) 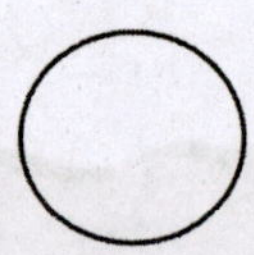

(c) 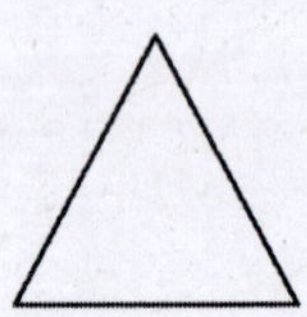

(d) Both (a) and (c)

5. Which of the following tools cannot be fixed in the collet of a multipurpose tool?
   (a) a file (b) poker
   (c) a screw driver (d) hammer

6. Which of the following tools are useful in cutting a small piece of metal?
   (a) Vice (b) Hacksaw blade
   (c) Screwdriver (d) Both (a) and (b)

7. A tin-cutter is used to cut a thin metallic circular plate. Then the angle between the forces which are applied at both the handles is ______.
   (a) 30° (b) 60°
   (c) 180° (d) 90°

8. A farmer ploughs his field, to ______.
   (a) prevent the escape of moisture, present in the surface of field
   (b) increase the evaporation of water from the surface of field
   (c) make the land dry
   (d) None of the above

9. Motion of plough in a field is ______.
   (a) translatory (b) rotatory
   (c) random (d) oscillatory

10. Choose the correct alternative(s) among the following statements.
    (a) Seed drill is used to sow seeds.
    (b) Four or five ploughs are attached to the plank of the seed drill to sow the seeds deeper.
    (c) Speed drill is also used to put manure near the roots of the small plants.
    (d) All of the above

11. Which of the following agricultural tools is used to remove weeds in a field?
    (a) Harrow (b) Leveller
    (c) Plough (d) Wooden plank

12. The use of the metal blade in a plough is ________.
    (a) to penetrate deep into the soil easily.
    (b) to give strength to the L-shaped log.
    (c) to avoid breaking of wooden log when it strikes a stone.
    (d) All of the above

13. Which of the following agent(s) is (are) used to pull a plough?
    (a) Tractor (b) Bull
    (c) Man (d) Both (a) and (b)

Directions for question from 14: **Match the entries given in Column A with the appropriate ones in Column B.**

14.

	Column A		Column B
A.	To loosen the vice	a.	Seed drill
B.	Poker	b.	Vice
C.	Plough	c.	Breaks mud rocks
D.	Funnel	d.	Fix nails on a wall
E.	Working table	e.	Sharpen knives
F.	Spring	f.	Holes
G.	File	g.	Tin-cutter
H.	Wooden plank	h.	Anti-clockwise direction
I.	Hammer	i.	Grooves in soil
J.	Hacksaw	j.	To cut metals

Directions for questions from 15 to 25: **Answer the following questions.**

15. How are wooden tools and metal tools maintained?

16. Name the tool which is used to put fertilizer near the roots of a plant.

17. What is the use of collet in a multipurpose tool?

18. Name few tools which can be fixed on a multipurpose tool.

19. Which among Divider, Harrow, Vice, Hammer is an agricultural tool?

20. Which tool among Vice, Hack-saw, Tin cutter, or Drilling tool has a spring attached to it?

21. What are the uses of jaws in a vice?

22. What are the advantages of using seed drill?

23. Why is oil or grease applied to tools?

24. What is the use of the long pole in a wooden plough?

25. What are the different kinds of hammers?

Short Answer Type Questions

26. What are the disadvantages in using a vice?

27. Between the maintenance of agriculture tool or workshop tool, which is difficult? Why?

28. What are the advantages of sowing seeds by using seed drill over that done by hand?

29. Write the uses of a divider.

30. Which part of the wooden plough is made of steel? What is the use of this part?

31. A leveller with one metre long metal strip is used to level the surface of the soil. If the farmer takes the leveller from one end to the other end of the field which is of length 30 m, then the area of the field which is levelled is ________ square meters.

32. To cut a thick metallic plate, it is placed between the jaws of a vice. The handle is rotated through fine complete rotations. What is the thickness of rod, if the distance moved by the movable jaw is 0.5 cm per rotation?

33. What are the three different parts of a wooden plough?

34. What is the use of a leveller?

35. Why is the tip of the screw driver magnetized?

36. Why is the maintenance of tool very important?

Essay Type Questions

37. Describe a wooden plough.

38. Describe a hacksaw blade.

39. Describe a seed-drill.

40. Write the difference between wooden plough and an improvized plough.

PRACTICE QUESTIONS COMPETITION WING

Level 1: Apply your Concepts

***Directions for questions from 1 to 15:* Fill in the blanks.**

1. _______ can be used to remove nails from a wall or a piece of wood.
2. Tools can not reduce the _______ done by the effort.
3. The _______ tools should be cleaned and oiled after every use.
4. A _______ can be used to level the wet field before transplantation.
5. Tools help us to do work with less _______.
6. To prevent tools from _______, oil is applied.
7. _______ is used to cut thin sheets of metal.
8. In a vice, screw is rotated in _______ direction to tighten the vice.
9. We can tighten or loosen screws by using _______.
10. To make a hole in a wooden plank, _______ is fixed in the multipurpose tool.
11. Tools used to make articles or to repair them are called _______.
12. Plough which is made up of iron or steel plates is called _______ plough.
13. _______ is used to level the surface of the soil.
14. _______ is used to remove weeds in a field.
15. _______ is used to sow the seeds.

***Directions for questions from 16 to 24:* State whether the following statements are true or false.**

16. Harrow is used to remove weeds in the field.
17. The diameter of a metallic plate can be measured by using a divider.
18. The hacksaw blade cannot be removed from a hacksaw.
19. A harrow can be used to level the wet field before transplantation.
20. A hammer is made of a soft metal.
21. Handle, blade, long pole are all parts of the wooden plough.
22. When the screw used to fix the object between the jaws is rotated in the anti-clockwise direction, both the jaws of the vice move towards each other.
23. Poker is used to make the surface of a metal smoother.
24. There are two screws in a vice.

***Directions for questions from 25 to 45:* For each of the questions, four choices have been provided. Select the correct alternative.**

25. Which of the following tools can be used to cut the metal plates of smaller thickness?
    (a) Tin cutter (b) Scissors
    (c) Plier (d) Hacksaw
26. Which of the following tools has a spring attached to it?
    (a) Hacksaw (b) Vice
    (c) Tin-cutter (d) Drilling tool
27. The motion of the pulley while drawing water from a well is _______ about its fixed axis.
    (a) translatory (b) rotatory
    (c) oscillatory (d) to and fro
28. Which of the following can be used as a measuring tool?
    (a) Hammer (b) Divider
    (c) Multipurpose tool (d) Hacksaw
29. Which of the following is not a part of wooden plough?
    (a) Handle (b) Blade
    (c) Long pole (d) None of the above
30. Which of the following is an example for agriculture tool?
    (a) Screwdriver
    (b) Wooden plough
    (c) Divider
    (d) Hacksaw black

31. Which of the following cannot be attached to a multi-purpose tool?

(a) Poker (b) Chisel
(c) Screw driver (d) Hammer

32. Which of the following is not a workshop tool?

(a) Divider (b) Hammer
(c) Wooden plank (d) Vice

33. The farmer controls the direction of the plough and depth of the soil ploughed, by the ________.

(a) handle (b) blade
(c) long pole (d) main plough

34. A thin piece of steel with sharp teeth on one edge is known as ________.

(a) tin cutter (b) hacksaw blade
(c) drill bit (d) hammer

35. Which among the following angles can be the maximum angle through which a divider can be stretched to draw a circle?

(a) 180° (b) 90°
(c) 45° (d) 160°

36. Which of the following tools can be fixed in the collet of a multipurpose tool to drill holes in to a wooden plank?

(a) Chisel (b) Drill bit
(c) Poker (d) All the above

37. Choose the correct statement(s) among the following alternatives for a 'vice'.

(a) To loosen the vice, the handle of the screw should be rotated in a clockwise direction.
(b) To tighten the vice, the handle of the screw should be rotated in an anti-clockwise direction.
(c) The vice has only one movable jaw.
(d) Both (a) and (b)

38. The angle between the direction of applied force and the main plough (or blade of plough), in a wooden plough is ______ .

(a) greater than 90° (b) 90°
(c) 60° (d) less than 90°

39. The use of the handle of the plough, when the farmer ploughs his field is ______ .

(a) to control the direction of plough
(b) to control the direction of bulls
(c) to control the depth of the soil ploughed
(d) Both (a) and (c)

40. Which of the following agricultural tools is used to level the surface of the soil?

(a) Wooden plank (b) Harrow
(c) Leveller (d) Plough

41. Which of the following is not a workshop tool?

(a) Hammer (b) Tin-cutter
(c) Scale (d) Seed drill

42. Which of the following agricultural tool is used to sow the seeds in a field?

(a) Seed-drill (b) Plough
(c) Harrow (d) Both (b) and (c)

43. **Assertion (A):** Metal tools are to be oiled or greased at regular intervals.

Reason (R): Metals tools are to be oiled or greased to prevent them from rusting.

(a) A and R are true and R is the correct explanation of A.
(b) A and R are true, but R is not the correct explanation of A.
(c) A is true but R is false.
(d) Both A and R are false.

44. **Assertion (A):** Wood, cork, petrol, etc., float on water.

Reason (R): Densities of the above substances is lesser than that of water.

(a) A and R are true and R is the correct explanation of A.
(b) A and R are true, but R is not the correct explanation of A.
(c) A is true but R is false.
(d) Both A and R are false.

45. Arrange the following steps in a sequential order in the working of a rocket.

(A) Gases are produced when the fuel in the combustion chamber is burnt.
(B) The gases come out with great force which is the action.
(C) The hot gases are allowed to escape through a nozzle.
(D) Due to this, the rocket moves with great speed in the other direction.

(E) As a reaction, the gases exert an opposite force on the rocket.

(a) ABCED
(b) ADCBE
(c) ACBED
(d) BDAED

Directions for question 46: **Match the entries given in Column A with the appropriate ones in Column B.**

46.

Column A	Column B
A. Poker	a. Sharpen knives
B. Funnel	b. Tin cutter
C. File	c. Holes
D. Spring	d. Seed drill

Level 2: Review your Concepts

47. A screw of length 8 cm has the pitch of 1 mm. In one second, a hammer applied 10 dyne force to displace the screw into the wooden block through a distance equal to its pitch. Find the total force required to fix the screw up to its 75th thread in it.

48. Why do we use a sharp continuous metal blade for cutting a mango and a blade with many small teeth for cutting metals?

49. Sriharsha had a doubt as to why the head of a screw driver is made of plastic material and not metal. Clarify his doubt.

50. The square shaped metallic strip of a leveller covers an area of 400 cm^2 in 1 s. Then, how much time it will take to level a field of area one hectare and find its speed?

51. A thick metallic cylindrical rod which is to be cut when placed between the jaws of a 'vice', the handle rotated through $4 \times 360°$, if the distance moved by the movable jaw is 0.5 cm per rotation then calculate the radius of the rod. (Assume that initially the jaws are in contact with each other)

52. A leveller with one metre long metal strip is used to level the surface of the soil. If the farmer takes the leveller from one end to another end of the field of length 25 m, then calculate the area of the field which is levelled.

53. Chachu is a young farmer. To grow a new crop in his field he is using seed drill having five ploughs. In one second span of time, he can sow five seeds simultaneously at the separation of 10 cm from each other. At the end of 20 s how many seeds Chachu can sow in the field? How many rows he can fill with seeds in 20 s?

54. The movable jaw of a vice moves through a distance of 7 mm for one complete rotation of the handle. Through how many rotations should the handle be rotated so that it holds a metal plate of thickness 3.5 cm firmly.

55. A leveller with a 1.5 meters long metallic strip is used to level an area of 45 square metres. Then calculate the length of the field which is levelled.

Level 3: Assess Your Concepts

56. Venkat went to a factory workshop where he saw hot metallic square plates. He measured the surface area of the hot plates. How did he do it?

57. What is the use of spring in a tin cutter?

58. Using a vice, a metal coin of thickness 2.7 cm is to be held firmly. The movable jaw of the vice moves through a distance of 9 mm for one complete rotation of the handle. Calculate the number of times the handle is to be rotated, so that the coin is held firmly.

59. Rahul, by using a hacksaw blade, was cutting metal pipes to supply water to his house. What will happen if he starts moving the hacksaw blade very fast over the metal, due to lack of time.

60. Why does an axe has a curved sharp edge?

61. A circular metal plate at room temperature has a radius of 6.8 cm. When it is heated, its area becomes 154 cm^2. What is the increase in its radius? Suggest a method to measure the radius of the plate when it is hot.

62. What are the advantages and disadvantages in using a vice?

63. Komali found that most of the agricultural tools her father uses are made up of wood. Explain why it is so.

AT

ANSWER KEYS

Crossword

Across

3. Nails 5. Vice 7. Dividers 9. Tractor

Down

1. Wodden plank 2. Weeds 4. Scissors 6. Collet 8. Manure

Classroom Wing

Very Short Answer Type Questions

1. movable, fixed 2. dividers 3. seed drill 4. (d) 5. (d)
6. (d) 7. (c) 8. (a) 9. (c) 10. (d)
11. (a) 12. (a) 13. (d)
14. A → h, B → f, C → i, D → a, E → b, F → g, G → e, H → c, I → d, J → j 19. Harrow
20. tin cutter 32. 2.5 cm

Competition Wing

Level 1: Apply your concepts

1. A hammer with a fork 2. work 3. metal 4. harrow
5. effort 6. rusting 7. Tin-cutter 8. clockwise 9. screw driver
10. drill bit 11. workshop tools 12. improvised 13. Leveller 14. Harrow
15. Seed drill 16. True 17. True 18. False 19. True
20. False 21. True 22. False 23. False 24. True
25. (a) 26. (c) 27. (b) 28. (b) 29. (d)
30. (b) 31. (d) 32. (c) 33. (a) 34. (b)
35. (d) 36. (d) 37. (c) 38. (d) 39. (d)
40. (c) 41. (d) 42. (a) 43. (a) 44. (a)
45. (c) 46. A → c, B → d, C → a, D → b

Level 2: Review your Concepts

47. 740 dyne 50. 69.444 h; 0.2 m/s 51. 1 cm 52. 25 m^2
53. 5 seeds; 20 rows 54. (n) = 5 55. 30 m

Level 3: Assess Your Concepts

58. 3 61. 2 mm

Hints and Explanations

Classroom Wing

Very Short Answer Type Questions

1. (movable, fixed)
When the screws are rotated in clockwise direction the movable jaw moves towards the fixed jaw.

2. (Dividers)
Dividers can be used to draw circles, half circles on the soft bodies like wood, plastic etc.

3. The tool used to sow seeds is seed drill.

4. (d)
By fixing one arm of the divider and by rotating another arm about this fixed arm we can draw a circle, but it is not possible to draw either a triangle or a rectangle.

5. (d)
It is not possible to use hammer in combination with the collet of a multipurpose tool.

6. (d)
We can fix a small piece of metal in between the jaws of a vice and by using a hack saw blade we can cut it.

7. (c)
When we cut the metal plate, we apply force by means of our hand in two opposite directions and hence the angle between the direction of applied forces is 180°.

8. (a)
A farmer ploughs his field to prevent the moisture present in the surface of field from escaping, which is necessary for the growth of plants. When he ploughs, the soil spreads in such a way that it prevents the water from evaporation.

9. (c)
As the plough moves from one place to another as a whole it is an example of random motion.

10. (d)
All the given options are true.

11. (a)
A Harrow is used to remove weeds in a field.

12. (a)
The use of metal blade in a plough is to penetrate deep into the soil easily.

13. (d)
Tractor or bulls can be used to pull a plough.

14. A → h The screws are rotated in the anti-clockwise direction to loosen the vice.
B → f Using a poker we can make holes in metal rods or strips.
C → i Plough is a tool used to make shallow grooves in the soil.
D → a Funnel is a part of seed drill.
E → b Vice is fixed to the working table.
F → g Spring is present in the tin cutter.
G → e File is used to sharpen knives.
H → c A wooden plank is used to break mud rocks.
I → d Hammer is used to fix nails on a wall.
J → j Hack-saw is used to cut soft metal, soft wood, plastic etc.

15. All tools, including the agricultural tools should be maintained properly. After every use, the wooden tools are to be cleaned. Metal tools are to be oiled or greased at regular intervals to prevent them from rusting.

16. Through the seed drill the fertilizer or manure can be dropped near the roots of the plants.

17. The tools which can be fixed in the collet is used for fixing the tools to a multipurpose tool.

18. A screw driver, a poker, a drill bit and a file are some of the tools which can be fixed to a multipurpose tool.

19. Harrow is an agricultural tool.

20. Among the given options, tin cutter has a spring attached to it.

21. Metal plates and pipes can be cut by fixing them between the jaws of a vice. Threads can be easily made on pipes by fixing them between the jaws.

22. Used to sow seeds, to make shallow grooves on the soil.

23. Metal tools are to be oiled or greased at regular intervals to prevent them from rusting.

24. One end of the long pole is fixed to the plough and the other end to the yoke of the bullocks.

25. There are two kinds of hammers:
   (i) An ordinary hammer
   (ii) A hammer with a fork.

Short Answer Type Questions

26. **Disadvantages:** Very thin and soft metals cannot be held on a vice. If it is soft metal, the vice change its dimension also it put some markings on the metal surface. Similarly, a work piece of bigger size cannot be held in the vice.

27. Maintenance of agricultural tool is more difficult compare to workshop tool because, the agricultural tools are always in contact with moist surface, water, etc. And also sometimes it is in contact with manure which is acidic in nature and may damage or corrode the tool.

28. The advantages in using seed drills are:
   (i) The seeds fall into the soil at equal distances.
   (ii) The distance between the rows of seed sown remain the same.
   (iii) We can do the work in a shorter time.
   (iv) We can also put manure or fertilizer near the roots of the small plants.

29. A pair of dividers is used to measure distance and to take equal measures. They can also be used to draw circles on plastics and wood.

30. The main plough of a wooden plough slightly bent like an 'L'. At the top, there is a provision to fix the handle, and a hole is also provided to fix a long pole into it. One end of this is sharply pointed and on this pointed end there is a metallic blade made of steel fixed with nails. The blade helps the plough to go deep into the soil more easily.

31. Length of the metallic strip $p = 1$ m
Length of the field = 30 m
Thus, Area of the field = 30×1 m = 30 m^2

32. The distance moved by the jaw per rotation is 0.5 cm.
The distance moved by the jaw for 5 rotations is $5 \times 0.5 = 2.5$ cm

33. The Wooden Plough: A wooden plough is used by a farmer to plough his fields. It consists of three main parts.
   (i) The main plough
   (ii) The long pole
   (iii) The handle

34. The Leveller is used to level the surface of the soil.

35. The tip of the screw driver is magnetised so that the metallic screw get attracted to it and the screw will not fall down.

36. Every tool must be used properly and after use they must be preserved for future use. If we are not cleaning the tool properly or not applying oil or grease to the tool, rust will be formed on the surface of the tool. It will reduce the efficiency of the tool.

Essay Type Questions

37. The Wooden Plough: A wooden plough is used by a farmer to plough his fields. It consists of three main parts.
   (i) The main plough: This is made of wood and is slightly bent like an 'L'. At the top, there is a provision to fix the handle, and a hole is also provided to fix a long pole into it. One end of this is sharply pointed and on this pointed end there is a metallic blade fixed with nails. The blade helps the plough to go deep into the soil more easily.
   (ii) The long pole: The long pole is a long wooden pole of length $2\frac{1}{2}$ m. One end of it is fixed to the plough and the other end to the yoke of the bullocks.
   (iii) The handle: This is fixed on the other side of the pointed end of the plough. The farmer uses it to change the direction of ploughing. It can also be used to control the depth of the soil to be ploughed.

38. The Hack-saw and Hack-saw blade: This is used for cutting metal rods. It consists of a blade made of steel with sharp teeth on it. This blade is fixed to a metal frame with a handle. It can also be used to cut soft materials like wood and plastics.

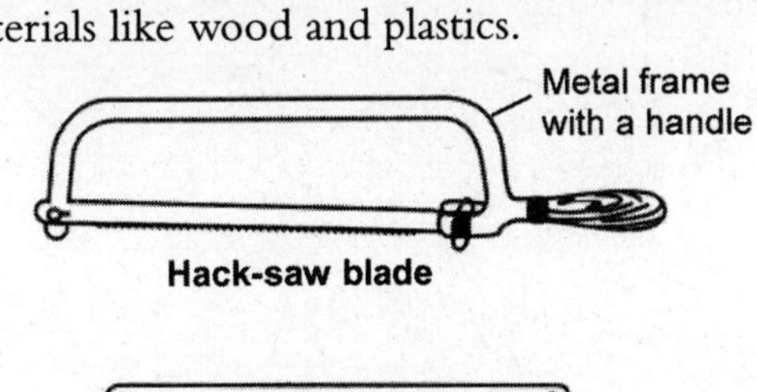

Hack-saw and Hack-saw blade

39. The Seed Drill: It is a tool used to sow seeds, to make shallow grooves on the soil by using this.

Four or five wooden ploughs with holes are fixed to a horizontal wooden plank or a metal tube. The holes on the wooden plank are connected by using plastic tubes. The other ends of these plastic tubes are connected to a funnel. The seeds are put into the funnel and they pass through the plastic tubes and fall into the soil. By using this the distance between two rows of seeds sown can be maintained constant and the seeds are made to fall at equal distances. Through the seed drill the fertilizer or manure can be dropped near the roots of the plants too.

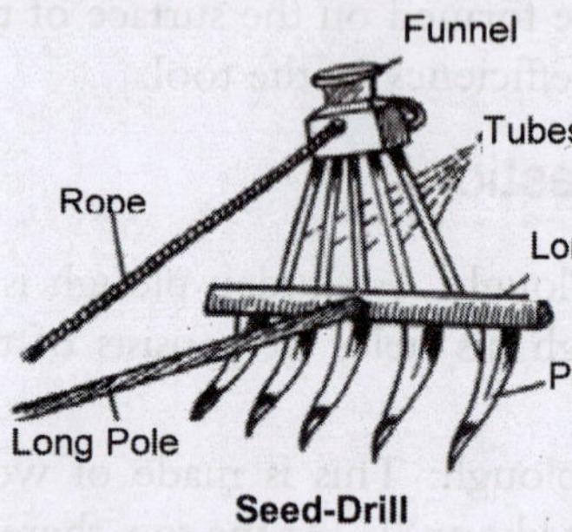

Seed-Drill

40. **The Wooden Plough:** A wooden plough is used by a farmer to plough his fields. It consists of three main parts.

(i) The main plough: This is made of wood and is slightly bent like an 'L'. At the top, there is a provision to fix the handle, and a hole is also provided to fix a long pole into it. One end of this is sharply pointed and on this pointed end there is a metallic blade fixed with nails. The blade helps the plough to go deep into the soil more easily.

(ii) The long pole: The long pole is a long wooden pole of length $2\frac{1}{2}$ m. One end of it is fixed to the plough and the other end to the yoke of the bullocks.

(iii) The handle: This is fixed on the other side of the pointed end of the plough. The farmer uses it to change the direction of ploughing. It can also be used to control the depth of the soil to be ploughed.

The Improvized Plough: All the parts of the improvized plough are made of iron or steel plates and strips. This lasts for a longer period of time as compared to a wooden plough and it can plough the soil deeper. This is also helpful in making shallow grooves in the soil and sow seeds into them. By changing the angle of blades these shallow grooves can also be covered after sowing of the seeds is done.

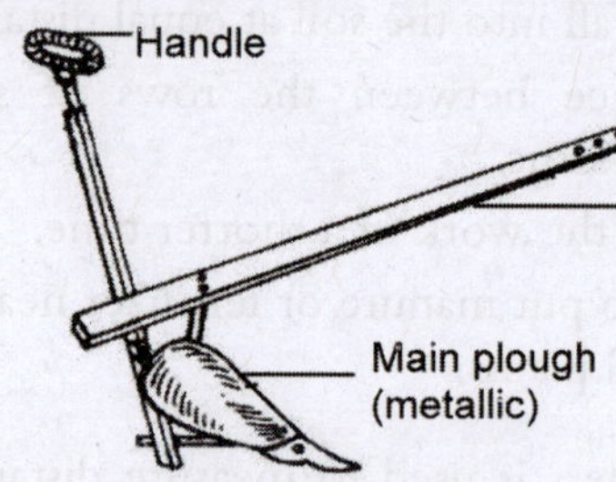

Improvised plough

Competition Wing

Level 1: Apply your Concepts

1. Hammer with a fork is used to remove nails from a wall or a piece of wood.
2. Tools can not be used to reduce the work done by the effort.
3. All metal tools should be cleaned and oiled after every use.
4. The harrow is used to remove weeds in a field. This is also used to level the wet field before transplantation.
5. Tools help us to do work with less effort.
6. Tools made of metal should be cleaned and oiled to prevent from rusting.
7. We can use tin cutter to cut thin sheets of metal.
8. In a vice screws are rotated in clockwise direction to tighten the vice.
9. We can tighten or loosen screws by using a screw driver.
10. We can make holes in wooden planks by fixing a drill bit in the multipurpose tool.
11. Tools used to make articles or to repair them are called workshop tools.
12. A plough which is made up of iron or steel plates is called improvized plough.
13. Leveller is used to level the surface of the soil.
14. Harrow is used to remove weeds in a field.
15. Seed drill is used to sow the seeds.
16. True. Harrow is used to remove weeds in the field.
17. We can measure the diameter of a metallic plate by using a divider.
18. We can remove the hacksaw blade from a hacksaw.
19. The harrow is used to remove weeds in a field. This is also used to level the wet field before transplantation.
20. A hammer is made of a hard and heavy metal.
21. True. Handle, blade, long pole are all parts of the wooden plough.
22. When the screws are rotated in anti-clock wise direction, the movable jaw moves away the fixed jaw.
23. Poker is used to make holes in the metal rods or strips.
24. Two types of screws are there in a vice one is used to fix the vice to table and another one is used to move the movable jaw.
25. Tin-cutter is the tool which is used to cut the metal plates of smaller thickness.
26. A tin-cutter is similar to a pair of scissors, but a strong spring linking the handle of one blade and the other blade is fixed.
27. When the person pulls the rope over the pulley, the pulley rotates about the axis which is passing through it, and hence, the motion is rotatory.
28. The dividers are used for measurements.
29. Handle, blade and long pole are part of the wooden plough.
30. Wooden plough is an example for agriculture tool.
31. Hammer cannot be attached to a multipurpose tool.
32. A wooden plank is an agriculture tool.
33. The farmer uses the handle to control the direction of the plough and depth of the soil ploughed.
34. A thin piece of steel with sharp teeth on one edge is known as hacksaw blade.
35. If the position (angle) of the arms of a divider is as shown in figure, it is not possible to draw a circle, and hence, the maximum angle through which a divider can be stretched to draw a circle among given options is 160°.

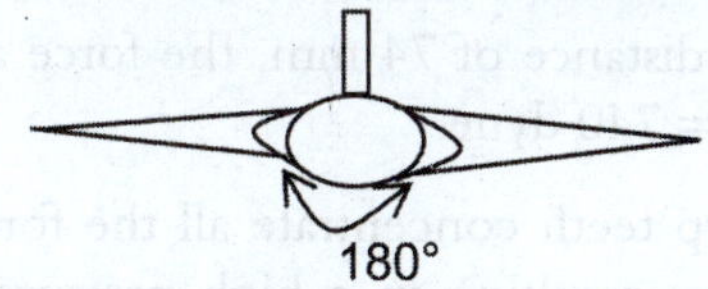

36. All tools which are given in the options can be used to drill holes in a wooden plank in combination with a multipurpose tool.
37. To loosen the vice, the handle of the screw should be rotated in an anti-clock wise direction and the vice has one movable and one fixed jaw.
38. From the adjacent figure, it is clear that the angle is less than 90°. If the angle is 90°, then it is difficult to pull the plough, and hence, the angle is always acute.

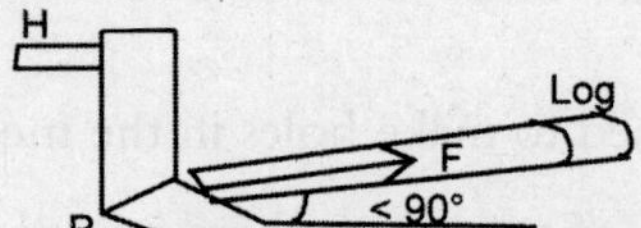

39. The farmer controls the direction of the plough, depth of the soil ploughed by means of the handle attached to the plough.

40. A leveller is used to level the surface of soil.

41. Seed drill is not a workshop tool, it is an agricultural tool.

42. Seed drill is used to sow seeds in a field.

43. Metal tools are to be oiled or greased at regular intervals to prevent them from rusting.
Hence, the correct option is (a).

44. If the density of a substance is more than that of water, then it will sink, otherwise it will float.
Hence, the correct option is (a).

45. (c)
The correct order is A C B E D.

46. (a) Poker is used to make holes on metal sheets.
(b) Funnel is a part of seed drill to hold the seeds.
(c) File is used to sharpen the knives.
(d) Spring is used in tin cutter.

Level 2: Review your Concepts

47. Length of the screw = 8 cm
Pitch = 1 mm
For a distance of 1 mm, which is the pitch of the screw, the force applied is 10 dyne.
The total distance advanced by the screw = 74 mm (as the screw is to be fixed up to its 75th thread)
∴ For a distance of 74 mm, the force applied = 74 × 10 dyne = 740 dyne.

48. The sharp teeth concentrate all the force onto a very small area, resulting in a high pressure which allows it to penetrate into the work piece. Mango is a soft material. So, for cutting it, we require only small effort. Therefore, we use a continuous pointed edge knife.

49. The head of the screw drivers are made up of plastic material to avoid the electric contact between the screw and the hand. So, a plastic handle is provided to avoid electric shock.

50. Area levelled in 1 s = $400\ cm^2 = 400 \times 10^{-4}\ m^2$
1 hectare = $10000\ m^2$
Time taken to level 1 hectare = $10000\ m^2 / 400 \times 10^{-4}\ m^2 = 250000\ s = 69.444\ h$
Speed = Distance / time
Distance = $\sqrt{400\ cm^2} = 20\ cm = 0.2\ m$
Hence, speed = 0.2 m/s.

51. From the question, it is clear that the handle was rotated through '4' rotations (n).
∴ $n = 4$.
The distance moved by the movable jaw per rotation = 0.5 cm.
∴ Total distance moved by the jaw = 4 × 0.5 cm = 2 cm
∴ The diameter of the rod = distance between jaws when rod is placed between them.
$d = 2$ cm
$\Rightarrow 2r = 2\ cm \Rightarrow r = 1\ cm$
∴ Radius of the rod = 1 cm

52. Length of the metal strip, (ℓ) = 1 m.
Length of the field, (ℓ^1) = 25 m
∴ The area of field which can be levelled (A) $= \ell^1 \times \ell$
= 25 m × 1m
= $25\ m^2$

53. Number of seeds sowed in 1 second = 5
Hence, the number of seeds sowed in 20 s = 20 × 5 = 100
In one row, there are 5 seeds.
∴ 100 seeds are sowed in 20 rows.

54. Number of rotations through which a handle is rotated, (n) = ?
Thickness of the metal plate, (t) = 3.5 cm.
∴ Distance moved by the jaw = thickness of plate which is held
∴ 3.5 cm = n × Distance moved by jaw per one rotation.
3.5 cm = n × 7 mm
3.5 × 10 mm = n × 7 mm
$$n = \frac{35}{7} = 5$$
∴ Number of rotations made by handle, (n) = 5

55. Area of the field which is ploughed, (A) = $45\ m^2$
the length of the metal strip = 1.5 m
∴ Area of the field ploughed = length of field ploughed × length of metal strip.

$\therefore$ 45 m^2 = $\ell \times 1.5$ m

$$\ell = \frac{45\,\text{m}^2}{1.5\,\text{m}} = 30 \text{ m}$$

Level 3: Assess Your Concepts

56. If a metallic plate is hot, we cannot take the readings by direct methods. So, we use a divider to measure it. Adjust the screw of the divider and place the pointed ends over the metallic plate and measure the distance between the two pointed nails by comparing it with a meter scale. This gives the length (ℓ) of the side.

    Now area can be determined as $A = \ell^2$

57. A tin cutter is similar to a pair of scissors, but a strong spring is fixed between the handle of one blade and the other blade. When we cut the metal by pressing the handle, the spring gets stretched, so, energy is stored in the spring. This energy of the spring is used to move the jaw apart after the operations.

58. Thickness of the given coin, t = 2.7 cm = 27 mm

    Distance moved by the vice in one complete rotation of the handle, x = 9 mm

    Hence, the total distance required to be moved = 27 mm

    Thus, the number of rotations made by the handle to fix the coin = 27 mm / 9 mm = 3

59. If we move the hack-saw blade very fast over the work piece, due to friction, the blade gets heated up and it will damage the sharpness of teeth. So, the efficiency of the blade will be reduced, and when we move it very fast over the cutting metal, there is a chance of breaking the hack-saw blade.

60. As the sharp edge is curved it can exert a higher pressure on the wooden log, and hence, it can penetrate into the wooden log.

61. Radius of the circular plate at room temperature, r_1 = 6.8 cm

    Area of the plate when heated, $A = \pi r_2^2 = 154$ cm^2

    $$\Rightarrow r_2^2 = \frac{154}{\pi} = \frac{154}{\frac{22}{7}} = 154 \times \frac{7}{22} = 49 \Rightarrow r_2 = \sqrt{49} = 7 \text{ cm}$$

    Hence, increase in the radius of the plate, $\Delta r = r_2 - r_1$ = 7 cm − 6.8 cm = 0.2 cm = 2 mm

    When the plate is hot, its radius can be measured by using a divider.

62. Vice is used to hold work pieces.

    Advantages: This tool is very useful if the wok piece small. Piece of metal is to be cut. The metal is fixed between the jaws of the vice tightly and then it can be cut easily. Vice holds the object to be worked on tightly at a position. So, the hands of the worker are free to work on the work piece.

    Disadvantages: Very thin and soft metals cannot be held on a vice. If it is soft metal, the vice change its dimension also it put some markings on the metal surface. Similarly, a work piece of bigger size cannot be held in the vice.

63. Agriculture tools are always in contact with the moisture, manure, etc., so, the chance of getting corroded is more when compared to workshop tools. The size of the agriculture tools is more than the size of workshop tools. But the weight of wood is less compared to the weight of metal. Thus, most of the parts are made up of wood.

$\therefore 45\ m^2 = \ell \times 1.5\ m$

CHAPTER

8

Our Universe

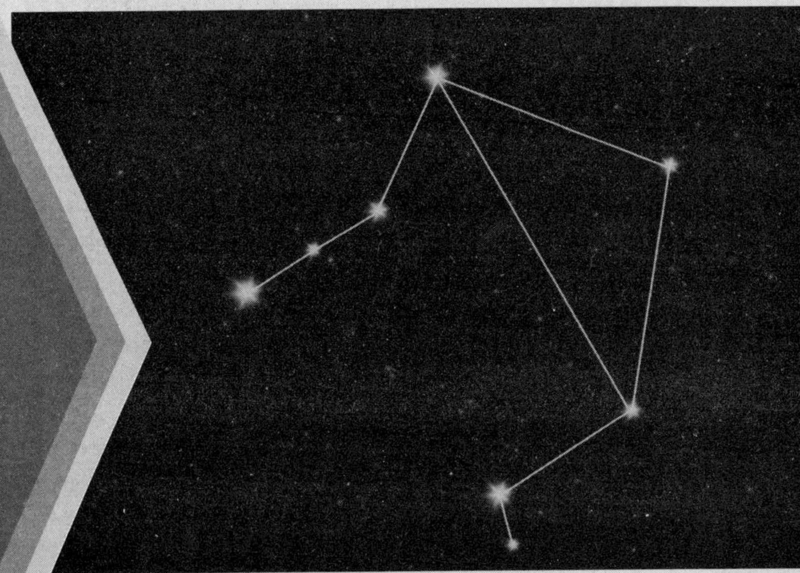

Remember

Before beginning this chapter, you should be able to:

- Define universe, galaxy, heavenly bodies, planets, starts, etc.
- Understand gravitation

Key Ideas

After completing this chapter, you should be able to:

- Explain the universal law of gravitation
- Learn applications of law of gravitation in scientific development
- Define terms, such as gravity, escape velocity, Moon's gravitation, etc.
- Study the formation of wind, storms, cyclones and tides

Scientific Crypt

A Tribute to Galileo Galilei (1564–1642)

On February 15, 1564, in Pisa, Italy, Galileo was born curious and brilliant. His musician father, Vincenzo Galilei, influenced his love of the arts and sciences. Galileo studied at Camaldolese monastery. Later, he studied medicine at Pisa University. Despite his father's reservations, he loved mathematics and natural philosophy.

Galileo's scientific journey contains remarkable discoveries and inventions. Improvements to the telescope allowed him to make unprecedented sky observations. His observations confirmed Venus's phases and Jupiter's moons, supporting the Copernican theory that the Earth orbits the Sun. He studied motion and gravity, dropping two balls of different masses from the Leaning Tower of Pisa to prove that their descent time was independent of mass.

Galileo revolutionised our understanding of the universe despite Church opposition to the heliocentric model. His careful experimental testing of hypotheses was revolutionary. We question, explore, and never stop learning because of Galileo's bravery and pursuit of truth. He proved that knowledge is noble and can change the world. Galileo symbolises curiosity, perseverance, and the infinite possibilities of the human mind as well as a brilliant scientist.

FUN TIME

CROSSWORD

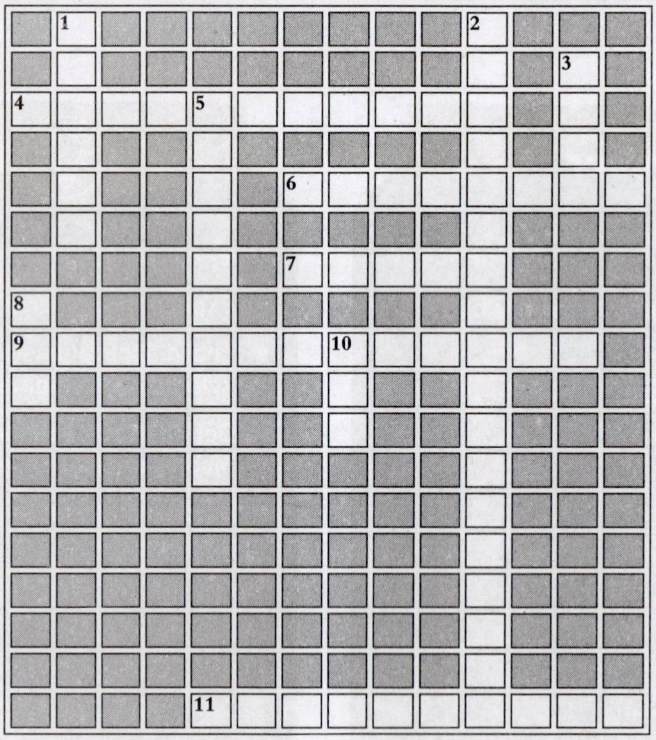

Across

4. The place from where India launched a spacecraft to the moon, for the first time.
6. The acceleration due to gravity on earth is _____ to that on the moon.
7. The Zodiac sign of a person born on the 10th of October.
9. The reason for generation of wind currents.
11. The name of the scientist who designed a barometer for the first time.

Down

1. The tides which occur on full moon day.
2. Force responsible for the formation of tides.
3. For a freely falling body, the velocity is directly proportional to _____.
5. A device used to measure the speed of wind.
8. In solar system, the maximum value of acceleration due to gravity is on _____.
10. The centre of cyclone is called _____.

INTRODUCTION

Man has been fascinated from centuries, by the movement of the heavenly bodies in the sky. Different hypotheses were put forward by a number of scientists, from time to time, to explain the motion of heavenly bodies. Notable among them were the ones put forward by Galileo, Copernicus, and Kepler. Finally, the English scientist Sir Isaac Newton succeeded in formulating the exact principle involved.

Gravitation

Sir Isaac Newton discovered that any two material bodies in the universe attract each other with a force called gravitation. He showed that it is the force of gravitation which is responsible for motion of heavenly bodies as well as certain other natural phenomena, such as the bodies getting attracted to the earth. The force of gravitation is universal as it exists every where in the universe, unaffected by the heat, pressure, electric field and magnetic field.

The Law of Gravitation

The law of gravitation states that in the universe, any two material bodies attract each other with a force which is (i) directly proportional to the product of their masses and (ii) inversely proportional to the square of the distance between them; the mutual force acts along the line joining the centres of mass of the bodies.

Here, directly proportional means the two quantities are related in such a way that if one increases (or decreases) a certain number of times, the other also increases (or decreases) the same number of times. For example, if the number of a certain kind of books one buys increases two times, then the price one has to pay also increases two times. Mathematically, the above statement is written as $N \propto P$ where, 'N' stands for the number of books and 'P' stands for price and '$\propto$' stands for proportional.

Inversely proportional means the two quantities are so related that if one of the quantities increases (or decreases) a certain number of times, the other quantity decreases (or increases) the same number of times. For example, if the number of labourers (N) required to complete a given work is doubled, the time (T) taken to complete the same work decreases the same number of times. We can write $N \propto \frac{1}{T}$.

The force of gravitation is mutual, i.e., if one body exerts a certain force on the other body, the other body also exerts the same force on the first body. If the sun attracts the earth, the earth also attracts the sun with the same attractive force.

Let the two bodies, with masses 'M' and 'm', respectively be separated by a distance 'd' as shown in the Fig. 8.1.

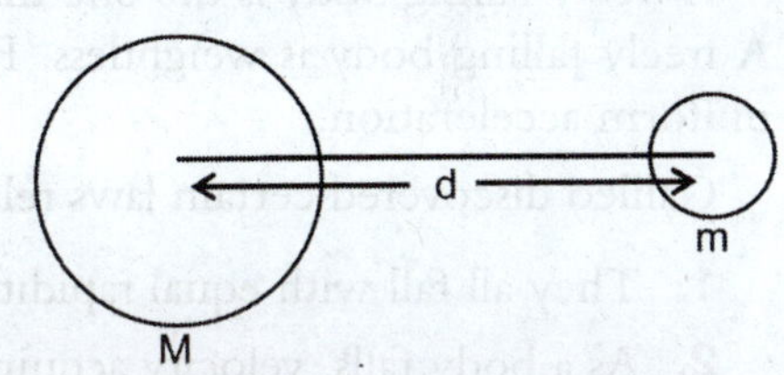

Figure 8.1 Force of attraction between two bodies

The mutual force of attraction, F, between them is:

$$F \propto M\,m \tag{8.1}$$

$$F \propto \frac{1}{d^2} \tag{8.2}$$

Combining the above two expressions,

$$F \propto \frac{Mm}{d^2} \quad \text{or} \quad F = G\frac{Mm}{d^2}$$

Where G is a constant of proportionality known as Universal Gravitational Constant.

Here, 'G' is a universal constant as it is independent of the medium surrounding the two bodies and their masses. It is also independent of external influences, such as heat, pressure, electric and magnetic field, etc.

Dependence of Gravitational Force on Mass and Distance

Force of gravitation between any two bodies is directly proportional to the product of their masses. Thus, if bodies involved have large masses, then the force of gravitation is also large. The gravitational force between earth and a body of mass 10 kg is much more than the force of gravitation between the two bodies of mass 10 kg each.

If the distance between two given bodies is halved, the force between them is quadrupled and if the distance is doubled, the force reduces to (1/4)th the initial force.

The value of G in C.G.S. system is 6.67×10^{-8} dyne cm^2 g^{-2} and in SI system, it is 6.67×10^{-11} N m^2 kg^{-2}.

Gravity

When the earth is one of the bodies involved in the force of gravitation, then the particular case of gravitation is called gravity. Thus, the gravity is defined as the force of attraction between the earth and any other body on or near it.

There is a mutual force of attraction between any body and the earth. The weight of a body is the force of attraction exerted by the earth on the body. The body exerts an equal force of attraction on the earth but as earth is huge, it does not move from its place. Instead, the body moves towards the earth, if it is free to move. Its velocity increases as it falls and a constant acceleration is produced in it which is called acceleration due to gravity denoted by '*g*'. The value of '*g*' in C.G.S system is 980 cm s^{-2} and in S.I. system, it is 9.8 m s^{-2}.

The value of '*g*' is different on different heavenly bodies. It depends on mass as well as radius of the heavenly body. In our solar system, the maximum value of 'g' is on the Sun (274.1 m s^{-2}) and minimum on Pluto (0.610 m s^{-2}). The '*g*' on moon is 1.625 m s^{-2}.

The weight of a body and '*g*' are related to each other. They are related as weight of the body = mass of the body × acceleration due to gravity.

The value of '*g*' varies from place to place on the earth. As weight depends on '*g*', it also changes from place to place on the earth. The value of '*g*' is maximum at poles (9.831 m s^{-2}) and minimum at equator (9.781 m s^{-2}).

The weight of a body of mass 1 kg is written as 1 kilogram weight or in short 1 kgwt. Similarly, the weight of body of mass 1 *g* is 1 gwt.

When different bodies are released from the same height, it appears that the lighter bodies, such as a piece of paper take longer time to reach the ground than the heavier bodies, such as a piece of stone. This happens due to air resistance. In the case of a piece of paper, air resistance is much more than its own weight whereas in the case of a piece of stone, the air resistance is less compared to its weight.

A freely falling body is the one that does not experience any force other than gravitational force, due to which it falls. A freely falling body is weightless. For the same reason, we feel our weight to be decreased in the lift descending with uniform acceleration.

Galileo discovered certain laws related to the freely falling bodies. They are as follows:

1. They all fall with equal rapidity in vacuum.
2. As a body falls, velocity acquired by it is directly proportional to the time.
3. The distance travelled is directly proportional to the square of time.

Newton, through his 'Guinea' experiment proved the 1st law, as mentioned above. He allowed a guinea and a feather to fall through a hollow glass tube, first with air in the tube and then after removing the air from the tube. It was found that with air present in the tube, the guinea fell rapidly compared to the feather and reached the bottom earlier. With air taken out and after inverting the tube, it was found that both the guinea and the feather reached the bottom at the same time, falling with equal rapidity.

Thus, in the absence of any opposing force, gravity causes all the bodies, light or heavy, to fall simultaneously, if they start from rest.

Escape Velocity

When a body is thrown vertically upwards, it is our common experience that it falls back on the earth. At large distance, earth's gravity is weak so that if the body is thrown with sufficient velocity, it may overcome force of gravity and may not fall back on the earth. Such a velocity is called escape velocity.

Thus, the escape velocity is defined as the minimum velocity which a body must acquire so that it escapes earth's gravity. The escape velocity on earth is about 11.27 km s^{-1}.

Moon's Gravitation

The value of '*g*' on the moon is (1/6)th that on the earth. The reason for small value of '*g*' on moon is due to its small mass compared to the earth's mass. Thus, a body of 6 kgwt on the earth will weigh 1 kgwt on the moon.

The Moon Has No Atmosphere

The escape velocity on moon is small due to its small mass. The velocity of gas particles is greater than the escape velocity on moon. This is the reason why there is no atmosphere on moon.

EXAMPLE 8.1 If a planet's mass is three times and its radius is half that of the Earth, then find the escape velocity of the planet.

SOLUTION

Given the escape velocity formula for Earth as:

$$v_e = \sqrt{2G \times \frac{M_e}{R_e}}$$

For the new planet with mass $3M_e$ and radius $0.5R_e$:

$$v_p = \sqrt{2G \times \frac{3M_e}{0.5R_e}}$$

$$\therefore V_p = \sqrt{12G \times \frac{M_e}{R_e}}$$

Given that $V_e = \sqrt{2G \times \frac{M_e}{R_e}}$, we can substitute:

$$V_p = \sqrt{12} \times V_e$$

$$V_p = 3.46 \times V_e$$

Thus, if the escape velocity on Earth V_e is 11.27 m/s, then the escape velocity of the planet V_p would be:

$$V_p = 3.46 \times 11.27 = 39.02 \text{ m/s}$$

Info Bytes!

The gravitational force on the moon is only about 1/6th as strong as Earth's gravity. That's why astronauts bounce around when they walk on the moon!

Tides

The level of water in the oceans rises and falls, alternatively, after 12 hours and 26 minutes. This rise and fall of water level is referred to as tides.

The tides are caused due to gravitational forces exerted by the moon and the sun on earth. The gravitational force of the sun on the earth is 46% of the gravitational force of the moon on the earth.

Other than the gravitational forces, the tides are also caused by the spinning motion of the earth about its own axis. The rotational motion of the earth gives rise to centrifugal forces, which act on every object present on the earth, in the outward direction. Under the action of centrifugal force, the objects on earth tend to fly away from the centre. They do not actually fly off due to another force, called centripetal force, which acts in a direction opposite to centrifugal force. The centripetal force is provided by the gravity.

Thus, the water particles on the earth tend to move outward due to centrifugal force. This reinforcement the cause of tides.

There are mainly two types of tides viz., high tides and low tides. Further, the high tides may be direct (or primary) and antipodal (or secondary). During the motion of earth about its own axis, say a place A faces the moon, as shown in Fig. 8.2.

The water at A gets attracted towards the moon and swells up producing a direct or primary tide at A.

The moon's attraction at antipodal position (diametrically opposite) B is weak as place B is farther away from moon. The water at B swells up producing antipodal or secondary tides, due to centrifugal force and a reaction force caused by the pull of moon on water at place A.

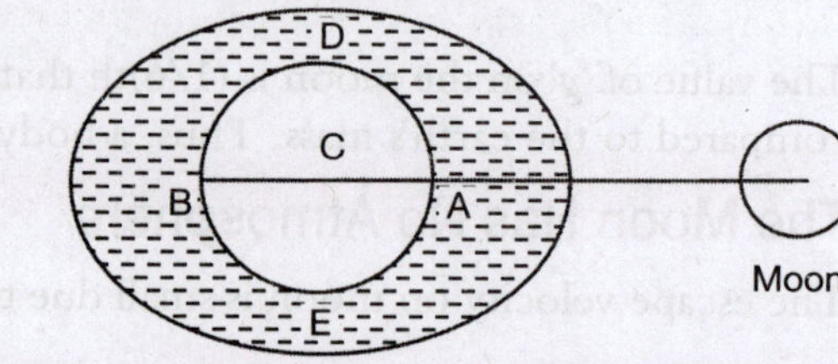

Figure 8.2 Formation of tides

As the water level at A and B rises, the water level at places D and E (See Fig. 8.2) goes down, producing low tides.

As earth completes one rotation about its own axis in 24 hours, the places A and B are interchanged after 12 hours. Thus, we expect direct tide to occur at B and antipodal tide to occur at A after 12 hours. But calculations show that the direct tide at A occurs after 12 hours and 26 minutes. Why is this so? The reason is, by the time B reaches A, the moon advances in its orbit as shown in the Fig. 8.3. It takes 26 minutes for place B to face the moon again.

Thus, the time interval between the occurrences of two successive primary or secondary tides at a given place on earth is 24 hours and 52 minutes [2 × (12 hours and 26 minutes)].

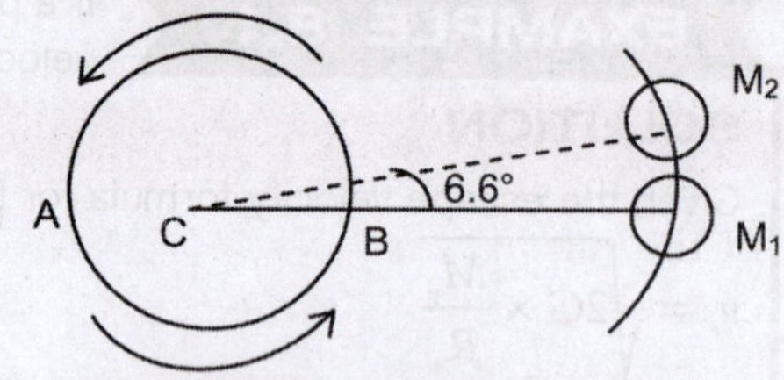

Figure 8.3 Relation between movement of earth and formation of tides

Types of Tides

1. **Spring tides:** These are high tides that occur during full moon or new moon day when sun, earth, and moon come in straight line.

   On a full moon day, the sun and the moon are present on either sides of the earth, in a straight line, as shown in the Fig. 8.4.

   Thus, the place on the earth where primary tides are produced due to moon's attraction are reinforced by secondary tides produced by sun's attraction and vice versa.

   On a new moon day, both moon and sun produce primary tides at the same place on earth as both are on the same side of earth, as shown in the Fig. 8.5.

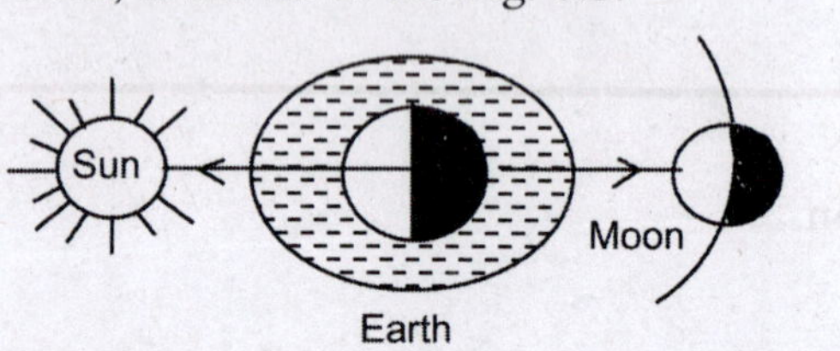

Figure 8.4 Spring tides during full moon

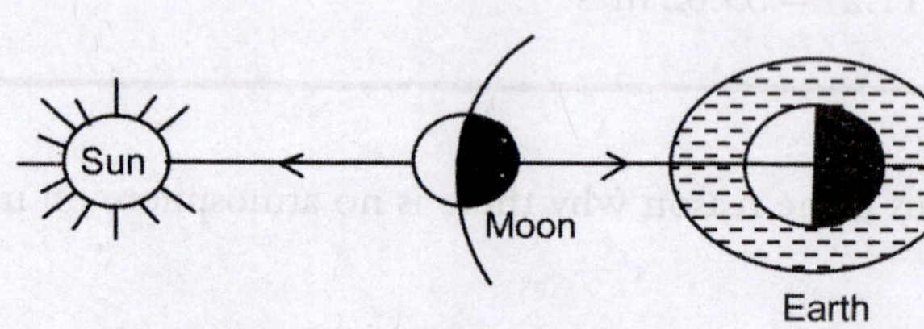

Figure 8.5 Spring tides during new moon

   The spring tides formed on a new moon day are much stronger than that formed on full moon day as water is attracted jointly by both the moon and the sun.

2. **Neap tides:** Neap tides occur when gravitational pull of moon and sun on earth are perpendicular to each other as shown in the Fig. 8.6.

   - Neap tides are low tides as the net gravitational pull on earth is small.
   - Neap tides occur during the first and the last quarter phases of moon.

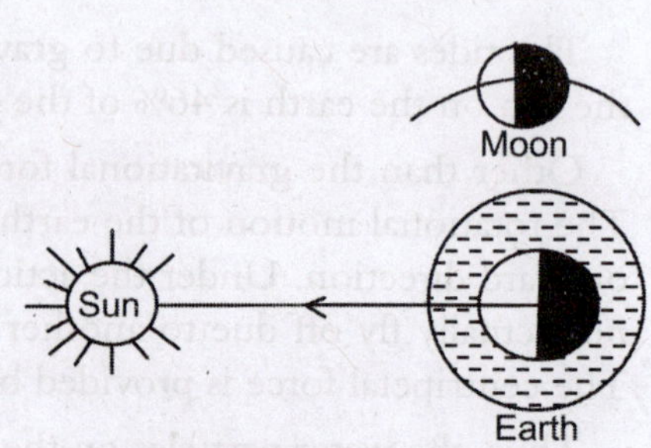

Figure 8.6 Neap tide

Tides have good as well as bad effects. The good effects of tides are as follows:

- The rivers become navigable when tidal water rushes into rivers. The wastes from rivers are flushed out by receding tidal water. This makes river water drinkable and pollution free. The fishes, such as Salmon and Hilsa lay their eggs in river water. Such fishes which climb up rivers to lay eggs are called Anadormous fishes. The tidal water helps them get in to the rivers. The fishermen catch them in rivers, in good numbers. The salt is made from sea water, when sea water rises on land during high tides. The energy of tidal waters is utilized for generating electrical energy.

- The bad effects of tides are as follows. The tidal water makes river water undrinkable since sometimes the tidal waters carry sediments and deposit them in a river so that it becomes difficult to navigate. Some times, tides make fishing difficult for fishermen and the rivers overflow due to tidal waters, damaging crops and coastal habitants.

Constellations and the Zodiac

The stars in the night sky are divided into small groups, called constellations. The ancient scholars named them after names of persons, animals or articles. In recent time, the astronomers have identified many more constellations in different regions of the sky. They are visible from different regions on earth and in different seasons. The study of these constellations is useful to identify and study other stars.

When seen from the earth, the Sun appears to be moving in the sky from east to west. The ancestors divided the path of the sun in twelve parts and named constellations present in these twelve parts according to their shape. The twelve constellations together are called zodiac whereas each constellation is called sign.

The shapes of the twelve constellations are given in Fig. 8.7.

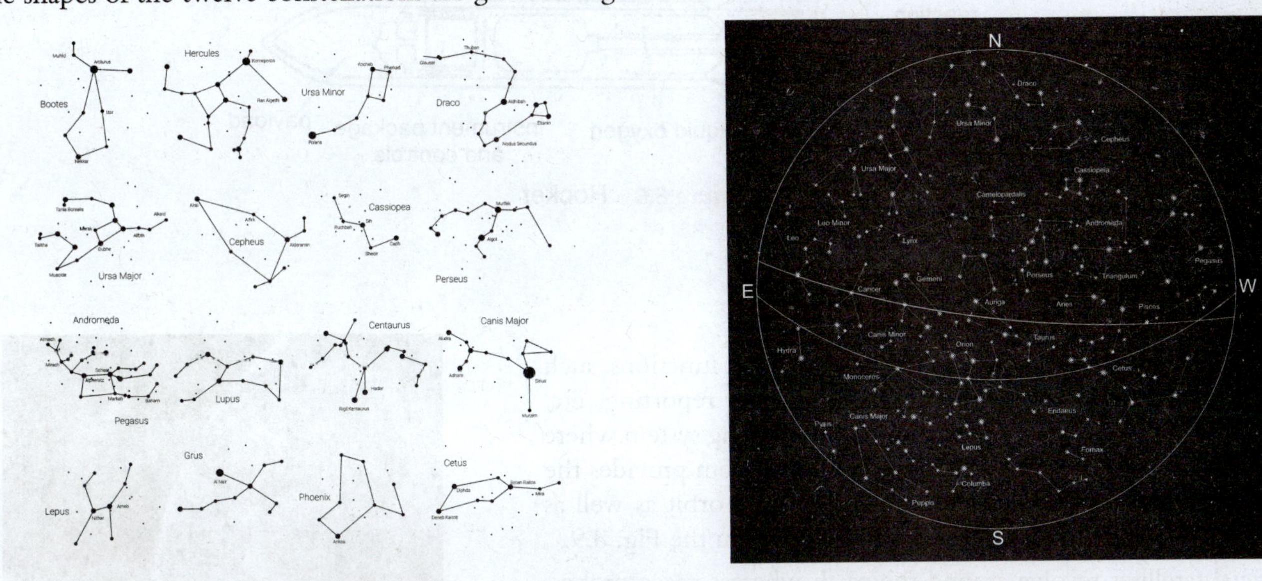

(a) (b)

Figure 8.7 (a) Constellations and (b) Signs of Zodiac

The table given below shows the time during which various constellations are visible.

Table 8.1 Visualizations of constellations

Sl. No	Constellation	Shape	Duration
1	Aries	The ram	21 Mar to 19 Apr
2	Taurus	The bull	20 Apr to 20 May
3	Gemini	The twins	21 May to 21 June
4	Cancer	The crab	22 June to 22 July
5	Leo	The lion	23 July to 22 Aug
6	Virgo	The virgin	23 Aug to 22 Sep
7	Libra	The balance	23 Sep to 23 Oct
8	Scorpion	The scorpion	24 Oct to 21 Nov
9	Sagittarius	The archer	22 Nov to 21 Dec
10	Capricorn	The crocodile	22 Dec to 19 Jan
11	Aquarius	The pot	20 Jan to 18 Feb
12	Pisces	The fish	19 Feb to 20 Mar

Info Bytes!

There are 88 recognized constellations in the night sky, and 12 of them form the zodiac signs used in astrology!

The astrologers and those who make the almanac do calculations based on the dates given in the table. Today, the astronomers have discovered eighty eight (88) constellations and the biggest of the constellations is Hydra which contains at least 78 very big stars.

Rocket

Rockets are of two types—The one used at the time of war and the other for studying atmosphere and outer space. A rocket's working is based on Newton's third law of motion according to which, for every action, there is an equal and opposite reaction. In a rocket, the gases are produced by burning fuel in the combustion chamber and the hot gases are allowed to escape through a nozzle at a great speed. The gases come out with great force which is an action. As a reaction, the gases exert an opposite force on rocket due to which rocket moves with great speed in the other direction. The various parts of the rocket are as shown in the Fig. 8.8.

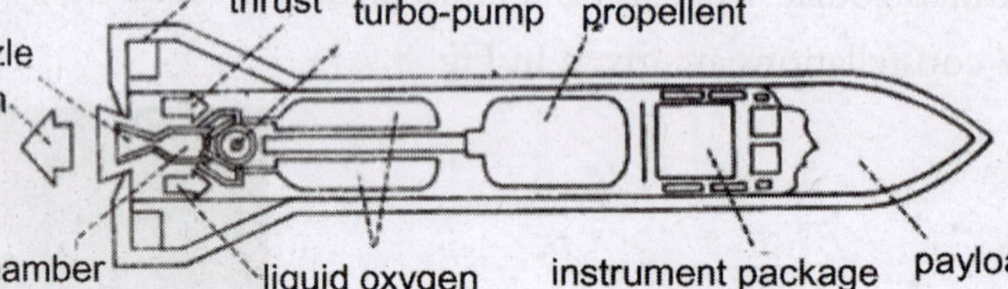

Figure 8.8 Rocket

Artificial Satellites

These are put into various orbits and perform different functions, such as communication, radio, TV transmission, weather reporting, etc. Satellites are sent into space using multi-stage launching system where different rockets are fired at different stages. This system provides the satellite to get the least speed required to reach the orbit as well as revolve in a given orbit with proper speed as shown in the Fig. 8.9.

Figure 8.9 A satellite orbiting around earth

Artificial satellites revolve around the earth whereas space probes, such as VENUS 13, VENUS 14, PIONEER 10 and VOYAGER 2 are used for studying and doing research on other planets.

Space Exploration and Mission to the Moon

Space exploration is an investigation that involves the use of astronomy and space technology to explore outer space. Astronomers use telescopes to explore space. For physical exploration, uncrewed robotic space probes and human spaceflight are used. Astronomy refers to the observation of objects in space. The advent of large and efficient rockets during the mid-20th century made physical space exploration possible. There are several reasons for exploring space, including advancing scientific research, enhancing national prestige, fostering unity among different nations, ensuring the survival of humanity, and developing military and strategic advantages over other countries.

Info Bytes!

The first human-made object to land on the Moon was the Soviet Union's Luna 2 in 1959.

Space Exploration by Astronomers

In 1609, Galileo Galilei became the first person to use a telescope to observe the motion of the planets. Later, in 1668, Isaac Newton built his own reflecting telescope, which was the first of its kind and had superior features compared to the earlier Galilean telescope. This became a landmark for future developments in the field of telescopes. Using telescopes many things were discovered like, the mountains of the Moon, the phases of Venus, the main satellites of Jupiter and Saturn, the rings of Saturn, many comets, the asteroids, the new planets Uranus and Neptune, and many more. The Orbiting Astronomical Observatory 2 was the first space telescope launched in 1968. However, the launching of the Hubble Space Telescope in 1990 marked a major milestone in the field of space exploration. As of December 1st, 2022, there have been 5,284 confirmed exoplanets discovered. It is estimated that the Milky Way contains anywhere from 100 to 400 billion stars, with over 100 billion planets. To put things into perspective, there are at least 2 trillion galaxies within the observable universe.

Physical Exploration of Space

On October 4th, 1957, the Soviet Union launched the first human-made object to orbit Earth, named Sputnik 1. Weighing approximately 83 kg and orbiting at a height of 250 km, it had two radio transmitters, emitting "beeps" that could be heard globally using radios. Analysis of these signals helped to gather information about the ionosphere's electron density, temperature, and pressure.

The Soviet space program achieved numerous milestones, such as launching the first living being into orbit in 1957 and sending Yuri Gagarin, the first human in space, aboard Vostok 1 in 1961. The spacecraft travelled around the globe once, completing the journey in approximately 1 hour and 48 minutes. Other notable accomplishments include the first spacewalk by Alexei Leonov on March 18th, 1965, the first automatic landing on a celestial body in 1966, and the launch of the first space station, Salyut 1, in 1971.

The first artificial object to reach another celestial body was 'Luna 2' reaching the Moon in 1959. The first soft landing on another celestial body was performed by Luna 9 landing on the Moon on 3 February 1966. Luna 10 became the first artificial satellite of the Moon, entering a lunar orbit on 3 April 1966. The first crewed landing on another celestial body was performed by Apollo 11 on 20 July 1969, landing on the Moon. After 20 years of exploration, the focus shifted from one-off flights to renewable hardware such as the Space Shuttle program, and from competition to cooperation with the International Space Station (ISS).

Space Station

A space station is a spacecraft orbiting Earth where crew members can live for extended periods to conduct experiments as part of space exploration. Salyut 1 was the first space station of any kind, launched into low Earth orbit by the Soviet Union on 19 April 1971. The International Space Station is currently the largest and oldest of the two space stations currently fully functional space stations, inhabited continuously since the year 2000. The other, Tiangong space station built by China, is now fully crewed and operational.

The International Space Station (ISS) is the largest modular space station orbiting the Earth at a low altitude. The first component of ISS was launched in 1998. It is a joint project of five space agencies - NASA from the United States, Roscosmos from Russia, JAXA from Japan, ESA from Europe, and CSA from Canada. The ownership and use of the space station are governed by intergovernmental treaties and agreements. The ISS is a research laboratory where scientific research is conducted in fields such as astrobiology, astronomy, meteorology, physics, and others, taking advantage of microgravity and space environment. It is an ideal platform for testing spacecraft systems and equipment that may be required for future long-duration missions to the Moon and Mars.

The crew on board the International Space Station (ISS) provides various opportunities for students on Earth. They run student-developed experiments, demonstrate educational activities, allow for student participation in classroom versions of ISS experiments, and directly engage with students through radio and email. ESA (European Space Agency) offers free teaching materials that can be downloaded and used in classrooms. In one of the lessons, students can navigate a 3D model of the interior and exterior of the ISS and face spontaneous challenges in real time that they must solve.

Mission to the Moon

The Moon has the distinction of being the first celestial object to be explored by humans. It was the first remote celestial object in history to be flown by, orbited, and landed upon by spacecraft. Since the mid-20th century, uncrewed spacecraft have been sent into orbit around other planets such as Saturn, Jupiter, Mars, Venus, and Mercury. As part of human exploration of the Moon, numerous space missions have been undertaken to study Earth's natural satellite. Luna 2, a spacecraft of the Soviet Union, was the first to reach the Moon's surface successfully. In total, six crewed missions were conducted by the United States to land humans on the Moon as part of the Apollo program between 1968 and 1972. Apollo 8 was the first crewed mission to enter orbit in December 1968, followed by Apollo 10 in May 1969. Finally, Apollo 11 landed humans on the Moon in July 1969, where Neil Armstrong became the first person to walk on the Moon.

India's Mission to the Moon

Numerous countries continue to explore the Moon through unmanned missions, with occasional deployments of lunar orbiters. In 2008, India's national space agency, the Indian Space Research Organisation (ISRO), developed the Indian Moon Impact Probe (MIP). The MIP was a lunar probe that was released by the Chandrayaan-1 lunar remote sensing orbiter, also developed by ISRO, which was launched on 22 October 2008. The spacecraft carried high-resolution remote sensing equipment for visible, near-infrared, and soft and hard X-ray frequencies. Its primary goal was to survey the lunar surface and produce a complete map of its chemical characteristics and three-dimensional topography. The polar regions were of special interest as they may have possible ice deposits. The mission lasted for 312 days, during which Chandrayaan-1 provided valuable insights into the Moon's surface.

On 22 July 2019, India launched the Chandrayaan-2 mission, which was the second mission to the Moon. The mission comprised an orbiter, a lander, and a rover. The GSLV Mk III rocket was used for the launch. The spacecraft had three components, a lunar orbiter, the Vikram lander, and the Pragyan lunar rover, all of which were developed in India. The mission was aimed at exploring the lunar south pole region, which had not been explored. The main purpose of the Chandrayaan-2 mission was to land a robotic rover on the Moon's surface to conduct various studies. The Vikram lander, carrying the Pragyan rover, was supposed to land on the near side of the Moon, in the south polar region on 7 September 2019. Unfortunately, the lander deviated from its intended trajectory and the telemetry was lost just before touchdown. India made its second attempt to soft-land on the Moon with the Chandryaan-3 mission, following the partial failure of Chandrayaan-2. This mission involved only a lander-rover set, which will communicate with the orbiter from the previous mission. On August 23, 2023, the Indian Space Research Organisation (ISRO) became the first space agency to successfully land a spacecraft on the lunar south pole region. This achievement also made ISRO the fourth space agency in history to successfully land on the Moon.

Mission to the Mars

The exploration of Mars has been an important aspect of space programs for several countries including the Soviet Union (later Russia), the United States, Europe, Japan, and India. Since the 1960s, dozens of robotic spacecraft such as orbiters, landers, and rovers have been launched towards Mars, with the aim of gathering data about current conditions and answering questions about the planet's history. The scientific community has raised several questions, and the answers to these questions are expected to provide not only a better understanding of Mars but also further insights into the past and possible future of Earth.

Info Bytes!

ISRO, the Indian Space Research Organization, made global headlines with its Mars Orbiter Mission (Mangalyaan) in 2014, making India the first Asian nation to reach Martian orbit.

Winds, Storms, and Cyclones

The Earth is surrounded by an envelope of air. The air covers the earth and extends up to 1000 km from its surface. We call this air cover atmosphere. The atmospheric gases consist of molecules of different gases. The whole weight of these gases act on earth's surface. Because of its weight atmospheric air exerts pressure.

How can we conclude that air exerts pressure? Take a metallic container that is half filled with water. Heat the container for some time and then place a cap on the container firmly. What happens to the shape of the container if it is cooled to very low temperatures? As the container is cooled, some steam in the container condenses into water and reduces the pressure inside the container. The container gets compressed because of the pressure exerted by the air from outside the container.

The pressure exerted by atmospheric air is called atmospheric pressure. Barometer is a device used to find the atmospheric pressure. Torricelli was the first scientist to design a barometer to measure atmospheric pressure and it is known as Torricelli's barometer.

Construction of a Barometer

Take a glass tube closed at one end and of a narrow uniform bore of diameter 1 cm and length of 1 m. Fill the glass tube with pure and dry mercury carefully so that no air bubbles are trapped inside and cover the open end with the thumb. Place the tube inverted in a trough containing mercury and remove the thumb. Certain amount of mercury in the tube falls down into the trough leaving an empty space above the surface of mercury column, known as 'Torricellian vacuum'. When mercury column is positioned vertically, the pressure exerted by it is equal to the atmospheric pressure. The height of the mercury column in the barometer gives the atmospheric pressure at that place. Usually, at sea level, the height of mercury column is 76 cm. we can say that the atmospheric pressure at sea level is 76 cm of mercury. Atmospheric pressure decreases with an increase in altitude.

Uses of Barometer

1. Barometer is used to find the atmospheric pressure at a place.
2. It can also be used as altimeter, to know the height of a place above sea level.
3. By observing the variations in atmospheric pressure with the help of a barometer, rainfall and arrival of storms can be forecasted.

Wind

Moving air is called wind.

Is the air pressure the same at all places? No the air pressure at different places on the surface of the earth is different due to differences in temperatures at these places. Because of change in pressure, air moves from one place to another place. Air moves from a region of high pressure to a region of low pressure. The greater the difference in pressure, the faster the air moves.

Most of the substances, including air, expands on heating and contracts on cooling. When they expand, their volume increases and they occupy more space. As a result, the density of the substance decreases.

Air also expands on heating. Expanded air occupies more space and becomes lighter. The warm air is lighter than the cold air. So, warm air moves up and cold air moves down.

Why does smoke always rise up? Why are exhaust fans fixed high on the walls of a room? Smoke is warm and lighter, and hence goes up. Exhaled warm air moves up in a room, and exhaust fans push it out making way for fresh air to enter the room.

In nature there are several situations where warm air rises at a place. The air pressure at that place is lowered. The cold air from the surrounding area rushes in to fill its place. This sets up convection currents in air. Wind currents are generated due to uneven heating on the earth.

The equator receives maximum heat from the sun and the air present at equator gets heated and moves upwards, cooler air moves in from the regions 0° to 30° latitude belt present on either side of equator. The warm air at these latitudes moves upwards and the cold air from the poles moves in. The movement of these winds are effected by the rotation of the earth.

Monsoon

A monsoon is a seasonal prevailing wind which lasts for several months. In summer, the land near the equator warms up faster and for most of the time the temperature of the land is higher than that of the water in the oceans. This produces winds carrying water vapour to flow from above the oceans toward the land and bring rain.

These winds are called monsoon winds. In winter, the direction of the wind gets reversed from the land to the ocean. These colder winds carry little water, hence bring small amount of rain water.

Thunderstorms

A storm of heavy rain accompanied by lightening, thunder, wind, and sometimes hail is called thunderstorm. In hot, humid tropical regions, thunderstorms are very common. The temperature is high at these places, because of this strong upward rising winds are produced. These winds carry water droplets along with them. When they freeze and fall down, the swift movement of the falling water droplets along with the rising air create lightning and sound.

Precautions to Be Taken During Thunderstorm Accompanied by Lightning

1. Avoid taking shelter under tall isolated trees.
2. A vehicle with closed windows is a safe place to take shelter.
3. Avoid sitting near a window.
4. Shelter under an umbrella with a metallic end, open garages, metal sheds are not safe places.
5. Do not stay in water during lightning. Come out of water and stay inside the building.

Cyclone

Cyclone is a violent rotating windstorm when water vapour in the atmosphere condenses to rain drops, it releases heat into the atmosphere and warms the air around. This warm air tends to move up and causes a drop in pressure. Then more and more cool air rushes in towards the centre of the storm. Some times the events end with the formation of a very low pressure system with very high speed winds revolving around it. This weather condition forms a cyclone.

Factors that contribute to the development of cyclone are wind speed, wind direction, temperature, humidity, etc. The centre of a cyclone, is called eye which is a calm area of diameter 10 to 30 km. It is a region free of clouds and has light winds. Large cyclone contains a violently rotating mass of air about 10 to 15 km high from the ground. Around the eye there is a clouded region of about 150 km in size where high speed winds and thick clouds along with heavy rain exist.

Destruction Caused by Cyclones

The destruction caused by cyclones is immense. The low pressure existing in the eye can lift water surface as high as 3–12 metre. As a result, low lying coastal areas are filled with the ocean water. Continuous heavy rain fall and high speed winds can cause severe loss to life and property.

If roofs of buildings are weak and high speed winds blew over these roofs, then the roofs could be lifted and blown away. What makes the roof be blown away? This happens when high speed winds are blowing above the roof of a building; air pressure above the roof gets reduced. The air pressure inside the building is much more than the air pressure above the roof. This difference in air pressure makes the roof be blown away. In general, increased wind speed is accompanied by a reduced air pressure.

Place a paper on a table and blow air from one side to the other side over the paper. Will the paper rise above the table or is it pressed to the table? We observe the paper rising above the table.

Let us take two ping-pong balls and hang them on a stick such that they are 10–12 cm apart. Blow air through the space between the balls. Will they move closer to each other or move away from each other? They move closer to each other.

With the help of these examples, we can conclude that high speed wind is always accompanied by a reduced air pressure.

Tornadoes

A tornado is a dark funnel shaped cloud that reaches from the sky to the ground. The diameter of a tornado can be between one metre to 1 kilometre. Usually tornadoes are weak, but a violent tornado moves with a speed of about 300 km h^{-1}. Because of low pressure, the funnel of a tornado sucks dust, debris and everything near it at the base and throws them out near the top.

Storms and cyclones are low pressure systems. Wind speed plays an important role in the formation of storms. A device called anemometer is used to measure the speed of wind. Meteorological department, with the help of satellites and radars, makes a forecast of the arrival of cyclones and warns the people. In case of any expected storm, a cyclone alert or a cyclone watch is issued 48 hours in advance and 24 hour in advance, a cyclone warning is issued. This helps the government and the people to take necessary safety measures.

People living in cyclone prone areas should not ignore the warnings issued by the meteorology department and be well prepared to meet the situation. If we are in a cyclone hit area, we should not drink contaminated water, touch wet switches and power lines and go out for the sake of fun. We should cooperate fully with other members in our neighbourhood and concerned authorities to meet the situation in a planned manner.

Floatation and Density

The density of water is 1 g cm^{-3}. Some substances have densities less than that of water while others have densities more than that of water. The density of wood, cork, petrol, kerosene, vegetable oil, etc., is less than the density of water whereas the density of iron, gold, silver, stone, glass, etc., is greater than that of water.

The substances whose densities are greater than that of water sink into water whereas those substances whose densities are less than that of water, float on water.

When a solid of density lesser than the density of liquids is placed over surfaces of different liquids, it is found that it immerses more in a liquid of smaller density and it immerses lesser and lesser as the density of the liquid increases.

There is a change in the density of sea water due to a change in temperature at different geographic locations and also due to addition of fresh water. This poses a serious threat to the ships. The density of sea water is greater than the density of fresh water. Thus, a ship that moves from a higher density to a lower density region of the sea may sink. For safety considerations, all the ships have markings on their hull to show how much they can be submerged, at a given location.

S.I. unit: kg/m^3

$$1\ kg/m^3 = 10^{-3}\ g/cm^3$$

$$1\ g/cm^3 = 1000\ kg/m^3 \text{ (For Water)}$$

POINTS TO REMEMBER

- Any two material bodies in the universe attract each other with a force called gravitational force.
- Newton's universal law of gravitation states that every body in the universe attracts every other body with a force (*F*) which is directly proportional to the product of their masses and inversely proportional to the square of the distance (*d*) between them.

$$F \propto \frac{M_1 M_2}{d^2}, F = G\frac{M_1 M_2}{d^2}$$

Where G is the universal gravitational constant.

- The weight (*W*) of a body is the force of attraction exerted by the earth on the body.

$$W = m \times g$$

Where *m* is the mass of the body and *g* is the acceleration due to gravity.

The value of *g* on the surface of earth is 980 cm s^{-2} or 9.8 m s^{-2}.

- The value of '*g*' varies from place to place on the earth. The value of *g* is maximum at the poles (9.831 m s^{-2})and minimum at the equator (9.781 m s^{-2}).
- Substances whose density is greater than the density of water, sink in water, whereas substances whose density is less than the density of water, float in water.
- (i) All bodies falling freely and starting from rest, fall with equal rapidity in vacuum.
  (ii) As the body falls, velocity acquired by it is directly proportional to the time of fall.
  (iii) The distance travelled by a freely falling body is directly proportional to the square of time of fall.
- (i) Escape velocity is the minimum velocity which a body must acquire so that it can escape from the earth's gravity.
  (ii) The escape velocity on the earth is 11.27 km s^{-1}.
- The value of acceleration due to gravity (*g*) on the moon is $\frac{1}{6}$ times the value of *g* on the earth.
- (i) Density = $\frac{\text{mass}}{\text{volume}}$.
  (ii) Density of water is 1 g cm^{-3}.
- Barometer is used to measure the atmospheric pressure, the height of mercury column near the sea level will be 76 cm.

PRACTICE QUESTIONS CLASSROOM WING

Very Short Answer Type Questions

Directions for questions from 1 to 25: **For each of the questions, four choices have been provided. Select the correct alternative.**

1. The escape velocity on the surface of the moon is small because ______.
   (a) The moon's gravitational pull is small
   (b) The moon has no atmosphere
   (c) The moon is not a planet
   (d) The moon is revolving around the earth

2. The value of escape velocity on the surface of the earth is ______.
   (a) 11.27 m s^{-1} (b) 11.27 mile s^{-1}
   (c) 7 m s^{-1} (d) 7 mile s^{-1}

3. The time interval between two successive primary and secondary tides at a place is more than 12 hours because ______.
   (a) Of the rotation of earth about its axis
   (b) The moon also moves round the earth in the same direction of the earth's rotation
   (c) The moon also moves round the earth in the opposite direction of the earth's rotation
   (d) The earth revolves round the sun

4. Spring tides occur during ______ .
   (a) A full-moon day
   (b) A new-moon day
   (c) The first and last quarter phases of the moon
   (d) Both (a) and (b)

5. Two bodies of masses 'm' and $2m$ are separated by a distance 'd'. The body of mass 'm' attracts another body of mass $2m$ with a force F, then the body of mass $2m$ attracts m with the force of ________.
   (a) F (b) $2F$
   (c) $\frac{F}{2}$ (d) $3F$

6. Which of the following is incorrect about the value of g?
   (a) The value of 'g' is different on different heavenly bodies.
   (b) It depends on mass as well as radius of the heavenly body.
   (c) In our solar system, the maximum value of 'g' is on the Pluto (274.1 m s^{-2}).
   (d) None

7. Two identical solid spheres each of radius 'r' are in contact with each other. If the gravitational attraction between them is F, then which of the following relations is correct?
   (a) $F \propto \frac{1}{r}$ (b) $F \propto \frac{1}{r^2}$
   (c) $F \propto \frac{1}{r^3}$ (d) $F \propto \frac{1}{r^4}$

8. The gravitational effect of which of the following causes tides in the sea?
   (a) Jupiter (b) Sun
   (c) Moon (d) Both (b) and (c)

9. The mass of a planet is double the mass of the earth and its radius is half of that of the earth. If F is the force of attraction on an object on the surface of earth, then the force of attraction on the same object on the surface of that planet is ________.
   (a) $2F$ (b) $4F$
   (c) $\frac{F}{2}$ (d) $8F$

10. A ball is dropped from a height of 10 m, as it falls,
   (a) Its velocity increases and acceleration decreases.
   (b) Its velocity decreases and acceleration increases.
   (c) Its velocity increases and acceleration remains constant.
   (d) Its velocity and acceleration remains constant.

11. A barometer can be used to determine the ______ of a particular place.
   (a) Temperature (b) Humidity
   (c) Altitude (d) None of these

12. If the mass of a body on the surface of moon is denoted by M_m and that on the earth by M_e, then
   (a) $M_m = \frac{M_e}{6}$ (b) $M_m = 6\,M_e$
   (c) $M_m = \frac{Me}{2}$ (d) $M_m = M_e$

13. The acceleration due to gravity on the surface of earth depends upon the
(a) Mass of the earth (b) Mass of the body
(c) Both (a) and (b) (d) None of these

14. Which of the following statement(s) is/are wrong?
(a) The mass of a moving object in the earth's atmosphere is zero.
(b) The weight of an object at rest on the earth's surface can be zero.
(c) The weight of a moving object in the earth's atmosphere can be 2 times its weight, when it is at rest on the earth's surface.
(d) All of the above

15. Two identical spheres of radius 2 cm and mass 1 kg are placed 1 cm apart on the surface of the earth. Then,
(a) The two spheres move towards each other.
(b) The two spheres move away from each other.
(c) There is no force of attraction between the two spheres.
(d) None of these

16. Which of the following statements is correct?
(a) The value of '*g*' on the moon is (1/6)th that on the earth.
(b) The reason for small value of '*g*' on moon is due to its small mass compared to the earth's mass.
(c) Thus, a body of 6 kgwt on the earth will weigh 1 kgwt on the moon.
(d) All of these

17. The gravitational constant depends upon
(a) The size of the bodies
(b) The mass of the bodies
(c) Distance between the bodies
(d) None of these

18. Arrange the following steps in a sequence involved in the working of a rocket.
(A) Gases are produced when the fuel in the combustion chamber is burnt.
(B) The gases come out with great force which is an action.
(C) The hot gases are allowed to escape through a nozzle.
(D) Due to this, the rocket moves with great speed in the other direction.
(E) As a reaction, the gases exert an opposite force on rocket.
(a) ACBED (b) AECBD
(c) BEACD (d) CABED

19. Write the following steps of an experiment in a sequence to conclude that atmospheric air exerts pressure.
(A) Stop heating the container and cool it to very low temperatures.
(B) Take a metallic container that is half filled with water.
(C) The container gets compressed because of the pressure exerted by the air from outside the container.
(D) Heat the container for some time and place a cap on the container firmly.
(a) DBCA (b) BDAC
(c) DABC (d) BADC

20. Write the following steps involved in the formation of thunderstorms, in a sequential order.
(A) These winds carry water droplets along with them.
(B) When they freeze and fall down, the swift movement of the falling water droplets along with rising air create lightning and sound.
(C) As the temperature is high in hot, humid tropical regions, strong upward rising winds are produced.
(a) BAC (b) BCA
(c) CAB (d) CBA

21. Match the following.

	Column A		Column B
A.	Spring tides	a.	Occur when the gravitational pull of the moon and sun on the earth are perpendicular to each other
B.	Constellation	b.	Chandrayan – 1
C.	Artificial Satellites	c.	Hydra
D.	Neap tides	d.	Occur during full moon day

(a) A → d, B → c, C → b, D → a
(b) A → c, B → d, C → b, D → a
(c) A → a, B → b, C → c, D → d
(d) A → b, B → d, C → a, D → c

22. **Assertion (A):** If the distance between two given bodies is halved, the force between them is quadrupled.
Reason (R): In the universe, any two material bodies attract each other with a force which is inversely proportional to the square of the distance between them.

(a) Both (A) and (R) are correct and (R) is the correct explanation of (A).

(b) Both A and R are correct but R is not the correct explanation of A.

(c) A is correct and R is incorrect.

(d) Both A and R are incorrect.

23. Two objects A and B of masses 2 kg and 20 kg are dropped from a height of 10 m simultaneously. Then

(a) Both A and B experience same gravitational force.

(b) The accelerations of both A and B are same.

(c) Both A and B reach the ground simultaneously.

(d) Both (b) and (c).

24. **Assertion (A):** Weight of a body on the Jupiter will be more than that on the Earth.

Reason (R): Weight of a body on the Earth is the force with which a body is attracted towards the Earth.

(a) Both (A) and (R) are correct and (R) is the correct explanation of (A).

(b) Both A and R are correct but R is not the correct explanation of A.

(c) A is correct and R is incorrect.

(d) Both A and R are incorrect.

25. The gravitational force of the earth on a freely falling ball of mass one kilogram is 9.8 N. The acceleration of the earth towards the ball is

(a) 9.8 m s^{-2}.

(b) Negligible

(c) Slightly less than 9.8 m s^{-2}

(d) More than 9.8 m s^{-2}

Directions for questions from 26 to 28: **Match the entries given in Column A with the appropriate ones in Column B.**

26.

Column A	Column B
A. Full moon day	a. Newton's third law
B. New moon day	b. Less stronger spring tide
C. Rocket	c. Strong spring tide
D. Outward direction	d. Generation of electricity
E. Tidal energy	e. Centrifugal force

27.

Column A	Column B
A. Neap tides	a. 11.27 km s^{-1}
B. Escape velocity on earth	b. Full moon day or new moon day
C. Spring sides	c. First and last quarter phases of moon

28.

Column A	Column B
A. Gravitational force	a. 6.67×10^{-11} N m^2 kg^{-2}
B. Universal gravitational constant (G)	b. Attractive in nature
C. Acceleration due to gravity at the poles	c. Anemometer
D. Acceleration due to gravity at the equator	d. Wind
E. Wind speed	e. Atmospheric pressure
F. Change in air pressure	f. 9.831 m s^{-2}
G. Barometer	g. 9.781 m s^{-2}

Directions for questions from 29 to 52: **Answer the following questions.**

29. What happens to the pressure when the speed of air is increased?

30. What is a tornado?

31. What is 'anemomter'?

32. Why are wind currents generated?

33. What is gravitation?

34. What is weight of a body?

35. What is a freely falling body?

36. What is acceleration due to gravity? What is its average value?

37. In which duration, constellation Aries is seen?

38. What is the time interval between two successive tides at a given place on the earth?

39. What is the value of escape velocity on the earth?

40. When does a solid float in a given liquid? When does it sink?

41. Till now, how many constellations have been discovered? Name the biggest of the constellations.

42. What is the difference between 'air' and 'wind'?

43. What is gravity? Does it change from place to place?

44. Define escape velocity.

45. What is the ratio of acceleration due to gravity on earth to moon?

46. What are constellations?

47. Name the device used to find the atmospheric pressure.

48. What is torricellian vacuum?

49. (a) Two bodies A and B fall freely from heights h_1 and h_2, respectively, where, $h_1 > h_2$. Which body will take more time to reach the ground? Explain.

(b) What is the weight of a body on the moon whose weight is 12 kgwt on the earth?

50. When a solid body is placed over the surface of a liquid A, half of its volume gets immersed in it. When the same body is made to float on liquid B, one-fourth of its volume is seen above the surface of the liquid. Explain.

51. What are the precautions to be taken during thunder-storm accompanied by lightning?

52. What are monsoon winds?

Short Answer Type Questions

53. What are neap tides? Explain the formation of neap tides.

54. If mass and radius of the Earth are double those of a planet, then acceleration due to gravity on the surface of the planet is ______ of its value on the Earth.

55. What happens to a ship that moves from a high density region to a low density region of the sea? Explain.

56. The force existing between two masses is *F*. If one of the masses is reduced to one-fourth and the distance between them is halved, then the new force between them is ______.

57. (a) What are the destructions caused by cyclones?

(b) What happens when high speed winds blow over the roofs of the buildings that are weak?

58. A body is placed over the surfaces of two liquids of densities d_1 and d_2 ($d_1 > d_2$) separately. If the density of the object is less than both the liquids, in which liquid the body immerses more?

59. What are the weather conditions that lead to the formation of a cyclone?

60. If the mass of a planet is half that of the earth and the radius of the planet is equal to that of earth, then calculate the ratio of acceleration due to gravity of earth to that of the planet.

61. The difference between the weights of a body on the earth and on the planet of acceleration due to gravity $\frac{1}{4}$ of that of earth is 10 N. If the acceleration due to gravity on earth surface is 10 m s^{-2}, the mass of the body is ______.

62. Explain why do we feel that our weight is decreased in a lift descending with uniform acceleration.

63. What are the functions of artificial satellites?

64. What are the bad effects of tides?

Essay Type Questions

65. What are spring tides? Why are they formed? Explain.

66. Explain the working of a rocket.

67. A body dropped from a height of 5 m, reaches the ground in 1 s. If it takes 2 s to reach the ground, find the height from which it is dropped.

68. A body is dropped from a certain height and it reaches the ground in 2 s. Another body which has twice the mass as that of the first body, when dropped reaches the ground in 4 s. Find the ratio of velocities acquired by them when they reach the ground.

69. Explain the construction of a barometer.

70. State and explain the law of gravitation.

71. What are tides? Discuss the causes of the occurence of tides.

72. State the laws of freely falling bodies and describe Newton's 'guinea and feather' experiment. What is the inference drawn from the experiment?

PRACTICE QUESTIONS COMPETITION WING

Level 1: Apply your Concepts

***Directions for questions from 1 to 16:* Fill in the blanks.**

1. The constellation ______ has the shape of balance.
2. The value of escape velocity on the Earth is ______.
3. For a freely falling body, its acceleration ________ as it falls.
4. For a freely falling body the distance covered is directly proportional to the ________.
5. Development of cyclone depends on the wind ________ and ________.
6. At higher altitudes the height of mercury column in a barometer will be ______.
7. If the distance between two given bodies is halved, then the force between them is ______.
8. Low pressure system with very high speed wind revolving around it is known as a ________.
9. When water vapour in the atmosphere condenses to raindrops it releases ________.
10. Wind currents are generated due to ________ on the earth.
11. The constellation ________ is seen between 22 December and 19 January.
12. The gravitational force of attraction between any two objects is directly proportional to the product of their ________.
13. Newton's law of gravitation is called ________ law of gravitation.
14. The minimum velocity which a body must acquire so that it escapes from the gravity of a planet is ________.
15. To break the mud rocks on the surface of the soil, ________ can be used.
16. Constellation Aquarius has the shape of ________.

***Directions for questions from 17 to 22:* State whether the following statements are true or false.**

17. There exists an attractive force between any two bodies on the earth.
18. For a freely falling body the distance covered is directly proportional to the square of time.
19. Gravitational force is affected by the temperature and pressure.
20. A body on the surface of the earth attracts the earth with a force equal to its weight.
21. The constellation Aries has the shape of a bull.
22. Venus-13 is an artificial satellite.

***Directions for questions from 23 to 52:* For each of the questions, four choices have been provided. Select the correct alternative.**

23. The Moon has no atmosphere because ______
    (a) Acceleration due to gravity on the surface of the moon is greater than that on the surface of the earth.
    (b) It is far away from the earth.
    (c) It is not a planet.
    (d) The escape velocity on its surface is very small.
24. Which of the following statements about the gravitational constant is true?
    (a) It has no units.
    (b) It has the same value in all systems of units.
    (c) Its value depends upon the mass of the body.
    (d) Its value does not depend upon the nature of the medium in which the object is placed.
25. The gravitational force of earth on a ball is 10 N then the gravitational force of attraction of the ball on the earth is ______.
    (a) 10 N (b) Zero
    (c) Slightly less than 10 N (d) More than 10 N
26. If the distance between two given bodies is halved, then the force of attraction between them
    (a) Is halved. (b) Is quadrupled.
    (c) Becomes twice. (d) Remains constant.
27. A man is carrying a load equal to half of his weight (W) on his head. If he jumps from roof of a building, during his fall the weight experienced by the man will be ______
    (a) $\frac{W}{2}$ (b) $\frac{3W}{2}$
    (c) $2W$ (d) Zero

28. The value of acceleration due to gravity on the surface of moon is ______ m s^{-2}.
(a) 274.1 (b) 0.610
(c) 9.81 (d) 1.625

29. A piece of paper and a cricket ball are dropped from a particular height. The piece of paper has taken a longer time to reach the ground than the cricket ball because
(a) Weight of the ball is more than the weight of the paper.
(b) Acceleration due to gravity is more on the ball compare to that on the paper.
(c) Air resistance is more on the paper and is not negligible as compared to its weight.
(d) Both (b) and (c)

30. A ball is dropped from a particular height, the velocity acquired by it is,
(a) Directly proportional to the time of fall.
(b) Directly proportional to the square of the time of fall.
(c) Directly proportional to mass of the body.
(d) Both (a) and (c)

31. Which of the following factors contribute(s) to the development of cyclones?
(a) Humidity (b) Wind direction
(c) Temperature (d) All of the above

32. The height of mercury column of a barometer at the sea level is ______.
(a) 76 m (b) 76 cm
(c) 1 m (d) 0.76 mm

33. Sudden fall in the height of mercury column in a barometer forecast the occurrence of ______.
(a) Rain (b) Storms
(c) Normal weather (d) Sea breeze

34. The change in the density of sea water is due to
(a) Change in temperature
(b) Addition of fresh water
(c) Density is independent of external factors.
(d) Both (a) and (b)

35. Write the following steps in a sequence in the construction of a barometer.
(A) Fill the glass tube with pure and dry mercury carefully so that no air bubbles are trapped inside.
(B) Place the tube inverted in a trough containing mercury and remove the thumb.
(C) Take a glass tube closed at one end and a narrow uniform bore of diameter 1 cm and of length of 1 m.
(D) Cover the open end with the thumb.
(a) ABCD (b) ADCB
(c) CADB (d) CDAB

36. Arrange the following steps in a sequence involved in the formation of a cyclone.
(A) The water vapour in the atmosphere condenses to rain drops releasing heat into the atmosphere and warming the air around.
(B) Then more and more cool air rushes in towards the centre of the storm.
(C) The warm air tends to move up and causes a drop in the pressure.
(D) This ends with the formation of a very low pressure system with very high speed winds revolving around it.
(a) BDAC (b) CABD
(c) ABCD (d) ACBD

37. An iron ball and a cork ball of the same radius are released from the same height in vacuum. Both of them reach the ground simultaneously. Which of the following statement is the correct explanation for this?
(a) Acceleration due to gravity is independent of the mass of the falling bodies.
(b) Acceleration due to gravity in vacuum is independent of the size of the bodies.
(c) In vacuum, the acceleration due to gravity is zero.
(d) In vacuum, there is resistance to the motion of the bodies.

38. Two bodies of masses 5 kg and 20 kg are separated by a distance of 300 m. A body of mass 1 kg is placed between the two masses in a straight line. If the forces of attraction due to the two masses on the body of 1 kg mass are the same, the distance between the 1 kg body and the 5 kg body is ______
(a) 100 (b) 200
(c) 300 (d) 400

39. A container filled with a liquid A is floating on the surface of another liquid 'B' as shown in the figure, then volume of the liquid displaced by the container

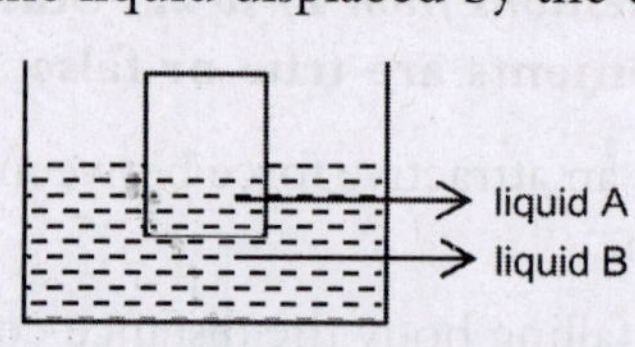

(a) Is equal to the volume of the liquid A.

(b) Is greater than the volume of the liquid A.

(c) Is less than the volume of the liquid A.

(d) Cannot be determined

40. Two objects similar in all respects are floating in two liquids 'A' and 'B' as shown in the figure. If d_A is the density of liquid A, d_B is the density of liquid B, and d_o is the density of the object, which among the following is the correct relation between the densities of the objects and the liquid?

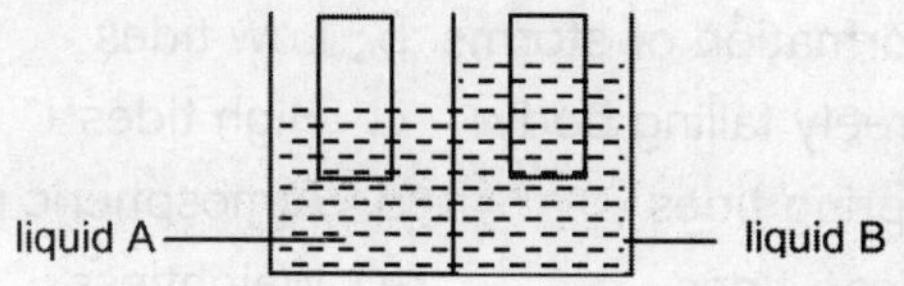

(a) $d_A > d_B > d_O$ (b) $d_O > d_B > d_A$
(c) $d_B > d_A > d_O$ (d) $d_A > d_O > d_B$

41. Spring tides on a new moon day are much stronger than those formed on a full moon day. Which of the following is the correct explanation for the phenomenon?

(a) On a new moon day, the sun and the moon position themselves on either side of the earth along a straight line.

(b) On a new moon day, the sun and the moon lie on the same side of the earth and along the same straight line.

(c) On a full moon day the sun and the moon lie on the same side of the earth and along the same straight line.

(d) On a new moon day the gravitational pull of the moon on the earth is at right angles to that of the sun on the earth.

42. A body of mass 1 kg is placed between two bodies of masses 10 kg and 90 kg and they are arranged in a straight line. If the forces of attraction due to the two masses on the body of mass 1 kg are equal, then the ratio of the distance between the masses 10 kg and 1 kg to the distance between the masses of 1 kg and 90 kg is ______

(a) 1 : 1 (b) 2 : 3
(c) 1 : 3 (d) 1 : 9

43. Two objects A and B of masses 2 kg and 20 kg are dropped from a height of 10m simultaneously. Then

(a) Both A and B experience same gravitational force.

(b) The accelerations of both A and B are same.

(c) Both A and B reach the ground simultaneously.

(d) Both (b) and (c)

44. Three masses A, B and C are arranged as shown in the figure, the mass of 'A' is 2 times the mass of 'B' and the mass of B is 10 kg. If the force of attraction between A and B, and B and C is equal then the mass of C is ______ kg.

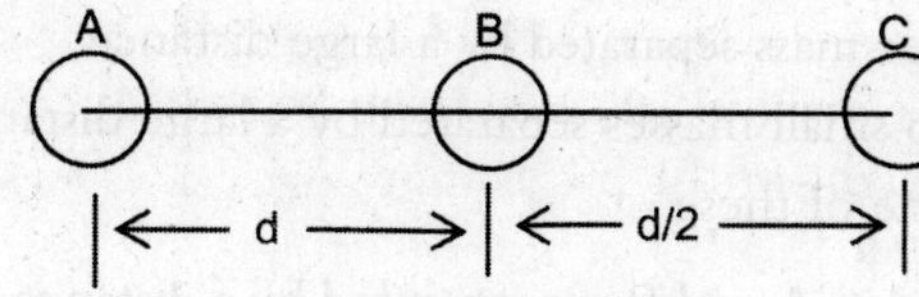

(a) 10 (b) 5
(c) 2.5 (d) 2

45. The gravitational force between two bodies is affected by ______.

(a) The electric field (b) The magnetic field
(c) Heat (d) None of these

46. The weight of a body A on the surface of the earth is equal to the weight of the body B on the surface of moon, the ratio of the mass of A to that of B is ______.
[The acceleration due to gravity on the surface of earth is six times the acceleration due to gravity on the surface of moon].

(a) 1 : 1 (b) 1 : 6
(c) 6 : 1 (d) 1 : 2

47. The acceleration due to gravity of a body on the surface of planets depends upon the ______

(a) Position of the body. (b) Size of the planets.
(c) Mass of the planets. (d) All of the above

48. The weight of a body is ______.

(a) The same every where on the earth.

(b) The gravitational force experienced by the body.

(c) The mass of the body.

(d) Independent of mass of the body.

49. If two metalic balls are placed in space, where the weight of the balls is zero, then ______

(a) They move towards each other.

(b) They repel each other.

(c) They remain in their position.

(d) We cannot say anything about their status.

50. The weight of a body on the surface of earth is W_e. When the density of the body is doubled by keeping its radius constant, its weight on the surface of the moon is found to be W_m; then $\frac{W_m}{W_e}$ = ______ ($g_e = 6g_m$)

(a) 1 : 1 (b) 1 : 3
(c) 3 : 1 (d) 6 : 1

51. Newton's gravitational law is not applicable in the case of _____.
(a) Two bodies at different temperatures separated by a distance of 1 km.
(b) A body of a smaller mass and another body of a larger mass separated by a large distance.
(c) Two small masses separated by a large distance.
(d) None of these

52. Two masses A and B are separated by a distance of 1 m. To increase the force of attraction by 2 times, the distance between them should be _____ m.
(a) 0.5 (b) $\frac{2}{3}$
(c) 2 (d) $\frac{1}{\sqrt{2}}$

***Directions for questions from 53 to 55:* Match the entries given in Column A with the appropriate ones in Column B.**

53.

Column A	Column B
A. Weight of atmosphere	a. Rotation of the earth
B. Monsoon	b. Eye
C. Movement of the winds	c. Exerts pressure
D. Thunderstorms	d. Seasonal wind
E. Centre of a cyclone	e. Humid tropical regions

54.

Column A	Column B
A. Height of mercury column	a. Wind speed
B. Formation of storms	b. Low tides
C. Freely falling body	c. High tides
D. Spring tides	d. Atmospheric pressure
E. Neap tides	e. Weightless

55.

Column A	Column B
A. Artificial satellites	a. Aries
B. Space probes	b. 300 km h^{-1}
C. The Ram	c. Doing research on other planets
D. Exhaust fans	d.. Revolve around the earth
E. Violent tornado	e Convectional air currents

Level 2: Review your Concepts

56. The height of the mercury column on a barometer at sea level is 76 cm and that at a particular height is 63.3 cm. Calculate the height from the sea level (For every 272.7 m of height from the sea level 2.54 centimetres of pressure decreases).

57. Tides are formed mainly due to the gravitational force of attraction between water, the sun and the moon. Why are tides not created by the effect of other planets?

58. In a barometer the height of the mercury column suddenly changes from 76 cm to 60 cm at a particular place. What does it indicate?

59. Is energy required to be supplied for an artificial satellite to revolve in a given orbit?

60. In a barometer, the height of the mercury column sud denly changes from 76 cm to 80 cm at a place 'A'. At a place 'B', the height of mercury column suddenly changes from 76 cm to 60 cm. What does these indicate?

61. The atmosphere exerts pressure on us. Why do we not feel it?

62. Akhilesh took sea water and river water in two containers. He made a body float in the river water and then in the sea water. What happens to the immersed part of the body when it is immersed in the river water and in the sea water?

63. Find the gravitational force between the sun and the Jupiter. Given that the mass of the sun = 2×10^{30} kg, the mass of the Jupiter = 1.89×10^{27} kg, the radius of the Jupiter's orbit = 7.73×10^{11} m and the value of universal gravitational constant G = 6.67×10^{-11} N m^2 kg^{-2}.

64. W_P and W_e be the weight of a body at the pole and at the equator, respectively. If the earth stops rotating, then what happens to the value of W_P and W_e? Are the values of W_e and W_P equal?

65. If the mass of a body is 20 kg, what is its weight at the equator and at poles on Earth? (At equator, g = 9.78 m s^{-2}; at poles, g = 9.83 m s^{-2})

66. An object of mass 2 kg is placed on the surface of the earth and another object of mass 6 kg is placed on the surface of the moon. Determine the ratio of their weights.

67. Aparna drops a body of mass '*m*' from the top of a tower and she found that it reaches the ground in 4 s. Another body of mass 10 m is dropped from the top of another tower and it reaches the ground in 8 s. Using this information she found the ratio of the height of the towers. What is the ratio of their heights?

68. A student placed two identical spheres A and B as shown in the figure. Then if another ball C identical to A and B is placed in between the balls A and B, determine the ratio of force of attraction between A and B in the two cases.

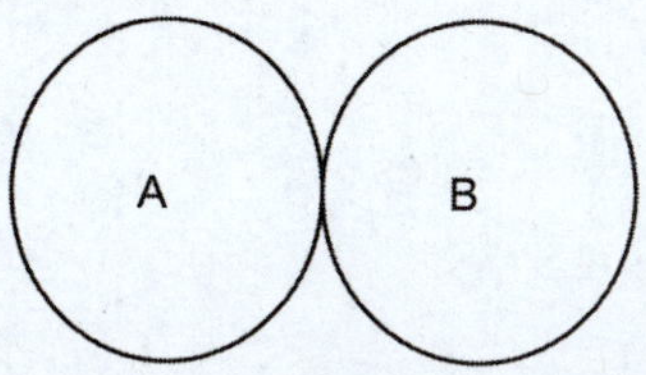

69. If the density of the earth is doubled keeping its radius constant, then the new value of force of attraction on an object on the surface of the earth is how many times that in the previous case?

70. The radius and mass of three planets are given below. Arrange them in the decreasing order of acceleration due to gravity. $\left[g = \frac{GM}{R^2}\right]$; g is acceleration due to gravity on a planet, M is mass of the planet and R is the radius of the planet.

Planet	Mass	Radius
P_1	m	R
P_2	2m	$R/2$
P_3	m/4	$R/4$

71. Sindhu wanted to know the variation in the gravitational force of attraction with height. So, she took a body of mass 'm' from the surface of the earth to a height equal to the radius of the earth. She then determined the change in gravitational force of attraction. What is her answer?

72. If the mass and radius of earth are doubled, then what is the weight of an object on the surface of the earth whose mass is 10 kg on the surface of the moon?

Level 3: Assess Your Concepts

73. We know that gravitational force is present between any two bodies in the universe. But when we stand near a rock, we are not pulled by the rock. Why?

74. The mass and radius of a planet are double that of the Earth. Calculate the escape velocity from the surface of the planet. Given that the escape velocity from the surface of Earth is 11.2 km/s.

75. Why do we use a common balance to measure the mass of an object instead of a spring balance? Can we determine the mass of an object by using a spring balance?

76. The gravitational force of attraction between two celestial bodies is *F*. If these two bodies are moving away from each other and the new distance between them is twice that of the original distance after 5 years, then calculate the change in gravitational force between them.

77. Two bodies are separated by a distance '*d*' and the force between them is *F*. What is the decrease in the distance if the new gravitational force between them is 9*F*?

78. Explain why the number of meteorites striking the surface is quite large whereas very few reach the surface of the earth even though the gravitational force of attraction of moon is less than that of the earth.

79. How does a perfume sprayer work?

80. What is the relation between the force of gravitation on the Moon and on the Earth? Consider a body of mass 'm' on the surface of Earth. What will be the relation between its mass and weight with that on the Moon?

81. An object is made to float in two immiscible liquids as shown in figure. Compare the densities of two liquids A and B and the object.

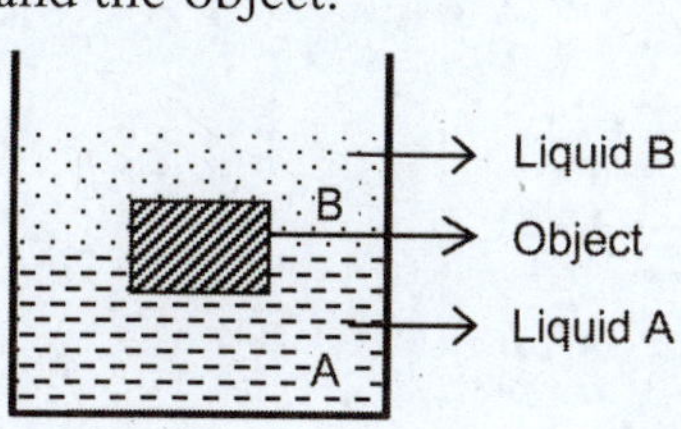

82. The gravitational attraction of the earth on any object is proportional to its mass. Then, why do heavy objects not fall faster than light objects?

83. A lighted candle is placed inside a rectangular box having two holes at its top, and a wheel made up of paper is placed inside it as shown in figure. In which direction will the wheel rotate? Why?

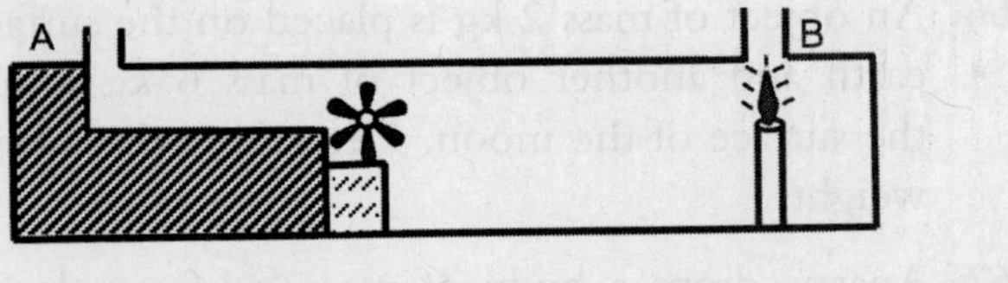

84. The value of Universal gravitational constant (G) in MKS system is 6.67×10^{-11} N m^2 kg^{-2}. Find its value in the CGS system. What will be the change in the value of 'G' if the masses of two bodies is doubled and the distance between them is halved?

ANSWER KEYS

Crossword

Across

4. Srikharikota **6.** Six times **7.** Libra **9.** Uneven heating **11.** Torricelli

Down

1. Spring **2.** Gravitational force **3.** Time **5.** Anemometer **8.** Sun
10. Eye

Classroom Wing

Very Short Answer Type Questions

1. (a) **2.** (d) **3.** (b) **4.** (d) **5.** (a)
6. (c) **7.** (b) **8.** (d) **9.** (d) **10.** (c)
11. (c) **12.** (d) **13.** (a) **14.** (d) **15.** (d)
16. (d) **17.** (d) **18.** (a) **19.** (b) **20.** (c)
21. (a) **22.** (a) **23.** (d) **24.** (b) **25.** (b)
26. A → b, B → c, C → a, D → e, E → d
27. A → c, B → a, C → b
28. A → b, B → a, C → f, D → g, E → c, F → d, G → e **37.** 21st March to 19th April

Competition Wing

Level 1: Apply your concepts

1. Libra **2.** 11.27 km s^{-1} **3.** remains constant **4.** square of time **5.** speed, direction
6. low **7.** quadrupled **8.** cyclone **9.** heat **10.** uneven heating
11. Capricorn **12.** masses **13.** Universal **14.** escape velocity **15.** wooden plank
16. pot **17.** True **18.** True **19.** False **20.** True
21. False **22.** False **23.** (d) **24.** (d) **25.** (a)
26. (b) **27.** (d) **28.** (d) **29.** (c) **30.** (a)
31. (d) **32.** (b) **33.** (b) **34.** (d) **35.** (c)
36. (d) **37.** (a) **38.** (a) **39.** (b) **40.** (a)
41. (b) **42.** (c) **43.** (d) **44.** (b) **45.** (d)
46. (b) **47.** (d) **48.** (b) **49.** (a) **50.** (b)
51. (d) **52.** (d)
53. A → c, B → d, C → a, D → e, E → b
54. A → d, B → a, C → e, D → c, E → b
55. A → d, B → c, C → a, D → e, E → b

Level 2: Review your Concepts

56. 1.36 km **63.** 4.22×10^{23} N **65.** 196.6 N; 195.6 N **66.** 2 : 1
67. 1 : 4 **68.** 4 : 1 **71.** 3/4 **72.** 5 kgwt

Hints and Explanations

Classroom Wing

Very Short Answer Type Questions

1. (a)
The escape velocity on the surface of moon is small, because the moon's gravitational force is small.

2. (d)
The value of escape velocity on the surface of earth is 7 miles s^{-1}

3. (b)
The time interval between two successive primary and secondary tides at a place is more than 12 hours because the moon also moves round the earth in the same direction of the earth's rotation.

4. (d)
Spring tides occur during the full-moon or the new moon day when the earth, the sun and the moon come in a straight line.

5. (a)
Two bodies attract each other with the same force.

6. (c)
In our solar system, the maximum value of '*g*' is on the Sun (274.1 m s^{-2}) and minimum on Pluto (0.610 m s^{-2}). The '*g*' on moon is 1.625 m s^{-2}.

7. (b)
When the two spheres are in contact with each other the distance between the centre of two spheres is equal to $r + r = 2r$

The force of attraction is inversely proportional to the square of the distance between them, so $F \propto \frac{1}{(2r)^2}$

$$F \propto \frac{1}{4r^2} \Rightarrow F \propto \frac{1}{r^2}$$

8. (d)
Tides are formed due to the gravitational pull of moon and sun on earth.

9. (d)

$$F \propto \frac{m_1 m_2}{r^2}$$

On earth $F_e = G\frac{M_e m}{R_e^2}$

On planet $F_P = G\frac{M_P m}{R_P^2}$

$$F_P = G\frac{2M_e m}{\left(\frac{R_e}{2}\right)^2} = 8G\frac{M_e m}{R_e^2}$$

$F_P = 8\ F_e$

M_e = mass of earth.

R_e = radius of earth.

M_P = mass of the planet.

R_P = radius of the planet.

$M_P = 2\ M_e$

$R_P = \frac{R_e}{2}$

10. (c)
For a freely falling body, its velocity increases as it falls under gravity and a constant acceleration is produced in it, which is called acceleration due to gravity.

11. (c)
By using a barometer we can measure the height of a particular place from sea level.

12. (d)
The mass of an object is constant at any given place any where in the universe. So $M_m = M_e$.

13. (a)
The acceleration due to gravity on the earth depends on the mass of the earth and the radius of the earth.

14. (d)
The gravitational force acting on a body by the earth is known as its weight on the earth. As the gravitational force is not zero, the weight of the object is not zero on the earth. Its mass is also not zero in the earth's atmosphere.

15. (d)
The small balls do not move towards each other because the force of attraction between them is negligible compared to the force of attraction by the earth.

16. (d)
The value of '*g*' on the moon is (1/6)th that on the earth. The reason for small value of '*g*' on moon is due to its

small mass compared to the earth's mass. Thus, a body of 6 kgwt on the earth will weigh 1 kgwt on the moon.

17. (d)

The gravitational constant does not depend on the size, and mass of the bodies or the distance between the bodies.

18. (a)

(i) Gases are produced when the fuel in the combustion chamber is burnt (a).

(ii) The hot gases are allowed to escape through a nozzle (c).

(iii) The gases come out with great force which is action (b).

(iv) As a reaction, the gases exert an opposite force on rocket (e).

(v) Due to this, the rocket moves with great speed in the other direction (d).

19. (b)

(i) Take a metallic container that is half filled with water (b).

(ii) Heat the container for some time and place a cap on the container firmly (d).

(iii) Stop heating the container and cool it to very low temperatures (a).

(iv) The container gets compressed because of the pressure exerted by the air from outside the container (c).

20. (c) As the temperature is high in hot, humid tropical regions, strong upward rising winds are produced.

(a) These winds carry water droplets along with them.

(b) When they freeze and fall down, the swift movement of the falling water droplets along with rising air create lightning and sound.

21. A → d Spring tides occur during full moon or new moon day when the sun, earth and moon come in a straight line.

B → c Among the eighty eight constellations discovered the biggest constellation is Hydra which contains 78 very big stars.

C → b Chandrayan – 1 is the artificial satellite launched by Indians successfully on October 22, 2008.

D → a Neap tides occur when the gravitational pull of the moon and sun on the earth are perpendicular to each other.

22. As per the universal law of gravitation, $F \propto \dfrac{m_1\, m_2}{d^2}$

F = force of attraction, m_1 and m_2 are the masses of two objects.

d is the distance between them.

$$F \propto \frac{1}{d^2}$$

$$F_1 = \frac{k}{d_1^2}$$

$$d_2 = 2d_1$$

$$F_2 = \frac{k}{4d_1^2}$$

$$\frac{F_1}{F_2} = \frac{k}{d_1^2} \times \frac{4d_1^2}{k}$$

$F_1 = 4F_2$, Force quadruples

23. The accelerations of both the bodies are same and they reach the ground simultaneously.

24. Weight of a body on Jupiter will be more than that on the earth as the mass of Jupiter is more than the mass of Earth, hence, the value of g on Jupiter is more than that of earth, $W = mg$.

25. Force = mass × acceleration

$$\text{acceleration } (a) = \frac{\text{force}}{\text{mass}} = \frac{9.8\text{N}}{(\text{mass of earth})}$$

The mass of the earth is very high, so, its acceleration is negligible.

26. A → b The spring tides formed on full moon day are less stronger than those on a new moon day.

B → c The spring tides formed on a new moon day are much stronger than those on full moon day.

C → a Rocket works on the principle of Newton's third law.

D → e Centrifugal force acts in the outward direction of the circular path.

E → d The energy from the tides is utilized to generate electricity.

27. The correct match is

A → r, B → p, C → q.

28. A → b Gravitational force is always attractive in nature.

B → a The value of universal gravitational constant is 6.67×10^{-11} N m² kg⁻².

C → f The value of acceleration due to gravity at the poles is 9.831 m s⁻².

D → g The value of acceleration due to gravity at the equator is 9.781 m s⁻².

E → c The instrument that measures wind speed is called an anemometer.

F → d Winds are produced due to change in air pressure.

G → e Barometer is used to measure atmospheric pressure.

29. The pressure decreases when the speed of air is increased.

30. A tornado is a dark funnel shaped cloud that reaches from the sky to the ground.

31. Anemometer is a device used to measure the speed of the wind.

32. Wind currents are generated due to uneven heating on the earth.

33. Any two material bodies in the universe attract each other with a force called gravitation.

34. The force with which the earth attracts a body towards itself is called the weight of a body.

35. A body, which moves only under the influence of gravitational force is called freely falling body.

36. The acceleration produced in a body when it moves towards the earth is called acceleration due to gravity.

37. Constellation Aries is seen during 21st March to 19th April.

38. The time interval between the occurrence of two successive tides at a place is 24 h and 52 min.

39. The escape velocity on the earth is 11.27 km s^{-1}.

40. A solid floats in a given liquid, when its density is less than that of the liquid. It sinks when its density is more than that of the liquid.

41. Today, there are 88 constellations and the biggest among them is Hydra.

42. Moving air is called wind.

43. The gravity is defined as the force of attraction between the earth and any other body on or near it. Yes, it changes from place to place.

44. The maximum velocity which a body must acquire so that it escapes the earth's gravity is called the escape velocity.

45. The ratio of acceleration due to gravity on earth to moon is 6 : 1.

46. The stars in the night sky are divided into small groups, called constellations.

47. Barometer is used to find the atmospheric pressure.

48. The empty space above the surface of mercury column, in barometer is called Toricellian vacuum.

49. (a) When a body falls freely, the distance travelled by it is directly proportional to the square of time. Hence, the body dropped from larger height, i.e., h_1, takes more time to reach the ground.

(b) A body of 6 kg wt on the earth will weigh 1 kg wt on the moon. Hence, a body of 12 kg wt on the earth will weigh 2 kg wt on the moon.

50. In liquid A, half of the volume of the body gets immersed. In liquid B, three fourth of the volume of the same body gets immersed. This means the density of liquid B is less than that of liquid A. This is because a body immerses more in liquid of smaller density and it immerses lesser and lesser as the density of the liquid increases.

51. Precautions to be taken during thunderstorm accompanied by lightning

(i) Avoid taking shelter under tall isolated trees.

(ii) A vehicle with closed windows is a safe place to take shelter.

(iii) Avoid sitting near a window.

(iv) Shelter under an umbrella with a metallic end, open garages, metal sheds are not safe places.

(v) Do not stay in water during lightning. Come out of water and stay inside the building.

52. Monsoon: A monsoon is a seasonal prevailing wind which lasts for several months.

In summer, the land near the equator warms up faster and for most of the time the temperature of the land is higher than that of the water in the oceans. This produces winds carrying water vapour to flow from above the oceans towards the land and bring rain.

These winds are called the monsoon winds. In winter, the direction of the wind gets reversed from the land to the ocean. These colder winds carry little water, hence bring small amount of rain water.

Short Answer Type Questions

53. Neap tides

Neap tides occur when gravitational pull of moon and sun on earth are perpendicular to each other as shown in the figure.

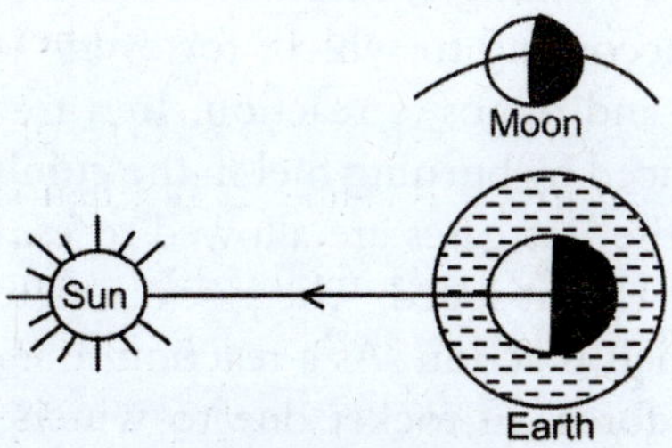

Neap tide

Neap tides are low tides as the net gravitational pull on earth is small.

Neap tides occur during the first and the last quarter phases of moon.

54. $n_p = m$, $m_e = 2m$

$R_p = R$, $R_e = 2R$

$$\frac{g_p}{g_e} = \frac{m_p}{m_e} \times \left(\frac{R_e}{R_p}\right)^2$$

$$= \frac{m}{2m} \times \left(\frac{2R}{R}\right)^2 = 2$$

$= gp = 2ge$

Hence, if mass and radius of the Earth are double those of a planet, then acceleration due to gravity on the surface of the planet is double of its value on the Earth.

55. There is a change in the density of sea water due to a change in temperature at different geographic locations and also due to addition of fresh water. This poses serious threat to the ships. The density of sea water is greater than the density of fresh water. Thus, a ship that moves from a higher density to a lower density region of the sea may sink.

56. $F_1 = G\frac{m_1 m_2}{d^2}$

$$F_2 = \frac{G\frac{m_1}{4}m_2}{\left(\frac{d}{2}\right)^2}$$

$$F_2 = \frac{Gm_1m_2}{4} \times \frac{4}{d^2}$$

$F_2 = F_1$

57. **(a) Destruction:** The destruction caused by cyclones is immense.

The low pressure existing in the eye can lift water surface as high as 3–12 metre. As a result, low lying coastal areas are filled with the ocean water. Continuous heavy rainfall and high speed winds can cause severe loss to life and property.

(b) If roofs of buildings are weak and high speed winds blew over these roofs, then the roofs could be lifted and blown away. What makes the roof be blown away? This happens when high speed winds are blowing above the roof of a building; air pressure above the roof gets reduced. The air pressure inside the building is much more than the air pressure above the roof. This difference in air pressure makes the roof be blown away.

58. The body immerses more in a liquid of smaller density i.e., d_2, because the upward force exerted by the liquid on the body increases with the density of the liquid.

59. **Cyclone:** Cyclone is a violent rotating wind storm. When water vapour in the atmosphere condenses to raindrops it releases heat into the atmosphere and warms the air around. This warm air tends to move up and causes a drop in pressure. Then more and more cool air rushes in towards the centre of the storm. Some times the events end with the formation of a very low pressure system with very high speed winds revolving around it. This weather condition forms a cyclone.

60. $m_e = m$, $m_p = \frac{m}{2}$

$R_e = R_p = R$

$$\frac{g_e}{g_p} = \frac{m_e}{\frac{m}{2}} = \frac{m}{1} \times \frac{2}{m}$$

$$\frac{g_e}{g_p} = \frac{2}{1} = 2:1$$

61. $mg_e - mg_p = 10$ N

$$m\left(10 - \frac{10}{4}\right) = 10$$

$$m = \frac{40}{30}$$

$$= m = \frac{4}{3} \text{ kg}$$

62. A freely falling body is the one that does not experience any force other than gravitational force, due to which it falls. A freely falling body is weightless. For the same reason, we feel our weight to be decreased in the lift descending with uniform acceleration.

63. **Artificial satellites:** These are put into various orbits and perform different functions such as communication, radio, TV transmission, weather reporting etc., these satellites are sent into space using multi-stage launching system where different rockets are fired at different stages. This system provides the satellite to get the least speed required to reach the orbit as well as revolve in a given orbit with proper speed.

64. The bad effects of tides are as follows. The tidal water makes river water undrinkable since sometimes the tidal waters carry sediments and deposit them in a river so that it becomes difficult to navigate. Some times, tides make fishing difficult for fishermen and the rivers overflow due to tidal waters, damaging crops, and coastal habitants.

Essay Type Questions

65. **Spring tides**

These are high tides that occur during full moon or new moon day when sun, earth, and moon come in straight line.

On a full moon day, the sun and the moon are present on either sides of the earth, in a straight line, as shown in the figure.

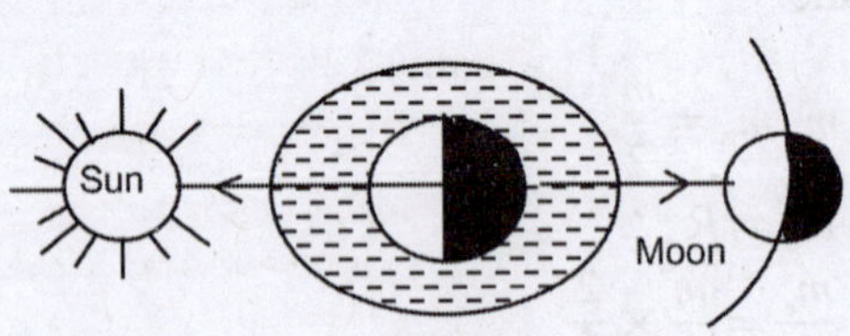

Spring tides during full moon

Thus, the place on the earth where primary tides are produced due to moon's attraction are reinforced by secondary tides produced by sun's attraction and vice versa.

On a new moon day, both moon and sun produce primary tides at the same place on earth as both are on the same side of earth, as shown in the figure.

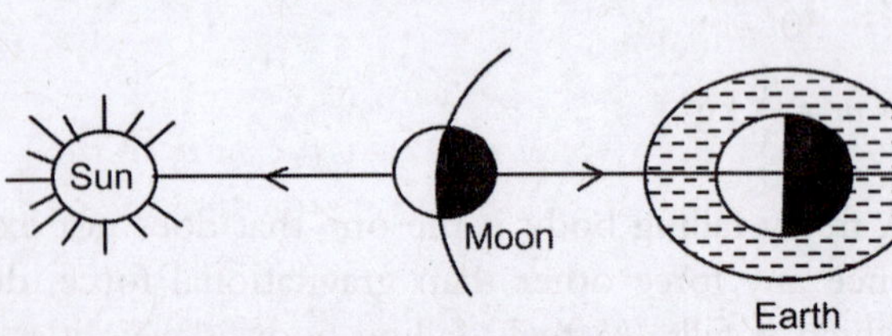

Spring tides during new moon

The spring tides formed on a new moon day are much stronger than that formed on full moon day as water is attracted jointly by both the moon and the sun.

66. A rocket's working is based on Newton's third law of motion according to which, for every action, there is an equal and opposite reaction. In a rocket, the gases are produced by burning fuel in the combustion chamber and the hot gases are allowed to escape through a nozzle at a great speed. The gases come out with great force which is action. As a reaction, the gases exert an opposite force on rocket due to which rocket moves with great speed in the other direction. The various parts of the rocket are as shown in the figure.

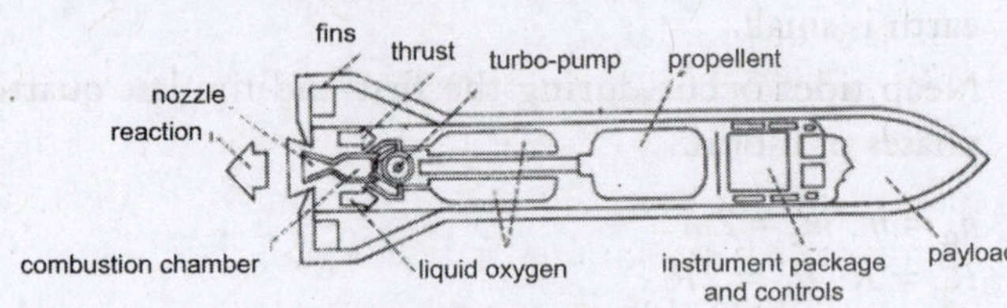

Working of rocket

67. We know that height $(h) \propto t^2$ (time)

Given $h_1 = 5$ m, $t_1 = 1$ s, $t_2 = 2$ s

$$h_1 \propto t_1^2 \quad (1)$$

$$h_2 \propto t_2^2 \quad (2)$$

$$\therefore \frac{h_1}{h_2} = \frac{t_1^2}{t_2^2}$$

$$\frac{5}{h_2} = \frac{1}{2^2} = \frac{1}{4}$$

$$h_2 = 5 \times 4 = 20 \text{ m}$$

68. When a body falls freely, the velocity (v) acquired by it is directly proportional to the time (t).

Given $t_1 = 2$ s

$t_2 = 4$ s

$$v_1 \propto t_1 \quad (1)$$

$$v_2 \propto t_2 \quad (2)$$

$$\frac{v_1}{v_2} = \frac{t_1}{t_2} = \frac{2}{4} = \frac{1}{2}$$

$$\therefore v_1 : v_2 = 1 : 2$$

69. **Construction of a barometer**

Take a glass tube closed at one end and of a narrow uniform bore of diameter 1 cm and length of 1 m. Fill the glass tube with pure and dry mercury carefully so that no air bubbles are trapped inside and cover the open end with the thumb.

Place the tube inverted in a trough containing mercury and remove the thumb. Certain amount of mercury in the tube falls down into the trough leaving an empty space above the surface of mercury column, known as 'Torricellian vacuum'. When mercury column is positioned vertically, the pressure exerted by it is equal to the atmospheric pressure. The height of the mercury column in the barometer gives the atmospheric pressure at that place. Usually, at sea level, the height of mercury column is 76 cm, we can say that the atmospheric pressure at sea level is 76 cm of mercury. Atmospheric pressure decreases with an increase in altitude.

70. The law of gravitation states that in the universe, any two material bodies attract each other with a force which is (i) directly proportional to the product of their masses and (ii) inversely proportional to the square of the distance between them; the mutual force acts along the line joining the centres of mass of the bodies. Let the two bodies, with masses M and m respectively be separated by a distance '*d*' as shown in the figure.

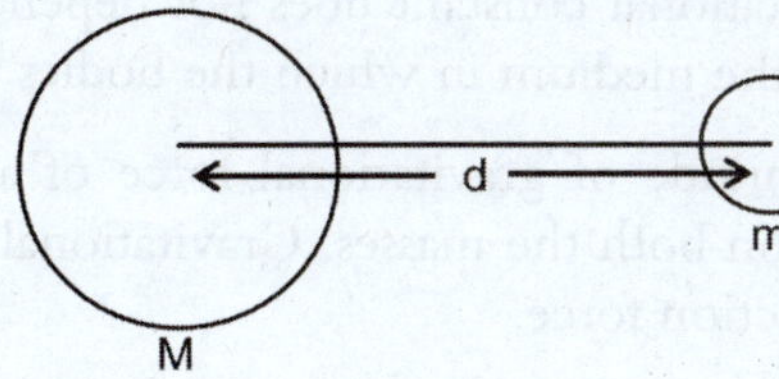

The mutual force of attraction, F, between them is

$F \propto M\text{m}$ (1)

$$F \propto \frac{1}{d^2} \quad (2)$$

Combining the above two expressions,

$$F \propto \frac{Mm}{d^2} \text{ or } F = G\frac{Mm}{d^2}$$

Where, G is a constant of proportionality known as Universal Gravitational Constant.

71. Occurrence of tides: The level of water in the oceans rises and falls, alternatively, after 12 hours and 26 minutes. This rise and fall of water level is referred to as tides.

The tides are caused due to gravitational forces exerted by the moon and the sun on earth. The gravitational force of the sun on the earth is 46% of the gravitational force of the moon on the earth.

Other than the gravitational forces, the tides are also caused by the spinning motion of the earth about its own axis. The rotational motion of the earth gives rise to centrifugal forces, which act on every object present on the earth, in the outward direction. Under the action of centrifugal force, the objects on earth tend to fly away from the centre. They do not actually fly off due to another force, called centripetal force, which acts in a direction opposite to centrifugal force. The centripetal force is provided by the gravity.

Thus, the water particles on the earth tend to move outward due to centrifugal force. This reinforces the cause of tides.

There are mainly two types of tides viz., high tides and low tides. Further, the high tides may be direct (or primary) and antipodal (or secondary). During the motion of earth about its own axis, say a place A faces the moon, as shown in figure.

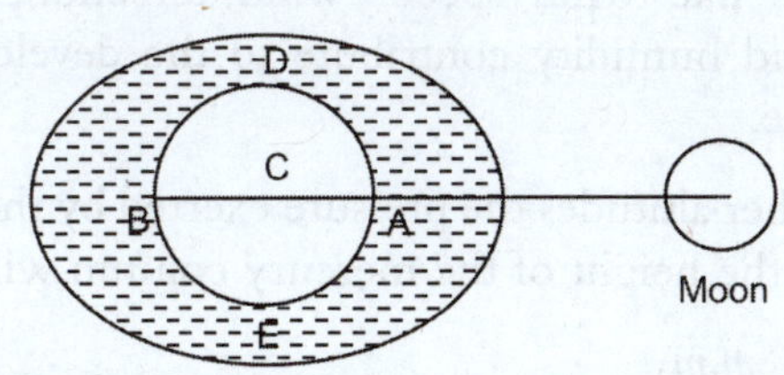

The water at A gets attracted towards the moon and swells up producing a direct or primary tide at A.

The moon's attraction at antipodal position (diametrically opposite) 'B' is weak as place B is farther away from moon. The water at 'B' swells up producing antipodal or secondary tides, due to centrifugal force and a reaction force caused by the pull of moon on water at place A.

As the water level at A and B rises, the water level at places D and E (see figure) goes down, producing low tides.

72. Galileo discovered certain laws related to the freely falling bodies. They are as follows.

(i) They all fall with equal rapidity in vacuum.

(ii) As a body falls, velocity acquired by it is directly proportional to the time.

(iii) The distance travelled is directly proportional to the square of time.

Newton, through his 'Guinea' experiment proved the 1st law, as mentioned above. He allowed a guinea and a feather to fall through a hollow glass tube, first with air in the tube and then after removing the air from the tube. It was found that with air present in the tube, the guinea fell rapidly compared to the feather and reached the bottom earlier. With air taken out and after inverting the tube, it was found that both the guinea and the feather reached the bottom at the same time, falling with equal rapidity.

Thus, in the absence of any opposing force, gravity causes all the bodies, light or heavy, to fall simultaneously, if they start from rest.

Competition Wing

Level 1: Apply your Concepts

1. The constellation Libra has the shape of balance.
2. The escape velocity on Earth is 11.27 km s^{-1}.
3. For a freely falling body, its acceleration is constant and that is equal to the acceleration due to gravity.
4. The distance travelled by a freely falling body is directly proportional to the square of time.
5. Factors like wind speed, wind direction, temperature and humidity contribute to the development of cyclone.
6. At higher altitudes the pressure exerted by the air is less hence the height of the mercury column will be low.
7. $F_1 = G\frac{m_1 m_2}{d^2}$

   $F_2 = G\frac{m_1 m_2}{\frac{d^2}{4}}$

   $F_2 = 4F_1$

   Hence, if the distance between two given bodies is halved, then the force between them is quadrupled.
8. Low pressure system with very high speed wind revolving around it is known as a cyclone.
9. When water vapour in the atmosphere condenses, it releases heat to the atmosphere.
10. Wind currents are generated due to uneven heating on the earth.
11. The constellation seen between 22 December and 19 January is Capricorn.
12. The gravitational force of attraction between any two objects is directly proportional to the product of their masses.
13. Newton's law of gravitation is called universal law of gravitation.
14. The minimum velocity required by a body to escape from the planet is called escape velocity.
15. To break the mud rocks on the surface of soil, wooden plank is used.
16. The constellation Aquarius has the shape of a pot.
17. Any two material bodies in the universe attract each other with a force.
18. The distance travelled is directly proportional to the square of time.
19. Gravitational force is unaffected by temperature and pressure.
20. The weight of a body is the force of attraction exerted by the earth on the body. The body exerts an equal force of attraction on the earth.
21. The constellation Aries has the shape of ram.
22. Venus-13 is an example of space probe.
23. The moon has no atmosphere because the escape velocity of a body on it is small. The escape velocity of gas particles on the moon is almost equal to their usual velocity. So, the gas particles fly away from the moon's surface. Hence, the moon has no atmosphere.
24. The gravitational constant does not depend upon the nature of the medium in which the bodies are placed.
25. The magnitude of gravitational force of attraction is the same on both the masses. Gravitational force is an action-reaction force.
26. If the distance between two given bodies is halved, then the force of attraction is quadrupled.
27. The apparent weight of a freely falling body is zero.
28. The value of acceleration due to gravity on the surface of the moon is 1.625 m s^{-2}.
29. The ball reaches the ground first because the air resistance is more on paper as compared to that on the ball.
30. For a freely falling body the velocity acquired by it is directly proportional to time.
31. Factors like wind speed, wind direction, temperature, and humidity contribute to the development of cyclones.
32. The height of the mercury column near the sea level is 76 cm.
33. Sudden fall in the height of mercury column forecasts the occurrence of storms.
34. The density of sea water changes due to change in temperature and due to the addition of fresh water into it.
35. (i) Take a glass tube closed at one end and a narrow uniform bore of diameter 1 cm and of length of 1 m.

(ii) Fill the glass tube with pure and dry mercury carefully so that no air bubbles are trapped inside.

(iii) Cover the open end with the thumb.

(iv) Place the tube inverted in a trough containing mercury and remove the thumb.

36. (i) The water vapour in the atmosphere condenses to rain drops releasing heat into the atmosphere and warming the air around.

(ii) The warm air tends to move up and causes a drop in the pressure.

(iii) Then more and more cool air rushes in towards the centre of the storm.

(iv) This ends with the formation of a very low pressure system with very high speed winds revolving around it.

37. Both of them reach the ground simultaneously because the acceleration due to gravity is independent of the mass of the falling bodies.

38. $F = \frac{Gm_1m_2}{r^2}$

$$\frac{G \times 5 \times 1}{x^2} = \frac{G \times 20 \times 1}{r^2}$$

$r^2 = x^2\ 4$

$r = 2x$

Total distance $= r + x = 300$ m

$2x + x = 300$ m

$3x = 300;\ x = 100$ m

39. From the figure, it is clear that the volume of the liquid displaced by the container is greater than the volume of the liquid A.

40. When the object is in liquid A, the portion of the object above the liquid surface is more compared to that when it is in liquid B, so, the density of the liquid A is greater than that of the liquid B, which is greater than the density of the object.

41. On a new moon day the sun and the moon lie on the same side of the earth and along the same straight line. Thus, the joint attraction by the sun and the moon at a place on the earth creates a strong spring tide.

42. $\leftarrow x \rightarrow \quad \leftarrow y \rightarrow$

10 kg —— **1 kg** —— **90 kg**

$$F_1 = \frac{G \times 10 \times 1}{x^2}$$

$$F_2 = \frac{G \times 90 \times 1}{y^2};\ \text{But } F_1 = F_2$$

$$\frac{10}{x^2} = \frac{90}{y^2} \text{ or } \frac{1}{x} = \frac{3}{y}\quad \frac{x}{y} = \frac{1}{3}$$

43. The accelerations both the bodies are same and they reach the ground simultaneously.

44. $F_{AB} = F_{BC},\ m_A = 2m_B$

$$\frac{Gm_Am_B}{d^2} = \frac{Gm_Bm_C}{(d/2)^2}$$

$$\frac{2m_Bm_B}{d^2} = \frac{m_Bm_C}{(d/2)^2} \qquad (\therefore m_A = 2m_B)$$

$$\frac{2m_B}{d^2} = \frac{m_C}{(d/2)^2}, \Rightarrow \frac{2m_B}{d^2} = \frac{4m_C}{d^2}$$

$$2m_B = 4m_C,\ m_C = \frac{2m_B}{4} = \frac{m_B}{2} = \frac{10}{2} = 5 \text{ kg}$$

45. Gravitational force is a mutual attractive force between any two bodies in the universe. The phenomenon is universal because it is true for any two bodies of the whole creation and is unaffected by heat, pressure, electric field and magnetic field, etc.

46. Weight of A $= m_A \times g_e$

weight of B $= m_B \times g_m$

g_e and g_m are the acceleration due to gravity on the surface of the earth and on the surface of the moon, respectively.

$$g_m = \frac{g_e}{6}$$

$$m_A g_e = m_B g_m$$

$$m_A g_e = m_B \times \frac{g_e}{6}$$

$$m_A = \frac{m_B}{6},\ \frac{m_A}{m_B} = \frac{1}{6} = 1:6$$

47. The acceleration due to gravity on the surface of the planet depends upon the radius or size, mass of the planet and the position of the body.

48. Weight of a body is the gravitational force experienced by the body.

49. Weight of the two bodies is zero that means gravitational force by the earth is zero. So, when they are placed nearer to each other, due to gravitational pull they attract each other.

50. Density $= \dfrac{\text{mass}}{\text{volume}}$

mass = density × volume, $m = d \times v$

$W_e = m_e \times g_e = d_e \times v_e \times g_e$

$W_m = m_m \times g_m = d_m \times v_m \times g_m$

$\dfrac{W_m}{W_e} = \dfrac{d_e \times v_e \times g_e}{d_m \times v_m \, g_m}$

$v_e = v_m$

$d_m = 2d_e$

$g_m = \dfrac{g_e}{6}$

$\dfrac{W_e}{W_m} = \dfrac{d_e \times v_e \times g_e \times 6}{2d_e \times v_e \times g_e} = \dfrac{3}{1}$

$W_e : W_m = 3 : 1$

Therefore, $\dfrac{W_m}{W_e} = \dfrac{1}{3}$

51. Newton's gravitational law is not applicable in case of two atoms or any two particles separated by a distance of 10^{-7} centimeter or less.

52. The gravitational force 'F' between two masses m_A and m_B is $F = \dfrac{Gm_A m_B}{d^2}$

When the force of attraction is increased by 2 times, then $\dfrac{2Gm_A m_B}{d^2} = \dfrac{Gm_A m_B}{x^2}$

x is the new distance between the masses

$\dfrac{x^2}{d^2} = \dfrac{1}{2}, x^2 = \dfrac{1}{2}, x = \sqrt{\dfrac{1}{2}} = \dfrac{1}{\sqrt{2}}$

53. A → c Due to the weight of atmospheric gases, it exerts pressure.

B → d A monsoon is a seasonal wind that lasts for several months.

C → a The movement of the winds is effected by the rotation of the earth.

D → e Thunderstorms are very common in hot, humid tropical regions.

E → b The centre of a cyclone is called eye.

54. A → d The height of mercury column in the barometer gives the atmospheric pressure at that place.

B → a Formation of storms is dependent on wind speed.

C → e A freely falling body experiences weightless.

D → c Spring tides are high tides which occur during full moon or new moon day.

E → b Neap tides are low tides occur during the first and the last quarter phases of moon.

55. A → d The artificial satellites revolve around the earth.

B → c Space probes are used for studying and doing research on other planets.

C → a The shape of the constellation Aries is 'the Ram'.

D → e Exhaust fans use the principle of convectional air currents.

E → b A violent tornado moves with a speed of 300 km h^{-1}.

Level 2: Review your Concepts

56. Change in pressure = 76 – 63.3 = 12.7 cm.

For each 272.7 m height 2.54 cm of pressure decreases so, when the pressure is 63.3 cm,

height from the sea level is $= 272.7 \times \dfrac{(76 - 63.3)}{2.54}$

= 1363.5 m = 1.36 km.

57. The gravitational force of attraction is directly proportional to the product of masses and inversely proportional to the square of the distance between the objects. The distance between the earth and moon is less compared to that between earth and other planet. Because the gravitational effect caused by planet is less, they cannot produce tides.

58. Rain, storm, etc., can be forecast with the help of atmospheric pressure. Sudden fall in the height of mercury column forecasts occurrence of storm.

59. Satellite is revolving around a planet due to the gravitational force of attraction between the planet and the satellite. So, energy is not required to make a satellite revolve around the planet with particular velocity.

60. In a barometer, if the height of the mercury column suddenly changes from 76 cm to 80 cm at the place 'A', it indicates a rapid increase in atmospheric pressure, which pushes out the cloudy and rainy weather out, clearing the skies and bringing in cool, dry air.

In a barometer, if the height of the mercury column suddenly changes from 76 cm to 60 cm at the place 'B', it indicates a rapid decrease in atmospheric pressure, with an approaching storm, bringing in heavy rain and strong winds.

61. The atmosphere exerts enormous pressure on us. But we do not feel it because our blood exerts a pressure slightly more than that of the atmospheric pressure.

62. The density of the sea water is greater than the density of the river water. So, when a body rises a little when it is immersed in the sea water compared to that in the river water.

63. Mass of the sun, $m_1 = 2 \times 10^{30}$ kg.

Mass of the Jupiter, $m_2 = 1.89 \times 10^{27}$ kg.

Radius of the Jupiter's orbit, $r = 7.73 \times 10^{11}$ m.

Gravitational force between the Sun and the Jupiter,

$$F = \frac{G\,m_1\,m_2}{r^2}$$

$$= \frac{6.67\times10^{-11}\times2\times10^{30}\times1.89\times10^{27}}{(7.73\times10^{11})^2}$$

$$= 4.22 \times 10^{23}\text{ N.}$$

64. The value of '*g*' varies from place to place on the surface of the earth. As the weight depends on '*g*', it also changes from place to place. The distance between the centre of the earth and the pole is less compared to that between the equator and the centre. So, the value of '*g*' is maximum at poles and minimum at equator. So, $W_P > W_e$. The earth has maximum speed of rotation at the equator. So, the centrifugal force (outward force) is also more at the equator compared to that on the poles. If the earth were not rotating, then the value of W_e will increase and W_P remains unchanged but still there will be difference in their values.

65. Weight of a body is given by the expression, $W = mg$, where '*m*' is the mass of the body and '*g*' is acceleration due to gravity.

Given,

Mass of the body, $m = 20$ kg

Acceleration due to gravity at poles of the earth, $g_p = 9.83\text{ m s}^{-2}$

Acceleration due to gravity at equator of the earth, $g_e = 9.78\text{ m s}^{-2}$

Hence, weight of the body at the poles of the earth, $W_P = mg_p = 20\text{ kg} \times 9.83\text{ m s}^{-2} = 196.6\text{ N}$

Weight of the body at the equator of the earth, $W_e = mg_e = 20\text{ kg} \times 9.78\text{ m s}^{-2} = 195.6\text{ N}$

66. Weight = mass × acceleration due to gravity.

$W = m \times g$

$g_e = 6 \times g_m$

where g_m and g_e are acceleration due to gravity on the surface of the moon and on the surface of the earth, respectively.

$W_1 = 2 \times g_e = 2g_e = 2 \times 6g_m = 12g_m$

$W_2 = 6 \times g_m = 6g_m$

$$\frac{W_1}{W_2} = \frac{12\,g_m}{6\,g_m} = \frac{2}{1} = 2:1.$$

67. The distance travelled is directly proportional to the square of time. $S \propto t^2$

$$\frac{S_1}{S_2} = \left(\frac{t_1}{t_2}\right)^2 = \left(\frac{4}{8}\right)^2 = \frac{16}{64} = \frac{1}{4} = 1:4.$$

68.

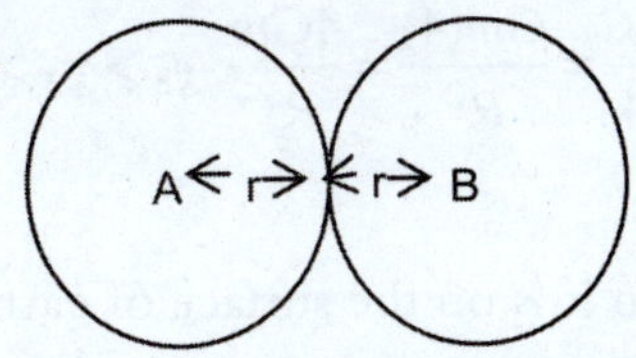

Force of attraction between ball A and B,

$$F_1 = \frac{mm}{(2r)^2}\,G,$$

where '*m*' is the mass of the ball and '*r*' is the radius of the ball.

$$F_1 = G\,\frac{m^2}{4r^2}$$

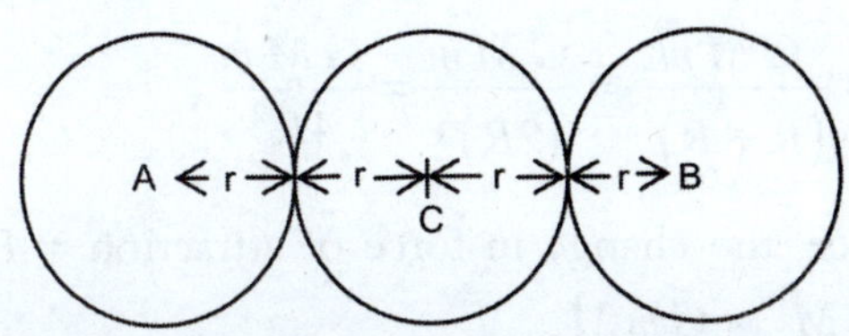

Force of attraction between *A* and *B* after placing the ball *C* in between them,

$$F_2 = \frac{G\,mm}{(4r)^2} = \frac{G\,m^2}{16r^2}$$

Ratio of the forces in two cases

$$\frac{F_1}{F_2} = \frac{\dfrac{G\,m^2}{4r^2}}{\dfrac{G\,m^2}{16r^2}} = \frac{16}{4} = \frac{4}{1} = 4:1.$$

69. The density of the earth is doubled by keeping its radius constant. But density = $\frac{\text{mass}}{\text{volume}}$

Thus, the mass of the earth is doubled.

As force of attraction is directly proportional to the product of the masses, the force of attraction is also doubled.

70. Acceleration due to gravity 'g'

$g = \frac{GM}{R^2}$, M is the mass of the planet and R is the radius of the planet.

$$g_1 = \frac{GM}{R^2};\ g_2 = \frac{G \times 2m}{\left(\frac{R}{2}\right)^2} = \frac{Gm(8)}{R^2} = \frac{8Gm}{R^2}$$

$$g_3 = \frac{G \times \left(\frac{m}{4}\right)}{\left(\frac{R}{4}\right)^2} = \frac{Gm}{R^2} \times \frac{16}{4} = \frac{Gm(4)}{R^2} = \frac{4Gm}{R^2};\ g_2 > g_3 > g_1.$$

71. Force of attraction when it is on the surface of earth is

$$F_1 = \frac{GmM}{R^2},$$

Where G is universal gravitational constant.

m is mass of the body.

M is mass of the earth.

R is radius of the earth.

Force of attraction when it is at a height equal to the radius of earth

$$F_2 = \frac{GMm}{(R+R)^2} = \frac{GMm}{(2R)^2} = \frac{GMm}{4R^2}$$

Hence, the change in force of attraction $= F_1 - F_2 =$

$$\frac{GmM}{R^2} - \frac{GmM}{4R^2}$$

$$\frac{GmM}{R^2}\left[1 - \frac{1}{4}\right] = \frac{3}{4}F_1$$

Hence, the change in force of attraction is $\frac{3}{4}$ times the original force.

72. Gravitational force of attraction on the surface of the earth on an object of mass 'm',

$F = \frac{GmM}{R^2}$, M is mass of the earth, R is radius of the earth.

New gravitation force of attraction on the surface of the earth after the mass and radius of the earth get doubled be F^1.

$$F^1 = \frac{Gm(2M)}{(2R)^2} = \frac{GMm}{R^2} \times \frac{1}{2} = \frac{1}{2}F$$

Weight of an object is equal to the gravitational force of attraction on that object.

$$W = \frac{GmM}{R^2} = 5 \text{ kgwt.}$$

Level 3: Assess Your Concepts

73. The gravitational force of attraction between the person and the rock is very less compared to the gravitational force of attraction between earth and person as the mass of the person and rock are very less compared to the mass of the earth. Therefore, the gravitational force of attraction between the rock and the person is negligible.

74. Given, mass of the planet $M_p = 2M_e$, where M_e is the mass of the Earth.

Also given, radius of the planet $R_p = 2R_e$, where R_e is the radius of the Earth.

Escape velocity on a planet is given by the expression,

$$v_{escape} = \sqrt{\frac{2GM}{R}}$$

Given, the escape velocity on the surface of the Earth

$$v_e = 11.2 \text{ km / s}$$

Hence, $v_e = \sqrt{\frac{2GM_e}{R_e}}$ and

$$v_p = \sqrt{\frac{2GM_p}{R_p}} = \sqrt{\frac{2G2M_e}{2R_e}} = \sqrt{\frac{2GM_e}{R_e}} = 11.2 \text{ km / s}$$

75. Spring balance is used for measuring the weight of an object, $w = m \times g$.

If we know the value of acceleration due to gravity (g) at that place, we can determine the mass of the object as, $m = w/g$

But the value of acceleration due to gravity on the surface of the earth changes from place to place. So, we use a common balance to measure the mass of an object instead of a spring balance.

76. $d_1 = d,\ d_2 = 2d$

$F_1 = F,\ F_2 = ?$

$$F_1 = G\frac{m_1 m_2}{d^2}$$

$$F_2 = G\frac{m_1m_2}{(2d)^2}$$

$$= F_2 = \frac{1}{4} \qquad F_1 = \frac{F}{4}$$

Change in force $= F - \frac{F}{4} = \frac{3F}{4}$

77. $d_1 = d,\ F_1 = F$

$d_2 = ?\ F_2 = 3F$

$$F = G\frac{m_1m_2}{d^2}$$

$$d = \sqrt{\frac{Gm_1m_2}{F}}$$

$$d_1 = d = \sqrt{\frac{Gm_1m_2}{F}}$$

$$d_2 = \sqrt{\frac{Gm_1m_2}{9F}}$$

$$d_2 = \sqrt{\frac{Gm_1m_2}{F}}$$

$$d_2 = \frac{1}{3}\ d_1 = \frac{d}{3}$$

Decrease in distance

$$= d - \frac{d}{3} = \frac{2d}{3}$$

78. The escape velocity of an object on the moon is small due to its small mass. The velocity of the atmospheric air particle is greater than the escape velocity on the moon. So, there is no atmosphere on moon. The number of meteorites striking on the moon's surface is quite large because moon has no atmosphere (air) to burn the falling meteorites by producing the frictional heat. On the other hand, the earth has an atmosphere containing air; so many of the meteorites burn up completely on entering the earth's atmosphere due to the heat produced by friction between falling meteorite and air.

79. Pressure in a fluid decreases with increase in the velocity of the fluid.

When the piston of a sprayer is pushed, air moves in the upper end of a tube whose lower end is dipped in the liquid to be sprayed. Due to the increased velocity of air, the pressure near the upper end of the tube is reduced. The atmospheric pressure in the container, therefore, pushes the liquid to the top, from where it is carried away by the stream of air.

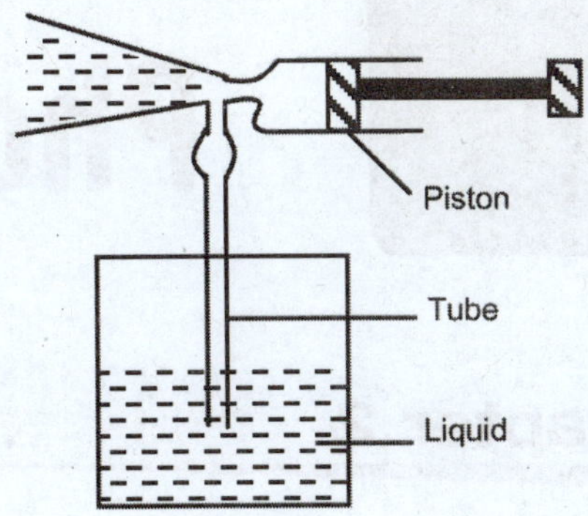

80. Mass is the amount of matter contained in a body and it does not change from one place to another and-hence, remains constant throughout the universe.

The radius of Moon is about ¼th that of Earth and mass of Moon is about 1/80th that of Earth.

Hence, the force of gravitation on Moon is 1/6 th that of Earth.

81. The density of the liquid A is more than the density of liquid B. So, liquid A occupies the lower portion and liquid B on the upper portion. The density of the object is greater than the density of liquid B so that it sinks in it and the density of the object is less than the density of liquid A, so, it floats on its surface. Then we can say that density of liquid A > density of the object > density of the liquid B.

82. Gravitational attraction of the earth on any body is proportional to its mass. But the acceleration caused in a body is due to the gravitational pull of the earth on the body ($\because$ 'g' is independent of mass). Hence, all the bodies fall towards the earth with equal rapidity irrespective of their masses.

83. Due to the lighted candle, the air above it gets heated up. Then it expands and becomes lighter, and hence goes up. When hot air moves in the upward direction through hole B, fresh air enters through the hole A. So, it creates a air current or wind from A to B. So, the wheel starts rotating in clockwise direction.

84. The value of Universal Gravitational Constant (G) is same everywhere in the universe. Its value is not affected by the masses of two bodies or the distance between. Hence, there will be no change in the value of 'G'.

Photo Credits

Chapter 2

Page 2.6—Sanjay Charadva. Pearson India Education Services Pvt. Ltd
Page 2.6—Mohd Suhail. Pearson India Education Services Pvt. Ltd

Chapter 3

Page 3.8—photoiconix. Shutterstock
Page 3.15—HL Studios. Pearson Education Ltd

Chapter 5

Page 5.10—Alila Medical Media. Shutterstock

Chapter 6

Page 6.6—Designua. Shutterstock
Page 6.9—Designua. Shutterstock

Chapter 8

Page 8.7—Kirasolly. Shutterstock
Page 8.7—shooarts. Shutterstock